Free Radical Reactions in
Preparative Organic Chemistry

Free Radical Reactions

in Preparative

Organic Chemistry

GEORGE SOSNOVSKY

*Associate Professor, Illinois Institute
of Technology, Chicago, Illinois*

THE MACMILLAN COMPANY, NEW YORK

COLLIER-MACMILLAN LIMITED, LONDON

First Printing

Library of Congress catalog card number: 64-13258

THE MACMILLAN COMPANY, NEW YORK
COLLIER-MACMILLAN CANADA, LTD., TORONTO, ONTARIO

Printed in the United States of America

DESIGN BY R. A. KASELER

Preface

Free radical reactions provide the experimental chemist with a valuable tool for many syntheses that are inaccessible by classical methods. The importance of these reactions is also recognized in biological processes.

Until about 1930 the study of free radicals was restricted almost exclusively to the reactions of radicals of the triphenylmethyl type in solution and to the reactions of a few hydrocarbon radicals in the gas phase. Since 1930, however, the chemistry of free radical processes in solution has received increasing attention. In the past few decades the decomposition of peroxides to radicals has been studied; the addition of halides, sulfites, mercaptans, and other compounds to unsaturated systems under free radical conditions has been investigated; and chlorination, sulfonation, carboxylation, and polymerization in the presence of peroxides and other radical initiators have been studied. The mechanisms for many of these processes have been elucidated.

To date, no book has been written dealing exclusively with the preparative aspects of free radical chemistry. In most books the preparative aspects and the theoretical discussions are so closely interwoven that it is often difficult to assess the scope of any particular reaction and a laborious literature search is required to obtain this information. In *Free Radical Reactions in Preparative Organic Chemistry* the existing free radical literature was evaluated from a preparative viewpoint. In order to present a wide coverage of free radical reactions, theoretical aspects, detailed mechanistic interpretations, historical developments, etc., were not included. We believe that discussions of theory would not have served any useful purpose, since they would for the most part be a repetition of the excellent discussions in standard free radical chemistry books, which are listed in the last chapter.

Since the chemistry of free radical reactions is complex and the literature voluminous, the scope of this book had to be restricted. With few exceptions, only free radical reactions in solution are discussed. Preparations of polymers, higher telomers, and compounds having ill-defined structures are omitted.

Reactions involving electrode processes and heterogeneous catalysis are not included. Reactions of oxygen, decomposition of peroxides, reactions of peroxides in the presence of metal salt catalysts, aromatic substitution reactions, Grignard reactions, reactions of azo and diazo compounds, dimerization reactions, and preparations and reactions of stable free radicals and other miscellaneous free radicals are also excluded. Reactions which seem to follow a general free radical pattern are generally included even if the reaction mechanism is unknown or not well established.

The literature up to about 1960 was reviewed. In some cases more recent works were included. While the references on any one subject are not considered to be exhaustive, we believe that all significant free radical reactions with preparative usefulness are included and that the references supplied will enable the reader to find other pertinent works on any particular subject. It is obvious that we could make errors in judgment in evaluating and selecting various publications, and we will be grateful to the reader for calling our attention to serious omissions or errors.

In the selection of preparative methods, original publications giving a reasonable preparative description along with yields and physical constants were chosen. In a number of cases references had to be included which did not meet these requirements. Their inclusion was justified either because no other references were available or because the products or processes are of interest. Although we were critical in selecting the preparative methods and tabulating the products, there is no criticism of the work reported. The original nomenclature was adhered to as closely as possible in order to facilitate checking of the original work by the reader.

The general arrangement of the book is as follows. It is divided into chapters on general classes of compounds. The chapters, in turn, are divided into sections. Each section is an independent unit on a particular type of compound but is loosely connected to the other sections. Some sections are further subdivided. Each section begins with a general discussion of the preparative method and is followed by a list of the various reaction conditions under which a particular result was achieved. Next such factors as temperature, pressure, catalyst, initiator, inhibitor, and solvents are discussed and appropriate references cited. Then a number of examples are described in some detail. These examples were usually chosen because they have some unusual feature, such as a rare starting material, an unexpected product, or the need for a catalyst. The chapters are accompanied by tables which summarize the more common reaction products. A list of references, arranged alphabetically by author, is included with each chapter.

Throughout the book, idealized equations and reaction schemes showing mainly starting materials and products are used. Intermediate chain sequences are seldom shown. We believe that this method of presentation is justified from a preparative point of view. The level of presentation is for the experimental organic chemist. A basic knowledge of free radical reactions is assumed.

It is our hope that this book will serve not only as a reference book for preparative free radical reactions but also as a stimulant for new preparative work and for studies of the mechanisms of free radical chemistry.

G. S.

Acknowledgements

I express my sincere appreciation and gratitude to the following persons who helped me in the preparation of this book. My deep thanks go to Mrs. Dorothy W. Green for her expert editorial assistance in preparing the manuscript and the index and in proofreading the galley and page proof. I acknowledge the assistance of IIT Research Institute (formerly Armour Research Foundation) and, in particular, of Dr. James J. Brophy, Vice President, without whose understanding and continued administrative support I could not have completed this work. I am grateful to Dr. Laszlo F. Biritz, who critically surveyed the entire manuscript and gave excellent advice; to Dr. Donald Laskowski, who encouraged me to write this book; and to Dr. Evan Baltazzi, who gave many helpful suggestions. I express my appreciation to Mrs. Ann P. Wennerberg for her invaluable help in surveying the literature. I also thank Miss Mary F. Wrenn for her editorial assistance and Miss Barbara A. Munro for her assistance in proofreading. I acknowledge with gratitude the assistance of Miss Dolores Podolak, who typed the entire final manuscript with exceptional skill, and of Miss Waltraud M. Reckert and Miss Ann R. Healey, who typed parts of the manuscript.

Table of Contents

List of Tables

Explanation of the Tables

Each chapter is accompanied by one or more tables listing the reactions of interest. The reagents, products, yields, selected physical constants, and literature sources are tabulated. The experimental details for the reactions are not tabulated, as the general experimental procedures are given in the corresponding chapter and specific details can be found in the references cited.

Compounds in the tables are arranged by the number of carbon atoms in the substrate and also by the reagent employed. For example, in Table 10, on addition of mercaptans to olefins, for each mercaptan the olefins are arranged in order of increasing number of carbon atoms.

The yields listed are either from the original publication or were calculated from the data available in the original publication. Some compounds are included for which yields were not available. These are included because: (a) they merit inclusion independently of yield, or (b) analogous reactions reported by the same author indicate that the yield would be in an acceptable range.

If available, boiling points, melting points, and refractive indices are included. Densities and other physical constants are omitted. The melting points are listed in parentheses in the column with the boiling points. The refractive indices are for sodium light. Pressure and temperature are recorded in millimeters of mercury and in degrees centigrade, respectively. If the original author specified the prevailing "normal" barometric pressure for the boiling point, it is included. If no value for the "normal" barometric pressure was available, a blank space follows the boiling point value. When several values were found for the same physical constant, only one was taken unless there was a large discrepancy between two values, in which case both values were listed.

In preparative organic chemistry it is customary to report a boiling or melting point range for a given substance. To simplify tabulation, we departed from this custom by using only one value, usually an average, for compounds with narrow boiling or melting ranges. We believe that this procedure does not sacrifice accuracy. The practicing organic chemist will appreciate that b.p. 113.8–115.8°/10 mm and m.p. 114–116° are no more useful than b.p. 114°/10 mm and m.p. 115°, respectively. In fact, he will find that, as a result of his individual technique, some slight deviation from the quoted literature value will usually occur.

Free Radical Reactions in Preparative Organic Chemistry

Introduction to

Preparative Free Radical Work

The characteristic feature of all free radical processes is that the reactive species possesses an odd electron. Therefore, from the preparative point of view, we are concerned with the production of these free radical species and their reactions with various substrates. Radical-forming sources are many and are widely varied. The most commonly used sources and initiators are peroxides, azonitriles, and light. Initiation or acceleration of a reaction by a radical source is characteristic of free radical reactions and can be regarded as evidence of a free radical process.

Radical formation, which is caused by bond dissociation, depends largely on temperature. Some molecules with covalent bonds dissociate even at room temperature. Examples are peroxides, organic azo compounds, some organometallic compounds, and disulfides. A number of compounds can dissociate at comparatively low temperatures, around 200°. Many more substances form radicals at elevated temperatures. Most organic substances produce radical species at temperatures above 500°, but such reactions are outside our sphere of interest.

As a rule, radical reactions are not sensitive to polar solvents, and acids and bases usually have no catalytic effect. Nevertheless, nonpolar solvents are usually employed in free radical work because they suppress or eliminate possible competing polar reactions.

Many peroxides can be used conveniently as initiators in laboratory work. Those most frequently used are dialkyl peroxides, diacyl peroxides, hydroperoxides, and peresters. Hydrogen peroxide itself produces radicals at 50–115°. Of the dialkyl peroxides, di–t–butyl peroxide (I) is the most widely used, in particular for initiation of reactions above 100°.

$$(CH_3)_3C—O—O—C(CH_3)_3$$

I

Di–t–butyl peroxide has a half life of 200 hr and 2 hr at 100° and 140°, respectively. The most frequently used diacyl peroxides are acetyl peroxide (II) and benzoyl peroxide (III).

$$CH_3C(O)—O—O—C(O)CH_3 \qquad C_6H_5C(O)—O—O—C(O)C_6H_5$$

II   III

Benzoyl peroxide is comparatively harmless, but acetyl peroxide can explode without warning and large quantities, in particular, should be

1

handled with care. In inert solvents both diacyl peroxides decompose at approximately the same rate and are convenient sources of radicals between 60° and 100°. The half life for benzoyl peroxide at 90° and 100° is 2 hr and 0.5 hr, respectively. The rates of decomposition of acyl peroxides vary somewhat with the medium in which they are decomposed.

The most commonly used peresters are t–butyl peracetate (IV), t–butyl perbenzoate (V), and t–butyl perphthalate.

$$CH_3C(O)—O—O—C(CH_3)_3 \qquad C_6H_5C(O)—O—O—C(CH_3)_3$$

$$IV \qquad\qquad\qquad\qquad V$$

The rate of decomposition of t–butyl perbenzoate at 115° compares with that of benzoyl peroxide at 80°. The half life of t–butyl perbenzoate at 100° and 120° is 20 hr and 2 hr, respectively.

Of the hydroperoxides, t–butyl hydroperoxide is readily available and relatively safe to handle. It decomposes quantitatively in approximately 24 hr at 95–100°. Cumene hydroperoxide is also widely used. The rate of decomposition of cumene hydroperoxide varies with different solvents. In aromatic solvents the half life at 113° is approximately 25 hr. Peroxy dicarbonates (VI) are sometimes employed as initiators.

$$ROC(O)—O—O—C(O)OR$$

$$VI$$

R = alkyl

At 20–60° most of these peroxides decompose faster than benzoyl peroxide, and they undergo rapid self-induced decomposition. Therefore, the utmost care must be used in handling them.

In the early work with free radical reactions in solution, ascaridole (VII) was frequently used. It explodes when heated to about 130° and is seldom employed nowadays.

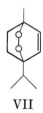

VII

When peroxide initiators are used in conjunction with such metallic ions as iron, cobalt, manganese, and copper, they are redox systems. Ferrous ion and hydrogen peroxide (Fenton's reagent) was the first such system to be used in organic chemistry. These one-electron redox systems are particularly useful in polymerizations. Organic peroxides, particularly t–butyl and cumene hydroperoxides, can also be used with trace amounts of metals to give reaction-initiating species.

The amount of initiator necessary for a particular reaction depends largely on the system involved. In general, only a small percentage of peroxide is used. The peroxide is added all at once at the beginning of a reaction, or a solution of the peroxide in an inert solvent is added in small portions throughout the reaction. Most free radical processes are exothermic, building up heat and creating almost explosive conditions. Therefore with systems involving chain reactions, particularly when large quantities of peroxide are used, preliminary runs with small amounts of reactants are advisable.

A convenient and versatile radical source is azobisisobutyronitrile (VIII) and its homologues.

$$(CH_3)_2(CN)CN\!=\!NC(CN)(CH_3)_2$$

VIII

These substances decompose to radicals, with evolution of nitrogen. Their decomposition is independent of solvents and, in contrast to peroxides, they have no tendency to undergo induced decomposition. Their rate of decomposition depends on their structural features and on temperature. The half life for azobisisobutyronitrile at 80° and 100° is 2 hr and 0.1 hr, respectively. The decomposition rates of a number of azonitriles are listed in Walling's book *Free Radicals in Solution*.

The persulfate ion is another free radical source and has about the same half life as azobisisobutyronitrile, about 2 hr at 80°. Organometallic compounds are other radical sources, but these are used much less than peroxides and azonitriles. Dimethyl mercury and tetraethyl lead are examples.

There are also substances which retard or inhibit radical reactions. They may be stable radicals, such as nitric oxide and oxygen, which are unable to initiate chain reactions themselves but which react with chain-propagating species. They may be nonradicals, such as phenols, quinones, amines, aromatic nitro compounds, and sulfur, which react with radicals to form new radicals which in turn are not capable of propagating chains. Or they may be inorganic ions, such as ferric ions, which destroy radicals in the following manner.

$$R\cdot + FeCl_3 \rightarrow RCl + FeCl_2$$

Thus, in preparative free radical chemistry, impurities which might act as inhibitors or retarders must be avoided.

Oxygen plays an interesting role in free radical reactions. Not only is oxygen present in many liquids, but also it is difficult to be entirely excluded from most systems. Oxygen is a diradical. As such, it can participate in many free radical processes and can also interfere with them. Oxygen accounts for the induction period in many reactions. A small amount can initiate a reaction; a large quantity may retard or completely inhibit the reaction and induce oxidative processes instead. Since the action of oxygen is unpredictable, it is seldom used to initiate free radical reactions. To exclude oxygen, all reactants and solvents are purified immediately before use and all reactions are carried out in an oxygen-free atmosphere. When traces of oxygen cannot be removed, its action can be suppressed by addition of inhibitors such as hydroquinone. The reactions are initiated with peroxides or other initiators to ensure controlled reaction conditions.

When they absorb light, many molecules produce radicals at temperatures below those at which thermal decomposition occurs. The energy of a quantum of light is equivalent to 48 kcal at 6000 A and to 96 kcal at 3000 A. These energies are sufficient for dissociation of most covalent bonds. Consequently, absorption of a light quantum of appropriate wavelength by a molecule with a covalent bond results in cleavage of the bond to form two radicals, which react exactly as though they were produced thermally. Photochemical production of radicals is convenient, since it can be easily initiated and interrupted.

When the quantum yield is equal to one, the absorbed quanta are transformed stoichiometrically into the products. In many instances the light is absorbed directly by the reacting molecules. In some instances, however, the light must first be absorbed by a photosensitizer, which itself does not undergo permanent change but transmits the absorbed energy to the reacting molecules. Dyes such as eosin and methylene blue act as such sensitizers. Another frequently used sensitizer is mercury metal. When the quantum yield is higher than one, the reactions are photoinduced chain reactions, for example, halogenation, sulfochlorination, oxidation, and polymerization. Below a certain characteristic temperature for each reaction, photoinduced chain reactions become stoichiometric reactions with quantum yields equal to one.

Peroxides absorb light appreciably only at wavelengths below 3200 A and thus can be utilized efficiently only in equipment that transmits ultraviolet light. Therefore silica vessels should be used. Organometallic compounds such as dimethyl mercury and tetraethyl lead, which absorb light below 2800 A, should also be used in silica vessels. Azobisisobutyronitrile, on the other hand, strongly absorbs light between 3450 and 4000 A and therefore can be used with ordinary glass equipment.

There are a number of compounds which do not dissociate easily thermally but which dissociate easily photochemically. Of most importance are various carbonyl compounds. Acetone, for example, absorbs light at 2700 A and dissociates to radicals.

$$CH_3COCH_3 \rightarrow CH_3CO\cdot + CH_3\cdot$$

Methylethyl ketone behaves similarly. Diacetyl dissociates in light of 3600 A and can be used as a photoinitiator in chain processes. Benzoin and its derivatives are used for this purpose also.

For the most effective photochemical work, the following factors should be remembered. (a) Inhibitors, oxygen in particular, should be excluded. Therefore all operations should be carried out in an oxygen-free atmosphere. (b) For well-controlled reaction conditions which ensure uniform mixing and cooling, the reactions should be carried out in solvents. Neither the solvents nor the reaction products should act as light filters. (c) Reaction products should not be deposited on the walls of the reaction vessels.

In most preparative photochemical work a spectral range of 2500–6000 A is used. A variety of illuminating devices is available for the visible spectrum, and many projection lamps can be adapted. For work under pressure, special lamps are commercially available. Sodium vapor lamps give monochromatic light at 5890 A. Much work has been done with mercury vapor lamps, which emit ultraviolet light around 2500 A. Perhaps the best known of these are produced by Quarzlampèngeschellschaft (Hanau/Main, Germany) and by the General Electric Company. Xenon and krypton lamps have a continuous spectrum and are well suited for imitation of natural daylight. Ordinary glass equipment can be used for light down to about 3500 A. Quartz or other ultraviolet-transmitting equipment should be used with light of 3500 A or lower.

For optimum utilization of light energy, it is advantageous to surround the light source with the reaction mixture. Since most lamps develop heat, it is advisable to have a cooling chamber between the light source and the reaction mixture. Comparatively simple equipment has been devised for this purpose, and some is available commercially. An excellent discussion on the preparative photochemical techniques is presented by Schenck in Schönberg's book *Präparative Organische Photochemie*.

Another radical-producing process is the high-energy radiation produced by α, β, γ, or x rays. This process is seldom used because high-energy radiation frequently results in fragmentation of many molecules, with the production of complex mixtures.

CHAPTER I

Addition of Hydrogen Halides to Unsaturated Compounds

ADDITION OF HYDROGEN BROMIDE

Depending on the reaction conditions, addition of hydrogen bromide to unsaturated compounds proceeds by one of two mechanisms: ionic or radical. In most instances the products of the two types of reactions are different. If reaction conditions favor the ionic mechanism, addition occurs in accordance with Markownikoff's rule, and the "normal" product is obtained; the halogen atom attaches itself to the carbon atom of the unsaturated compound which carries the least hydrogen atoms or the most alkyl groups. If reaction conditions favor the radical mechanism, addition occurs contrary to Markownikoff's rule, and the "abnormal" product is obtained; the halogen atom attaches itself to that unsaturated carbon atom which carries the most hydrogen atoms.

$$RCH{=}CH_2 + HBr \left< \begin{array}{l} \longrightarrow RCHBrCH_3 \\ \text{Normal product} \\ \longrightarrow RCH_2CH_2Br \\ \text{Abnormal product} \end{array} \right.$$

Although this description is an oversimplification of the experimental results, and exceptions have been observed, the description holds for the overwhelming number of reactions, particularly those involving terminal olefins. In some reactions the ionic and the radical process each lead to the same mixture of products. For example, the addition of hydrogen bromide to cis– or to trans–2–pentene under either radical or ionic conditions produces an equimolar mixture of 2– and 3–bromopentane.[44,48] The addition of hydrogen bromide to crotonic acid or to its ethyl ester under either radical or ionic conditions produces, respectively, β–bromobutyric acid and ethyl β–bromobutyrate.[81] The reaction of hydrogen bromide with cinnamic acid in the presence of benzoyl peroxide at 60° in benzene or under antioxidant conditions results in the same product, β–bromohydrocinnamic acid.[63]

The factors affecting hydrogen bromide addition are of both theoretical and practical significance. Thus it is not surprising that this addition reaction has been studied extensively, in particular by Kharasch, Mayo, and associates.[28-44,47-49] The subject is discussed in all books and review articles dealing with free radical chemistry. Of special interest are the articles by Mayo and Walling[49] and by Mayo.[48]

In working with hydrogen bromide and unsaturated compounds, it is important to select certain experimental conditions to obtain the product desired. For example, if the last traces of oxygen are not removed from some olefins, a mixture of normal and abnormal products may be obtained. In such cases the use of radical inhibitors such as mercaptans, diphenylamines, and hydroquinones prevents the formation of the abnormal product.

Pioneers in these studies used oxygen and ascaridole as initiators for producing the abnormal product.[36,71,72] For example, the reaction of hydrogen bromide with allyl bromide in the presence of oxygen produces the abnormal product in as high as 97% yield.[36,71,72] A variety of more reliable radical initiators is now available commercially. Among these are benzoyl peroxide, azonitriles, haloketones,[59,60] and photosensitizers such as ketones[77] and tetraethyl lead.[8,9]

In the absence of air, peroxide, or light, hydrogen bromide reacts slowly with many absolutely pure, freshly prepared olefins to form the normal product. This addition is accelerated by ferric, aluminum, and other metal halides. In the presence of air, peroxide, light, or a combination of these, the abnormal product is formed predominantly or exclusively. Reversal of the normal addition reaction by peroxide is known as the "peroxide effect."[48,49] It does not occur with all olefins.[48,49,79] For example, the reaction of hydrogen bromide with atropic acid produces β–bromohydratropic acid and the presence of benzoyl peroxide does not reverse the normal addition.[69]

Bromoacetone in the absence of air catalyzes abnormal addition. For example, the addition of hydrogen bromide to propylene or to butene–1 in the presence of bromoacetone produces n–propyl and n–butyl bromide, respectively, even in the dark.[59,60] Acetone does not catalyze this reaction in the dark, but it can act as a photosensitizer. Light of a wavelength that does not initiate the addition of hydrogen bromide to olefins by the radical mechanism may have sufficient energy to dissociate acetone into radicals, which in turn initiate the abnormal addition reaction. This effect is demonstrated in the reaction of hydrogen bromide with propylene in the presence of acetone.[77] Tetraethyl lead also promotes the abnormal addition of hydrogen bromide to olefins when the reaction mixture is irradiated with light.[8,9] Neither tetraethyl lead alone nor light of 3600 A initiates the reaction; the light of this wavelength dissociates the tetraethyl lead, which in turn initiates the reaction. Thus, the reaction of hydrogen bromide with propylene in the presence of tetraethyl lead produces n–propyl bromide in high yield.[8,9]

Large amounts of oxygen inhibit photochemical processes. The reactions of hydrogen bromide with olefins in the presence of equimolar amounts of oxygen have a complex pattern.[59,62,68,69] These reactions have little preparative significance because mixtures of products are always produced. For example, the reaction of hydrogen bromide with either ethylene or propylene in the presence of an equimolar amount of oxygen yields n–monobromides, dibromides, bromohydrin, and water.[59] In the reaction with propylene, bromoacetone is also formed. The reaction of hydrogen bromide with crotonic acid in the presence of an equimolar amount of oxygen produces β–bromobutyric acid, crotonic acid dibromide, and α–hydroxy–β–bromobutyric acid.[62] The addition reaction with cinnamic acid under like conditions produces cinnamic acid dibromide, ω–bromoacetophenone, and carbon dioxide.[68] Catechol inhibits this reaction, but nitrobenzene has no effect. The addition reaction with atropic acid in the presence of an equimolar amount of oxygen produces α–hydroxy–β–bromohydratropic acid and small amounts of ω, ω–dibromoacetophenone and carbon dioxide.[69] The same reaction with diphenylethylene yields a complex mixture of 1, 1–diphenyl–β–bromoethylene, ω–bromoacetophenone, diphenylethylene dibromide, diphenylbromoethane, phenol, and carbon dioxide.[69] And the reaction with styrene yields a mixture of styrene dibromide, α–bromoethylbenzene, and phenolic substances.[69]

Polar solvents such as acetic acid, propionic acid, and water promote normal addition, whereas nonpolar solvents promote abnormal addition. Higher temperatures generally promote abnormal addition; temperatures from −78° to 100° are used.

Most additions of hydrogen bromide to olefins and acetylenes are carried out with compounds containing terminal unsaturation. Reversal of the normal addition reaction—the peroxide effect—is not confined to such compounds, however. For example, the reaction of hydrogen bromide with 2–methyl–Δ²–nonadecene produces the normal product, 2–bromo–2–methylnonadecane; whereas in the presence of oxygen, ascaridole, or both the reaction produces the abnormal product, 3–bromoisomeride.[15] A number of compounds containing nonterminal unsaturation also react with hydrogen bromide according to a free radical mechanism.[1,2,11−15,18,21,45,50,55,65,80,81]

Table 1 lists the more interesting addition reactions of hydrogen bromide and deuterium bromide to olefins and acetylenes under free radical conditions. The first addition reaction of hydrogen bromide to acetylene was described by Bauer.[4,5] The reaction was initiated by oxygen, ozonized oxygen, or light. Leitch and More prepared deuterated 1, 2–bromoethane and deuterated acetylene by reaction with hydrogen bromide in ultraviolet light.[46]

Under antioxidant conditions hydrogen bromide adds to propylene to form isopropyl bromide, whereas in the presence of peroxide, n–propyl bromide is formed.[37-39] Likewise, the reaction of hydrogen bromide with vinyl bromide[38] or with vinyl chloride[30] produces both normal and abnormal products depending on the experimental conditions, and the peroxide effect is tremendously accelerated by light. In the absence of oxygen or peroxide, hydrogen bromide adds to 2–butyne to form 2, 2–dibromobutane; but in the presence of peroxide, 2, 3–dibromobutane is formed.[80] The addition reaction of hydrogen bromide with butene–1 produces sec–butyl bromide in the absence of peroxide and n–butyl bromide in the presence of peroxide.[32] Although heat or light catalyzes abnormal addition, air does not, probably because oxygen does not readily form a peroxide with butene–1. Similarly, under antioxidant conditions the reaction of hydrogen bromide with pentene–1 produces the normal product, 2–bromopentane, whereas in the presence of ascaridole the reaction produces the abnormal product, 1–bromopentane.[33]

Hydrogen bromide reacts with butadiene under antioxidant conditions to give a mixture of 80% 3–bromo–1–butene, b.p. 7°/10 mm, n_D 1.4602 (25°), and 20% 1–bromo–2–butene, b.p. 13°/10 mm, n_D 1.4794 (25°), in 90% yield.[35] In the presence of air or peroxide the yields are reversed: 80% 1–bromo–2–butene and 20% 3–bromo–1–butene. Interpretation of these results is complicated by the fact that both bromides are an equilibrium mixture of 85% 1–bromobutene–2 and 15% 3–bromobutene–1 even at −12°.

Hydrogen bromide does not react with trichloroethylene under antioxidant conditions even at 100°, whereas it reacts in the presence of oxygen, air, peroxide, or light to form 1–bromo–1, 2, 2–trichloroethane.[34,41] Hydrogen bromide reacts with isopropylethylene in the presence of air or ascaridole at −78° to form 80% primary isoamyl bromide; and 15–19% secondary bromide and 6–10% tertiary bromide are formed by rearrangement.[51] In the presence of hydroquinone no primary bromide is formed.

The addition of hydrogen bromide to fluorinated olefins and acetylenes is usually carried out in a sealed silica tube and is initiated by ultraviolet radiation. Often the vapor phase above the liquid phase is irradiated, and the liquid phase is shielded from the light source.[19,20,26] In most cases excellent yields (51–93%) are obtained. When pyrex is used instead of silica, the yield decreases and the reaction time increases. In most cases no reaction occurs in the dark. The reaction time ranges from a few hours (for trifluoropropyne[18]) to several days (for hexafluoropropene[19]). The reaction temperature ranges from −60° (for trifluoropropyne[18]) to 20° (for trifluoropropylene[26]). A mixture of hydrogen bromide and trifluoroethylene irradiated with ultraviolet light in a silica vessel forms a mixture of 1–bromo–1, 2, 2–trifluoroethane and 1–bromo–1, 1, 2–trifluoroethane in 98%

yield.[25] The mixture can be separated by fractionation: the first product (38%) boils at 41°/735 mm and the second at 25°.

Hydrogen bromide does not add to the double bond of vinyltrimethylsilane in the absence of peroxide. In the presence of benzoyl peroxide, however, β–bromoethyltrimethylsilane is obtained in 79% yield.[67] In the presence of peroxide, hydrogen bromide adds to 4–trimethylsilyl–1–butene to form the abnormal product.[56] Surprisingly, hydrogen bromide adds to allyltrimethylsilane in the absence or presence of peroxide to form the normal product in high yield.[66]

$$(CH_3)_3SiCH=CH_2 + HBr \rightarrow (CH_3)_3SiCH_2CH_2Br$$

$$(CH_3)_3SiCH_2CH=CH_2 + HBr \rightarrow (CH_3)_3SiCH_2CHBrCH_3$$

$$(CH_3)_3Si(CH_2)_2CH=CH_2 + HBr \rightarrow (CH_3)_3Si(CH_2)_4Br$$

An unusual reaction occurs with 3, 3, 3–trichloropropene. Initially the product of the reaction was believed to be 1, 1, 1–trichloro–3–bromopropane, $CCl_3CH_2CH_2Br$.[43] Subsequently it was shown that the product is the rearranged compound 1, 1, 2–trichloro–3–bromopropane.[53,54]

$$CCl_3CH=CH_2 + HBr \rightarrow CHCl_2CHClCH_2Br$$

Similarly, the addition of hydrogen bromide to 1, 1, 1–trichloro–2–methylpropene at 70° in carbon tetrachloride in the presence of benzoyl peroxide produces 1, 1, 2–trichloro–3–bromo–2–methylpropane.[52,54]

In recent years the stereochemistry of hydrogen bromide addition to unsaturated systems has received much attention, and interesting new compounds have been prepared. Hydrogen bromide reacts with propyne rapidly and stereospecifically by a *trans* mechanism to form *cis*–1–bromo–1–propene.[64] The reaction is initiated by ultraviolet light at −60° to −78°. The stereospecific reaction of hydrogen bromide with 1–bromo–2–methyl acetylene at −75° in ultraviolet light proceeds by a *cis* addition and forms 1, 2–dibromopropene, b.p. 64°/61 mm, n_D 1.5302 (20°), in 92% yield; the dibromopropene contains 75 ± 7.5% of the *trans* isomer.[6]

The addition of both hydrogen and deuterium bromides to isomeric *cis*– and *trans*–2–bromo–2–butene is also stereospecific; ultraviolet illumination is used at temperatures ranging from −80° to 25°.[13] In the absence of illumination the ionic reaction, leading to 2, 2–dibromobutane, competes strongly with the radical process. At low temperatures the ionic reaction predominates, whereas at elevated temperatures the radical reaction does. Hydrogen bromide addition to either *cis*– or *trans*–2–chloro–2–butene also proceeds under ultraviolet illumination.[55] In pentane even at −78° hydrogen bromide causes the starting olefins to isomerize rapidly; a mixture of diastereoisomers is obtained in high yield. The product, b.p. 63°/60 mm, contains 70% *threo* and 30% *erythro* compounds. Pure *erythro–* and *threo–* 3–deuterio–2–bromobutane are prepared by radical addition of deuterium bromide to *trans–* and *cis*–2–butene, respectively.[65] The reaction is stereospecific, proceeds via a *trans* mechanism, and is initiated by irradiation with a sun lamp.

Hydrogen bromide reacts with 1–methylcycloheptene at 70° in ultraviolet light by *trans* addition to form more than 95% *cis*–1–methyl–2–bromocycloheptane in 74–84% yield.[1] Hydrogen bromide reacts smoothly with various 1–bromocycloalkenes to give a resolvable mixture of *cis* and *trans* isomers.[2] This reaction takes place with 1–bromocyclobutene, 1–bromocyclopentene, and 1–bromocycloheptene. The ratios of the *cis* to *trans* isomers are 79:21, 94:6, and 91:9, respectively, and the yields are 85–90%. The reaction is carried out in pentane in a quartz vessel with a quartz–mercury arc lamp as an ultraviolet source.

Hydrogen bromide reacts with 1–bromocyclohexene in pentane in the presence of benzoyl peroxide or ultraviolet light at 25–35° via the free radical process to form *cis*–1, 2–dibromocyclohexane.[11,14] The reaction of hydrogen bromide with 1–methylcyclohexene at 0–65° produces two products: 1–bromo–1–methylcyclohexane, by an ionic mechanism, and *cis*–1–bromo–2–methylcyclohexane, by a radical process.[11] Hydrogen bromide and 1–chlorocyclohexene subjected to ultraviolet irradiation in pentane react to form *cis*–1–bromo–2–chlorocyclohexane.[14] No addition via the radical mechanism occurs in ether and 1–bromo–1–chlorocyclohexane is formed.[14] In a mixture of ether and pentane the abnormal addition product is obtained in a low yield (36%).[14]

Hydrogen bromide adds to 2–bromo–2–norbornene (I) in ultraviolet light to form a mixture of *trans*–2, 3–dibromonorbornane (II) and *exo–cis*–2, 3–dibromonorbornane (III).[45]

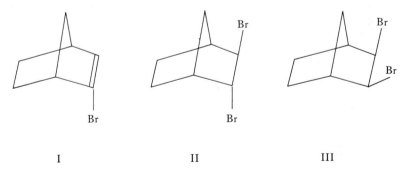

I   II   III

The reaction is carried out in pentane at 0–65°. Since the ionic addition is suppressed, the formation of the *exo–cis* product represents a *trans* addition to norbornylene. The total yield is 70–97%.

ADDITION OF HYDROGEN CHLORIDE, HYDROGEN FLUORIDE, AND HYDROGEN IODIDE

In general, the addition of hydrogen chloride, fluoride, and iodide to olefins proceeds by the ionic mechanism and yields the normal product. Early workers believed that hydrogen chloride adds to olefins by the ionic mechanism only, since before 1940 all attempts to obtain abnormal addition failed. However, it was shown later that abnormal products can be obtained in the presence of peroxide.[16] For example, hydrogen chloride reacts with ethylene under pressure in the presence of benzoyl peroxide or tetraphenyl lead to give a mixture of telomers, and with t–butylethylene to give 24% of the primary halide 1–chloro–3, 3–dimethylbutane.[7]

Hydrogen chloride also reacts with propene or with allyl chloride to give a mixture of normal and abnormal products. In the reaction of hydrogen chloride with styrene no radical addition occurs.[47] These results indicate that addition of hydrogen chloride to an alkene–1 under free radical conditions is difficult but possible.

Table 1. Addition of Hydrogen Bromide to Unsaturated Compounds

C_n	Unsaturated compound	Product	% Yield	°C b.p./mm (m.p.)	n_D (°C)	Ref.
C₂	C₂H₂	Vinyl bromide	80			4
		Ethylene bromide	85	130		5
	C₂D₂	1,2-Dibromoethane	100	129	1.5360 (20)	46
	CH₂=CHCl	CH₂BrCH₂Cl	80	104/735	1.4908 (20)	30, 74, 75, 78
	CH₂=CHBr	1,2-Dibromoethane				38
	CH₂=CCl₂	1-Bromo-2,2-dichloroethane	62	134	1.5054 (25)	10
	CH₂=CCl₂+DBr	1-Bromo-2,2-dichloroethane-2-D	64			10
	1,1-Difluoroethylene	2-Bromo-1,1-difluoroethane	85	56		21
	Trifluoroethylene	1-Bromo-1,2,2-trifluoroethane+	57	40/735		25
		1-Bromo-1,1,2-trifluoroethane	43	25/735		
	CF₂=CFCl	1-Bromo-2-chloro-1,1,2-trifluoroethane	93	53	1.3705 (20)	22
	Trichloroethylene	1,1,2-Trichloro-2-bromoethane	90	171/760	1.5302 (20)	34, 41
	Chloro-1,1-difluoroethylene	1-Bromo-2-chloro-1,1-difluoroethane	99	70/776	1.404 (20)	24
	Tetrafluoroethylene	1-Bromo-1,1,2,2-tetrafluoroethane+	66	12.5		22
		1-Bromo-1,1,2,2,3,3,4,4-octafluorobutane	12	66	1.309 (20)	
C₃	Propyne	cis-1-Bromo-1-propene	88			64
	CH₃C=CBr	CH₃CBr=CHBr	92	64/61	1.5302 (20)	6
	Propylene	n-Propyl bromide	87	70	1.4340 (20)	8, 9, 37, 39, 59-61, 74-78
	1-Bromopropene	1,2-Dibromopropane	84	141/740	1.5200 (20)	28

Table 1. (cont.)   Addition of Hydrogen Bromide to Unsaturated Compounds

C_n	Unsaturated compound	Product	% Yield	°C b.p./mm (m.p.)	n_D (°C)	Ref.
	1-Chloropropene	1-Chloro-2-bromopropane		117/740	1.4795 (20)	28
	2-Bromopropene	1, 2-Dibromopropane	80	141/740	1.5200 (20)	28
	2-Chloropropene	1-Bromo-2-chloropropane		118/740	1.4778 (20)	28
	Allyl bromide	1, 3-Dibromopropane	87–96	167	1.5230 (20)	29, 36, 71–73, 78
	Allyl chloride	1-Bromo-3-chloropropane	91			3
	Methyl acetylene	1, 2-Dibromopropane	100	140	1.5192 (20)	40
	$CCl_3CH=CH_2$	1, 1, 2-Trichloro-3-bromopropane	77	76/9	1.5290 (20)	43, 53, 54
	Trifluoropropyne	1-Bromo-3, 3, 3-trifluoropropene	83	40	1.357 (20) 1.3580 (23)	18 27
	Trifluoropropylene	$CF_3CH_2CH_2Br$	90	61	1.3603 (20) 1.358 (25)	26 17
	1, 1-Difluoropropene-1	2-Bromo-1, 1-difluoropropane	93	72		20
	1, 1, 3, 3, 3-Pentafluoropropene	1-Bromo-1, 1, 3, 3, 3-penta-fluoropropane+	40	44	1.319 (20)	23
		1, 2-Dibromo-1, 1, 3, 3, 3-penta-fluoropropane	50	87	1.379 (20)	
	Hexafluoropropene	1-Bromo-1, 1, 2, 3, 3, 3-hexa-fluoropropane	88	36		19
C_4	$CH_3C=CCH_3$	2, 3-Dibromobutane	95	63/30	1.5147 (20)	80
	Butene-1	n-Butyl bromide	92		1.4393 (20)	32, 59–61, 74, 75, 78
	cis-2-Butene	threo-3-Deuterio-2-bromobutane	95		1.4348 (24)	65
	trans-2-Butene	erythro-3-Deuterio-2-bromobutane	98		1.4345 (24)	65
	Isobutylene	Isobutyl bromide	86	89	1.4357 (20)	42, 74, 75, 78

Table 1. (cont.) Addition of Hydrogen Bromide to Unsaturated Compounds

C_n	Unsaturated compound	Product	% Yield	°C b.p./mm (m.p.)	n_D (°C)	Ref.
	cis-2-Bromo-2-butene	meso-2,3-Dibromobutane		103/160	1.5093 (25)	12, 13
	trans-2-Bromo-2-butene	dl-2,3-Dibromobutane		107/160	1.5126 (25)	13
	1,1,1-Trichloro-2-methylpropene	1,1,2-Trichloro-3-bromo-2-methylpropane	59	123/55	1.5250 (20)	52
	3,3,3-Trifluoro-2-trifluoromethyl-prop-1-ene	2-Bromomethyl-1,1,1,3,3,3-hexafluoropropane	93	78		20
	Hexafluorobut-2-yne	2-bromo-hexafluorobut-2-ene	87	55		18
	$CF_3CF=CFCF_3$	2-Bromo-1,1,1,2,3,4,4,4-octafluorobutane+	60	53	1.307 (17)	21
		2,3-Dibromooctafluorobutane	40	96	1.354 (18)	
	Perfluorocyclobutene	1-Bromo-1,2,2,3,3,4-hexafluorocyclobutane+	33	96	1.389 (20)	21
		1,2-Dibromohexafluorocyclobutane	49	62		
C_5	Pentene-1	1-Bromopentane	96	128	1.4443 (20)	33
	Trimethylethylene	$(CH_3)_2CHCHBrCH_3$	99	115/760	1.4454 (20)	50, 81
	$CH_2=C(CH_3)CO_2CH_3$	Methyl β-bromoisobutyrate	100	67/17	1.4551 (20)	57
	1-Bromocyclopentene	cis-1,2-Dibromocyclopentane+	85	92/13	1.5483 (25)	2
		trans-1,2-Dibromocyclopentane		73/15	1.5460 (25)	
	$(CH_3)_3SiCH=CH_2$	$(CH_3)_3SiCH_2CH_2Br$	79	64/39	1.4575 (20)	67
C_6	Butyl acetylene	1-Bromo-1-hexene	73	140/751	1.4596 (20)	83
	Butyl acetylene (+ 2 moles HBr)	1-Bromo-1-hexene+	50			83
		1,2-Dibromohexane	37	90/18	1.5023 (20)	
	Diallyl	1,6-Dibromohexane	65	114/15	1.5037 (20)	3, 78
	1-Chlorocyclohexene	cis-1-Bromo-2-chlorocyclohexane	88	88/7	1.5238 (25)	14
	1-Bromocyclohexene	cis-1,2-Dibromocyclohexane+	76	104/9	1.5534 (25)	2, 11, 14
		trans-1,2-Dibromocyclohexane		92/9	1.5507 (25)	

Table 1. (cont.) Addition of Hydrogen Bromide to Unsaturated Compounds

C_n	Unsaturated compound	Product	% Yield	°C b.p./mm (m.p.)	n_D (°C)	Ref.
C$_7$	4,4-Dimethylpentene-1	1-Bromo-4,4-dimethylpentane	88	70/35	1.4485 (20)	31, 82
	1-Bromocycloheptene	cis-1,2-Dibromocycloheptane+	85	97/2	1.5526 (25)	2
		trans-1,2-Dibromocycloheptane		83/1.9	1.5530 (25)	
	4-Trimethylsilylbutene-1	4-Trimethylsilyl-1-bromobutane		66/12	1.4558 (20)	56
	2-Bromo-2-norbornene	trans-2,3-Dibromonorbornane+	48–68	64/0.4	1.5560 (25)	45
		exo-cis-2,3-Dibromonorbornane	23–35	(61)		
C$_8$	Styrene	β-Phenylethyl bromide	75	75/4	1.5543 (23)	70, 81
	1-Methylcycloheptene	cis-1-Methyl-2-bromocycloheptane	74	98/25	1.5003 (22)	1
C$_9$	$C_6H_5CH_2CH{=}CH_2$	$C_6H_5CH_2CH_2CH_2Br$	80	114/16		58
C$_{10}$	$o\text{-}CH_3C_6H_4CH_2CH{=}CH_2$	$o\text{-}CH_3C_6H_4CH_2CH_2CH_2Br$	66	75/0.35		58
	$m\text{-}CH_3C_6H_4CH_2CH{=}CH_2$	$m\text{-}CH_3C_6H_4CH_2CH_2CH_2Br$	80	85/1.1		58
	$p\text{-}CH_3C_6H_4CH_2CH{=}CH_2$	$p\text{-}CH_3C_6H_4CH_2CH_2CH_2Br$	70	76/0.7		58
	$p\text{-}CH_3OC_6H_4CH_2CH{=}CH_2$	$p\text{-}CH_3OC_6H_4CH_2CH_2CH_2Br$	70	85/0.8		58
	$3,4\text{-Di-}CH_3C_6H_3CH_2CH{=}CH_2$	$3,4\text{-Di-}CH_3C_6H_3CH_2CH_2CH_2Br$	55	109/0.01		58
C$_{20}$	2-Methyl-Δ^2-nonadecene	3-Bromo-2-methylnonadecane		(3)		15

REFERENCES

[1] Abell and Bohm, *J. Org. Chem.*, **26,** 252 (1961).

[2] Abell and Chiao, *J. Am. Chem. Soc.*, **82,** 3610 (1960).

[3] N. V. de Bataafsche Petroleum Maatschappij, Dutch 55,728 (1943).

[4] Bauer, U.S. 1,414,852 (1922).

[5] Bauer, U.S. 1,540,748 (1925).

[6] Bergelson, *Izvest. Akad. Nauk,* **1958,** 1499.

[7] Ecke, Cook, and Whitmore, *J. Am. Chem. Soc.*, **72,** 1511 (1950).

[8] Evans, Vaughan, and Rust, U.S. 2,376,675 (1945).

[9] Evans, Vaughan, and Rust, Brit. 567,524 (1945).

[10] Francis and Leitch, *Can. J. Chem.*, **35,** 500 (1957).

[11] Goering, Abell, and Aycock, *J. Am. Chem. Soc.*, **74,** 3588 (1952).

[12] Goering and Larsen, *J. Am. Chem. Soc.*, **79,** 2653 (1957).

[13] Goering and Larsen, *J. Am. Chem. Soc.*, **81,** 5937 (1959).

[14] Goering and Sims, *J. Am. Chem. Soc.*, **77,** 3465 (1955).

[15] Grimshaw, Guy, and Smith, *J. Chem. Soc.*, **1940,** 68.

[16] Hanford and Harmon, U.S. 2,440,801 (1948).

[17] Haszeldine, *J. Chem. Soc.*, **1952,** 2504.

[18] Haszeldine, *J. Chem. Soc.*, **1952,** 3490.

[19] Haszeldine, *J. Chem. Soc.*, **1953,** 3559.

[20] Haszeldine, *J. Chem. Soc.*, **1953,** 3565.

[21] Haszeldine and Osborne, *J. Chem. Soc.*, **1956,** 61.

[22] Haszeldine and Steele, *J. Chem. Soc.*, **1954,** 3747.

[23] Haszeldine and Steele, *J. Chem. Soc.*, **1955,** 3005.

[24] Haszeldine and Steele, *J. Chem. Soc.*, **1957,** 2193.

[25] Haszeldine and Steele, *J. Chem. Soc.*, **1957,** 2800.

[26] Henne and Nager, *J. Am. Chem. Soc.*, **73,** 5527 (1951).

[27] Henne and Nager, *J. Am. Chem. Soc.*, **74,** 650 (1952).

[28] Kharasch, Engelman, and Mayo, *J. Org. Chem.*, **2,** 288 (1937).

[29] Kharasch, Haefele, and Mayo, *J. Am. Chem. Soc.*, **62,** 2047 (1940).

[30] Kharasch and Hannum, *J. Am. Chem. Soc.*, **56,** 712 (1934).

[31] Kharasch, Hannum, and Gladstone, *J. Am. Chem. Soc.*, **56,** 244 (1934).

[32] Kharasch and Hinckley, *J. Am. Chem. Soc.*, **56,** 1212 (1934).

[33] Kharasch, Hinckley, and Gladstone, *J. Am. Chem. Soc.*, **56,** 1642 (1934).

[34] Kharasch, Kleiger, and Mayo, *J. Org. Chem.*, **4,** 428 (1939).

[35] Kharasch, Margolis, and Mayo, *J. Org. Chem.*, **1,** 393 (1936).

[36] Kharasch and Mayo, *J. Am. Chem. Soc.*, **55,** 2468 (1933).

[37] Kharasch and McNab, *J. Am. Chem. Soc.*, **56,** 1425 (1934).

[38] Kharasch, McNab, and Mayo, *J. Am. Chem. Soc.*, **55,** 2521 (1933).

[39] Kharasch, McNab, and Mayo, *J. Am. Chem. Soc.*, **55,** 2531 (1933).

[40] Kharasch, McNab, and McNab, *J. Am. Chem. Soc.*, **57,** 2463 (1935).

[41] Kharasch, Norton, and Mayo, *J. Org. Chem.*, **3,** 49 (1938).

[42] Kharasch and Potts, *J. Am. Chem. Soc.*, **58,** 57 (1936).

[43] Kharasch, Rossin, and Fields, *J. Am. Chem. Soc.*, **63,** 2558 (1941).

[44] Kharasch, Walling, and Mayo, *J. Am. Chem. Soc.*, **61,** 1559 (1939).

[45] Le Bel, *J. Am. Chem. Soc.*, **82,** 623 (1960).

[46] Leitch and More, *Can. J. Chem.*, **30,** 924 (1952).

[47] Mayo, *J. Am. Chem. Soc.*, **76,** 5392 (1954).

[48] Mayo, *Vistas in Free Radical Chemistry*, edited by Waters, Pergamon Press, New York (1959).

[49] Mayo and Walling, *Chem. Revs.*, **27**, 351 (1940).

[50] Michael and Weiner, *J. Org. Chem.*, **4**, 531 (1939).

[51] Michael and Weiner, *J. Org. Chem.*, **5**, 389 (1939).

[52] Nesmeyanov, Freidlina, and Belyavskii, *Izvest. Akad. Nauk*, **1959**, 1028.

[53] Nesmeyanov, Freidlina, and Firstov, *Izvest. Akad. Nauk*, **1951**, 505.

[54] Nesmeyanov, Freidlina, and Zakharin, *Dok. Akad. Nauk*, **81**, 199 (1951).

[55] Neureiter and Bordwell, *J. Am. Chem. Soc.*, **82**, 5354 (1960).

[56] Perklev, *Svensk Kem. Tidskr.*, **65**, 216 (1953).

[57] Price and Coyner, *J. Am. Chem. Soc.*, **62**, 1306 (1940).

[58] Quelet, Durand-Dran, and Pineau, *C. r.*, **244**, 1218 (1957).

[59] Rust and Vaughan, *J. Org. Chem.*, **7**, 491 (1942).

[60] Rust and Vaughan, U.S. 2,299,411 (1943).

[61] Rust and Vaughan, Brit. 557,602 (1943).

[62] Simamura, *Bull. Chem. Soc. Jap.*, **17**, 326 (1942).

[63] Simamura and Takahasi, *Bull. Chem. Soc. Jap.*, **22**, 60 (1949).

[64] Skell and Allen, *J. Am. Chem. Soc.*, **80**, 5997 (1958).

[65] Skell and Allen, *J. Am. Chem. Soc.*, **81**, 5383 (1959).

[66] Sommer, Tyler, and Whitmore, *J. Am. Chem. Soc.*, **70**, 2872 (1948).

[67] Sommer, *et al.*, *J. Am. Chem. Soc.*, **76**, 1613 (1954).

[68] Takahasi, *Bull. Chem. Soc. Jap.*, **29**, 625 (1956).

[69] Takahasi, *Bull. Chem. Soc. Jap.*, **29**, 973 (1956).

[70] Takebayashi, *J. Chem. Soc. Jap.*, **62**, 1107 (1941).

[71] Takebayashi, *J. Chem. Soc. Jap.*, **64**, 191 (1943).

[72] Urushibara and Takebayashi, *Bull. Chem. Soc. Jap.*, **11**, 692, 798 (1936).

[73] Urushibara and Takebayashi, *Bull. Chem. Soc. Jap.*, **12**, 138, 173 (1937).

[74] Vaughan and Rust, U.S. 2,307,552 (1943).

[75] Vaughan and Rust, Brit. 554,499 (1943).

[76] Vaughan and Rust, U.S. 2,398,481 (1946).

[77] Vaughan and Rust, Brit. 581,775 (1946).

[78] Vaughan, Rust, and Evans, *J. Org. Chem.*, **7**, 477 (1942).

[79] Walling, *Free Radicals in Solution*, p. 272, John Wiley, New York (1957).

[80] Walling, Kharasch, and Mayo, *J. Am. Chem. Soc.*, **61**, 1711 (1939).

[81] Walling, Kharasch, and Mayo, *J. Am. Chem. Soc.*, **61**, 2693 (1939).

[82] Whitmore and Homeyer, *J. Am. Chem. Soc.*, **55**, 4555 (1933).

[83] Young, Vogt, and Nieuwland, *J. Am. Chem. Soc.*, **58**, 1806 (1936).

CHAPTER II

Addition of Alkyl Polyhalides
to Unsaturated Compounds

ADDITION OF CARBON TETRACHLORIDE AND CARBON TETRABROMIDE

Carbon tetrachloride and carbon tetrabromide react with many olefins under free radical conditions to give 1:1 adducts.

$$RCH{=}CH_2 + XCX_3 \rightarrow RCHX{-}CH_2CX_3$$

X = Br, Cl

The reactions are usually carried out at 70–100°. Higher temperatures are rarely employed. The reactions are commonly carried out in an atmosphere of nitrogen gas and are initiated by peroxides such as acetyl or benzoyl peroxide, by azonitriles, or by light.

The addition of carbon tetrabromide proceeds readily in visible light. However, visible light does not initiate carbon tetrachloride reactions, and ultraviolet illumination is required. A large excess of carbon tetrachloride over the olefin is usually employed to avoid telomer formation. With carbon tetrabromide only a small excess of the halomethane is required to achieve 1:1 addition.

The reaction of carbon tetrabromide with olefins proceeds so much faster than that with carbon tetrachloride that the tetrachloride can be used as a solvent in condensations of carbon tetrabromide. Polynuclear hydrocarbons, such as styrene, 1, 2–benzanthracene, anthracene, naphthacene, and 3, 4–benzopyrene, are effective retarders in these reactions. Some additions of carbon tetrachloride to olefins are accompanied by dehydrohalogenation and yield halogenated olefins. Occasionally the addition of carbon tetrachloride is accompanied by isomerization. Carbon tetrachloride does not react with acetylenes.

Carbon tetrachloride reacts with ethylene in the presence of benzoyl peroxide or azobisisobutyronitrile at 95–105°.[18,85] The reaction is carried out in a stainless steel autoclave and the ethylene pressure is maintained at

1650–1750 psi. A complex mixture of products is obtained, the main products being the telomers I and II.

$$Cl(CH_2)_4CCl_3 \qquad\qquad Cl(CH_2)_6CCl_3$$

I   II

An additional product, which is believed to be the 1:1 adduct, b.p. 59°/24 mm, n_D 1.4794 (25°), is obtained in only 8.7% yield. The product is converted by hydrolysis to β–chloropropionic acid, b.p. 110°/20 mm, m.p. 41°. Carbon tetrabromide and ethylene react readily in visible light to give 1, 1, 1, 3–tetrabromopropane, b.p. 67°/0.3 mm, n_D 1.6090 (20°), in almost quantitative yield.[109] Carbon tetrachloride or carbon tetrabromide reacts with tetrafluoroethylene at 225–260° in 30 min to 1 hr to give 1, 1, 1, 3–tetrachloro- and 1, 1, 1, 3–tetrabromotetrafluoropropane in 20 and 26% yield, respectively.[72]

Both carbon tetrachloride and carbon tetrabromide react with higher olefins such as propene,[70,71] isobutylene,[108–110] heptene,[12,71] and octene[58,59,109] to give the corresponding 1:1 adducts in good yield. Carbon tetrabromide reacts with undecylenic acid in visible light to give a tetrabromo derivative, which was not characterized.[109] In contrast to carbon tetrachloride, carbon tetrabromide adds to styrene to give a 1:1 product, m.p. 57°, in excellent yield.[58,59,109]

Carbon tetrachloride reacts with vinyl alkyl ethers,[3,15,78,97] with vinyl aryl ethers,[3,97] or with vinyl acetate[19,90] to form the expected tetrachloro derivatives. The reactions are promoted by azonitriles, light, or benzoyl peroxide. In one case, a trace of pyridine was used in conjunction with benzoyl peroxide.[15] The influence of the ratio of reactants upon the yield of the products was investigated.[3,97]

Boiling carbon tetrachloride reacts with cyclohexyl vinyl ether in ultraviolet light or in the presence of azoisobutyronitrile to give a 1:1 adduct in 54% yield.[3] The adduct dehydrochlorinates during the distillation to give 1, 1, 3–trichloroallylcyclohexyl ether, b.p. 111°/2 mm, n_D 1.5000 (20°).

$$CCl_3CH_2CHClOR \rightarrow CCl_2=CHCHClOR$$

R = cyclohexyl

The 1:1 addition product of butyl vinyl ether undergoes a similar thermal reaction.[78] Boiling carbon tetrachloride reacts with acryloaldehyde diethyl acetal in 22 hr to give a 1:1 adduct.[17] The free acryloaldehyde itself does not undergo the reaction. The product is extremely stable against hydrolysis. Boiling concentrated hydrochloric acid is required to hydrolyze it.[17]

Carbon tetrachloride reacts with allyl compounds to give products in low yield.[59] For instance, the reaction of carbon tetrachloride with biallyl produces tetrachloroheptene in 31% yield.[59] The reaction of carbon tetrachloride with allyl ethyl ether at 70° in the presence of benzoyl peroxide yields mainly ethyl 2, 4, 4, 4–tetrachlorobutyl ether, b.p. 85°/5 mm, n_D 1.4711 (25°), and ethyl 4–ethoxymethyl–2, 6, 6, 6–tetrachlorohexyl ether, b.p. 119°/1 mm, n_D 1.4732 (25°).[91] The reaction of carbon tetrachloride with allyl acetate in ultraviolet light or in the presence of benzoyl peroxide at 95–100° yields a 1:1 product, which was not well defined.[109] The reaction of carbon tetrachloride with allylbenzene under similar conditions results in tetrachloro–4–phenylbutane in 12% yield.[71]

Interesting reactions occur between carbon tetrachloride or tetrabromide and β–chlorovinyl mercury compounds.[4] The reaction of carbon tetrachloride with either III or IV at 70° in the presence of acetyl or benzoyl peroxide produces 1, 1, 1, 3–tetrachloropropylene.

$$ClCH{=}CHHgCl + CCl_4 \rightarrow CCl_3CH{=}CHCl + HgCl_2$$

$$III$$

$$(ClCH{=}CH)_2Hg + CCl_4 \rightarrow CCl_3CH{=}CHCl + HgCl_2$$

$$IV$$

Under similar conditions carbon tetrabromide and III react to give two products.

$$ClCH{=}CHHgCl + CBr_4 \Big\langle \begin{matrix} \rightarrow CBr_3CH{=}CHCl \\ \rightarrow CBr_3CHBrCHBrCl \end{matrix}$$

Carbon tetrachloride reacts with vinylsilanes under free radical conditions.[2,16,93] Thus, carbon tetrachloride reacts with triethylvinylsilane at 84–103° in the presence of benzoyl peroxide to give the 1:1 adduct.[93] Carbon tetrabromide and vinylmethyldichlorosilane react in 11 hr at 191° in ultraviolet light to give 1, 1, 1, 3–tetrabromo–n–propylmethyldichlorosilane, b.p. 117°/1 mm, n_D 1.5796 (25°); no yield is reported.[16] The reaction of carbon tetrachloride with triphenylvinylsilane is carried out at 67–90° in the presence of benzoyl peroxide to give the expected product in high yield.[2]

$$R_3SiCH{=}CH_2 + ClCCl_3 \rightarrow (C_6H_5)_3SiCHClCH_2CCl_3$$

$$R = C_2H_5, C_6H_5$$

Prolonged heating at 100° of carbon tetrachloride with triethylvinyl tin in the presence of benzoyl peroxide produces the expected product.[96]

$$(C_2H_5)_3SnCH{=}CH_2 + CCl_4 \rightarrow (C_2H_5)_3SnCHClCH_2CCl_3$$

The reaction of carbon tetrachloride with butadiene at 110° in 4 hr results in the 1, 4–addition product in 23% yield.[92] The reaction is carried out in a pressure vessel of steel in the presence of a small amount of a mixture of ethanol, pyrogallol, and benzoyl peroxide.

$$CH_2=CHCH=CH_2 + CCl_4 \rightarrow CCl_3CH_2CH=CHCH_2Cl$$

A higher yield (62%) of the same compound is obtained when butadiene is produced *in situ* by using 2, 5–dihydrothiophene–1–dioxide.[49,92] However, 3–chloro–4–trichloromethyltetrahydrothiophene–1–dioxide (V) is also formed.[57]

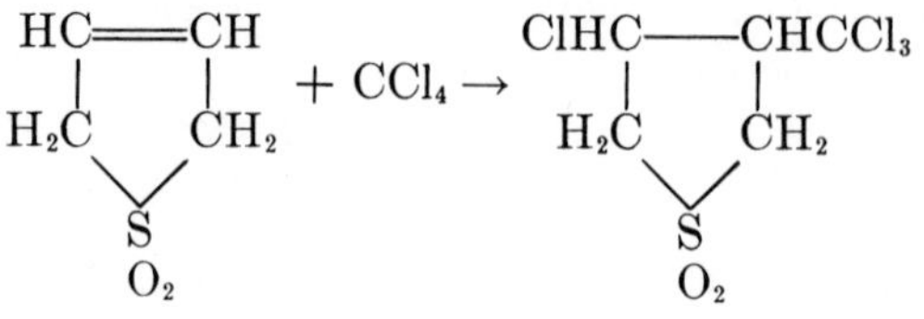

$$
\begin{array}{ccc}
HC\!\!=\!\!\!=\!\!CH & & ClHC\!\!-\!\!\!-\!\!CHCCl_3 \\
| \quad\quad | & + CCl_4 \rightarrow & | \quad\quad\quad | \\
H_2C \quad CH_2 & & H_2C \quad\quad CH_2 \\
\diagdown\!\diagup & & \diagdown\!\!\diagup \\
S & & S \\
O_2 & & O_2
\end{array}
$$

V

Boiling carbon tetrachloride reacts with dibutylethyleneboronate (VI, R = H) or with dibutylpropene–2–boronate (VI, R = CH₃) in the presence of azobisisobutyronitrile to give adducts in fair yield.[79]

$$CH_2=C(R)B(OC_4H_9)_2 \rightarrow CCl_3CH_2CRClB(OC_4H_9)_2$$

VI

Dibutyl–1–propene–1–boronate (VII), however, does not react efficiently with carbon tetrachloride.[79]

$$CH_3CH=CHB(OC_4H_9)_2$$

VII

Carbon tetrachloride reacts with several terpines, such as d–limonene, β–pinene, and camphene.[7-11,50,86,95] Carbon tetrachloride and d–limonene react slowly (24 hr) at 80–90° in the presence of benzoyl peroxide.[7,50] The reaction in ultraviolet light proceeds at a slower rate—50 hr. The addition apparently is accompanied by dehydrochlorination to give an unsaturated product (VIII).

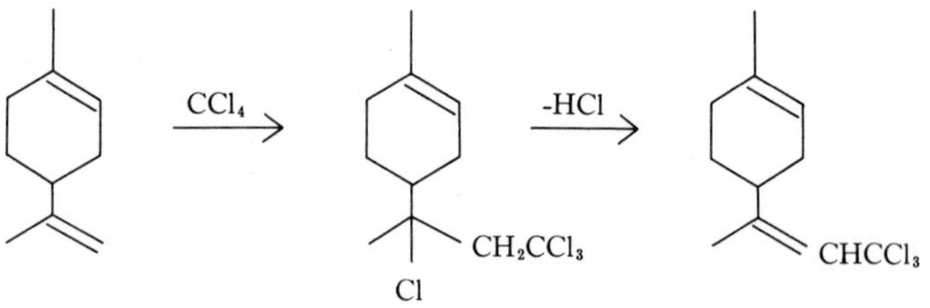

VIII

Similarly, the reaction of carbon tetrachloride with camphene, initiated with acetyl peroxide, gives the 1:1 adduct, in 45% yield, which partially dehydrochlorinates during the distillation to give IX.[10] The 1:1 adduct or compound IX can be hydrolyzed to the corresponding acid, X.

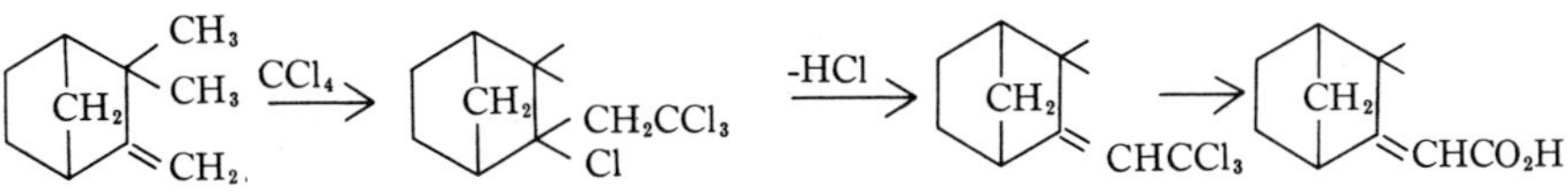

IX   X

Carbon tetrachloride adds readily to β–pinene to give XI in high yield, 85–97%.[7-11,86,95] Acetyl peroxide, benzoyl peroxide, or ultraviolet light is used as the initiator. The addition is accompanied by isomerization. The product still contains a double bond. It can be converted to the corresponding acid by saponification.

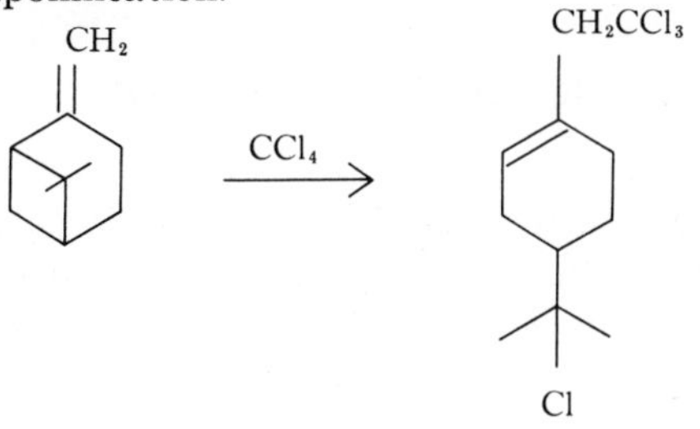

XI

The reaction of boiling carbon tetrachloride with aldrin in the presence of benzoyl peroxide for 40 hr produces a solid product (XII), m.p. 137°.[6] The addition appears to proceed by a *trans* mechanism.

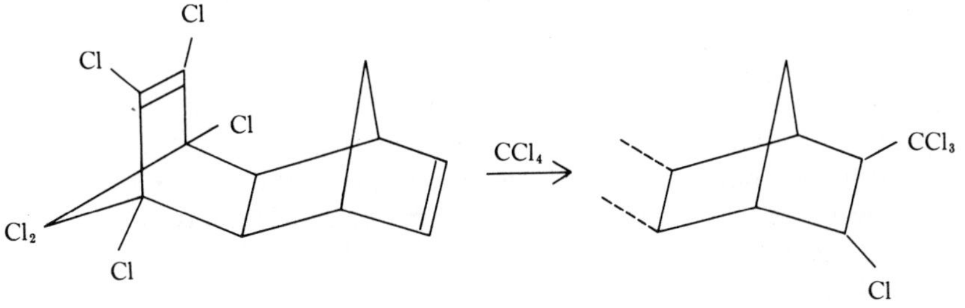

XII

The reaction of carbon tetrachloride with 5–methylenebicyclo[2.2.1]-hept–2–ene is induced by benzoyl peroxide.[48] The reaction is carried out at 86° and produces a complex mixture of products in 73% yield. The main product is believed to have structure XIII.

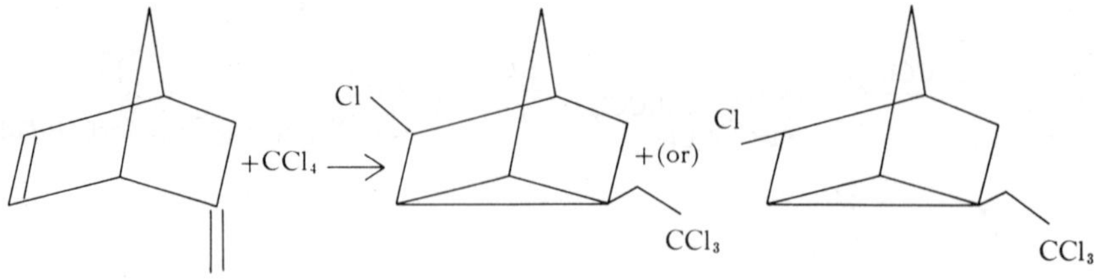

XIII

The results of the addition reactions of carbon tetrachloride and carbon tetrabromide are summarized in Table 2.

ADDITION OF BROMOTRICHLOROMETHANE

Bromotrichloromethane undergoes addition to unsaturated compounds in a manner similar to carbon tetrachloride and carbon tetrabromide. The scission of the molecule occurs preferentially at the carbon-bromine bond. The addition of bromotrichloromethane to unsaturated compounds proceeds so much faster than that of carbon tetrachloride that the reaction can be carried out in a solution of carbon tetrachloride. Little excess bromotrichloromethane over the unsaturated compound is required to give good yields of adduct without the formation of telomers. The reaction can be initiated at room temperature by visible light, by near-ultraviolet light, or with γ rays. The customary peroxide and azonitrile initiators are also widely used. With acyl peroxides or azonitriles as the initiator, the reaction is usually carried out at temperatures between 65° and 160°. The photochemical reactions are often performed at lower temperatures, between 20° and 50°.

$$RCH{=}CH_2 + BrCCl_3 \rightarrow RCHBrCH_2CCl_3$$

Skinner and co-workers[99] showed that free radical reaction of bromotrichloromethane with olefins also proceeds in the absence of initiators at temperatures around 100°. However, the yields of the products are somewhat lower than those obtained from peroxide-initiated reactions. Peroxide-initiated reactions are inhibited by 2, 6–t–butyl–4–methyl phenol, air, and nitromethane.

The reaction of bromotrichloromethane with 1–alkynes or 1–alkenes yields 1:1 products.[60] In general, the alkynes are less reactive than their

Table 2. Addition of Carbon Tetrachloride and Carbon Tetrabromide to Unsaturated Compounds

C_n	Unsaturated compound	Halocarbon	Product	% Yield	°C b.p./mm (m.p.)	n_D (°C)	Ref.
C_2	CH_2=CH_2	CCl_4	$Cl(CH_2)_4CCl_3$ + $Cl(CH_2)_6CCl_3$	57 24	112/24 143/24	1.4859 (25) 1.4824 (25)	18
	CH_2=CH_2	CBr_4	1, 1, 1, 3-Tetrabromopropane	100	67/0.3	1.6090 (20)	58, 109
	ClCH=CHHgCl (trans-β-chlorovinyl mercury)	CCl_4	CCl_3CH=CHCl	46	144	1.5072	4
	ClCH=CHHgCl	CBr_4	1, 1, 1-Tribromo-3-chloro-propylene+ $HCBrClCHBrCBr_3$	60 20	74/80 86/63	1.5408 (20) 1.5764 (20)	4
	CF_2=CF_2	CBr_4	1, 1, 1, 3-Tetrabromotetra-fluoropropane	26	91/25	1.5019 (23)	72
	CF_2=CF_2	CCl_4	1, 1, 1, 3-Tetrachlorotetra-fluoropropane	20	113	1.3948 (25)	72
C_3	Propene	CCl_4	1, 1, 1, 3-Tetrachlorobutane	55	61/15	1.4794 (20)	70, 71
	CH_2=CH(CH$_3$)SiCl$_2$	CBr_4	$CBr_3CH_2CHBrSi(CH_3)Cl_2$		116/1	1.5796 (25)	16
C_4	Isobutylene	CCl_4	1, 1, 1, 3-Tetrachloro-3-methylbutane	70	64/7	1.4850 (20)	108, 110
	Isobutylene	CBr_4	1, 1, 1, 3-Tetrabromo-3-methylbutane		78/0.3		109
	Vinyl acetate	CCl_4	1, 3, 3, 3-Tetrachloropropyl acetate+ 3-Acetoxy-1, 5, 5, 5-tetra-chloroamyl acetate	39 44	58/1.5 107/1.5	1.4700 (28) 1.4759 (28)	19, 90
	Ethyl vinyl ether	CCl_4	$CCl_3CH_2CHClOC_2H_5$	92	79/11	1.4695 (25)	15, 97
	(ClCH=CH)$_2$Hg (trans-trans-di-β-chlorovinyl mercury)	CCl_4	1, 1, 1, 3-Tetrachloropropylene	36	144	1.5078 (20)	4

Table 2. (cont.)   Addition of Carbon Tetrachloride and Carbon Tetrabromide to Unsaturated Compounds

C_n	Unsaturated compound	Halocarbon	Product	% Yield	°C b.p./mm (m.p.)	n_D (°C)	Ref.
C4	1,3-Butadiene	CCl_4	1,1,1,5-Tetrachloropentene-3	23	129/60	1.5068 (25)	49, 92
	2,5-Dihydrothiophene-1-dioxide	CCl_4	3-Chloro-4-trichloromethyl-tetrahydrothiophene	10	(127)		57
			1,1,1,5-Tetrachloropentene-3	62	129/60	1.5068 (25)	49, 92
C5	Allyl ethyl ether	CCl_4	Ethyl 2,4,4,4-tetrachloro-butyl ether + Ethyl 4-ethoxymethyl-2,6,6,6-tetrachlorohexyl ether		82/5 120/1	1.4711 (25) 1.4732 (25)	91
C6	3,3-Dimethylbutene-1	CCl_4	1,1,1,3-Tetrachloro-4,4-dimethylpentane	42	105/20	1.4834 (20)	71
	n-Butyl vinyl ether	CCl_4	1,3,3,3-Tetrachloropropyl-butyl ether	98	68/1.2	1.4680 (25)	3, 15, 78, 97
	Biallyl	CCl_4	Tetrachloroheptene	31	58/0.4	1.4913 (20)	59
C7	$CH_2{=}CHCH(OC_2H_5)_2$	CCl_4	α,γ,γ-Tetrachloro-butaldehyde diethyl acetal	18	105/1	1.4668 (20)	17
	n-Heptene-1	CCl_4	Tetrachlorooctane	80	130/19	1.4772 (20)	12, 71
C8	Octene-1	CCl_4	1,1,1,3-Tetrachlorononane	85	78/0.1	1.4770 (20)	59
	Octene-1	CBr_4	1,1,1,3-Tetrabromononane	88	127/0.2	1.5484 (20)	58, 59, 109
	Styrene	CBr_4	1,1,1,3-Tetrabromo-3-phenylpropane	96	123/0.1 (58)		58, 59, 109
	$(C_2H_5)_3SiCH{=}CH_2$	CCl_4	$CCl_3CH_2CHClSi(C_2H_5)_3$	43	138/5	1.4974 (20)	93
	$(C_2H_5)_3SnCH{=}CH_2$	CCl_4	$(C_2H_5)_3SnCHClCH_2CCl_3$	59	100/0.3	1.5230 (25)	96
	$CH_2{=}CHOC_6H_5$	CCl_4	1,1,1,3-Tetrachloropropyl-phenyl ether	66	146/12	1.5430 (20)	3, 97

Table 2. (cont.) Addition of Carbon Tetrachloride and Carbon Tetrabromide to Unsaturated Compounds

C_n	Unsaturated compound	Halocarbon	Product	% Yield	°C b.p./mm (m.p.)	n_D (°C)	Ref.
C_9	Allylbenzene	CCl_4	1,1,1,3-Tetrachloro-4-penylbutane	12	100/0.3	1.5478 (20)	71
	d-Limonene	CCl_4	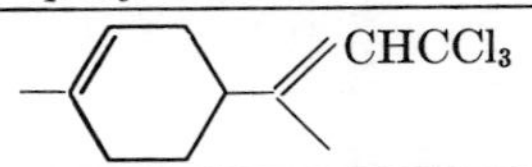 (structure) $CHCCl_3$	75	167/19	1.5260 (20)	50
C_{10}	β-Pinene	CCl_4	7-Trichloromethyl-8-chloro-p-menthene 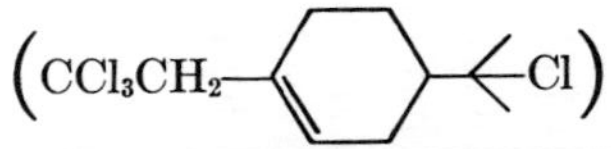 (CCl_3CH_2— structure —Cl)	85	(46)		7, 86, 95
	$CH_2{=}CHB(OC_4H_9)_2$	CCl_4	$CCl_3CH_2CHClB(OC_4H_9)_2$	45	92/0.07	1.4565 (29.3)	79
C_{11}	$CH_2{=}CB(OC_4H_9)_2$ with CH_3	CCl_4	$CCl_3CH_2C(Cl)B(OC_4H_9)_2$ with CH_3	53	94/0.07	1.4642 (22.5)	79
C_{20}	$(C_6H_5)_3SiCH{=}CH_2$	CCl_4	$(C_6H_5)_3SiCHClCH_2CCl_3$	75	(93)		2

corresponding alkenes. For example, phenyl acetylene is less reactive than styrene.

Bromotrichloromethane reacts with acetylenes such as propargyl acetate[72] or octyne–1[60] in the presence of azobisisobutyronitrile, acetyl peroxide, or ultraviolet light to give adducts in fair to good yield. Bromotrichloromethane reacts with phenyl acetylene at 60° in ultraviolet light to give a product which is believed to be 1–bromo–1–phenyl–3, 3, 3–trichloropropene.[52,60] Bromotrichloromethane reacts with ethylene or propylene in the presence of acetyl peroxide or ultraviolet light to give the corresponding products in high yield.[63] Higher olefins such as 2–methyl–1–butene, 2–ethyl–1–butene, isobutylene, allyl chloride, 2, 3–dichloropropene, methallyl chloride, allyl cyanide, vinyl acetate, octene–1, cyclohexene, allylbenzene, styrene, p–chlorostyrene, and 2, 4–dichlorostyrene also react with bromotrichloromethane; good yields of products are obtained.[52,63–66]

The acetyl peroxide-catalyzed reaction of bromotrichloromethane with butadiene yields a 1:1 product, b.p. 84°/1.5 mm, n_D 1.5349 (20°), which was not further identified.[52] The uncatalyzed reaction of bromotrichloromethane with butadiene in an autoclave at 100° produces 1–bromo–5, 5, 5–trichloropentene–2, b.p. 69°/1.6 mm, n_D 1.5328 (20°), in 10% yield.[99] When butadiene is bubbled through boiling bromotrichloromethane, 3–bromo–5, 5, 5–trichloropentene–1, n_D 1.5350 (20°), is obtained.[99]

The product of the reaction of bromotrichloromethane with α–methylstyrene reacts with ethanolic potassium hydroxide to give compound I, b.p. 67°/0.1 mm, in 40% yield.[66]

$$C_6H_5CCH_2CCl_3$$
$$\|$$
$$CH_2$$

I

Bromotrichloromethane reacts with isopropenyl acetate to give a 1:1 adduct, b.p. 38°/0.1 mm, which reacts with water to give 4, 4–dichloro–3–buten–2–one (II), 75–76°/40 mm, n_D 1.4904 (20°).[66]

$$CH_2{=}C(CH_3)OCOCH_3 + BrCCl_3 \rightarrow Cl_3CCH_2C(Br)(CH_3)OCOCH_3$$
$$\xrightarrow{H_2O} CCl_2{=}CHCOCH_3$$

II

The reaction of bromotrichloromethane with either cis–2–butene or trans–2–butene at about 10° using a 200-watt tungsten-filament lamp produces a mixture of equal quantities of two diastereomeric 1:1 addition products, b.p. 100°/20 mm.[98] Bromotrichloromethane reacts with cis– or with trans–cinnamonnitrile in the presence of benzoyl peroxide to give addition products, which cannot be purified.[46] They are converted to the same product, namely, α–dichloromethylene–β–hydroxy–β–phenylpropionitrile, b.p. 110° (bath)/0.2 mm, n_D 1.5549 (23°).[46]

The reactions between bromotrichloromethane and various alkenes are initiated by γ rays at room temperature.[45] Experiments with a 3.5-kilocurie Co^{60} source are described. The reactions are carried out in a nitrogen atmosphere for 40–60 hr. Generally the yields are high. The reaction of bromotrichloromethane with 1, 1–disubstituted alkenes results in a mixture of 1:1 adducts and dimers. In the reaction with 1, 2–disubstituted alkenes the yield of 1:1 adducts is usually poor. The reaction with cyclic alkenes produces 1:1 adducts plus 1, 2–dibromo- and 1, 2–ditrichloromethyl derivatives.

Bromotrichloromethane reacts with fluorinated olefins in the presence of benzoyl peroxide. The reaction with vinylidene fluoride at 90° in an autoclave gives the 1:1 product in good yield.[13]

$$CH_2{=}CF_2 + BrCCl_3 \rightarrow CCl_3CH_2CBrF_2$$

The reaction of bromotrichloromethane with chlorotrifluoroethylene results in a 45% yield of a product which was first assumed to have the structure III[42] but was subsequently assigned the structure IV.[43,44]

$$CCl_3CClFCF_2Br \qquad CCl_3CF_2CBrClF$$

$$III \qquad\qquad\qquad IV$$

Bromotrichloromethane reacts with difluoroprop–1–ene in the presence of acetyl peroxide to give 1–bromo–3, 3, 3–trichloro–1, 1–difluoro–2–methyl-propane in 60% yield.[29]

Bromotrichloromethane reacts with butadiene sulfone in the presence of acetyl peroxide or ultraviolet light to give 3–bromo–4–trichloromethyltetra-hydrothiophene–1–dioxide in 40–62% yield.[57] The reaction is carried out in a nitrogen atmosphere at 70–80% for 113 hr.

The photochemical reaction of bromotrichloromethane with allyl bromide is complex.[45,64,65] If excess halomethane is used, the products are 1, 2, 3–tribromopropane, in 41% yield, and 1, 1, 1, 5, 5, 5–hexachloro–3–bromo-pentane, b.p. 62°/0.05 mm, n_D 1.5456 (20°), in 36% yield. If excess allyl bromide is used, the main product is 4, 4, 4–trichloro–1–butene and the secondary product is 1, 2, 3–tribromopropane. The product boils over a wide range, 123–131°/760 mm, n_D 1.4678 (20°).

The reaction between bromotrichloromethane and 1, 1, 1–trichloropropylene at 100° in the presence of benzoyl peroxide leads mainly to a dehydrohalogenation product (V) and a rearranged product (VI).[84]

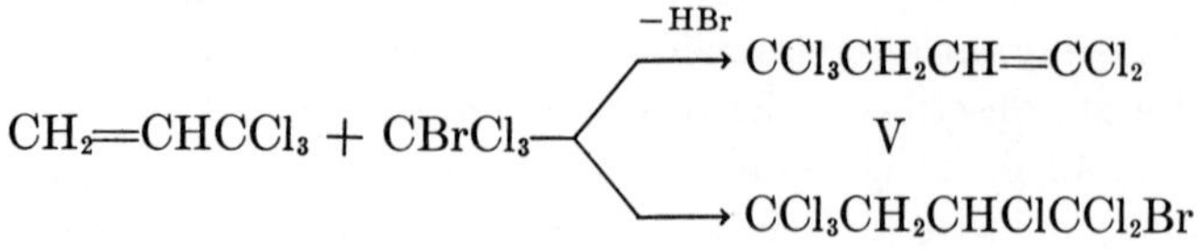

$$\text{CH}_2\text{=CHCCl}_3 + \text{CBrCl}_3 \begin{cases} \xrightarrow{-\text{HBr}} \text{CCl}_3\text{CH}_2\text{CH=CCl}_2 & \text{V} \\ \\ \longrightarrow \text{CCl}_3\text{CH}_2\text{CHClCCl}_2\text{Br} & \text{VI} \end{cases}$$

1, 1, 1, 4, 4–Pentachlorobutene–3 (V) boils at 45°/3 mm, n_D 1.5172 (20°), and 1, 1, 1, 3, 4, 4–hexachloro–4–bromobutane (VI) boils at 93°/3 mm, n_D 1.5478 (20°). The yields are 28% and 11%, respectively.

A mixture of bromotrichloromethane and dimethyl fumarate illuminated with a mercury vapor neon lamp at 50–60° for 24 hr gives a 1:1 adduct in 66% yield.[51,53] The product is first distilled at 95–108°/0.1 mm. The distillate sets to a solid (VII), m.p. 54°.

$$\text{Cl}_3\text{CCHCO}_2\text{CH}_3$$

$$\text{BrCHCO}_2\text{CH}_3$$

VII

The addition product can react with an olefin such as octene–1 in the presence of acetyl peroxide at 75–80°. When this addition product is distilled at about 160°/0.1 mm, it is dehydrobrominated to give 1, 1, 1–trichloro–2, 3–dicarbmethoxyundecene–4.

A series of interesting reactions occurs with bromotrichloromethane, various olefins, and dimethyl fumarate.[54] Heating a mixture of the three reactants to 80–90° in the presence of benzoyl peroxide produces 1:1:1 products, which on distillation eliminate hydrogen bromide to form products of the general formula VIII, containing all three starting materials.

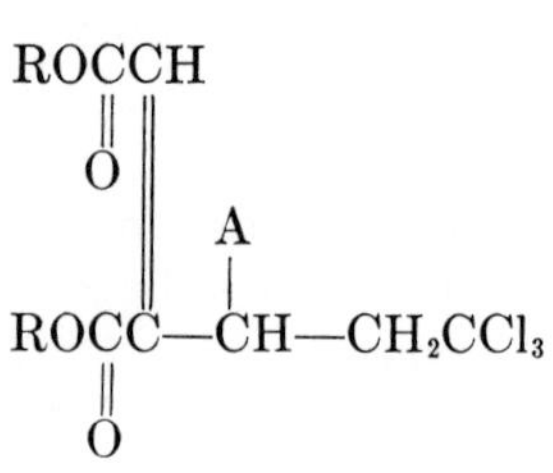

$$\begin{array}{c} \text{ROCCH} \\ \parallel \parallel \\ \text{O} \qquad \text{A} \\ \qquad \quad | \\ \text{ROCC—CH—CH}_2\text{CCl}_3 \\ \parallel \\ \text{O} \end{array}$$

VIII

R = CH₃

A = methyl, chloromethyl, vinyl, hexyl, phenyl

Table 3. Addition of Bromotrichloromethane to Unsaturated Compounds

C_n	Unsaturated compound	Product	% Yield	°C b.p./mm (m.p.)	n_D (°C)	Ref.
C_2	C_2H_4	1, 1, 1–Trichloro–2–bromopropane	95	113/104	1.5127 (20)	52, 63, 99
	$CH_2{=}CF_2$	1, 1, 1–Trichloro–3–bromo–3, 3–difluoropropane	62	85/100	1.4678 (20)	13
C_3	Vinyltrichlorosilane	$CCl_3CH_2CHBrSiCl_3$	70	139/30	1.5223 (25)	14, 16, 81
	$CH_3CH{=}CH_2$	1, 1, 1–Trichloro–3–bromobutane	95	82/20	1.5072 (20)	63
	$CH_2{=}CHCH_2Cl$	1, 1, 1, 4–Tetrachloro–3–bromo–butane	70	59/0.6	1.5337 (20)	45, 63, 99
	$CH_2{=}CClCH_2Cl$	$Cl_3CCH_2CClBrCH_2Cl$	8	52/0.03	1.5443 (20)	65
	$CH_2{=}CHCH_2Br$	1, 2, 3–Tribromopropane + 3–Bromo–1, 1, 1, 5, 5, 5–hexachloropentane	48 / 44	46/0.6 / 85/0.5	1.5456 (20)	45, 65
	1, 1–Difluoroprop–1–ene	1–Bromo–3, 3, 3–trichloro–1, 1–difluoro–2–methylpropane	65	62/0.1		29
	Vinylmethyldichlorosilane	$CCl_3CH_2CHBrSi(CH_3)Cl_2$	82	115/10	1.5175 (25)	16, 81
	2–Chloropentafluoropropene	$CF_3CBrClCF_2CCl_3$	43	119/100	1.4443 (20)	83
C_4	Butene–1	3–Bromo–1, 1, 1–trichloropentane	43	66/3		99
	Butene–2	2–Bromo–4, 4, 4–trichloro–3–methylbutane	13	95/10		98, 99
	Isobutylene	1, 1, 1–Trichloro–3–bromo–3–methylbutane	95	76/10	1.5108 (20)	52, 63
	Vinyl acetate	1–Bromo–3, 3, 3–trichloropropyl acetate	90	55/0.5	1.4969 (20)	1, 52, 63, 99
	$CH_2{=}C(CH_3)CH_2Cl$	$Cl_3CCH_2CBr(CH_3)CH_2Cl$	45	65/0.1	1.5341 (20)	65
	Allyl cyanide	3–Bromo–5, 5, 5–trichloropentano-nitrile	82	87/0.5 (15)	1.5276 (20)	45, 65

Table 3. (cont.)   Addition of Bromotrichloromethane to Unsaturated Compounds

C_n	Unsaturated compound	Product	% Yield	°C b.p./mm (m.p.)	n_D (°C)	Ref.
	Butadiene sulfone, 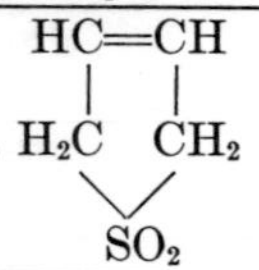 $\begin{array}{c}HC=CH\\ \mid\quad\mid\\ H_2C\quad CH_2\\ \diagdown SO_2\diagup\end{array}$	3-Bromo-4-trichloromethyltetra-hydrothiophene-1-dioxide	62	(141)		57
C_5	Propargyl acetate	2-Bromo-4, 4, 4-trichloro-2-butenyl acetate	30	88/0.6	1.5239 (20)	73
	Cyclopentene	2-Bromo-1-trichloromethyl-cyclopentane	62	61/0.8	1.5331 (20)	45, 56
	$CH_2=CHCHOC_2H_5$	$CCl_3CH_2CHBrCH_2OC_2H_5$	29	69/0.5	1.4940 (23)	106
	$CH_2=CHCH_2OCF_2CFClH$	$CCl_3CH_2CHBrCH_2OCF_2CFClH$	50	99/2	1.4645 (23)	106
C_6	$CH_2=C(C_2H_5)_2$	$Cl_3CCH_2CBr(C_2H_5)_2$	91	68/0.7	1.5156 (20)	65
	$CH_2=CHCH_2CO_2C_2H_5$	$Cl_3CCH_2CHBrCH_2CO_2C_2H_5$	92	74/0.06	1.4996 (20)	65
	Ethyl crotonate	Ethyl 2-bromo-3-trichloromethyl-butanoate	84	92/1	1.5007 (22)	46
	Dimethyl fumarate (maleate)	1, 1, 1-Trichloro-3-bromo-2, 3-dicarbomethoxypropane	66	(54)		51, 53
	Cyclohexene	2-Bromo-1-trichloromethyl-cyclohexane	64	72/0.2	1.5466 (20)	45, 56, 65
C_8	Octyne-1	1, 1, 1-Trichloro-3-bromo-2-nonene	80	mol. dist.	1.5136 (20)	60
	Octene-1	1, 1, 1-Trichloro-3-bromomonane	88	100/0.6	1.4943 (20)	45, 52, 63, 90
	$(C_2H_5)_3SnCH=CH_2$	$(C_2H_5)_3SnCHBrCH_2CCl_3$	34	115/0.65	1.5425 (25)	96
	$C_6H_5C\equiv CH$	1-Phenyl-1-bromo-3, 3, 3-trichloropropene-1	9		1.6148 (20)	52, 60

Table 3. (cont.)   Addition of Bromotrichloromethane to Unsaturated Compounds

C_n	Unsaturated compound	Product	% Yield	°C b.p./mm (m.p.)	n_D (°C)	Ref.
	Styrene	1,1,1-Trichloro-3-bromo-3-phenylpropane	78	92/0.2 (55)		45, 52, 63, 99
	p-Chlorostyrene	1-Chloro-4-(α-bromo-γ,γ,γ-trichloropropyl)benzene	80	(72)		66
C_9	CH_2=CHC_6H_3-2,4-Cl_2	$Cl_3CCH_2CHBrC_6H_3$-2,4-Cl_2	20	108/1	1.5973 (20)	65
	CH_2=$CHCH_2C_6H_5$	$Cl_3CCH_2CHBrCH_2C_6H_5$	49	79/0.05	1.5650 (20)	65
	Indene	3-Bromo-2-trichloromethylindane	79	112/0.5 (33)	1.6001 (20)	45, 56
C_{10}	CH_2=$CHB(OC_4H_9)_2$	Dibutyl 1-bromo-3,3,3-trichloro-propane-1-boronate	94	95/0.08	1.4710 (27)	79
	Benzylidene acetone	4-Bromo-4-phenyl-3-trichloro-methylbutan-2-one	43	(96)		47
C_{11}	CH_2=$C(CH_3)B(OC_4H_9)_2$	Dibutyl 2-bromo-4,4,4-trichloro-butane-2-boronate	90	112/0.1	1.4786 (24.4)	79
	CH_3CH=$CHB(OC_4H_9)_2$	Dibutyl 1-bromo-2-methyl-3,3,3-trichloropropane-1-boronate	79	113/0.08		79
	Ethyl cinnamate	Ethyl β-bromo-β-phenyl-α-trichloromethylpropionate	57	(65)		46, 65
	3,9-Divinylspirobimethadioxane	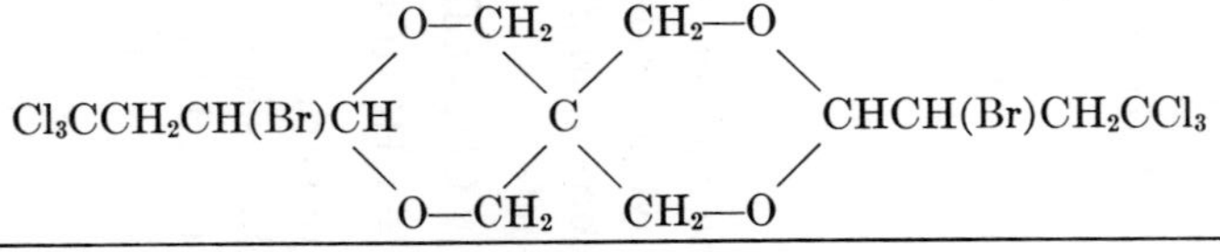 (see structure below)	57	(185)		99

Product structure for 3,9-Divinylspirobimethadioxane:

$$Cl_3CCH_2CH(Br)CH\!\!<\!\!\begin{array}{c}O-CH_2 \\ O-CH_2\end{array}\!\!>\!\!C\!\!<\!\!\begin{array}{c}CH_2-O \\ CH_2-O\end{array}\!\!>\!\!CHCH(Br)CH_2CCl_3$$

The 1:1 adducts between bromotrichloromethane and unsaturated hydrocarbons are formed as by-products. Sometimes Diels-Alder adducts are also isolated from this reaction mixture. The condensations are performed with propene, allyl chloride, butadiene, octene–1, or styrene.

Bromotrichloromethane reacts smoothly with dibutylethylene boronate (IX), dibutylpropene–2–boronate (X), and dibutyl–1–propene–1–boronate (XI) in the presence of azobisisobutyronitrile at 85–105° to give the expected addition products in excellent yield.[79] The reactions are carried out in an atmosphere of nitrogen gas.

$$CH_2{=}CHB(OC_4H_9)_2 + CBrCl_3 \rightarrow CCl_3CH_2CHBrB(O_4H_9)_2$$
IX

$$CH_2{=}CH(CH_3)B(OC_4H_9)_2 + CBrCl_3 \rightarrow CCl_3CH_2C(CH_3)BrB(O_4H_9)_2$$
X

$$CH_3CH{=}CHB(OC_4H_9)_2 + CBrCl_3 \rightarrow CH_3CH(CCl_3)CHBrB(O_4H_9)_2$$
XI

The reaction of bromotrichloromethane with allyl ethers is catalyzed by benzoyl peroxide.[106] The halomethane reacts with allyl ethyl ether or allyl β–chloro–α, α, β–trifluoroethyl ether at 90–95° in a few hours to give 1:1 products.

$$CH_2{=}CHCHOC_2H_5 + BrCCl_3 \rightarrow CCl_3CH_2CHBrCH_2OC_2H_5$$

$$CH_2{=}CHCHOCF_2CFClH + BrCCl_3 \rightarrow CCl_3CH_2CHBrCH_2OCF_2CFClH$$

Bromotrichloromethane reacts with vinyltrichlorosilane and vinylmethyldichlorosilane in ultraviolet light at 136° and 160°, respectively, to give the 1:1 adducts in high yield.[14,16,81] Similarly, bromotrichloromethane condenses with triethylvinyl tin at 90–95° in the presence of benzoyl peroxide.[96]

$$(C_2H_5)_3SnCH{=}CH_2 + BrCCl_3 \rightarrow (C_2H_5)_3SnCHBrCH_2CCl_3$$

Like carbon tetrachloride, bromotrichloromethane reacts with aldrin (XII) at 100° in the presence of benzoyl peroxide to give endo–6–bromo–6, 7–dihydro–exo–7–trichloromethylaldrin (XIII), m.p. 153°, in good yield.[6] The addition occurs in a trans manner.

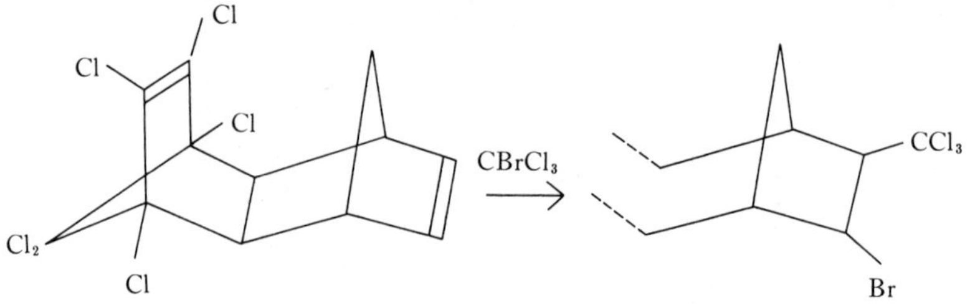

XII   XIII

Bromotrichloromethane reacts with [2.2.1]–bicyclo–2–heptene (XIV) or [2.2.2]–bicyclo–2–octene (XV) when illuminated with a mercury argon lamp to give 1:1 addition products (XVI), b.p. 72°/0.1 mm, n_D 1.5538 (20°), and XVII, b.p. 82°/0.1 mm, n_D 1.5632 (20°), respectively.[56] No yields were reported.

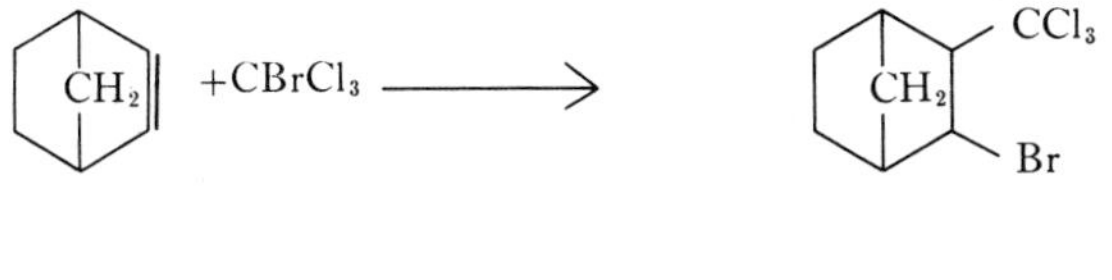

XIV   XVI

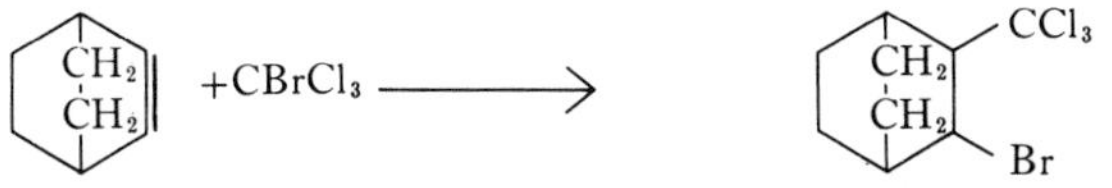

XV   XVII

The reaction of bromotrichloromethane with indene under similar conditions produces trichloromethyl–3–bromoindane (XVIII), b.p. 128°/0.1 mm, n_D 1.6001 (20°),[56] which can be hydrolyzed by 70% sulfuric acid to give indene–2–carboxylic acid (XIX), m.p. 234°. No yields were reported.

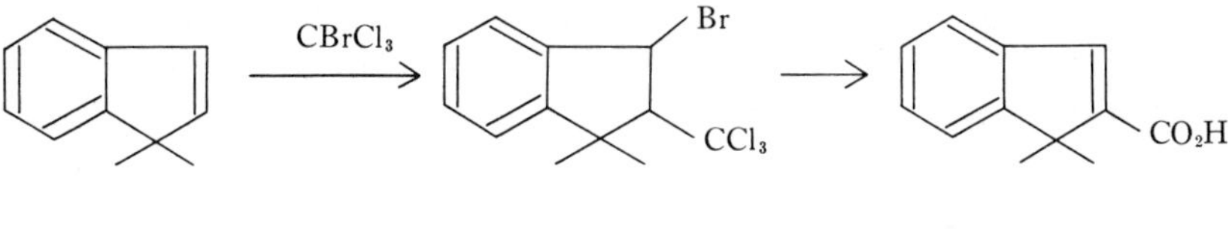

XVIII   XIX

The reaction of bromotrichloromethane with cyclopentadiene or with dicyclopentadiene produces 1:1 adducts.[56] The respective physical constants are: b.p. 42°/0.1 mm, n_D 1.5562 (20°), and b.p. 112°/0.1 mm, n_D 1.5753 (20°). No yields were reported. The reaction of bromotrichloromethane with 1, 3–cyclohexadiene probably gives product XX, m.p. 46°, in 32% yield, and product XXI, b.p. 62°/0.1 mm, n_D 1.5632 (20°), in 68% yield, by 1, 2– and 1, 4–addition, since dehydrochlorination of either XX or XXI results in the same compound, XXII.[56]

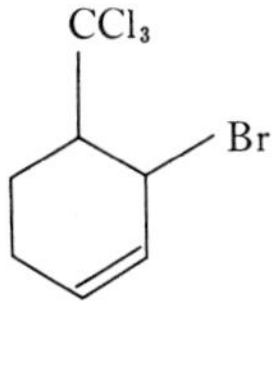

XX 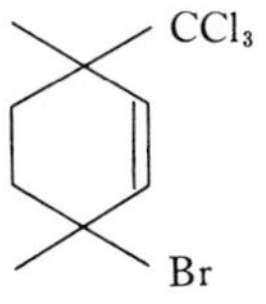   XXI 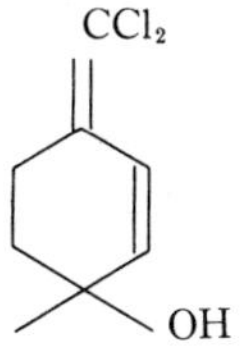   XXII

The free radical addition of bromotrichloromethane to 5–methylene-bicyclo [2.2.1] hept–2–ene (XX) is carried out at 75–80° in the presence of benzoyl peroxide and results in a complex mixture (in 61% yield) of addition products.[48] All the components of the mixture are 1:1 adducts.

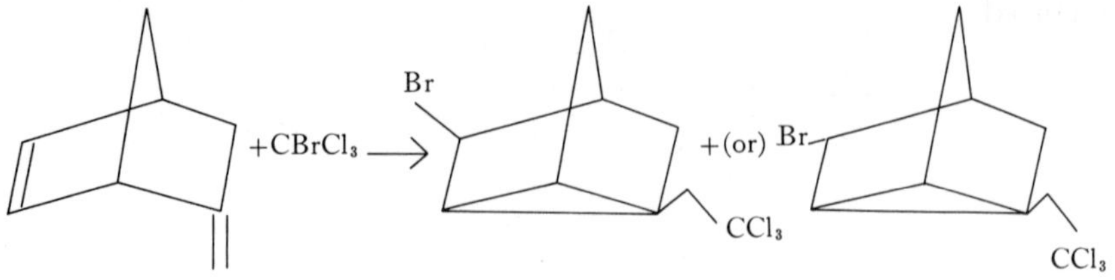

Apparently, a tricyclene derivative (XXIV) is the major addition product; this 1:1 adduct boils at approximately 120°/3 mm.

ADDITION OF TRIFLUORO- AND TRICHLOROIODOMETHANE

Trifluoroiodomethane

In most reactions of trifluoroiodomethane with acetylenes and olefins, 1:1 adducts are obtained in high yield.[28,37] The attack of the CF_3 radical upon an olefin of the structure $RCH=CH_2$ (R = CH_3, Cl, F, CO_2, CH_3, CF_3, CN) is exclusively on the terminal CH_2 group. Similarly, with perfluoroolefins of the type $RCF=CF_2$, the attack is usually on the CF_2 group.

$$CH_3C=CH + ICF_3 \rightarrow CH_3CI=CHCF_3$$

$$CH_3CH=CH_2 + ICF_3 \rightarrow CH_3CHICH_2CF_3$$

$$CF_3CF=CF_2 + ICF_3 \rightarrow CF_3CFICF_2CF_3$$

However, the CF_3 radical attacks the CH group in $CF_3CH=CF_2$ to give compound I.[38]

$$(CF_3)_2CH \cdot CF_2$$

I

The reactivity of trifluoroiodomethane is somewhere between that of carbon tetrachloride and that of bromotrichloromethane. In the dark no re-action occurs. The reactions are usually carried out in ultraviolet light of 2200–3000 A; peroxides are not used. A Hanovia fluorescent lamp can be used as a light source. All the reagents should be highly purified. The re-actions are usually carried out at room temperature in a sealed pyrex or

silica vessel. The reaction rate is faster in a silica vessel. Often the vapor
phase is illuminated while the liquid phase is shielded from the light source.
The extent of the reaction is proportional to the time of exposure to light.
The reaction time can be reduced drastically by addition of a small amount
of mercury.[21] Sometimes the addition reaction is achieved by heat.[21,32] Thermal reactions are usually carried out around 200°, and mercury increases
the rate of these reactions.

Prolonged exposure to ultraviolet light or heating above 250° may cause
the adduct to decompose, with cleavage of the carbon-iodine bond, and to
undergo further radical transformations. For example, the photochemical
reaction of trifluoroiodomethane with ethylene results in the formation of
two main products, 3–iodo–1, 1, 1–trifluoropropane and 5–iodo–1, 1, 1–
trifluoropentane.[21] The thermal reaction of these products produces 1, 1, 1–
trifluoropropane, in 33% yield, and 1, 1, 1–trifluoropentane, in 26% yield.
Acetylene,[22,23,32] ethylene,[21,32] propyne,[33,77] and propylene[27] all react with
trifluoroiodomethane to give 1:1 adducts in high yield. The reaction with
acetylene often stops at the ethylene stage. For example, the reaction of trifluoroiodomethane with excess acetylene produces 3, 3, 3–trifluoro–1–
iodopropene–1 in 80% yield.[22,23]

The photochemical reaction of trifluoroiodomethane with chlorotrifluoroethylene or with 1, 1–difluoroethylene yields 1–chlorohexafluoro–1–
iodopropane[39,42–44] and 1, 1, 1, 3, 3–pentafluoro–3–iodopropane,[37] respectively.

$$CF_3I + CF_2=CClF \rightarrow CF_3CF_2CClFI$$

$$CF_3I + CF_2=CH_2 \rightarrow CF_3CH_2CF_2I$$

A mixture of trifluoroiodomethane and 3, 3, 3–trifluoropropene–1 reacts
in 5 days under the influence of ultraviolet light to give trifluoroiodomethane, b.p. $-22°$, in 47% yield, trifluoropropane in 19% yield, 1, 1, 1, 4,
4, 4–hexafluoro–2–iodobutane in 65% yield, plus some other products in
much lower yields.[24] The 1:1 adduct is obtained in nearly quantitative yield
when the liquid phase is shielded from the irradiation; the reaction is completed after 3 days of irradiation.

The photochemical reaction of trifluoroiodomethane with allene yields one
product (II); the radical attack is on the CH_2 group exclusively.[34]

$$CH_2=C=CH_2 + CF_3I \rightarrow CF_3CH_2CI=CH_2$$

II

The photochemical condensation of trifluoroiodomethane with acrylonitrile
results in an adduct, which was not isolated in pure form.[25] However,

hydrolysis of the 1:1 adduct with alcoholic potassium hydroxide produces the expected γ, γ, γ–trifluorocrotonic acid.

$$CF_3I + CH_2{=}CHCN \rightarrow CF_3CH_2CHICN$$
$$CF_3CH_2CHICN \xrightarrow{\text{OH}^-} CF_3CH{=}CHCO_2H$$

The thermal condensation of trifluoroiodomethane with perfluoropropene at 1800–3500 psi and 200° for 113 hr produces a 1:1 adduct in 48% yield.[41]

Photochemical reactions of trifluoroiodomethane with allyl alcohol or propargyl alcohol produce the 1:1 adduct in 50% and 46% yield, respectively.[87]

$$CH_2{=}CHCH_2OH + CF_3I \rightarrow CF_3CH_2CHICH_2OH$$

$$HC{\equiv}CCH_2OH + CF_3I \rightarrow CF_3CH{=}CICH_2OH$$

Photochemical reactions also occur between trifluoroiodomethane and unsaturated silanes.[14]

$$CH_2{=}CHSi(CH_3)_3 + CF_3I \rightarrow CF_3CH_2CHISi(CH_3)_3$$

$$CH_2{=}CHSiCl_3 + CF_3I \rightarrow CF_3CH_2CHISiCl_3$$

Trichloroiodomethane

In contrast to trifluoroiodomethane, very little work has been done with trichloroiodomethane. Like the trifluoro compound, trichloroiodomethane reacts with fluorinated acetylenes and olefins at room temperature under the influence of ultraviolet light. The reactions can also be carried out thermally at about 200°.[26,82]

The photochemical reaction of trichloroiodomethane with trifluorochloroethylene for 5 days results in the 1:1 adduct in good yield.[82]

$$CCl_3I + CF_2{=}CClF \rightarrow CCl_3CF_2CClFI$$

The photochemical reaction of trichloroiodomethane with 3, 3, 3–trifluoropropyne for 36 hr results in 1, 1, 1–trichloro–4, 4, 4–trifluoro–3–iodobut–2–ene, which can be hydrogenated and the product hydrolyzed to give γ, γ, γ–trifluorocrotonic acid, m.p. 51°.[26] Similarly, the photochemical or thermal reaction of trichloroiodomethane with 3, 3, 3–trifluoropropene produces a 1:1 adduct, $CF_3CHICH_2CCl_3$, which on dehydrogenation and subsequent hydrolysis forms γ, γ, γ–trifluorocrotonic acid.[26] The photochemical reaction of trichloroiodomethane with hexafluorobutadiene results in a product, n_D 1.4562 (20°), with this possible structure[82]:

$$CCl_3CF_2CF{=}CFCF_2I$$

Table 4. Addition of Trifluoro- and Trichloroiodomethane to Unsaturated Compounds

C_n	Unsaturated compound	Halocarbon	Product	% Yield	°C b.p./mm	n_D (°C)	Ref.
C₂	C_2H_2	CF_3I	$CF_3CH=CHI$	78	70	1.420 (25)	22, 23
	C_2H_4	CF_3I	1, 1, 1–Trifluoro–3–iodopropane + 1, 1, 1–Trifluoro–5–iodopentane	82	90 153	1.423 (17) 1.439 (17)	21
	$CH_2=CHCl$	CF_3I	3–Chloro–1, 1, 1–trifluoro–3–iodopropane	97	120	1.453 (20)	27
	$CH_2=CHF$	CF_3I	1, 1, 1, 3–Tetrafluoro–3–iodopropane	84	86/757	1.4024 (20)	27
	1, 1–Difluoroethylene	CF_3I	1, 1, 1, 3, 3–Pentafluoro–3–iodopropane	90	72	1.373 (20)	37
	$CF_2=CHF$	CF_3I	1, 1, 1, 2, 3, 3, 3–Hexafluoro–3–iodopropane + 1, 1, 1, 2, 2, 3–Hexafluoro–3–iodopropane	85	62	1.355 (20)	40
	$CF_2=CFCl$	CF_3I	1–Chlorohexafluoro–1–iodopropane	84	58/330	1.381 (20)	36
	$CF_2=CFCl$	CCl_3I	CCl_3CF_2CClFI	77	74/10	1.5080 (20)	82
	Chloro–1, 1–difluoroethylene	CF_3I	3–Chloro–1, 1, 1, 2, 2,–pentafluoro–3–iodopropane	94	104	1.404 (20)	39
	$CH_2=CHSiCl_3$	CF_3I	Trichloro–(3, 3, 3–trifluoro–1–iodopropyl)silane	35	79/25		14
	$CF_2=CF_2$	CF_3I	Heptafluoro–1–iodopropane	94	39		30
C₃	$CH_3C≡CH$	CF_3I	1, 1, 1–Trifluoro–3–iodobut–2–ene	91	95	1.4352 (20)	33, 77
	$CH_3CH=CH_2$	CF_3I	1, 1, 1–Trifluoro–3–iodobutane	98	104/763	1.4277 (20)	27
	$CH_2=C=CH_2$	CF_3I	4, 4, 4–Trifluoro–2–iodobut–1–ene	96	58/160	1.4312 (20)	34

Table 4. (cont.)   Addition of Trifluoro- and Trichloroiodomethane to Unsaturated Compounds

C_n	Unsaturated compound	Halocarbon	Product	% Yield	°C b.p./mm	n_D (°C)	Ref.
	$CH_2=CHCH_2Cl$	CF_3I	1–Chloro–4, 4, 4–trifluoro–2–iodobutane	89	88/69	1.476 (20)	34
	$CF_3C≡CH$	CCl_3I	1, 1, 1–Trichloro–4, 4, 4–trifluoroiodobut–2–ene	74	108/27		26
	$CF_3C≡CH$	CF_3I	1, 1, 1, 4, 4, 4–Hexafluoro–2–iodobut–2–ene	38	76	1.3758 (16)	77
	$CF_3CH=CH_2$	CCl_3I	$CF_3CHICH_2CCl_3$	57	120/53		26
	$CF_3CH=CH_2$	CF_3I	1, 1, 1, 4, 4, 4–Hexafluoro–2–iodobutane	98	88	1.371 (25)	24
	1, 1–Difluoroprop–1–ene	CF_3I	1, 1, 1, 3, 3–Pentafluoro–3–iodo–2–methylpropane	77	95/760	1.394 (20)	29
	1, 1, 3, 3, 3–Pentafluoropropene	CF_3I	1, 1, 1, 3, 3–Pentafluoro–3–iodo–2–trifluoromethyl-propane	80	80	1.347 (20)	38
	$CF_3CF=CF_2$	CF_3I	Nonafluoro–2–iodobutane + $CF_3ClFCF_2CF_3$	94	66	1.340 (20) 1.3282 (25)	28, 41
	$CH≡CCH_2OH$	CF_3I	2–Iodo–4, 4, 4–trifluoro–2–butenol	46	75/10	1.4782 (20)	87
	$CH_2=CHCH_2OH$	CF_3I	4, 4, 4–Trifluoro–2–iodobutanol	50	105/60	1.4630 (25)	87
C_4	Methyl acrylate	CF_3I	Methyl–γ, γ, γ–trifluoro–α–iodobutyrate	88	82/42	1.440 (20)	27
	Perfluorocyclobutene	CF_3I	Hexafluoro–1–iodo–2–trifluoromethylcyclobutane	67	86		35
	Perfluorobutene–2	CF_3I	Octafluoro–2–iodo–3–trifluoromethylcyclobutane	79	86		35

Table 4. (cont.)   Addition of Trifluoro- and Trichloroiodomethane to Unsaturated Compounds

C_n	Unsaturated compound	Halocarbon	Product	% Yield	°C b.p./mm	n_D (°C)	Ref.
	3, 3, 3–Trifluoro–2–tri-fluoromethylprop–1–ene	CF_3I	1, 1, 1, 4, 4, 4–Hexafluoro–2–iodo–2–trifluoromethylbutane	71	20/20		29
	Pentafluoroethyl acetylene	CF_3I	1, 1, 1, 4, 4, 5, 5, 5–Octa-fluoro–3–iodopent–2–ene	29	85	1.3623 (16)	77
C_5	$CH_2{=}CHSi(CH_3)_3$	CF_3I	Trimethyl–(3, 3, 3–trifluoro–1–iodopropyl)silane	79	72/20		14
C_6	Perfluorocyclohexene	CF_3I	Decafluoro–1–iodo–2–tri-fluoromethylcyclohexane	68	132		35

ADDITION OF DIBROMODIFLUOROMETHANE AND BROMOCHLORODIFLUOROMETHANE

Dibromodifluoromethane adds readily to unsubstituted olefins and to fluoroolefins under free radical conditions to give 1:1 adducts.

$$CH_3CH{=}CH_2 + BrCBrF_2 \rightarrow CH_3CHBrCH_2CBrF_2$$

In condensations with fluoroolefins the BrF_2C radical combines with the carbon atom of the double bond which carries the fewer fluorine atoms.

$$CF_2{=}CFH + BrCBrF_2 \rightarrow CF_2BrCFHCBrF_2$$

Most of the condensations are carried out in the presence of benzoyl peroxide in an autoclave at 90–100°.[13,102,104,105] Reactions can also be initiated by γ rays from a Co^{60} source.[13]

The products obtained from these addition reactions are valuable intermediates, since they can be converted to fluoroolefins, dienes, and cyclic compounds. For example, the reaction product of dibromodifluoromethane and 2–methylpropene may lose both bromine atoms as hydrogen bromide, to give 1, 1–difluoro–3–methyl–1, 3–butadiene.[103] Substitution of one bromine atom in dibromodifluoromethane by chlorine does not appreciably change the reactivity of the molecule. Thus, bromochlorodifluoromethane reacts readily with a number of olefins in the presence of benzoyl peroxide.

The addition of bromochlorodifluoromethane follows the same course as that of dibromodifluoromethane and bromotrichloromethane. Namely, the carbon-bromine bond is ruptured and the $CClF_2$ radical adds to the methylene end of the terminal double bond. The reactions are carried out in an autoclave at 80–100°.[103]

$$CClF_2Br + CH_2{=}CHCH_3 \rightarrow CClF_2CH_2CHBrCH_3$$

The reaction of dibromodifluoromethane with trifluoroethylene in the presence of benzoyl peroxide was first reported to give the 1:1 product (I), b.p. 35°/79 mm, n_D 1.3816 (25°), in 9% yield, and the 2:1 product (II), b.p. 62°/25 mm, n_D 1.4237 (25°), in 18% yield.[105]

$CF_2BrCHFCF_2Br$	$CF_2Br(CHFCF_2)_2Br$	CF_2BrCF_2CFHBr
I	II	III

Later this condensation was repeated, and the 1:1 adduct was found to be composed of 80% of I and 20% of III.[40] This condensation was again repeated recently;[5] either benzoyl peroxide at 100° (4 hr) or t–butyl perbenzoate at 120° (6 hr) was used as the initiator. Mixtures of I and III in a ratio of 2.4 and 1.0, respectively, were obtained.

Table 5. Addition of Dibromodifluoromethane and Bromochlorodifluoromethane to Unsaturated Compounds

C_n	Unsaturated compound	Halomethane	Product	% Yield	°C b.p./mm	n_D (°C)	Ref.
C_2	$CH_2=CF_2$	$BrClF_2C$	$CF_2ClCH_2CF_2Br$	35	79/760	1.3669 (25)	103
C_3	Propylene	$BrClF_2C$	$CF_2ClCH_2CHBrCH_3$	42	55/55	1.4194 (25)	103
C_4	$CH_3CH=CHCH_3$	$BrClF_2C$	$CF_2ClCH(CH_3)CHBrCH_3$	73	62/49	1.4321 (25)	103
	Isobutylene	$BrClF_2C$	$CF_2ClCH_2CBr(CH_3)_2$	22	69/86	1.4281 (25)	103
C_2	$CH_2=CH_2$	Br_2F_2C	1,3-Dibromo-1,1-difluoro-propane	23	62/86	1.4450 (25)	102
	$CH_2=CHF$	Br_2F_2C	CF_2BrCH_2CHFBr	34	115/760	1.4256 (25)	105
	$CH_2=CF_2$	Br_2F_2C	$CF_2BrCH_2CF_2Br+$ $CF_2Br(CH_2CF_2)_2Br$	28 23	43/85 54/14	1.3974 (25) 1.4032 (25)	13, 105
C_3	$CH_3CH=CH_2$	Br_2F_2C	1,3-Dibromo-1,1-difluoro-butane	67	60/50	1.4469 (25)	102, 104
	$CH_3CF=CH_2$	Br_2F_2C	$CF_2BrCH_2CFBrCH_3$	58	52/35	1.4346 (25)	104, 105
	$CHF=CHCH_3$	Br_2F_2C	$CF_2BrCHFCHBrCH_3$	55	56/43	1.4403 (25)	105
C_4	2-Butene	Br_2F_2C	1,3-Dibromo-1,1-difluoro-2-methylbutane	75	72/39	1.4621 (25)	102, 104
	Isobutylene	Br_2F_2C	1,3-Dibromo-1,1-difluoro-3-methylbutane	64	79/66	1.4632 (25) 1.4527 (25)	102, 104 107
	$CH_3CF=CHCH_3$	Br_2F_2C	$CF_2BrCH(CH_3)CFBrCH_3$	75	65/30	1.4469 (25)	104, 105
	$CH_2=C(CF_3)CH_3$	Br_2F_2C	$CF_2BrCH_2CBr(CF_3)CH_3$		59/42	1.4715 (26.5)	104
C_5	Allyl acetate	Br_2F_2C	$CF_2BrCH_2CHBrCH_2OCOCH_3$	41	72/2		13
	$CH_2=CHCH_2OC_2H_5$	Br_2F_2C	$CF_2BrCH_2CHBrCH_2OC_2H_5$	31	55/2	1.4510 (23)	106
	$CH_2=CHCH_2OCF_2CFClH$	Br_2F_2C	$CF_2BrCH_2CHBrCH_2OCF_2CFClH$	46	65/2	1.4301 (23)	106
	$CH_2=CHSi(CH_3)_3$	Br_2F_2C	$CF_2BrCH_2CHBrSi(CH_3)_3$	79	95/25		14
C_8	$C_6H_{13}CH=CH_2$	Br_2F_2C	1,3-Dibromo-1,1-difluoro-nonane	55	76/1	1.4591 (25)	102

Dibromodifluoromethane condenses with allyl ethyl ether or with β–chloro–α, α, β–trifluoroethyl ether in the presence of benzoyl peroxide to the following adducts.[106]

$$CH_2{=}CHCH_2OC_2H_5 + CBr_2F_2 \rightarrow CF_2BrCH_2CHBrCH_2OC_2H_5$$

$$CH_2{=}CHCH_2OCF_2CFClH + CBr_2F_2 \rightarrow CF_2BrCH_2CHBrCH_2OCF_2CFClH$$

The products of bromochlorodifluoromethane and olefin reactions are different in their reactivity from those of dibromodifluoromethane and olefins, since they only lose one mole of hydrogen bromide to give olefins. For example, bromochlorodifluoromethane and 2–methylpropene adduct is dehydrobrominated to give 1–chloro–1, 1–difluoro–3–methyl–2–butene.[103]

ADDITION OF CHLOROFORM, BROMOFORM, IODOFORM, BROMODICHLOROMETHANE, AND DIBROMODICHLOROMETHANE

Chloroform, bromoform, and iodoform react with terminal olefins. These reactions readily produce telomers.[18,85] In chloroform, scission of the molecule occurs at the carbon-hydrogen bond. In contrast to chloroform, bromoform and iodoform cleave at the carbon-halogen bond to produce CHX_2 and X radicals (X = Br, I).[114]

$$RCH{=}CH_2 + HCCl_3 \rightarrow RCH_2CH_2CCl_3$$

$$RCH{=}CH_2 + BrCHBr_2 \rightarrow RCHBrCH_2CHBr_2$$

The reactions are initiated by azonitrile, acetyl or benzoyl peroxide, or ultraviolet light.[2,6,7,12,20,58,59,93,109,114] The reaction of chloroform with ethylene either at 95° in the presence of an azonitrile or benzoyl peroxide or at 160° in the presence of ethyl lead produces only a mixture of telomers.[18,20,85] In contrast to carbon tetrachloride, the condensation of chloroform with dibutylethylene boronate in the presence of azobisisobutyronitrile leads to a mixture of telomers.[79] Chloroform reacts with heptene–1 at 90° to give 1, 1, 1–trichlorooctane in 23% yield.[12] Chloroform reacts with octene–1 to give 1, 1, 1–trichloro-nonane in 22% yield.[59] The reaction of chloroform with β–pinene, as in carbon tetrachloride addition, gives a rearranged product.[7]

In reactions with alkenes, bromodichloromethane and dibromodichloro-methane resemble bromoform rather than chloroform in their behavior.[55,61] Thus cleavage of the carbon-bromine bond occurs.

$$RCH{=}CH_2 + BrCHCl_2 \rightarrow RCHBrCH_2CHCl_2$$

$$RCH{=}CH_2 + Br_2CCl_2 \rightarrow RCHBrCH_2CBrCl_2$$

The reactions can be initiated by ultraviolet light or by diacetyl peroxide at 70–100°. The yields range between 50 and 80%. The reaction of bromo-dichloromethane with propylene, isobutylene, vinyl acetate, or octene–1 produces 1:1 adducts.[55,61] The reaction of dibromodichloromethane with propylene or isobutylene also yields 1:1 adducts.[55,61]

Chloroform reacts with vinylsilanes such as dimethyldivinylsilane,[2] triethylvinylsilane,[2,93] and triphenylvinylsilane[2] in the presence of benzoyl peroxide at 67–90° to give 1:1 products in 12, 37–48, and 69% yield, respectively. Chloroform adds to tri–n–butylvinylgermane in the presence of benzoyl peroxide to give the expected 1:1 product.[80] The yield was not reported. Chloroform also reacts with triethylvinyl tin to give the 1:1 adduct in 25% yield.[96] The reaction of boiling chloroform with 6–chloro- or with 6–bromoaldrin (I) in the presence of benzoyl peroxide for about 200 hr produces the adduct II.[6]

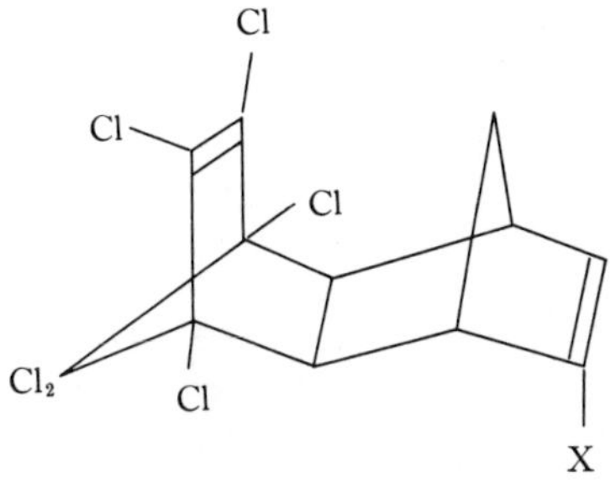

I   X = Br,Cl

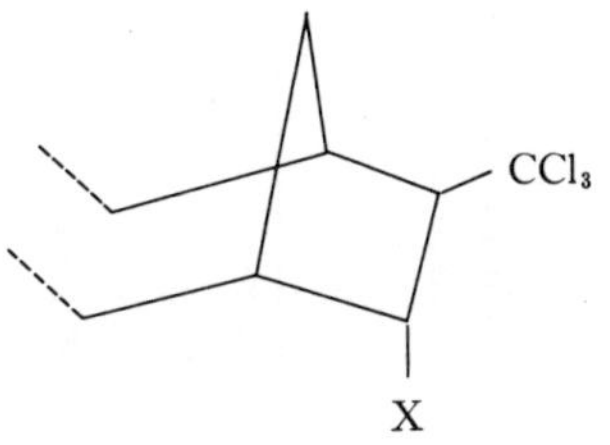

II   X = Cl, m.p. 137°

X = Br, m.p. 152°

The products are identical with those obtained from the reaction of aldrin with carbon tetrachloride or bromotrichloromethane.[6]

Bromoform adds to octene–1 in the presence of acetyl peroxide at 80° to give 1, 1, 3–tribromononane in good yield.[58,59,109] No reaction occurs under the influence of a mercury vapor lamp. Chloroform reacts with styrene in the presence of benzoyl peroxide to give phenyltribromopropane in 10% yield.[59] The addition of chloroform to 5–methylenebicyclo–[2.2.1]–hept–2–ene (III) is carried out at 70° in the presence of benzoyl peroxide; a complex mixture of products is formed in 42% yield.[48] The main product probably has the structure of IV.[48]

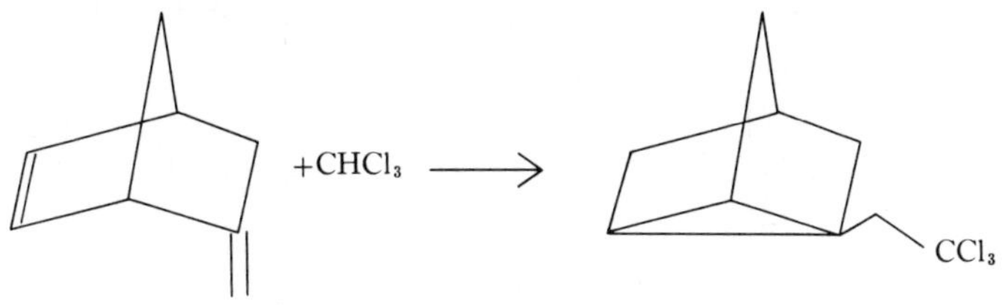

+CHCl$_3$ $\longrightarrow$

CCl$_3$

III   IV

Table 6.   Addition of Chloroform, Bromoform, Bromodichloromethane, and Dibromodichloromethane to Unsaturated Compounds

C_n	Unsaturated compound	Halomethane	Product	% Yield	°C b.p./mm (m.p.)	n_D (°C)	Ref.
C_3	$CH_3CH=CH_2$	$BrCl_2CH$	1,1-Dichloro-3-bromobutane		75/30	1.4912 (20)	55, 61
C_4	Isobutylene	$BrCl_2CH$	1,1-Dichloro-3-bromo-3-methylbutane		72/12	1.4950 (20)	55, 61
	Vinyl acetate	$BrCl_2CH$	1-Bromo-3,3-dichloropropyl acetate	100	58/0.2	1.4785 (20)	55, 61
C_8	Octene-1	$BrCl_2CH$	1,1-Dichloro-3-bromononane	82	65/0.03	1.4842 (20)	55, 61
C_6	Dimethyldivinylsilane	$CHCl_3$	$CH_2=CHSi(CH_3)_2(CH_2)_2CCl_3$	12	36/0.5	1.4743 (20)	2
C_8	Octene-1	$CHCl_3$	1,1,1-Trichlorononane	22	67/0.5	1.4620 (20)	59
	Octene-1	$CHBr_3$	1,1,3-Tribromo-n-nonane	31–100	100/0.3	1.5178 (20)	58, 59, 109
	$(C_2H_5)_3SiCH=CH_2$	$CHCl_3$	$(C_2H_5)_3Si(CH_2)_2CCl_3$	37	74/0.3 116/3	1.4767 (20) 1.4785 (20)	2 93
	$(C_2H_5)_3SnCH=CH_2$	$CHCl_3$	$(C_2H_5)_3SnCH_2CH_2CCl_3$	25	74/0.25	1.5086 (25)	96
C_{14}	$(n-C_4H_9)_3GeCH=CH_2$	$CHCl_3$	$(n-C_4H_9)_3Ge(CH_2)_2CCl_3$		156/0.5	1.4855 (20)	80
C_{20}	$(C_6H_5)_3SiCH=CH_2$	$CHCl_3$	$(C_6H_5)_3Si(CH_2)_2CCl_3$	69	(141)		2
C_3	$CH_3CH=CH_2$	Br_2Cl_2C	1,1-Dichloro-1,3-dibromobutane	90	36/0.05	1.5369 (20)	55, 61
C_4	Isobutylene	Br_2Cl_2C	1,1-Dichloro-1,3-dibromo-3-methylbutane	82	53/0.3	1.5385 (20)	61

Iodoform and limonene react in the presence of acetyl peroxide to give product V, b.p. 75°/25 mm.[114]

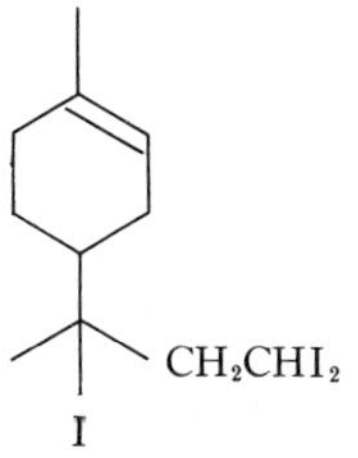

I

V

ADDITION OF DERIVATIVES OF α-HALOGENATED ALIPHATIC ACIDS

α–Bromo- and α–chloroesters,[62,67–69,111] -nitriles,[76] and -acid chlorides[68,69] react with unsaturated compounds in the presence of a free radical initiator to give 1:1 adducts.

$$RCH{=}CH_2 + XCH_2CO_2R \rightarrow RCHXCH_2CH_2CO_2R$$

$$RCH{=}CH_2 + XCH_2CN \rightarrow RCHXCH_2CN$$

$$RCH{=}CH_2 + XCH_2COCl \rightarrow RCHXCH_2COCl$$

R, R' = alkyl

In most cases a 4- to 5-fold excess of the α–halo compound over the olefin is used. The reactions are usually carried out at 70–100°. They are initiated by a small amount of diacetyl peroxide or dibenzoyl peroxide.[62,67–69,94,111]

When gaseous olefins such as propylene are used, the halogenated liquid reactant is first saturated with the olefins at 40–45 psi, the heavy pyrex glass vessel is sealed, and the reaction is then allowed to take place.[67] The reactions are not markedly exothermic. All the equipment is purged with nitrogen gas before the reaction is started. Most of the products can be purified by distillation. Very high-boiling compounds are purified by molecular distillation in high vacuum. Most of the products of such condensations are listed in Table 7 and need no further elaboration. However, a few condensations warrant comment.

The reaction of diethyl α, α–dichloromalonate with ethylene in the presence of benzoyl peroxide at 70° at 240 psi (autoclave) produces mainly the following products: diethyl α–chloro–α–(2–chloroethyl)malonate, b.p. 87°/2 mm, n_D 1.446 (20°); diethyl α–chloro–α–(4–chlorobutyl)malonate, b.p. 127°/2 mm, n_D 1.458 (20°); and diethyl α–chloro–α–(6–chlorohexyl)-malonate, b.p. 136°/2 mm.[74] The reaction of ethyl α, α–dichloroacetoacetate with octene–1 at 80° in the presence of benzoyl peroxide in 48 hr gives the 1:1 adduct, ethyl α–chloro–α–(2–chlorooctyl)acetoacetate (I), b.p. about 125°/0.3 mm, n_D 1.464 (20°), in 25% yield.[74]

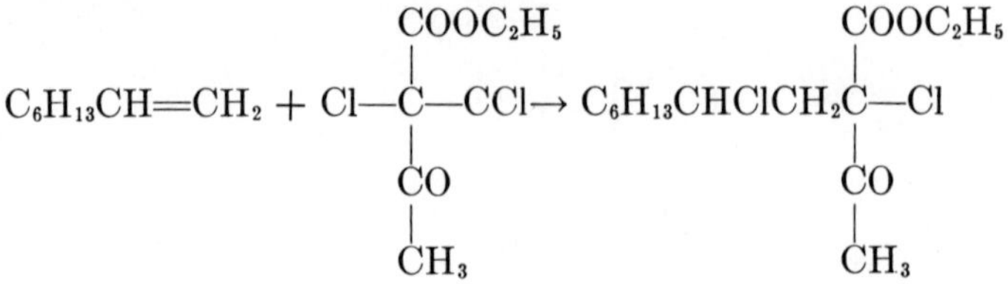

$$C_6H_{13}CH{=}CH_2 + Cl{-}\overset{\displaystyle COOC_2H_5}{\underset{\displaystyle \underset{\displaystyle CH_3}{CO}}{C}}{-}CCl \rightarrow C_6H_{13}CHClCH_2\overset{\displaystyle COOC_2H_5}{\underset{\displaystyle \underset{\displaystyle CH_3}{CO}}{C}}{-}Cl$$

$$I$$

Ethyl bromoacetate adds to triethylvinylsilane in the presence of benzoyl peroxide at 67–90°.[2]

$$(C_2H_5)_3SiCH{=}CH_2 + BrCH_2CO_2C_2H_5 \rightarrow C_2H_5SiCHBr(CH_2)_2CO_2C_2H_5$$

Ethyl α–bromoacetate also reacts with triethylvinylgermane.[80] The reaction of ethylbromoacetate with camphene in the presence of acetyl peroxide gives a 1:1 adduct (II) in 50% yield.[10] The adduct is converted with alcoholic potassium hydride to the unsaturated acid (III).

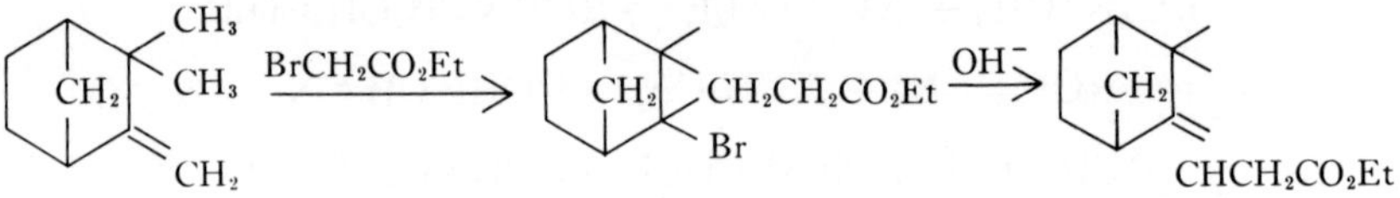

II

III

Like the addition reaction of carbon tetrachloride to β–pinene, the reaction of ethyl bromoacetate is accompanied by a rearrangement, to give ethyl bromo–7–menthene–3–yl–10–acetate (IV).[10]

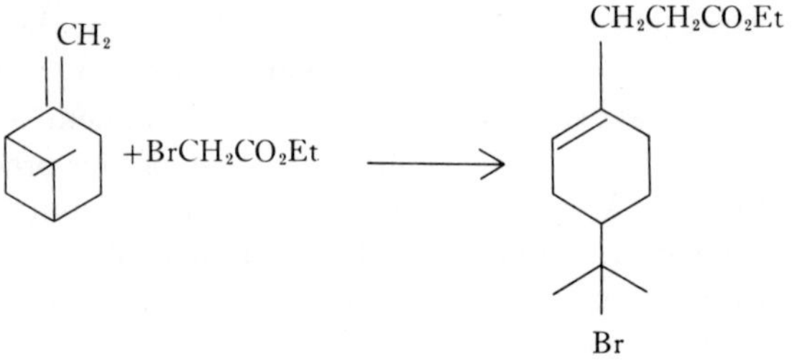

IV

The reaction of ethyl bromoacetate with bicyclo–[2.2.1]–2–heptene produces *exo–cis*–2–carbethoxymethyl–3–bromonorcamphene.[113] No rearrangement occurs.

Table 7.   Addition of Derivatives of α-Halogenated Aliphatic Acids to Unsaturated Compounds

C_n	Unsaturated compound	Halogenated derivative	Product	% Yield	°C b.p./mm	n_D (°C)	Ref.
C_3	Propylene	$BrCH_2CO_2C_2H_5$	Ethyl α-bromovalerate	17	82/8	1.4552 (20)	62, 67, 111
C_4	Butene-2	$BrCH_2CO_2C_2H_5$	Ethyl γ-bromo-β-methyl valerate	10	70/4	1.4588 (20)	62, 67, 111
C_8	Octene-1	$BrCH_2CO_2C_2H_5$	Ethyl 3-bromodecanoate	57	93/0.2	1.4599 (20)	62, 67, 111
	$(C_2H_5)_3SiCH=CH_2$	$BrCH_2CO_2C_2H_5$	$(C_2H_5)_3SiCHBr(CH_2)_2CO_2C_2H_5$	45	84/0.04	1.4830 (20)	2
	$(C_2H_5)_3GeCH=CH_2$	$BrCH_2CO_2C_2H_5$	$(C_2H_5)_3GeCHBr(CH_2)_2CO_2C_2H_5$		152/2	1.4871 (20)	80
C_3	Propylene	$CH_3CHBrCO_2C_2H_5$	Ethyl α-methyl-γ-bromovalerate	12	83/9.5	1.4521 (20)	62, 67, 111
	Allyl chloride	$CH_3CHBrCO_2C_2H_5$	Ethyl 4-bromo-5-chloro-2-methyl-n-valerate	27	99/1		62, 111
C_4	Isobutylene	$CH_3CHBrCO_2C_2H_5$	Ethyl α,γ-dimethyl-γ-bromo-valerate	70	70/4	1.4520 (20)	67
C_8	Octene-1	$CH_3CHBrCO_2C_2H_5$	Ethyl 1-methyl-3-bromodecanoate	77	92/0.1	1.4570 (20)	62, 67, 111
	Octene-1	Methyl α-bromo-isobutyrate	Methyl α,α-dimethyl-γ-bromo-caprate	22	98/0.3	1.458 (20)	67
	Octene-1	Ethyl α-bromo-n-butyrate	Ethyl 1-ethyl-3-bromodecanoate	62	108/0.6	1.4576 (20)	62, 67, 111
	Octene-1	Ethyl α-bromo-isobutyrate	Ethyl α,α-dimethyl-γ-bromo-caprate	12	mol. dist.	1.4572 (20)	67
	Octene-1	Methyl α-bromo-isovalerate	Methyl α-isopropyl-γ-bromo-caprate	46	84/0.03	1.4608 (20)	67
	Octene-1	Ethyl α-bromo-(d)-isovalerate	Ethyl α-isopropyl-γ-bromocaprate	14	mol. dist.	1.4592 (20)	67
	Octene-1	Methyl dichloro-acetate	α,α-Dichlorocaprate	40	74/0.3	1.4561 (20)	68, 69
	Octene-1	Trichloroacetyl chloride	α,α,γ-Trichlorocapryl chloride	81	124/0.3	1.4830 (20)	68, 69

Table 7. (cont.)   Addition of Derivatives of α–Halogenated Aliphatic Acids to Unsaturated Compounds

C_n	Unsaturated compound	Halogenated derivative	Product	% Yield	°C b.p./mm	n_D (°C)	Ref.
	Octene–1	Dimethyl bromosuccinate	Methyl-β–carbomethoxy-δ–bromocaprate	83	mol. dist.	1.4669 (20)	67
	Octene–1	Diethyl bromomalonate	Ethyl-α–carbethoxy-γ–bromocaprate	74	mol. dist.	1.4572 (20)	67
	Octene–1	Ethyl-α,α–dichloroacetate	Ethyl-α–chloro-α–(2–chlorooctyl)–acetoacetate ($CH_3COClCO_2C_2H_5CH_2CHClC_6H_{13}$)	25	125/0.3	1.464 (20)	74
C_5	Allyl acetate	Br_2CHCN	5–Acetoxy-2,4–dibromopentanenitrile	52	110/0.1	1.5123 (20)	76
C_8	Octene–1	$BrCH_2CN$	4–Bromodecanenitrile	75	97/0.2	1.4722 (20)	76
	Octene–1	CCl_3CN	2,2,4–Trichlorodecanenitrile	65	80/0.15	1.4715 (20)	76
C_5	Allyl acetate	2,2,3–Trichloropropionitrile	5–Acetoxy-2,4–dichloro-2–chloromethylpentanenitrile		131/2.2	1.4960 (20)	76
C_8	Octene–1	2,2,3–Trichloropropionitrile	2,4–Dichloro-2–chloromethyldecanenitrile	75	116/0.3	1.4960 (20)	76

ADDITION OF MISCELLANEOUS ALKYL POLYHALIDES

The interesting additions of various alkyl polyhalides to unsaturated systems are presented in Table 8. This table gives some idea about the synthetic usefulness of the reactions of polyhalo compounds with unsaturated systems. Several of the synthetic methods merit elaboration and amplification.

The condensation of ethyl iodide with ethylene in the presence of benzoyl peroxide yields a mixture of alkyl iodides.[18] The reaction is carried out at 95° in a silver-lined autoclave at about 955 atm of ethylene. n–Butyl, n–hexyl, and n–octyl iodides can be separated from the product mixture by distillation. Under similar experimental conditions the reaction of methylene chloroiodide (CH_2ClI) and ethylene also yields a mixture of telomers.[18,20] The condensates contain 16% of compound Ia, b.p. 57°/10 mm, n_D 1.5472 (20°), 20% of Ib, b.p. 95°/10 mm, n_D 1.5284 (20°), 19% of Ic, b.p. 95°/2 mm, n_D 1.5153 (20°), and 11% of Id, b.p. 122°/2 mm, n_D 1.5088 (20°).

$$Cl(CH_2)_nI$$

Ia, $n = 3$; Ib, $n = 5$; Ic, $n = 7$; Id, $n = 9$

Dichlorofluoroiodomethane reacts with 1, 1–difluoroethylene in the presence of benzoyl peroxide to give 1, 1–dichloro–1, 3, 3–trifluoro–3–iodopropane in high yield.[82] 1, 1–Difluoro–1–chloro–2–iodoethane condenses with ethylene in ultraviolet light to give a 1:1 adduct.[89]

$$CF_2ClCH_2I + CH_2{=}CH_2 \rightarrow CF_2ClCH_2CH_2CH_2I$$

Pentafluoroiodoethane (C_2F_5I) and heptafluoroiodopropane (C_3F_7I) react with acetylenes and olefins under ultraviolet light.[32,38,77,87,107] The reaction temperature ranges from room temperature to 200°, and the reaction period ranges from hours to days or even weeks.

The reaction of pentafluoroiodomethane with acetylene under ultraviolet light produces pentafluoro–1–iodobutene.[32]

$$HC{\equiv}CH + C_2F_5I \rightarrow C_2F_5CH{=}CHI$$

The reaction of pentafluoroiodomethane with 1, 1–difluoroethylene at 220° in an autoclave in 10 hr produces an adduct, in good yield, which can be converted in good yield to pentafluoropropionic acid.[38] The reaction of heptafluoroiodopropane with 1, 1, 1, 3, 3–pentafluoropropene in ultraviolet light at 100° for 8 days produces 1, 1, 1, 2, 2, 3, 3, 5, 5–nonafluoro–2–trifluoromethylpentane, b.p. 60°, which in turn can be transformed to perfluoropentene–2–one, b.p. 30°.[38] The over-all yield is about 53%. Similar addition reactions occur with higher perfluoroalkyl iodides, ·namely, the nonafluoro–2–iodobutane,[28,30] undecafluoroiodopentane,[30] and perfluoro-heptyl iodide.[107] The last compound is condensed with octene, octadecene, undecylenic acid, or vinylmethyldiethoxysilane in ultraviolet light.

A mixture of tetrachloroethylene and ethylene heated in the presence of water and benzoyl peroxide to 90–115° for 5 hr under 95 atm of pressure produces a 2:1 adduct in approximately 20% yield.[94]

$$CH_2{=}CH_2 + Cl_2C{=}CCl_2 \rightarrow ClCH_2CH_2CH_2CH_2CCl{=}CCl_2$$

Trifluoroiodoethylene (perfluorovinyl iodide) reacts with olefins in ultraviolet light similarly to give saturated perhaloalkyl iodide.[88]

$$CF_2{=}CFI + CH_2{=}CF_2 \rightarrow CF_2{=}CFCH_2CF_2I$$

The perfluorovinyl radical reacts with ethylenic carbon atoms in the following order: $CH_2 > CFH > CClH > CF_2 > CCl_2$.

Similarly, 1, 1–difluoro–2–iodoethylene condenses with ethylene, difluoro-ethylene, or trifluorochloroethylene in ultraviolet light to give 1:1 adducts.[89]

$$CF_2{=}CHI + CH_2{=}CH_2 \rightarrow CF_2{=}CHCH_2CH_2I$$

$$CF_2{=}CHI + CF_2{=}CH_2 \rightarrow CF_2{=}CHCH_2CF_2I$$

$$CF_2{=}CHI + CF_2{=}CFCl \rightarrow CF_2{=}CHCF_2CFClI$$

1, 1–Difluoro–2–chloro–2–iodoethylene reacts with ethylene, 1, 1–difluoro-ethylene, or trifluoroethylene to give 1:1 adducts containing one double bond.[89] These reactions result in moderate yields of the 1:1 adducts, which are valuable intermediates for the preparation of various dienes and perfluorobutadienes.

The reaction of chlorotrifluoroethylene with 1–chlorohexafluoro–1–iodo-propane in ultraviolet light gives 1, 3–dichlorononafluoro–1–iodopentane in 50% yield.[36] 1, 1–Dichloro–1, 3–dibromobutane (a condensation product of dibromodichloromethane and propylene) reacts in ultraviolet light or in the presence of acetyl peroxide at 80° with olefins such as propylene and octene–1 to give 1:1 adducts in good yield.[55,61]

1–Chloro–1, 2–dibromo–1, 2, 2–trifluoroethane is readily added to ethylene, propylene, isobutylene, butene–2, octene–1, allyl chloride, 1, 1–difluoropropene, difluoroethylene, or trifluoroethylene in the presence of benzoyl peroxide.[100,101] This polyhalocarbon is less reactive than bromotri-chloromethane and more reactive than dibromodifluoromethane. The general reaction scheme is:

$$F_2CBrCClFBr + CH_2{=}CHCH_2Cl \rightarrow CF_2BrCClFCH_2CHBrCH_2Cl$$

The condensations are carried out in an autoclave at 90–100°. The duration of the reaction is 4–6 hr. The products are separated by fractional distillation. 1–Chloro–1, 2–dibromo–1, 2, 2–trifluoroethane reacts with allyl ethyl ether or allyl β–chloro–α, α–trifluoroethyl ether at 90–95° in the presence of benzoyl peroxide.[106] Well-defined adducts are obtained.

$$CH_2{=}CH{-}CH_2OC_2H_5$$
$$+ \; F_2CBrCClFBr \rightarrow CF_2BrCFClCH_2CHBrCH_2OC_2H_5$$

$$CH_2{=}CHCH_2OCF_2CFClH$$
$$+ \; F_2CBrCClFBr \rightarrow CF_2BrCFClCH_2CHBrCH_2OCF_2CFClH$$

Under similar experimental conditions 1, 2–dichloro–2–iodo–1, 1, 2–trifluoroethane reacts with various unsaturated reactants to give excellent yields of products.[14,16,31,41,81,82,87,101] It even reacts with olefins which fail to react with 1–chloro–1, 2–dibromo–1, 2, 2–trifluoroethane.[101]

$$CF_2ClCFClI + CHF{=}CF_2 \rightarrow CF_2ClCClFCFHCF_2I$$

Photochemical reactions of this polyhaloethane with vinyltrichlorosilane,[14] methylvinyldichlorosilane,[14,16] and trimethylvinylsilane[14] result in 1:1 adducts.

$$(CH_2{=}CH)CH_3SiCl_2 + CF_2ClCFClI \rightarrow CF_2ClCFClCH_2CHISi(CH_3)Cl_2$$

$$CH_2{=}CHSi(CH_3)_3 + CF_2ClCFClI \rightarrow CF_2ClCFClCH_2CHISi(CH_3)_3$$

$$CH_2{=}CHSiCl_3 + CF_2ClCFClI \rightarrow CF_2ClCClFCH_2CHISiCl_3$$

Most of the products can be dehalogenated. This feature makes the method useful for the preparation of a variety of fluoroolefins and 1, 1, 2–fluorobutadienes.[101]

A polyhalogenated ethane derivative which has received little attention is 1, 1–difluoro–1, 2, 2–trichloro–2–iodoethane. It condenses with 1–chloro–1, 2, 2–trifluoroethylene at 100° in the presence of benzoyl peroxide to give a 1:1 adduct, b.p. 55°/1.5 mm, n_D 1.4800 (20°), in 70% yield.[82]

Free radical-catalyzed additions of perhaloalkanes are also carried out with unsaturated alcohols. Thus, light or peroxide catalyzes the reactions of pentafluoroethyl iodide, n–heptafluoropropyl iodide, 1, 2–dichloro–2–iodo–1, 1, 2–trifluoroethane, or 1–chloro–1, 2–dibromo–1, 2, 2–trifluoroethane with allyl alcohol or propargyl alcohol.[87] The product yields are 40–60%.

The addition of chloral in the presence of benzoyl peroxide to α–pinene, similarly to the addition reaction of chloroform and carbon tetrachloride, is accompanied by a rearrangement; 8–chloro–p–menthene–1–yl–7 dichloroacetaldehyde is obtained in 50% yield.[112]

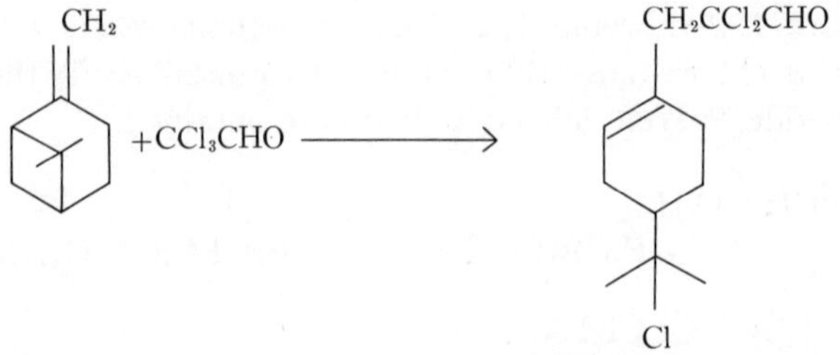

$$CH_2 \qquad\qquad CH_2CCl_2CHO$$

$$+CCl_3CHO \longrightarrow$$

Cl

The reaction is carried out at 95° in an atmosphere of nitrogen. Although no physical constants were reported for the product, its structure seems to be well established.

DDT reacts with ethylene at about 600 psi and 140° in the presence of t–butyl hydroperoxide to give mainly 1, 3, 3–trichloro–4, 4–bis(p–chlorophenyl)butane (n = 1), m.p. 106°, 1, 5, 5–trichloro–6, 6–bis(p–chlorophenyl)hexane (n = 2), and 1, 7, 7–trichloro–8, 8–bis(p–chlorophenyl)octane (n = 3).[75]

$$\begin{array}{c} ClC_6H_4 \\ \diagdown \\ CHCCl_3 + CH_2{=}CH_2 \rightarrow \\ \diagup \\ ClC_6H_4 \end{array} \qquad \begin{array}{c} ClC_6H_4 \\ \diagdown \\ CHCCl_2(CH_2CH_2)_nCl \\ \diagup \\ ClC_6H_4 \end{array}$$

Table 8. Addition of Miscellaneous Alkyl Polyhalides to Unsaturated Compounds

C_n	Unsaturated compound	Alkyl polyhalide	Product	% Yield	°C b.p./mm (m.p.)	n_D (°C)	Ref.
C_2	$CF_2=CH_2$	CCl_2FI	$CCl_2FCH_2CF_2I$	78	42/14	1.4658 (20)	82
	C_2H_2	C_2F_5I	3,3,4,4-Pentafluoro-1-iodo-butene-1	72	84	1.392 (25)	32
	$CH_2=CF_2$	C_2F_5I	1,1,1,2,2,4,4-Heptafluoro-4-iodobutane	91	88	1.354 (20)	38
	$CF_2=CF_2$	C_2F_5I	Nonafluoro-1-iodobutane	91	67		30
C_3	$CH\equiv CCH_2OH$	C_2F_5I	4,4,5,6,6-Heptafluoro-2-iodo-2-hexen-1-ol	60	66/3.4	1.4223 (20)	87
	$CH_2=CHCH_2OH$	C_2F_5I	4,4,5,5,5-Pentafluoro-2-iodopentanol	55	81/13.5	1.4310 (25)	87
	3,3,3-Trifluoropropyne	Heptafluoro-iodopropane	1,1,1,4,4,5,5,6,6,6-Decafluoro-2-iodohex-2-ene	38	110	1.3575 (13)	77
	$\overline{CH_2}=CH—CH_2OH$	Heptafluoro-iodopropane	4,4,5,5,6,6,6-Heptafluoro-2-iodohexanol	54	71/7	1.4125 (25)	87
	1,1,1,3,3-Pentafluoro-propene	Heptafluoro-iodopropane	1,1,1,2,2,3,3,5,5-Nonafluoro-5-iodo-4-trifluoromethylpentane				38
C_4	$(CH_3)_2C=CH_2$	n-C_3F_7I	n-$C_3F_7CH_2Cl(CH_3)_2$	91	63/40	1.3963 (25)	107
C_2	C_2H_2	Nonafluoro-2-iodobutane	3,4,4,5,5,5-Hexafluoro-1-iodo-3-trifluoromethylpentene-1 ($C_2F_5(CF_3)CFCH=CHI$)	83	75/148		28
C_3	Hexafluoropropene	$CF_3CF_2CFICF_3$	Dodecafluoro-2-iodo-4-trifluoro-methylhexane	51	137		28
C_7	Vinylmethyldiethoxysilane	n-$C_7F_{15}I$	n-$C_7F_{15}CH_2CH_2CHISi(CH_3)(OC_2H_5)_2$	62	150/20	1.3795 (25)	107
C_8	Octene	n-$C_7F_{15}I$	n-$C_7F_{15}CH_2CHIC_6H_{13}$	60	156/20	1.3846 (25)	107
C_{11}	Undecylenic acid	n-$C_7F_{15}I$	n-$C_7F_{15}CH_2CHI(CH_2)_8CO_2H$	73	190–240/0.01 (50)		107

Table 8. (cont.)   Addition of Miscellaneous Alkyl Polyhalides to Unsaturated Compounds

C_n	Unsaturated compound	Alkyl polyhalide	Product	% Yield	°C b.p./mm (m.p.)	n_D (°C)	Ref.
C_{18}	Octadecene-1	$n-C_7F_{15}I$	$n-C_7F_{15}CH_2CHIC_{16}H_{33}$	93	170–200 / 0.01	1.4107 (25)	107
C_2	$CH_2=CH_2$	CF_2ClCH_2I	$CF_2ClCH_2CH_2I$		44/7	1.4780 (20)	89
	$CH_2=CH_2$	$CF_2BrCBrClF$	2-Chloro-1, 4-dibromo-1, 1, 2-trifluorobutane	58	67/20	1.4563 (25)	100
	$CH_2=CHF$	$CF_2BrCBrClF$	$CF_2BrCFClCH_2CHFBr$	74	72/32	1.4405 (25)	101
	$CH_2=CF_2$	$CF_2BrCBrClF$	$CF_2BrCFClCH_2CF_2Br +$	44	70/50	1.4230 (27)	101
			$CF_2BrCFClCH_2CF_2CH_2CF_2Br$	23	90/20	1.4112 (27)	
	$CHF=CF_2$	$CF_2BrCBrClF$	$CF_2BrCFClCHFCF_2Br +$	16	61/40	1.4330 (23)	101
			$CF_2BrCFClCHFCF_2CHFCF_2Br$	20	80/15	1.3943 (25)	
C_3	$CH_3CH=CH_2$	$CF_2BrCBrClF$	2-Chloro-1, 4-dibromo-1, 1, 2-trifluoropentane	83	66/11	1.4560 (27)	100
	$CH_2=CHCH_2Cl$	$CF_2BrCBrClF$	1, 4-Dibromo-2, 5-dichloro-1, 1, 2-trifluoropentane	45	90/6	1.4762 (27)	100
	$CH_2=CHCH_2OH$	$CF_2BrCBrClF$	2, 5-Dibromo-4-chloro-4, 5, 5-trifluoropentanol		97/2.6	1.4808 (25)	87
C_4	Isobutylene	$CF_2BrCBrClF$	2-Chloro-1, 4-dibromo-4-methyl-1, 1, 2-trifluoropentane	43	44/2	1.4590 (25)	100
	2–Butene	$CF_2BrCBrClF$	2-Chloro-1, 4-dibromo-3-methyl-1, 1, 2-trifluoropentane	35	49/2.5	1.4592 (24)	100
C_5	Vinyl acetate	$CF_2BrCBrClF$	$CF_2BrCFClCH_2CHBr(OCOCH_3)$	50	73/2	1.4531 (25)	13
	Allyl acetate	$CF_2BrCBrClF$	$CF_2BrCFClCH_2CHBrCH_2CO_2CH_3$	76	86/1.4	1.4670 (20)	13
	Allyl ethyl ether	$CF_2BrCBrClF$	$CF_2BrCFClCH_2CHBrCH_2OC_2H_5$	26	75/1.5	1.4534 (23)	106
	$CH_2=CHCH_2OCF_2CFClH$	$CF_2BrCBrClF$	$CF_2BrCFClCH_2CHBrCH_2OCF_2-CFClH$	47	78/0.6	1.4350 (22)	106

Table 8. (cont.)   Addition of Miscellaneous Alkyl Polyhalides to Unsaturated Compounds

C_n	Unsaturated compound	Alkyl polyhalide	Product	% Yield	°C b.p./mm (m.p.)	n_D (°C)	Ref.
C_8	1-Octene	$CF_2BrCBrClF$	2-Chloro-1,4-dibromo-1,2-trifluorodecane	34	84/0.3	1.4612 (24)	100
C_2	CH_2=CFCl	$CF_2ClCFClI$	$CF_2ClCFClCH_2CFClI$	45	70/10	1.4741 (22)	101
	CHF=CF_2	$CF_2ClCFClI$	$CF_2ClCFClCHFCF_2I$	79	56/23	1.4224 (28)	101
	CClF=CF_2	$CF_2ClCFClI$	$CF_2ClCClFCF_2CClFI$	22	70/18	1.4428 (20)	82
				75	80/25		31
	CH_2=$CHSiCl_3$	$CF_2ClCFClI$	Trichloro-(3,4-dichloro-3,4,4-trifluoro-1-iodobutyl)-silane	26	124/1		14
C_3	CH_2CH=CF_3	$CF_2ClCFClI$	$CF_2ClCFClCH_2CHICF_3$	95	61/18	1.4275 (22)	101
	CF_2CH=CH_3	$CF_2ClCFClI$	$CF_2ClCFClC(CH_3)HCF_2I$	89	76/20	1.4567 (25)	101
	Vinylmethyldichlorosilane	$CF_2ClCFClI$	$CF_2ClCFClCH_2CHISi(CH_3)Cl_2$	58	117/33	1.4895 (25)	14, 16, 81
	CF_3CF=CF_2	$CF_2ClCFClI$	$CF_2ClCFClCF(CF_3)CF_2I$		59/20	1.3908 (25)	41
	CH_2=$CHCH_2OH$	$CF_2ClCFClI$	2-Iodo-4,5-dichloro-4,5,5-trifluoropentanol	42	84/1.6	1.4953 (25)	87
C_4	$CF_3(CH_3)C$=CH_2	$CF_2ClCFClI$	$CF_2ClCFClCH_2C(CF_3)ICH_3$	87	66/12	1.4418 (22)	101
C_5	CH_2=$CHSi(CH_3)_3$	$CF_2ClCFClI$	3,4-Dichloro-3,4,4-trifluoro-1-iodobutyltrimethylsilane	66	100/9		14
C_2	CH_2=CH_2	CCl_2=CCl_2	$Cl(CH_2)_4CCl$=CCl_2	20	100/10	1.5060 (25)	94
	CF_2=CH_2	CF_2=CHI	CF_2=$CHCH_2CF_2I$		87/632	1.4193 (20)	89
	CH_2=CH_2	CF_2=CHI	CF_2=$CHCH_2CH_2I$		58/81	1.4752 (20)	89
	CF_2=CHCl	CF_2=CHI	CF_2=$CHCF_2CFClI$		75/144		89
	CH_2=CH_2	CF_2=CClI	CF_2=$CClCH_2CH_2I$	71	142/631	1.4958 (20)	89
	CF_2=CH_2	CF_2=CClI	CF_2=$CClCH_2CF_2I$		120/627	1.4435 (20)	89
	CF_2=CHF	CF_2=CClI	CF_2=$CClCHFCF_2I$	69	58/90	1.4342 (20)	89

Table 8. (cont.)　　Addition of Miscellaneous Alkyl Polyhalides to Unsaturated Compounds

C_n	Unsaturated compound	Alkyl polyhalide	Product	% Yield	°C b.p./mm (m.p.)	n_D (°C)	Ref.
	$CH_2=CH_2$	$CF_2=CFI$	$CF_2=CFCH_2CH_2I$	67	112/623	1.4554 (20)	88
	$CH_2=CFH$	$CF_2=CFI$	$CF_2=CFCH_2CFHI$	50	107/633	1.4370 (20)	88
	$CH_2=CF_2$	$CF_2=CFI$	$CF_2=CFCH_2CF_2I$	24	92/633	1.4118 (20)	88
	$CF_2=CFH$	$CF_2=CFI$	$CF_2=CFCFHCF_2I$	39	83/631	1.4006 (20)	88
	$CF_2=CFI$	$CF_2=CFI$	$CF_2=CFCF_2CFI_2$	50	146/622	1.4794 (20)	88
	$CF_2=CFCl$	1-Chlorohexa-fluoro-1-iodo-propane	1, 3-Dichlorononafluoro-1-iodo-pentane	50	70/34		36
C_3	$CH_3CH=CH_2$	1, 1-Dichloro-1, 3-dibromo-butane	2, 6-Dibromo-4, 4-dichloro-heptane	76	76/0.5 76/0.05	1.5282 1.4282 (20)	61 55
C_8	Octene-1	1, 1-Dichloro-1, 3-dibromo-butane	2, 6-Dibromo-4, 4-dichloro-dodecane	62	mol. dist.	1.5120 (20)	55, 61

REFERENCES

[1] Bengough and Thomson, *Trans. Faraday Soc.*, **56**, 407 (1960).
[2] Benkeser, Bennett, and Hickner, *J. Am. Chem. Soc.*, **79**, 6253 (1957).
[3] Bogdanova and Shostakovskii, *Izvest. Akad. Nauk*, **1957**, 224.
[4] Borisov, *Izvest. Akad. Nauk*, **1951**, 524.
[5] Coscia, *J. Org. Chem.* **26**, 2995 (1961).
[6] Davies, *J. Chem. Soc.* **1960**, 3669.
[7] Du Pont, Dulou, and Clement, *Bull. soc. chim. France*, **1950**, 1056.
[8] Du Pont, Dulou, and Clement, *Bull. soc. chim. France*, **1950**, 1115.
[9] Du Pont, Dulou, and Clement, *C. r.*, **230**, 2027 (1950).
[10] Du Pont, Dulou, and Clement, *Bull. soc. chim. France*, **1951**, 257, 1002.
[11] Du Pont, Dulou, and Clement, *C. r.*, **236**, 2512 (1953).
[12] Du Pont, Dulou, and Pigerol, *C. r.*, **240**, 628 (1955).
[13] Durrell, Lovelace, and Adamczak, *J. Org. Chem.*, **25**, 1661 (1960).
[14] Geyer, *et al.*, *J. Chem. Soc.*, **1957**, 4472.
[15] Glickman, U.S. 2,560,219 (1951).
[16] Gordon, U.S. 2,715,113 (1955).
[17] Hall and Jacobs, *J. Chem. Soc.*, **1954**, 2034.
[18] Hanford, U.S. 2,440,800 (1948).
[19] Harmon, U.S. 2,396,261 (1946).
[20] Harmon, *et al.*, *J. Am. Chem. Soc.*, **72**, 2213 (1950).
[21] Haszeldine, *J. Chem. Soc.*, **1949**, 2856.
[22] Haszeldine, *J. Chem. Soc.*, **1950**, 3037.
[23] Haszeldine, *J. Chem. Soc.*, **1951**, 588.
[24] Haszeldine, *J. Chem. Soc.*, **1952**, 2504.
[25] Haszeldine, *J. Chem. Soc.*, **1952**, 3490.
[26] Haszeldine, *J. Chem. Soc.*, **1953**, 922.
[27] Haszeldine, *J. Chem. Soc.*, **1953**, 1199.
[28] Haszeldine, *J. Chem. Soc.*, **1953**, 3559.
[29] Haszeldine, *J. Chem. Soc.*, **1953**, 3565.
[30] Haszeldine, *J. Chem. Soc.*, **1953**, 3761.
[31] Haszeldine, *J. Chem. Soc.*, **1955**, 4291.
[32] Haszeldine and Leedham, *J. Chem. Soc.*, **1952**, 3483.
[33] Haszeldine and Leedham, *J. Chem. Soc.*, **1954**, 1261.
[34] Haszeldine, Leedham, and Steele, *J. Chem. Soc.*, **1954**, 2040.
[35] Haszeldine and Osborne, *J. Chem. Soc.*, **1956**, 61.
[36] Haszeldine and Steele, *J. Chem. Soc.*, **1953**, 1592.
[37] Haszeldine and Steele, *J. Chem. Soc.*, **1954**, 923.
[38] Haszeldine and Steele, *J. Chem. Soc.*, **1955**, 3005.
[39] Haszeldine and Steele, *J. Chem. Soc.*, **1957**, 2193.
[40] Haszeldine and Steele, *J. Chem. Soc.*, **1957**, 2800.
[41] Hauptschein, Brain, and Lawlor, *J. Am. Chem. Soc.*, **79**, 2549 (1957).
[42] Henne and Kraus, *J. Am. Chem. Soc.*, **73**, 1791 (1951).
[43] Henne and Kraus, *J. Am. Chem. Soc.*, **73**, 5303 (1951).
[44] Henne and Kraus, *J. Am. Chem. Soc.*, **76**, 1175 (1954).
[45] Heiba and Anderson, *J. Am. Chem. Soc.*, **79**, 4940 (1957).
[46] Huang, *J. Chem. Soc.*, **1956**, 1749.

[47] Huang, *J. Chem. Soc.*, **1957**, 1342.
[48] Huyser and Echegaray, *J. Org. Chem.*, **27**, 429 (1962).
[49] Imperial Chemical Industries, Ltd., Brit. 570,869 (1945).
[50] Israelashvili and Diamant, *J. Am. Chem. Soc.*, **74**, 3185 (1952).
[51] Kharasch, U.S. 2,264,869 (1949).
[52] Kharasch, U.S. 2,468,208 (1949).
[53] Kharasch, U.S. 2,485,099 (1949).
[54] Kharasch, U.S. 2,525,912 (1950).
[55] Kharasch, U.S. 2,574,832 (1951).
[56] Kharasch and Friedlander, *J. Org. Chem.*, **14**, 239 (1949).
[57] Kharasch, Freiman, and Urry, *J. Org. Chem.*, **13**, 570 (1948).
[58] Kharasch, Jensen, and Urry, *J. Am. Chem. Soc.*, **68**, 154 (1946).
[59] Kharasch, Jensen, and Urry, *J. Am. Chem. Soc.*, **69**, 1100 (1947).
[60] Kharasch, Jerome, and Urry, *J. Org. Chem.*, **15**, 966 (1950).
[61] Kharasch, Kuderna, and Urry, *J. Org. Chem.*, **13**, 895 (1948).
[62] Kharasch and Ladd, U.S. 2,476,668 (1949).
[63] Kharasch, Reinmuth, and Urry, *J. Am. Chem. Soc.*, **69**, 1105 (1947).
[64] Kharasch and Sage, *J. Org. Chem.*, **14**, 79 (1949).
[65] Kharasch and Sage, *J. Org. Chem.*, **14**, 537 (1949).
[66] Kharasch, Simon, and Nudenberg, *J. Org. Chem.*, **18**, 328 (1953).
[67] Kharasch, Skell, and Fisher, *J. Am. Chem. Soc.*, **70**, 1055 (1948).
[68] Kharasch and Urry, U.S. 2,471,570 (1949).
[69] Kharasch, Urry, and Jensen, *J. Am. Chem. Soc.*, **67**, 1626 (1945).
[70] Kooyman, *Rec. trav. chim.*, **70**, 684 (1951).
[71] Kooyman and Farenhorst, *Rec. trav. chim.*, **70**, 867 (1951).
[72] Krespan, Harder, and Drysdale, *J. Am. Chem. Soc.*, **83**, 3424 (1961).
[73] Ladd, U.S. 2,554,533 (1951).
[74] Ladd, U.S. 2,577,422 (1951).
[75] Ladd, U.S. 2,609,402 (1952).
[76] Ladd, U.S. 2,615,915 (1952).
[77] Leedham and Haszeldine, *J. Chem. Soc.*, **1954**, 1634.
[78] Levas, *Ann. chim. Paris*, **7**, 697 (1952).
[79] Matteson, *J. Am. Chem. Soc.*, **82**, 4228 (1960).
[80] Mazerolles and Lesbre, *C.r.*, **248**, 2018 (1959).
[81] Midland Silicones Ltd., Brit. 769,499 (1957).
[82] Miller, U.S. 2,880,247 (1959).
[83] Miller, U.S. 2,880,248 (1959).
[84] Nesmeyanov, Freidlina, and Zakharin, *Dok. Akad. Nauk*, **81**, 199 (1951).
[85] Nesmeyanov, Karapetyan, and Freidlina, *Dok. Akad. Nauk*, **109**, 791 (1956).
[86] Oldroyd, Fisher, and Goldblatt, *J. Am. Chem. Soc.*, **72**, 2407 (1950).
[87] Park, Rogers, and Lacher, *J. Org. Chem.*, **26**, 2089 (1961).
[88] Park, Seffl, and Lacher, *J. Am. Chem. Soc.*, **78**, 59 (1956).
[89] Park, *et al.*, *J. Org. Chem.*, **23**, 1661 (1958).
[90] Patrick, U.S. 2,676,981 (1954).
[91] Patrick, U.S. 2,683,749 (1954).
[92] Petersen, U.S. 2,401,099 (1946).
[93] Petrov, Chernyshev, and Bisku, *Izvest. Akad. Nauk*, **1956**, 1445.
[94] Roland, Brit. 589,065 (1947).
[95] Saunders, U.S. 2,776,325 (1957).
[96] Seyferth, *J. Org. Chem.*, **22**, 1252 (1957).
[97] Shostakovskii, *et al.*, *Izvest. Akad. Nauk*, **1956**, 1236.

[98] Skell and Woodworth, *J. Am. Chem. Soc.*, **77**, 4638 (1955).

[99] Skinner, *et al.*, *J. Org. Chem.*, **23**, 1710 (1958).

[100] Tarrant and Gillman, *J. Am. Chem. Soc.*, **76**, 5423 (1954).

[101] Tarrant and Lilyquist, *J. Am. Chem. Soc.*, **77**, 3640 (1955).

[102] Tarrant and Lovelace, *J. Am. Chem. Soc.*, **76**, 3466 (1954).

[103] Tarrant and Lovelace, *J. Am. Chem. Soc.*, **77**, 768 (1955).

[104] Tarrant and Lovelace, U.S. 2,750,431 (1956).

[105] Tarrant, Lovelace, and Lilyquist, *J. Am. Chem. Soc.*, **77**, 2783 (1955).

[106] Tarrant and Stump, *J. Org. Chem.*, **26**, 4646 (1961).

[107] Tiers, *J. Org. Chem.*, **27**, 2261 (1962).

[108] Topchiev, Bogomolova, and Goldfarb, *Dok. Akad. Nauk*, **107**, 420 (1956).

[109] United States Rubber Co., Brit. 620,855 (1949).

[110] United States Rubber Co., Brit. 638,414 (1950).

[111] United States Rubber Co., Brit. 646,960 (1950).

[112] Vilkas, Du Pont, and Dulou, *Bull. soc. chim. France*, **1955**, 799.

[113] Weinstock, *Am. Chem. Soc. Meeting, Abstract*, **128**, 19-O (1955).

[114] Weizmann, *et al.*, *J. Am. Chem. Soc.*, **69**, 2569 (1947).

ADDITION OF HYDROGEN SULFIDE TO UNSATURATED COMPOUNDS

Under free radical conditions the reaction of hydrogen sulfide with olefins is contrary to Markownikoff's rule. Mercaptans are formed initially.

$$RCH{=}CH_2 + HSH \rightarrow RCH_2CH_2SH$$

The subsequent reaction of the mercaptans with olefins produces various amounts of sulfide, depending largely on the relative amounts of hydrogen sulfide and olefins.

$$RCH{=}CH_2 + HSCH_2CH_2R \rightarrow (RCH_2CH_2)_2S$$

The reactions are initiated by common free radical initiators such as azo compounds,[115,135] peroxides,[131] tetraethyl lead,[40] tetraethyl lead with light,[39] ultraviolet light,[39,52,149,150] and ultraviolet light in conjunction with such sensitizers as acetone.[147,151] The reactions are usually carried out in a sealed vessel, preferably a quartz tube for light-catalyzed reactions, at temperatures from $-78°$ to room temperature.

Hydrogen sulfide reacts with ethylene in highly acidic medium in the presence of air to give a mixture of ethyl mercaptan, diethyl sulfide, and higher telomers.[58] The addition of hydrogen sulfide to propylene[39,40,147,149,151] or to butene[147,149] under ultraviolet light produces n–propyl and n–butyl mercaptan, respectively, in high yield. Free radical chain addition of hydrogen sulfide to 1–chlorocyclohexene at $-60°$ in ultraviolet light produces predominantly cis–2–chlorocyclohexanethiol.[52]

About a 35% yield of mercaptan is obtained by reacting hydrogen sulfide and tetramethylethylene in the presence of azobisisobutyronitrile for 11 hr at 75–100° and 225-psi hydrogen sulfide.[115] Hydrogen sulfide also adds to octene–1, octene–2, hexadecene–1, octadecene–1, styrene, allylidene diacetate, and dimethyl–Δ–4–tetrahydrophthalate under similar conditions to give the corresponding mercaptan in moderate to good yield and the corresponding sulfide in low yield.[115] The reaction of hydrogen sulfide with allyl alcohol or with allyl amine produces mercaptan and sulfide in low yield.[115]

The reaction of hydrogen sulfide with vinyl chloride produces a mixture of ethylene thiochlorohydrin and β, β'–dichlorodiethylthioether (mustard gas).[147,150] Russian chemists have thoroughly studied the interaction of hydrogen sulfide with various vinyl ethers.[118,119,131,132] They found the relative amounts of the mercaptan and sulfide produced depend on the ratio of hydrogen sulfide to vinyl ether. With two parts hydrogen sulfide to one part vinyl ether, the yield of mercaptan is 55–80%.[131,132]

$$\text{ROCH}{=}\text{CH}_2 + \text{H}_2\text{S} \left\langle \begin{array}{l} \rightarrow \text{ROCH}_2\text{CH}_2\text{SH} \\[2em] \rightarrow (\text{ROCH}_2\text{CH}_2)_2\text{S} \end{array} \right.$$

In addition, less than 10% of sulfide is formed by ionic addition. These products can be separated by distillation.

Hydrogen sulfide reacts with vinyl pyrrolidone (n = 3) or vinyl caprolactam (n = 5) in the presence of azobisisobutyronitrile to give the corresponding mercaptan and sulfide.[135]

$$\underset{(\text{CH}_2)_n}{\text{C(O)NCH}{=}\text{CH}_2} \overset{\text{H}_2\text{S}}{\rightarrow} \left[\underset{(\text{CH}_2)_n}{\text{C(O)NCH}_2\text{CH}_2}\right]_2 \text{S} + \underset{(\text{CH}_2)_n}{\text{C(O)NCH}_2\text{CH}_2\text{SH}}$$

n = 3 or 5

Each reaction is inhibited by oxygen. Dioxane can be used as a solvent. The reaction mixture is kept in a sealed tube at room temperature for 1–4 weeks. The products cannot be separated by distillation; separation is achieved by extraction of the mercaptan with potassium hydroxide solution. A 12-fold molar excess of hydrogen sulfide over the vinyl pyrrolidone produces β, β'–dipyrrolidonyldiethyl sulfide, m.p. 101.5°, in 60–80% yield, plus a small amount of the thiol, b.p. 118°/2 mm, n_D 1.5300 (20°). With an excess of hydrogen sulfide the reaction with vinyl caprolactam produces β, β'–dicaprolactamdiethyl sulfide, m.p. 83°, in 40% yield, and the thiol, b.p. 113°/2.5 mm, n_D 1.5254 (20°), in 41% yield.

Table 9.   Addition of Hydrogen Sulfide to Unsaturated Compounds

C_n	Unsaturated compound	Product	% Yield	°C b.p./mm (m.p.)	n_D (°C)	Ref.
C_3	Propylene	n–Propyl mercaptan			1.4380 (20)	147
	Propylene	n–Propyl mercaptan +	65	68	1.4351 (20)	149
		Di-n–propyl thioether	35	143	1.4493 (20)	
	$CH_2=CHCH_2OH$	3–Mercaptopropanol +	26	72/9	1.4921 (25)	115
		Bis(3-hydroxypropyl) sulfide	12	138/2		
	Allyl amine	3–Mercaptopropylamine +	21	(49)		115
		Bis(3-aminopropyl) sulfide	25	117/7		
C_4	Butene–1	n–Butyl mercaptan +	85	98	1.4431 (20)	147, 149
		Di-n–butyl thioether			1.4530 (20)	
	$C_2H_5OCH=CH_2$	$C_2H_5OCH_2CH_2SH$ +		127/760	1.4456 (20)	132
		$(C_2H_5OCH_2CH_2)_2S$		84/3.5	1.4560 (20)	
	$C_2H_5SCH=CH_2$	$C_2H_5SCH_2CH_2SH$ +	59	60/9	1.5273 (20)	133
		β,β'-Dimercaptoethyldiethyl sulfide	40	161/9	1.5460 (20)	
C_5	n-$C_3H_7OCH=CH_2$	n-$C_3H_7OCH_2CH_2SH$ +		64/40	1.4478 (20)	132
		$(n$-$C_3H_7OCH_2CH_2)_2S$		106/4	1.4553 (20)	
	i-$C_3H_7OCH=CH_2$	i-$C_3H_7OCH_2CH_2SH$ +		56/44	1.4424 (20)	132
		$(i$-$C_3H_7OCH_2CH_2)_2S$		100/6	1.4493 (20)	
C_6	n-$C_4H_9OCH=CH_2$	n-$C_4H_9OCH_2CH_2SH$ +		48/6	1.4488 (20)	131, 132
		$(n$-$C_4H_9OCH_2CH_2)_2S$		130/5	1.4560 (20)	
	i-$C_4H_9OCH=CH_2$	i-$C_4H_9OCH_2CH_2SH$ +		45/9	1.4444 (20)	132
		$(i$-$C_4H_9OCH_2CH_2)_2S$		126/5	1.4506 (20)	
	1-Chlorocyclohexene	cis-2-Chlorocyclohexanethiol +	61	90/12	1.5212 (25)	52
		trans-2-Chlorocyclohexanethiol				
C_7	i-$C_5H_{11}OCH=CH_2$	i-$C_5H_{11}OCH_2CH_2SH$ +		54/6	1.4489 (20)	132
		$(i$-$C_5H_{11}OCH_2CH_2)_2S$		144/4	1.4550 (20)	
	Allylidene diacetate	3–Mercaptopropylidene diacetate	61	87/2		115

Table 9. (cont.)   Addition of Hydrogen Sulfide to Unsaturated Compounds

C_n	Unsaturated compound	Product	% Yield	°C b.p./mm (m.p.)	n_D (°C)	Ref.
C_8	Cyclohexyl vinyl ether	$C_6H_{11}OCH_2CH_2SH+$ $(C_6H_{11}OCH_2CH_2)_2S$		74/4.5 183/5	1.4864 (20) 1.4982 (20)	132
	Styrene	2-Phenylethyl mercaptan+ Bis(2-phenylethyl) sulfide	61 20	100/18 172/3		115
C_{10}	n-$C_8H_{17}OCH=CH_2$	n-$C_8H_{17}OCH_2CH_2SH+$ $(n$-$C_8H_{17}OCH_2CH_2)_2S$		103/4.5 195/3	1.4556 (20) 1.4610 (20)	132
	Dimethyl 4-tetrahydrophthalate	Dimethyl 4-mercaptohexahydro-phthalate	52	142/2		115
C_{16}	Cetene–1	Di-n-cetyl sulfide	60	(62)		46, 62

ADDITION OF MERCAPTANS TO UNSATURATED COMPOUNDS

Mercaptans add to olefins to form thioethers. Acid, base, sulfur dioxide, air, peroxide, or ultraviolet light catalyzes the reaction, and the nature of the product depends largely on the catalyst used. A small amount of oxygen,[130,133,134,140,158] peroxide,[24-26,48,50,51,73,77,86,110,112,125,154,157] azobisisobuty-ronitrile,[24,157] or ultraviolet light[35,52,68,69,77,99,105,122-124,148,158] causes the reaction to proceed by a radical mechanism, contrary to Markownikoff's rule.

$$RCH{=}CH_2 + HSR' \rightarrow RCH_2CH_2SR'$$

This addition is suppressed by hydroquinone, copper, or sulfur.[123,140] Amyl disulfide or diphenyl disulfide in conjunction with ultraviolet light catalyze the reaction.[122-124] Sometimes light[1,15] or a metal salt[1,46,55,62] is used in conjunction with oxygen or peroxide to initiate the reaction, and in some cases no catalyst is used.[71,107,111,113,129,137] Sulfur dioxide or sulfur catalyzes the normal addition reaction.[73,130]

The reaction usually takes place at 25-100°; higher temperatures are rarely employed.[73] A sealed vessel is necessary with volatile materials.[59,148] In photochemical work involving sensitizers such as acetone, pyrex equipment is used. In the absence of sensitizers, quartz equipment is used.

Methanethiol or trifluoromethanethiol adds readily to terminal fluoro-olefins under the influence of ultraviolet light or x rays.[59] When methanethiol reacts with either trifluoroethylene or hexafluoropropene, both isomers are produced. The ultraviolet-initiated reactions are carried out in a quartz vessel at room temperature in a nitrogen atmosphere. Highly volatile reactants are sealed in a thick-walled pyrex tube and irradiated for 7 days. The x ray-initiated additions are performed in a stainless steel reactor. The reaction mixture is exposed to x rays for a few hours at an average rate of 16,000 rads/min. The products are isolated and purified by distillation, and the isomers are resolved by gas chromatography.

Mercaptans react with vinyl ethers or vinyl thioethers in the absence of a catalyst.[129,130,133,134] Sulfur dioxide accelerates the reaction to give normal addition products, while a small amount of oxygen induces the formation of abnormal products. A large amount of oxygen or of the products of ether oxidation inhibits the reaction.[130]

Thioglycolic acid or its ester condenses with oleic acid, methyl oleate, methyl ricinolate, or 10-undecenoic acid in the presence of peroxide.[86] In most cases lauroyl peroxide is used, and the reaction mixture is heated to 60-90° for several hours. The reaction with undecenoic acid produces a well-defined solid. All the other products are oils and are probably mixtures of isomers. Thioglycolic acid or its ester reacts with alkenyl silanes such as allyltrimethylsilane and allylpentamethyl disiloxane at room temperature.[25]

$$(CH_3)_3SiOSi(CH_3)_2CH_2CH{=}CH_2 + HSCH_2COO_2H$$
$$\rightarrow (CH_3)_3SiOSi(CH_3)_2(CH_2)_3SCH_2CO_2H$$

The reaction is exothermic and can be initiated, if necessary, with a trace of benzoyl peroxide. Thioglycolic acid also adds to 4–trimethylsilylbutene, in the absence of a catalyst, to give the abnormal 1:1 adduct.[113]

Benzyl mercaptan condenses with several vinylsilanes in the absence of a free radical catalyst.[111] The reaction is carried out at 100–130°. Because of these elevated temperatures and the pattern of addition, the condensation may very well be a radical process. The reaction of benzyl mercaptan with triethoxyvinylsilane forms $C_6H_5CH_2SCH_2CH_2CH_2Si(OC_2H_5)_3$, b.p. 125°/0.3 mm, in 34% yield; the reaction with diethoxymethylvinylsilane forms $C_6H_5CH_2SCH_2CH_2Si(CH_3)(OC_2H_5)_2$, b.p. 114°/0.2 mm, in 36% yield; and the reaction with ethoxydimethylvinylsilane forms $C_6H_5CH_2SCH_2CH_2Si-(CH_3)_2(OC_2H_5)$, b.p. 107°/0.5 mm, in 26% yield.

A series of interesting free radical condensations occurs with mercaptans, unsaturated compounds, and carbon monoxide.[26,48,125] The reactions are carried out at 100–130° in an oxygen-free atmosphere at pressures of 1000–3000 atm. The condensations are carried out over a period of 2.5 to 17 hr. The initiator is azobisisobutyronitrile or di–t–butyl peroxide. When n–butylthiol, acetylene, and carbon monoxide react, 3–(n–butylthio)-propenal, b.p. 74°/2 mm, n_D 1.5451 (25°), is obtained in 17% yield.[26,125] The same reactants with benzyl mercaptan produce 3–(benzylthio)-propenal, b.p. 110°/1.3 mm, n_D 1.6167 (25°), in low yield.[26] Ethyl mercaptan, propylene, and carbon monoxide undergo a similar reaction at 130° and 3000 atm in the presence of di–t–butyl peroxide; 3–ethylmercapto–2–methylpropanal, $C_2H_5SCH_2CH(CH_3)CHO$, is produced in 16% yield.[48] A concurrent addition, that of the thiol to the unsaturated compound, occurs in these reactions. For example, 1, 2–bis(n–butylthio)ethane, b.p. 150°/17 mm, n_D 1.4975 (25°), is obtained from n–butylthiol and acetylene; and 1, 2–bis(benzylthio)ethane, b.p. 175°/3 mm, m.p. 38°, is obtained from benzylthiol and acetylene.

Ethyl mercaptan condenses with propylene,[46,62,71] hexyne–1,[15,46,62] or cetene–1.[46,55,62] An increased yield of sulfide is obtained by using peroxide and a salt of iron, chromium, manganese, aluminum, uranium, vanadium, osmium, or magnesium. Light, peroxide, or metal ions catalyze the condensation of cetene–1, and hydroquinone or butadiene inhibits the reaction.[46,55,62] These additions are free radical reactions. They are exothermic and occur at 40–80°.[46,62] Ethylene thiochlorohydrin reacts with cyclohexene containing peroxide or chromic chloride to produce cyclohexychloroethyl sulfide, b.p. 133°, in 41% yield.[46,62]

Mercaptoethanol adds smoothly to vinyl chloride in the presence of benzoyl peroxide[50] or under ultraviolet light[123] and yields the product

2–chloroethyl–2–hydroxyethyl sulfide. If inhibitors such as sulfur or copper are present, amyl disulfide in conjunction with ultraviolet light induces the reaction.[123] Mercaptoethanol reacts with vinyl acetate in ultraviolet light to produce thiodiglycol monoacetate.[124] When the starting materials are pure, the reaction proceeds readily. When stabilized commercial products are used, a catalyst such as 1% diphenyl disulfide is required.

The reaction of benzyl mercaptan with 1, 1, 1–trichloropropene yields two products after 4 hr at 110–115°: 10% of 2, 3, 3–trichloropropylbenzyl sulfide (I), b.p. 114°/0.5 mm, n_D 1.5793 (20°), and 39% of 3, 3–dichloropropen–2–ylbenzyl sulfide (II), b.p. 91°/0.5 mm, n_D 1.5845 (20°).[105]

$$CCl_3CH{=}CH_2 + HSCH_2C_6H_5 \Bigg\langle \begin{array}{l} \longrightarrow CHCl_2CHClCH_2SCH_2C_6H_5 \\ \qquad\qquad\qquad I \\ \\ \longrightarrow CCl_2{=}CHCH_2SCH_2C_6H_5 + HCl \\ \qquad\qquad\qquad II \end{array}$$

The result was interpreted as a rearrangement of the initial radical, $CCl_3\dot{C}HCH_2SCH_2C_6H_5$, to $CCl_2CHClCH_2SCH_2C_6H_5$, followed by hydrogen abstraction and, in the case of II, loss of hydrogen chloride.

Deuterated mercaptan, CH_3SD, reacts with *cis*– or *trans*–2–butene at −70° to give the same product: a mixture of *erythro*– and *threo*–3–deuterio–2–methylthiobutane.[137] In the presence of deuteriobromide the same reaction with *cis*–2–butene produces *threo*–3–deuterio–2–methylthiobutane (III) and with *trans*–2–butene produces *erythro*–3–deuterio–2–methylthiobutane (IV).

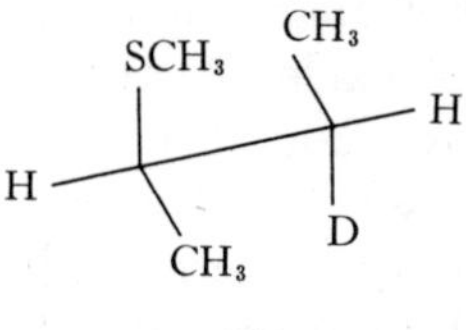

III 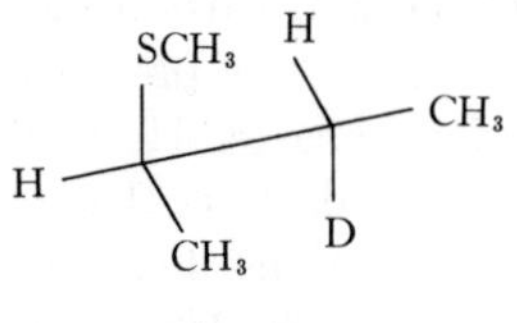   IV

Ethanedithiol and vinyl chloride condense in ultraviolet light in the presence of phenyl disulfide to give bis(2–chloroethylthio)ethane–1, 2.[122]

1, 3, 4–Thiadiazole–2, 5–dithiol and styrene react in the presence of benzoyl peroxide to form the 1:1 adduct (V) in high yield.[45]

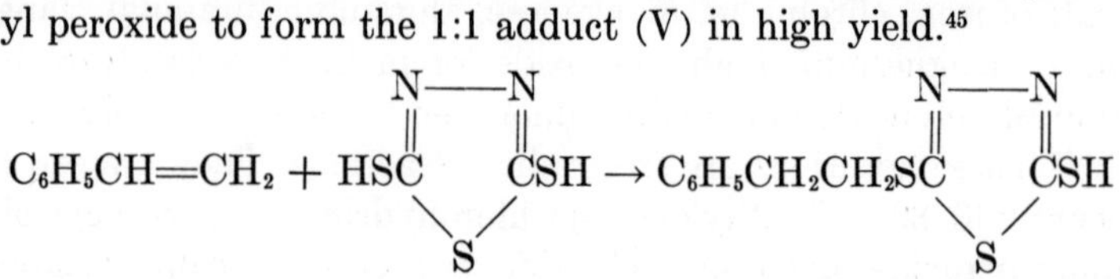

V

In addition, some of the 2:1 adduct, n_D 1.6742 (20°), is obtained.

Table 10. Addition of Mercaptans to Unsaturated Compounds

C_n	Unsaturated compound	Mercaptan	Product	% Yield	°C b.p./mm (m.p.)	n_D (°C)	Ref.
C_2	$CF_2{=}CF_2$	CF_3SH	$CF_3SCF_2CF_2H$ + / $CF_3S(CF_2CF_2)_2H$	53 / 17	33 / 84		59
	$CF_2{=}CFCl$	CF_3SH	CF_3SCF_2CFClH + / $CF_3S(CF_2CFCl)_2H$	62 / 20	66 / 145	1.3339 (25) / 1.3627 (25)	59
	$CF_2{=}CH_2$	CF_3SH	$CF_3SCH_2CF_2H$	72	58	1.3270 (25)	59
	$CF_2{=}CFH$	CF_3SH	$CF_3SCHFCF_2H$	83	52	1.3112 (25)	59
C_3	$CF_3CF{=}CF_2$	CF_3SH	$CF_3SCF_2CFHCF_3$ + / $CF_3SC(SF_3)FCF_2H$	56	53 / 55		59
	$CF_2{=}CFOCH_3$	CF_3SH	$CF_3SCF_2CFHOCH_3$	71	102	1.3303 (25)	59
	$CF_3CF{=}CF_2$	CF_3CH_2SH	$CF_3CH_2SCF_2CFHCF_3$ + / $CF_3CH_2SC(CF_3)FCF_2H$	65	105 / 98	1.3208 (24) / 1.3220 (24)	59
C_2	$CH_2{=}CHCl$	CH_3SH	$ClCH_2CH_2SCH_3$	74	44/20		68
	$CF_2{=}CFH$	CH_3SH	$CH_3SCHFCF_2H$ + / $CH_3SCF_2CFH_2$	60		1.3889 (23)	59
	$CF_2{=}CFCl$	CH_3SH	CH_3SCF_2CFClH	84	51/98	1.4024 (25)	59
C_3	Propargyl alcohol	CH_3SH	2,3-Dimethylmercapto-propanol	50	88/1	1.5431 (19)	158
	Allyl alcohol	CH_3SH	$CH_3S(CH_2)_3OH$	61	100/23		1
C_4	$CH_2{=}CHOCOCH_3$	CH_3SH	$CH_3S(CH_2)_2OCOCH_3$	95	79/21	1.4583 (30)	68, 69
C_3	Propene	C_2H_5SH	$C_2H_5SC_3H_7{-}n$	64	116/750	1.4471 (20)	46, 71
	Propargyl alcohol	C_2H_5SH	2,3-Bis(ethylmercapto)-1-propanol	95	119/3.4	1.5248 (25)	15
	Propiolic acid	C_2H_5SH	$C_2H_5SCH{=}CHCO_2H$		(74)		15
	Propiolic acid	C_2H_5SH (2 moles)	$C_2H_5SCH_2CH(SC_2H_5)CO_2H$		128/0.5		15
C_4	Isobutene	C_2H_5SH	$C_2H_5SC_4H_9{-}i$	94	132/749	1.4461 (20)	71

Table 10. (cont.)   Addition of Mercaptans to Unsaturated Compounds

C_n	Unsaturated compound	Mercaptan	Product	% Yield	°C b.p./mm (m.p.)	n_D (°C)	Ref.
	$C_2H_5SCH{=}CH_2$	C_2H_5SH	Bis-1,2-ethylmercaptoethane	88	94/7	1.5110 (20)	133
	Methyl acrylate	C_2H_5SH	Methyl 2-thioethyl propionate	37	84/14	1.4630 (20)	77
	$CH_2{=}CHOC_2H_5$	C_2H_5SH	$C_2H_5SCH_2CH_2OC_2H_5$	93	84/48	1.4508 (20)	130
C_5	Trimethylethylene	C_2H_5SH	$C_2H_5SC_5H_{11}\text{-}sec\text{-}i$	90	151/751	1.4527 (20)	71
	Propargyl acetate	C_2H_5SH	2,3-Bis(ethylmercapto)-1-propyl acetate	93	101/0.8	1.4978 (25)	15
	2-Methyl-3-butyn-2-ol	C_2H_5SH	3,4-Bis(ethylmercapto)-2-methyl-2-butanol		88/0.3	1.5080 (25)	15
C_6	1-Hexyne	C_2H_5SH	1,2-Bis(ethylmercapto)hexane	94	74/0.2	1.4934 (25)	15, 46, 62
	$CH_2{=}CHO\text{-}n\text{-}C_4H_9$	C_2H_5SH	$C_2H_5SCH_2CH_2O\text{-}n\text{-}C_4H_9$	96	62/4	1.4520 (20)	130
	Dimethyl acetylene dicarboxylate	C_2H_5SH	$CH_3O_2CCH{=}C(SC_2H_5)CO_2CH_3$		108/1	1.5132 (25)	15
	$CH_2{=}CHSC_4H_9$	C_2H_5SH	$C_2H_5SCH_2CH_2SC_4H_9$	100	99/3.5	1.5013 (20)	134
C_8	Octene-1	C_2H_5SH	$C_2H_5S\text{-}n\text{-}C_8H_{17}$	75	155/100		73
	Phenyl acetylene	C_2H_5SH	$C_6H_5CH_2CH(SC_2H_5)_2$	93	115/0.75	1.5604 (25)	15
	2-Butyn-1,4-diol diacetate	C_2H_5SH	2,3-Bis(ethylmercapto)-1,4-butanediol diacetate	93	145/1.4	1.4932 (20)	15
C_{16}	Cetene-1	C_2H_5SH	Cetylethyl sulfide	87	(18)		46, 62
C_3	$CH_3CH{=}CH_2$	$n\text{-}C_3H_7SH$	Di-n-propyl thioether	96	142	1.4480 (20)	148
C_4	Methyl acrylate	$n\text{-}C_3H_7SH$	Methyl 2-thiopropylpropionate	37	63/4	1.4629 (21)	77
C_3	Propargyl alcohol	$n\text{-}C_4H_9SH$	2,3-Di-n-butylmercapto-propanol	50	132/1	1.5089 (15)	158
C_4	Isobutylene	$n\text{-}C_4H_9SH$	$n\text{-}C_4H_9SC_4H_9\text{-}i$	66	174/745	1.4500 (20)	71
	Vinyl acetate	$n\text{-}C_4H_9SH$	$n\text{-}C_4H_9S(CH_2)_2OCOCH_3$		65/2.5	1.4581 (20)	157
C_9	Indene	$n\text{-}C_4H_9SH$	2-Indanyl n-butyl sulfide	93	118/2	1.5475 (20)	110

Table 10. (cont.)   Addition of Mercaptans to Unsaturated Compounds

C_n	Unsaturated compound	Mercaptan	Product	% Yield	°C b.p./mm (m.p.)	n_D (°C)	Ref.
C_{16}	3,3-Diphenyl-1-butene	n-C_4H_9SH	3,3-Diphenyl-1-butylbutyl sulfide	25	180/1.5	1.5682 (25)	154
C_4	Vinyl acetate	$(CH_3)_2CHCH_2SH$	$(CH_3)_2CHCH_2S(CH_2)_2OCOCH_3$		95/11	1.4572 (25)	157
	Vinyl acetate	$(CH_3)_3CSH$	$(CH_3)_3CS(CH_2)_2OCOCH_3$		60/3	1.4571 (20)	157
C_2	Vinyl chloride	$HO(CH_2)_2SH$	$HO(CH_2)_2S(CH_2)_2Cl$	100	87/0.5	1.5205 (24.5)	123
		$HO(CH_2)_2SH$		57	100/0.6	1.5260 (20)	50
C_4	$CH_2{=}CHOCOCH_3$	$HO(CH_2)_2SH$	$HO(CH_2)_2S(CH_2)_2OCOCH_3$	51	148/13	1.4879 (20)	124
C_6	$(CH_3)_3SiCH_2CH{=}CH_2$	HO_2CCH_2SH	$(CH_3)_3Si(CH_2)_3SCH_2CO_2H$	54	165/9	1.4790 (20)	25
	Cyclohexene	HO_2CCH_2SH	Cyclohexylthioglycolic acid	87	122/0.1		35
C_7	1-Methylcyclohexene	HO_2CCH_2SH	2-Methylcyclohexylthio-glycolic acid		135/0.1		35
	4-Trimethylsilyl-butene-1	HO_2CCH_2SH	$(CH_3)_3SiCH_2CH_2CH_2CH_2{-}SCH_2CO_2H$	73	173/14	1.4775 (20)	113
C_8	Octene-1	HO_2CCH_2SH	n-$C_8H_{17}SCH_2CO_2H$		138/0.35 (37)		140
	$(CH_3)_3SiOSi(CH_3)_2CH_2{-}CH{=}CH_2$	HO_2CCH_2SH	$(CH_3)_3SiOSi(CH_3)_2(CH_2)_3{-}SCH_2CO_2H$	48	201/50	1.4479 (20)	25
C_9	Nonene-1	HO_2CCH_2SH	n-$C_9H_{19}SCH_2CO_2H$		137/0.7		140
C_{10}	Decene-1	HO_2CCH_2SH	n-$C_{10}H_{21}SCH_2CO_2H$		157/0.67 (53)		140
	Dihydromyrcene	HO_2CCH_2SH	Dihydromyrcene monothio-glycolic acid	49	170/0.1		35
C_{11}	Undecene-1	HO_2CCH_2SH	n-$C_{11}H_{23}SCH_2CO_2H$		(63)		140
	4-Methyldecene-1	HO_2CCH_2SH	4-CH_3-n-$C_{10}H_{21}SCH_2CO_2H$		126/0.02		140

Table 10. (cont.)   Addition of Mercaptans to Unsaturated Compounds

C_n	Unsaturated compound	Mercaptan	Product	% Yield	°C b.p./mm (m.p.)	n_D (°C)	Ref.
	Undecenoic acid	HO_2CCH_2SH	$HO_2CCH_2S(CH_2)_{10}CO_2H$		(99)		86
C_6	$(CH_3)_3SiCH_2CH=CH_2$	$C_2H_5CO_2CH_2SH$	$(CH_3)_3Si(CH_2)_3SCH_2CO_2C_2H_5$	63	148/24	1.4630 (20)	25
	Cyclohexene	$(CH_2)_2CH(CH_2)_2SH$	Cyclohexylisoamyl sulfide	67	120/12		35
C_7	1–Methylcyclohexene	$(CH_2)_2CH(CH_2)_2SH$	Methylcyclohexylisoamyl sulfide		124/10		35
C_6	$CH_2=CHO-n-C_4H_9$	$C_4H_9O(CH_2)_2SH$	β,β'–Dibutoxydiethyl sulfide	94	130/4.5	1.4560 (20)	130
C_8	$C_4H_9OCH_2CH_2-SCH=CH_2$	$C_4H_9O(CH_2)_2SH$	$C_4H_9O(CH_2)_2S(CH_2)_2S(CH_2)_2-OC_4H_9$	96	175/3.2	1.4869 (20)	129
	$CH_2=CHSC_6H_5$	$C_4H_9O(CH_2)_2SH$	$C_6H_5SCH_2CH_2SCH_2CH_2OC_4H_9$	90	155/4	1.4900 (20)	134
C_{10}	$CH_2=CHB(OC_4H_9)_2$	$C_6H_{13}SH$	$C_6H_{13}SCH_2CH_2B(OC_4H_9)_2$	93	116/0.07	1.4501 (29.5)	99
C_3	Propargyl alcohol	$C_2H_5CH_2SH$	2, 3–Dibenzylmercaptopropanol		125/ 5×10^{-3}	1.6085 (24)	158
	Propiolic acid	$C_6H_5CH_2SH$	cis–β–Benzylthioacrylic acid	47	(144)		112
C_4	Vinyl acetate	$C_6H_5CH_2SH$	$C_6H_5CH_2S(CH_2)_2OCOCH_3$		108/2	1.5417 (20)	157
C_{15}	Benzalacetophenone	$C_6H_5CH_2SH$	β–Phenyl–β–benzylmercapto-propiophenone		(71)		107
C_{20}	$(C_6H_5)_3SiCH=CH_2$	$C_6H_5CH_2SH$	$(C_6H_5)_3SiCH_2CH_2SCH_2C_6H_5$	18	(72)		51
C_{11}	$CH_3(CH_2)_8CH=CH_2$	$C_{12}H_{25}SH$	$C_{12}H_{25}S(CH_2)_{10}CH_3$		(37)		73
C_{13}	$CH_3(CH_2)_{10}CH=CH_2$	$C_{12}H_{25}SH$	$C_{12}H_{25}S(CH_2)_{12}CH_3$		(39)		73
C_{15}	$CH_3(CH_2)_{12}CH=CH_2$	$C_{12}H_{25}SH$	$C_{12}H_{25}S(CH_2)_{14}CH_3$		(49)		73
C_{15}	$C_{12}H_{25}SCH_2CH=CH_2$	$C_{12}H_{25}SH$	$C_{12}H_{25}S(CH_2)_3SC_{12}H_{25}$		(47)		73
C_{17}	$CH_3(CH_2)_{14}CH=CH_2$	$C_{12}H_{25}SH$	$C_{12}H_{25}S(CH_2)_{16}CH_3$		(52)		73
C_{19}	$CH_3(CH_2)_{16}CH=CH_2$	$C_{12}H_{25}SH$	$C_{12}H_{25}S(CH_2)_{18}CH_3$		(53)		73

Table 10. (cont.)   Addition of Mercaptans to Unsaturated Compounds

C_n	Unsaturated compound	Mercaptan	Product	% Yield	°C b.p./mm (m.p.)	n_D (°C)	Ref.
C_8	2–Butyn–1, 4–diol diacetate	$HS(CH_2)_2SH$	1, 2–Bis(acetoxymethyl)–1, 4–dithiane	43	156/1	1.5252 (20)	15
C_{13}	Tridecene	$HS(CH_2)_2SH$	$n-C_{13}H_{27}S(CH_2)_2SC_{13}H_{27}-n$		(64)		73
	Tridecene	$HS(CH_2)_3SH$	$n-C_{13}H_{27}S(CH_2)_3SC_{13}H_{27}-n$		(53)		73
	Tridecene	$HS(CH_2)_4SH$	$n-C_{13}H_{27}S(CH_2)_4SC_{13}H_{27}-n$		(56)		73
	Tridecene	$HS(CH_2)_5SH$	$n-C_{13}H_{27}S(CH_2)_5SC_{13}H_{27}-n$		(57)		73
	Tridecene	$HS(CH_2)_6SH$	$n-C_{13}H_{27}S(CH_2)_6SC_{13}H_{27}-n$		(59)		73
	Tridecene	$HS(CH_2)_7SH$	$n-C_{13}H_{27}S(CH_2)_7SC_{13}H_{27}-n$		(60)		73
	Tridecene	$HS(CH_2)_8SH$	$n-C_{13}H_{27}S(CH_2)_8SC_{13}H_{27}-n$		(59)		73
	Tridecene	$HS(CH_2)_9SH$	$n-C_{13}H_{27}S(CH_2)_9SC_{13}H_{27}-n$		(64)		73
	Tridecene	$HS(CH_2)_{10}SH$	$n-C_{13}H_{27}S(CH_2)_{10}SC_{13}H_{27}-n$		(64)		73
	Tridecene	$HS(CH_2)_{11}SH$	$n-C_{13}H_{27}S(CH_2)_{11}SC_{13}H_{27}-n$		(65)		73
	Tridecene	$HS(CH_2)_{12}SH$	$n-C_{13}H_{27}S(CH_2)_{12}SC_{13}H_{27}-n$		(66)		73
	Tridecene	$HS(CH_2)_{18}SH$	$n-C_{13}H_{27}S(CH_2)_{18}SC_{13}H_{27}-n$		(73)		73

ADDITION OF THIOACIDS TO UNSATURATED COMPOUNDS

Thioacids react with many unsaturated compounds to give abnormal products.[9-11,13,17,18,24,36,52,64,66,67,71,104,106,114,136,154]

$$C_6H_5CH{=}CH_2 + CH_3COSH \rightarrow C_6H_5CH_2CH_2S(O)CCH_3$$

Even at room temperature the reaction proceeds readily in the absence of a catalyst.[11,13,36,64-67,71,104,136] It can be accelerated by heat,[24,67,71] benzoyl peroxide,[10,11,24,104] ascaridole,[10,11,24,104] t–butyl hydroperoxide,[106,154] or ultra-violet light.[10,11,17,18,52,106] Most of the reported reactions are reactions of thioacetic acid with acetylenes or olefins, although a few reactions of monochloro-, dichloro-, and trichlorothioacetic acid[36] and thiopropionic and thiobenzoic acid[13] have been reported. The resulting thioacetates can easily be hydrolyzed to thiols in good yield or can be converted to sulfonyl chlorides.

Depending on the relative amount of thioacid and acetylene, the reaction products are either olefins or saturated compounds.

$$RC{\equiv}CH + CH_3C(O)SH \rightarrow RCH{=}CHS(O)CCH_3$$

$$RCH{=}CHSOCCH_3 + CH_3COSH \rightarrow RCH(SCOCH_3)CH_2S(O)CCH_3$$

Thioacetic acid reacts with phenyl acetylene[13] to give a mixture of two isomers of I, which melt at 20° and 44°.

$$C_6H_5CH{=}CHS(O)CCH_3$$

I

Thioacetic acid and hex–1–yn–3–ol react in the presence of ascaridole to give 3–hydroxyhex–1–enyl thioacetate (II), b.p. 75°/5 × 10^{-4} mm, n_D 1.5050 (16°), in 67% yield.[10] In ultraviolet light a 51% yield is obtained plus 22% of 1, 2–diacetylthiohexan–3–ol (III), b.p. 80/10^{-3} mm, n_D 1.5208 (20°).[10]

$$C_3H_7CH(OH)CH{=}CHSCOCH_3$$

II

$$C_3H_7CH(OH)CH(SCOCH_3)CH_2SCOCH_3$$

III

Similarly, thioacetic acid and hex–4–en–1–yn–3–ol react in the presence of ascaridole to form compound IV, b.p. 67°/10^{-4} mm, n_D 1.5007 (26.5°), in 25% yield and compound V, b.p. 100°/10^{-4} mm, n_D 1.5407 (23.5°) in

11% yield.[10] Under ultraviolet light IV and V are produced in 12% and 13.5% yield, respectively.[10]

$$CH_3CH(SCOCH_3)CH_2CH(OH)C\equiv CH$$

IV

$$CH_3CH=CHCH(OH)CH(SCOCH_3)CH_2SCOCH_3$$

V

The most detailed reports of work with acetylenes are by Behringer[13] and Bader.[10,11]

Thioacetic acid reacts smoothly with $\alpha-$ or $\beta-$pinene in ultraviolet light.[17,18] The products seem to be a mixture of two thiolacetates. The radical addition of thioacetic acid to 1–chlorocyclohexene in ultraviolet light is less stereospecific (66% *cis* product) than the radical addition reactions of either thiophenol or hydrogen sulfide.[52] Thioacetic acid adds to *cis*– or *trans*–2–chloro–2–butene at $-78°$ to produce the same mixture of 90% *threo*– and 10% *erythro*–2–acetylmercapto–3–chlorobutane, b.p. $97°/27$ mm.[106] The addition is usually reversible, although at $-78°$ the reverse reaction is retarded.

O, O–dialkyl hydrogen phosphorodithioates (VI) add to olefins both according to Markownikoff's rule and contrary to it.[9,114]

$$(RO)_2P(S)SH$$

R = alkyl

VI

For example, compound VI adds to substituted allylsilanes to form normal products.[114]

$$R'_3SiCH_2CH=CH_2 + (RO)_2P(S)SH \rightarrow R'_3SiSH_2CH(CH_3)SP(S)(OR)_2$$

But compound VI adds to vinylsilanes to form abnormal products.[144]

$$R'_3SiCH=CH_2 + (RO)_2P(S)SH \rightarrow R'_3SiCH_2CH_2SP(S)(OR)_2$$

Specifically, the addition of VI (R = CH_3 or C_2H_5) to triethylvinylsilane results in VII, b.p. $121°/0.5$ mm, n_D 1.5102 (20°), and VIII, b.p. $133°/0.5$ mm, n_D 1.5021 (20°), respectively.[114]

$$(C_2H_5)_3SiCH_2CH_2SP(S)(OCH_3)_2$$

VII

$$(C_2H_5)_3SiCH_2CH_2SP(S)(OC_2H_5)_2$$

VIII

Table 11. Addition of Thioacids to Unsaturated Compounds

C_n	Unsaturated compound	Thioacid	Product	% Yield	°C b.p./mm (m.p.)	n_D (°C)	Ref.
C_3	Allyl alcohol	CH_3COSH	3-Acetylthio-n-propan-1-ol	97	73/1.5	1.4827 (20)	24
	Acraldehyde	CH_3COSH	β-(Acetylthio)propaldehyde	65	68/1	1.5079 (20)	24
	Acrylic acid	CH_3COSH	$CH_3COSCH_2CH_2COOH$	66	127/3 (53)	1.4902 (20)	66
	Allyl chloride	CH_3COSH	$CH_3COSCH_2CH_2CH_2Cl$	79	83/10		136
C_4	Crotyl alcohol	CH_3COSH	3-Acetylthio-n-butan-1-ol	55	85/15	1.4605 (20)	24
	Crotonaldehyde	CH_3COSH	β-(Acetylthio)-n-butaldehyde	100	59/2	1.5025 (20)	24
	Crotonic acid	CH_3COSH	$CH_3COSCH(CH_3)CH_2COOH$	68	129/3	1.4902 (20)	66
	Maleic acid	CH_3COSH	Acetylthiosuccinic acid	90	(125)		63, 65, 66
	Maleic anhydride	CH_3COSH	Acetylthiosuccinic anhydride	83	(76)		24
	Isobutylene	CH_3COSH	$CH_3COSC_4H_9$-i	60	151/744		71
	3-Methylallyl alcohol	CH_3COSH	3-Acetylthio-2-methyl-n-propan-1-ol	77	121/23	1.4856 (20)	24
C_5	Vinylacetic acid	CH_3COSH	$CH_3COS(CH_2)_3CO_2H$	85	139/3	1.4949 (20)	66
	4-Chlorobut-1-yne	CH_3COSH	3, 4-Bisacetylthiobutyl chloride	92	92/0.0001	1.5392 (15)	104
	Isopropylethylene	CH_3COSH	$CH_3COSC_5H_{11}$-i	86	176/748	1.4590 (20)	71
	Allyl acetate	CH_3COSH	3-Acetylthio-n-propyl acetate	100	125/24	1.4720 (20)	24
	Trimethylethylene	CH_3COSH	$CH_3COSC_5H_{11}$-sec-i	87	75/30	1.4621 (20)	71
	Propylidene acetic acid	CH_3COSH	$CH_3CH_2CH(SCOCH_3)CH_2CO_2H$	81	133/2 (44)		67
	Pent-4-yn-2-ol	CH_3COSH	$CH_3CH(OH)CH_2CH=CHSCOCH_3$	60	76/ 5×10^{-4}	1.5158 (22.5)	10
	β-Ethylidene propionic acid	CH_3COSH	$CH_3CH(SCOCH_3)CH_2CH_2CO_2H$	80	143/4		67
	Allylacetic acid	CH_3COSH	$CH_2(SCOCH_3)(CH_2)_3CO_2H$	87	(53)		67

Table II. (cont.)   Addition of Thioacids to Unsaturated Compounds

C_n	Unsaturated compound	Thioacid	Product	% Yield	°C b.p./mm (m.p.)	n_D (°C)	Ref.
	Itaconic acid	CH_3COSH	$CH_3COSCH_2CH(CO_2H)CH_2CO_2H$	75	(91)		66
C_6	Hex-1-yne	CH_3COSH	Hex-1-enyl thiolacetate ($C_4H_9CH=CHSCOCH_3$)	53	83/20	1.4899 (20)	11
	Hex-1-yne	CH_3COSH (3 moles)	$C_4H_9CH(SCOCH_3)CH_2SCOCH_3$	70	158/20	1.5094 (17)	11, 13
	Hexene-1	CH_3COSH	n-Hexyl thiolacetate	83	88/13	1.4591 (25)	18
	t-Butyl acetylene	CH_3COSH	$CH_3COSCH=CH(CH_3)_3$		77/12	1.4862 (23)	13
	Diallyl	CH_3COSH	$CH_3COS(CH_2)_6SCOCH_3$		(29)		13
	Crotyl acetate	CH_3COSH	3-Acetylthio-n-butyl acetate	74	110/11	1.4674 (20)	24
	2-Methylallyl acetate	CH_3COSH	3-Acetylthio-2-methyl-n-propyl acetate	80	133/24	1.4693 (20)	24
	Citraconic acid	CH_3COSH	1:1 adduct	13	(149)		66
	Mesityl oxide	CH_3COSH	4-Acetylthio-4-methyl-n-pentan-2-one	92	85/6		24
	$CH_2=CHO$-n-C_4H_9	CH_3COSH	$CH_3COSCH_2CH_2O$-n-C_4H_9	91	84/5	1.4600 (20)	130
	Vinylisobutyl ether	CH_3COSH	Acetylmercaptoisobutoxyethane	52	92/15	1.4579 (19)	13
	1-Methylcyclopentene	CH_3COSH	2-Methylcyclopentyl thiolacetate (71% cis, 29% trans)	80	100/25	1.4900 (25)	18
	Cyclohexene	CH_3COSH	Cyclohexyl thiolacetate	92	90/14	1.5197 (16)	36, 104
	1-Chlorocyclohexene	CH_3COSH	2-Chlorocyclohexyl thiolacetate	84	120/10	1.5191 (25)	52
C_7	1-Methylcyclohexene	CH_3COSH	2-Methylcyclohexyl thiolacetate	85	110/4	1.495 (25)	18, 36
C_8	Octene-1	CH_3COSH	n-Octyl thiolacetate	100	132/23	1.4648 (20)	24
	n-Hexyl acetylene	CH_3COSH	$CH_3COSCH=CHC_6H_{13}$	65	123/14	1.4891 (14)	13
	Cyclohexyl acetylene	CH_3COSH	$CH_3COSCH=CHC_6H_{11}$	96	117/13	1.5222 (14)	13

Table 11. (cont.) Addition of Thioacids to Unsaturated Compounds

C_n	Unsaturated compound	Thioacid	Product	% Yield	°C b.p./mm (m.p.)	n_D (°C)	Ref.
	Cyclohexyl acetylene	CH₃COSH (3 moles)	CH₃COSCH₂(SCOCH₃)CHC₆H₁₁	41	175/12 (44)		13
	Octa-1, 7–diyne (HC≡C((CH₂)₄C≡CH)	CH₃COSH	CH₃COSCH=CH(CH₂)₂C≡CH + CH₃COSCH₂(SCOCH₃)CH(CH₂)₄-C≡CH+	26 12	61/0.1 98/10⁻³	1.5115 (19) 1.5324 (18)	11
			CH₃COSCH=CH(CH₂)₄CH-(SCOCH₃)CH₂SCOCH₃	36	146/ 2 × 10⁻⁴	1.5458 (20)	
	1–Ethynylcyclohexanol	CH₃COSH	2–Cyclohex–1'–enylvinyl thiolacetate	55	(36)		10
	Styrene	CH₃COSH	β–Phenylethylthioacetate		137/14	1.5478 (20)	63–65
	Phenyl acetylene	CH₃COSH	CH₃COSCH=CHC₆H₅	85	142/16	1.6215 (17)	11, 13
C₉	p–Methoxyphenyl acetylene	CH₃COSH	p–Methoxystyryl 2–thiolacetate	75	(47)		11
	α–Methylstyrene	CH₃COSH	2–Phenyl–n–propyl thiolacetate	90	105/4	1.5429 (20)	24
	Cinnamaldehyde	CH₃COSH	β–(Acetylthio)–β–phenyl-propaldehyde	90	115/1 (44)		24
	Cinnamic acid	CH₃COSH	CH₃COSCH(C₆H₅)CH₂CO₂H	53	(95)		66
	1–Phenylprop–2–yn–1–ol	CH₃COSH	C₆H₅CH(OH)CH=CHSOCH₃	24	115/10⁻³	1.5730 (20)	10
C₁₀	Benzylidene acetone	CH₃COSH	4–Acetylthio–4–phenyl–n–butan–2–one	90	(67)		24
	Camphene	CH₃COSH	2–(S–Thioacetoxymethyl)–3, 3–dimethylbicyclo–[2.2.1] heptane	83	93/0.8		17, 18
	Eugenol	CH₃COSH	3'–Acetylthio–4–hydroxy–3–methoxy–n–propylbenzene	78	180/1.5		24
	Dihydromyrcene	CH₃COSH	Dihydromyrcene monothiolacetate	40	128/10		36
	Dihydromyrcene	CH₃COSH (excess)	Dihydromyrcene bisthiolacetate	60	125/0.05		36

Table 11. (cont.) Addition of Thioacids to Unsaturated Compounds

C_n	Unsaturated compound	Thioacid	Product	% Yield	°C b.p./mm (m.p.)	n_D (°C)	Ref.
C_{11}	Cinnamyl acetate	CH_3COSH	3-Acetylthio-3-phenyl-n-propyl acetate	38	127/1	1.5292 (20)	24
C_{16}	Hexadec-1-ene	CH_3COSH	n-Hexadecyl thiolacetate	75	168/1.5 (31)		24
	3, 3-Diphenyl-1-butene	CH_3COSH	3, 3-Diphenyl-1-butyl thiolacetate	95	215/1	1.5843 (25)	154
C_6	Cyclohexene	$ClCH_2COSH$	Cyclohexyl chlorothiolacetate		132/14		36
C_7	1-Methylcyclohexene	$ClCH_2COSH$	2-Methylcyclohexyl chloro-thiolacetate	91	137/11		36
C_{10}	Dihydromyrcene	$ClCH_2COSH$	Dihydromyrcene chloro-thiolacetate	51	99/0.1		36
C_6	Cyclohexene	$Cl_2CHCOSH$	Cyclohexyl dichlorothiolacetate	93	148/12		36
C_{10}	Dihydromyrcene	$Cl_2CHCOSH$	Dihydromyrcene dichloro-thiolacetate	28	118/0.1		36
C_6	Cyclohexene	Cl_3CCOSH	Cyclohexyl trichlorothiolacetate	97	151/12		36
C_7	1-Methylcyclohexene	Cl_3CCOSH	2-Methylcyclohexyl trichloro-thiolacetate	100	96/0.1		36
C_{10}	Dihydromyrcene	Cl_3CCOSH	Dihydromyrcene trichloro-thiolacetate	48	119/0.05		36
C_6	Vinylisobutyl ether	CH_3CH_2COSH	$CH_3CH_2COS(CH_2)_2O$-i-C_4H_9	30	81/11		13
C_8	Phenyl acetylene	CH_3CH_2COSH	$CH_3CH_2COSCH=CHC_6H_5$		161/15		13
C_3	Propargyl aldehyde	C_6H_5COSH	$C_6H_5COSCH=CHCHO$	16	(94)		13
C_8	Phenyl acetylene	C_6H_5COSH	$C_6H_5COSCH=CHC_6H_5$		(97)		13

O, O–dialkyl hydrogen phosphorodithioate reacts with octene–1 or styrene.

$$RCH{=}CH_2 + (C_2H_5O)_2P(S)SH \rightarrow RCH_2CH_2SP(S)(OC_2H_5)_2$$

R = hexyl or phenyl

When pure starting materials are used or when cumene hydroperoxide is present, the products are abnormal: O, O–diethyl–S–(n–octyl) phosphorodithioate and O, O–diethyl–S–(β–phenethyl) phosphorodithioate, respectively.

Condensations involving a variety of olefins and dialkyldithiophosphoric acid (VI) in the presence of base[101] and in the absence of a catalyst have been reported by Russian chemists.[114] The mechanism of the uncatalyzed reactions has not been investigated. However, the pattern of addition suggests a radical mechanism.

ADDITION OF THIOPHENOLS TO UNSATURATED COMPOUNDS

Aromatic thiols add readily to unsaturated compounds under various conditions. Generally the factors affecting free radical addition of hydrogen sulfide or mercaptans are applicable to thiophenols. Thiophenols add readily to unsaturated compounds in the absence of a free radical initiator and abnormal products are obtained. Thus, in the absence of peroxide under a nitrogen atmosphere at 120°, thiophenol reacts with propene, butene–1, isobutene, pentene–1, isopropylethylene, or trimethylethylene to form n–propyl, n–butyl, isobutyl, n–amyl, isoamyl, or sec–amylphenyl sulfide, respectively.[72] In the presence of an acid catalyst the normal product is formed.[72]

Thiophenol adds to triethoxyvinylsilane at 100–120° in the absence of a catalyst to form $C_6H_5S(CH_2)_2Si(OC_2H_5)_3$, b.p. 130°/0.8 mm, in 75% yield.[111] p–Methylthiophenol reacts with both vinyl groups of divinyl acetylene to produce di–(p–tolylthio)–1, 6–hexine–3 in 80% yield, and the acetylenic bond is preserved.[27] The reaction is accelerated by ultraviolet light.

$$CH_2{=}CHC{\equiv}CCH{=}CH_2 + 2CH_3C_6H_4SH$$
$$\rightarrow CH_3C_6H_4S(CH_2)_2C{\equiv}C(CH_2)_2SC_6H_4CH_3$$

The uncatalyzed reaction[116] between thiophenol and styrene as well as the photochemical reaction[5] yield phenylethylphenyl sulfide. Thiocresol adds to phenyl acetylene in the absence of a catalyst to form a mixture of two isomers of benzalmethyltolyl sulfide, $C_6H_5CH{=}CHSC_6H_4$–p–CH_3, m.p. 44° and 65°.[87]

Aromatic thiols react readily with indene to give 2–indanyl sulfide.[110] t–Butyl hydroperoxide or cumene hydroperoxide is used as the initiator, but the reaction proceeds well even without peroxide. In contrast, ionic addition of these thiols to indene results in 1–indanyl sulfide.[110] In the absence of a catalyst, p–tolyl mercaptan reacts with benzalacetophenone or benzalpyruvic acid to give the adducts in good yield.[107]

A catalyst is not required for the radical addition of p–thiocresol to compounds I and II at 100° to give the corresponding sulfide, III and IV, in high yield.[14]

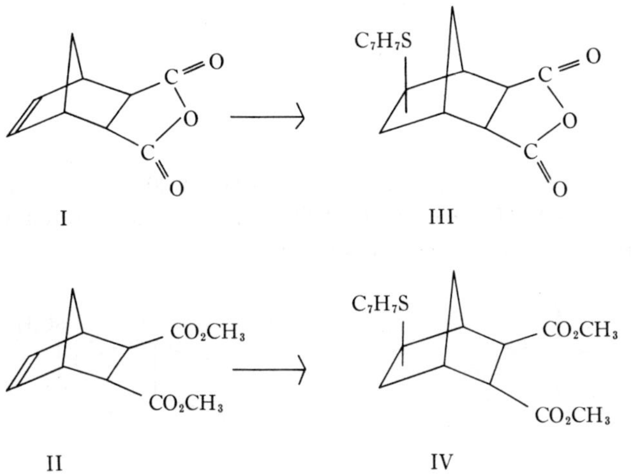

Likewise, a catalyst is not required for the radical addition of p–thiocresol to V to give VI.[31]

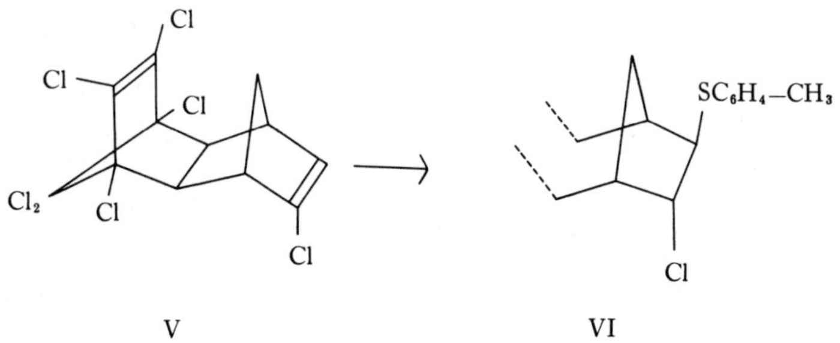

The uncatalyzed reaction of p–thiocresol with 11–chloro–9, 10–dihydro–9, 10–ethanoanthracene results in a mixture of cis and $trans$ isomers which can be separated by chromatography on alumina.[31]

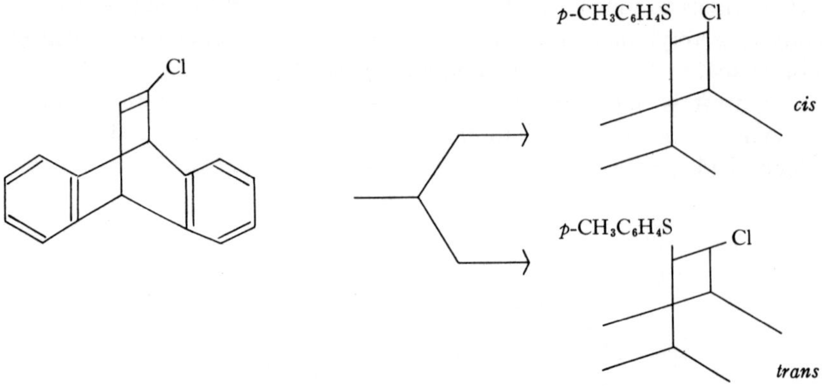

p-Thiocresol reacts with norbornylene (VII) at 60–75° in the absence of a catalyst to give VIII in 86% yield.[32] The reaction is accelerated by benzoyl peroxide and retarded by trinitrobenzene.

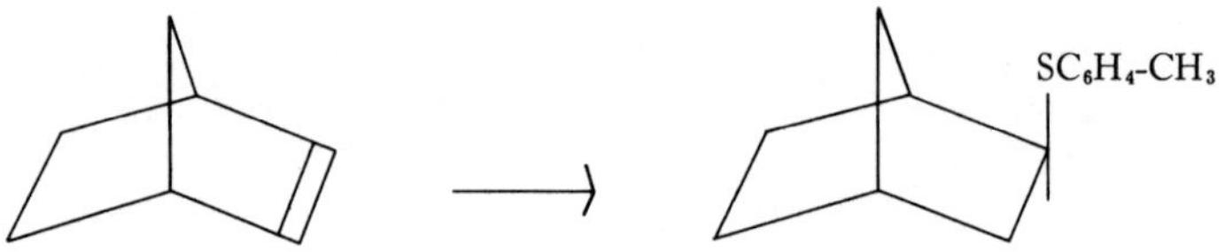

VII   VIII

p-Thiocresol or thiophenol reacts highly exothermically with 2, 5–norbornadiene (IX) to give an unresolvable mixture of two products, X and XI, in high yield.[33]

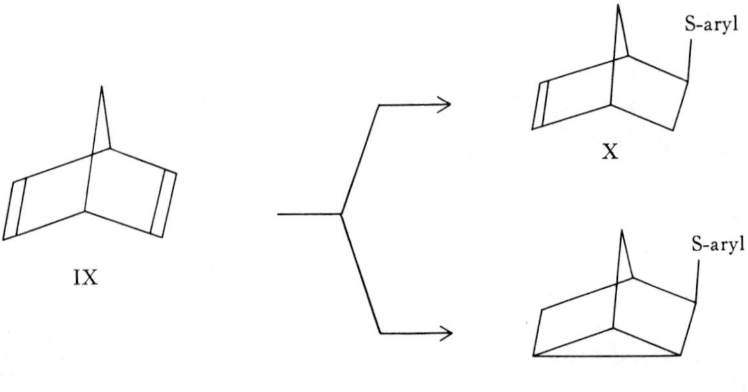

IX

X

XI

Thiophenol reacts with 1–chlorocyclohexene at 50° under ultraviolet light to form *cis*–2–chlorocyclohexylphenyl sulfide predominantly (94%).[52] The addition of thiophenol to benzothiophene–1–dioxide (XII) can be initiated by heat, peroxide, or ultraviolet light.[16] This reaction is carried out in boiling carbon tetrachloride in a nitrogen atmosphere. It is not catalyzed by diphenyl sulfide and is not inhibited by hydroquinone. The addition product is substituted at position 2 (XIII). In contrast, the base-catalyzed addition yields a product substituted at position 3.

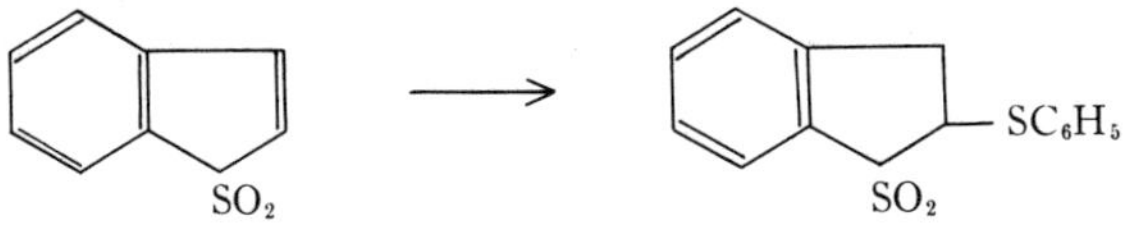

XII   XIII

In the presence of benzoyl peroxide, 4–mercaptobiphenyl adds readily at room temperature to a series of olefins to produce the corresponding solid sulfide.[95]

In the presence of peroxide, thiophenol and hexene–1 react to produce *n*–hexylphenyl sulfide; the yield is higher in the presence of ferrous ion.[46,62] Thiophenol and 1, 1, 1–trichloropropene (XIV) react to produce 2, 3, 3–trichloropropylphenyl sulfide (XV), b.p. 119°/2 mm, n_D 1.5908 (20), in 35% yield.[105] This unexpected product is attributed to the rearrangement of the initial radical, $CCl_3\dot{C}HCH_2X$, to $\dot{C}Cl_2CHClCH_2X$; $X = SC_6H_5$.

$$CCl_3CH{=}CH_2 + HSC_6H_5 \rightarrow CHCl_2CHClCH_2SC_6H_5$$

XIV   XV

Table 12. Addition of Thiophenols to Unsaturated Compounds

C_n	Unsaturated compound	Thiophenol	Product	% Yield	°C b.p./mm (m.p.)	n_D (°C)	Ref.
C_3	Propylene	C_6H_5SH	n–Propylphenyl sulfide	60	219/750	1.5571 (20)	72
C_4	Butene–1	C_6H_5SH	n–Butylphenyl sulfide	73	95/4	1.5463 (20)	72
	Isobutylene	C_6H_5SH	Isobutylphenyl sulfide	90	86/4	1.5430 (20)	72
	Vinyl acetate	C_6H_5SH	$C_6H_5S(CH_2)_2OCOCH_3$		111/3	1.5340 (20)	157
C_5	Pentene–1	C_6H_5SH	n–Amylphenyl sulfide	25	93/4.5	1.5396 (20)	72
	Isopropylethylene	C_6H_5SH	Isoamylphenyl sulfide	80	87/3.5	1.5378 (20)	72
	Trimethylethylene	C_6H_5SH	sec–Amylphenyl sulfide	60	99/5	1.5395 (20)	72
C_6	Hexene–1	C_6H_5SH	n–Hexylphenyl sulfide	32			46, 62
	Cyclohexene	C_6H_5SH	Cyclohexylphenyl sulfide	83	108/0.1		35
	1–Chlorocyclohexene	C_6H_5SH	cis–2–Chlorocyclohexylphenyl sulfide	35	128/1	1.5800 (25)	52
C_7	1–Methylcyclohexene	C_6H_5SH	2–Methylcyclohexylphenyl sulfide	35	120/0.1		35
C_8	$C_6H_5CH=CH_2$	C_6H_5SH	$C_6H_5CH_2CH_2SC_6H_5$	96	187/15		5, 116
	Benzothiophene–1–dioxide	C_6H_5SH	[bicyclic structure with SC_6H_5 and SO_2]	50	(112)		16
	CH_2=$CHSC_6H_5$	C_6H_5SH	$C_6H_5SCH_2CH_2SC_6H_5$	100	(68)		134
C_9	Indene	C_6H_5SH	2–Indanylphenyl sulfide	86	136/2 (46)		110
C_{10}	Dihydromyrcene	C_6H_5SH	Phenyldihydromyrcene sulfide + Dihydromyrcene bis–(phenyl) sulfide	63 / 17	135/0.05 / 185/0.05		35
C_{11}	$CH_3(CH_2)_8CH=CH_2$	C_6H_5SH	$C_6H_5S(CH_2)_{10}CH_3$		(34)		73
C_{13}	$CH_3(CH_2)_{10}CH=CH_2$	C_6H_5SH	$C_6H_5S(CH_2)_{12}CH_3$		(44)		73
C_{15}	$CH_3(CH_2)_{12}CH=CH_2$	C_6H_5SH	$C_6H_5S(CH_2)_{14}CH_3$		(51)		73

Table 12. (cont.) Addition of Thiophenols to Unsaturated Compounds

C_n	Unsaturated compound	Thiophenol	Product	% Yield	°C b.p./mm (m.p.)	n_D (°C)	Ref.
C_{17}	$CH_3(CH_2)_{14}CH=CH_2$	C_6H_5SH	$C_6H_5S(CH_2)_{16}CH_3$		(58)		73
C_{19}	$CH_3(CH_2)_{16}CH=CH_2$	C_6H_5SH	$C_6H_5S(CH_2)_{18}CH_3$		(61)		73
C_{20}	$(C_6H_5)_3SiCH=CH_2$	C_6H_5SH	$(C_6H_5)_3Si(CH_2)_2SC_6H_5$	65	(100)		51
C_6	Allyltrimethylsilane	$p\text{-}CH_3C_6H_4SH$	$p\text{-}CH_3C_6H_4S(CH_2)_3Si(CH_3)_3$	18	207/46 (73)	1.5267 (20)	25
	$CH_2=CHC\equiv CCH=CH_2$	$p\text{-}CH_3C_6H_4SH$	$p\text{-}CH_3C_6H_4S(CH_2)_2C\equiv C(CH_2)_2\text{-}SC_6H_4\text{-}p\text{-}CH_3$	80	(75)		27
C_7	2, 2, 1-Bicyclo-2-heptene (norbornylene)	$p\text{-}CH_3C_6H_4SH$	exo-Norbornyl p-tolyl thioether	86	175/11	1.5758 (20)	32
C_9	Indene	$p\text{-}CH_3C_6H_4SH$	2-Indanyl-p-tolyl sulfide	90	141/2 (86)		110
	exo-cis-3, 6-endo-Methylene–Δ–4-tetrahydrophthalic anhydride 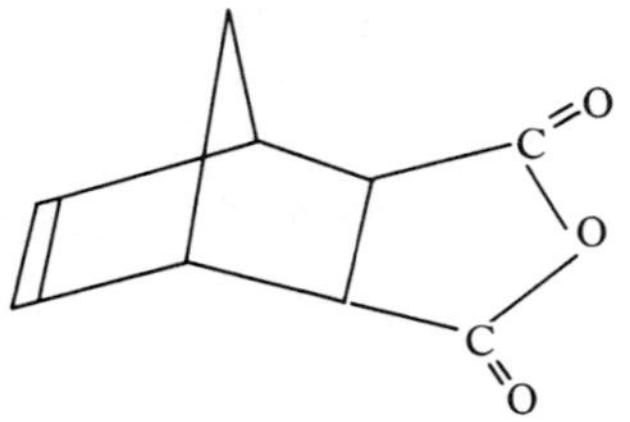	$p\text{-}CH_3C_6H_4SH$	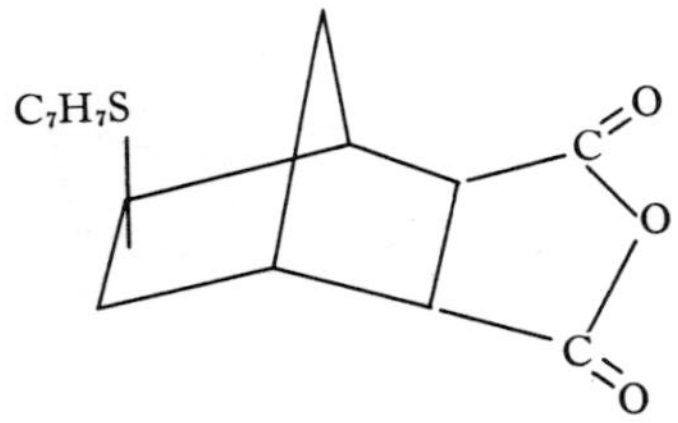 C_7H_7S (structure)	73	(124)		14
	Benzalpyruvic acid	$p\text{-}CH_3C_6H_4SH$	α-Keto-γ-p-tolylmercapto-γ-phenylbutyric acid		(97)		107

Table 12. (cont.) Addition of Thiophenols to Unsaturated Compounds

C_n	Unsaturated compound	Thiophenol	Product	% Yield	°C b.p./mm (m.p.) · n_D (°C)	Ref.
C_{11}	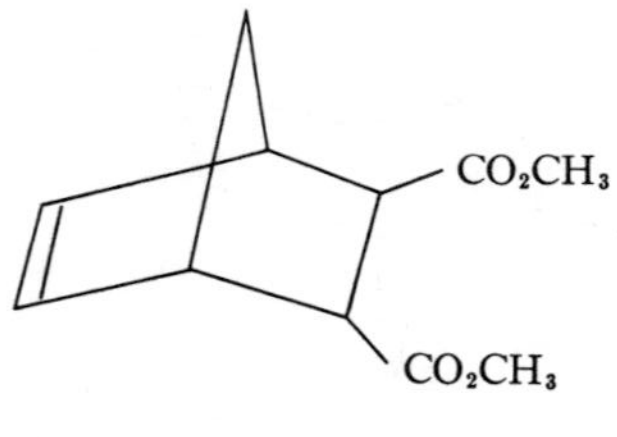	$p\text{-}CH_3C_6H_4SH$	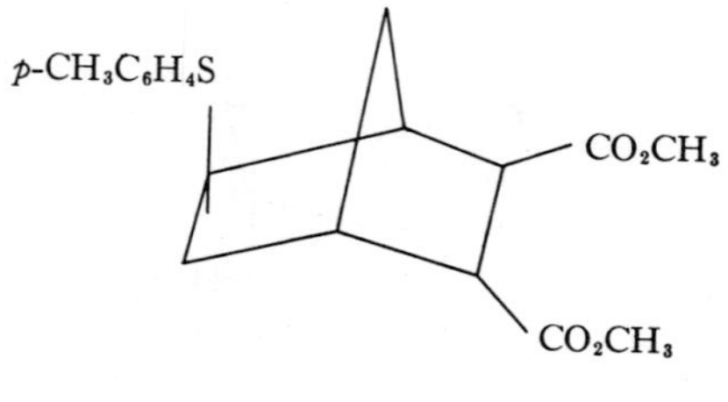	78	(74)	14
C_{12}	$CH_3(CH_2)_8CH=CH_2$	$p\text{-}CH_3C_6H_4SH$	$CH_3C_6H_4S(CH_2)_{10}CH_3$	85	(30)	73
	$endo\text{-}exo\text{-}1, 2, 3, 4, 6\text{-}10, 10\text{-}$ Heptachloro-1, 4, 4a, 5, 8, 8a– hexahydro-1, 4, 5, 8– dimethanonaphthalene 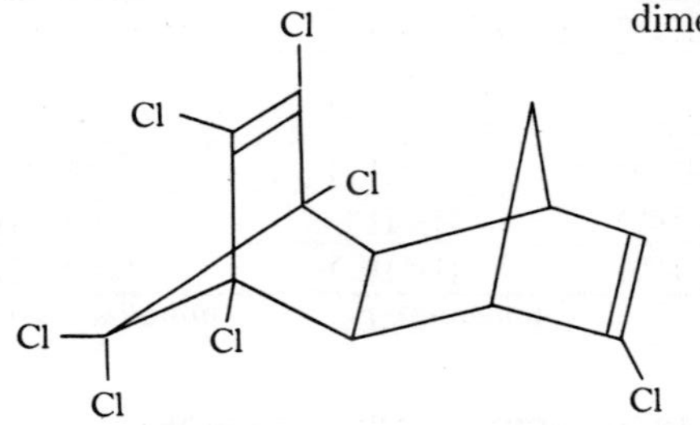	$p\text{-}CH_3C_6H_4SH$	$exo\text{-}2\text{-}p\text{-}$Thiocresoxy-$endo$-3, 5, 6, 7, 8, 9, 9-heptachloro-exo-$endo$-1, 2, 3, 4, 4a, 5, 8, 8a– octahydro-1, 4, 5, 8– dimethanonaphthalene 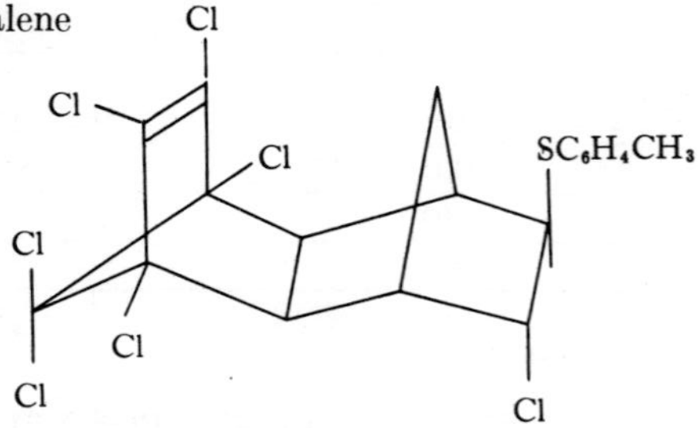		(130)	31

Table 12. (cont.)   Addition of Thiophenols to Unsaturated Compounds

C_n	Unsaturated compound	Thiophenol	Product	% Yield	°C b.p./mm (m.p.)	n_D (°C)	Ref.
C_{13}	$CH_3(CH_2)_{10}CH{=}CH_2$	$p\text{-}CH_3C_6H_4SH$	$CH_3C_6H_4(CH_2)_{12}CH_3$		(40)		73
C_{15}	$CH_3(CH_2)_{12}CH{=}CH_2$	$p\text{-}CH_3C_6H_4SH$	$CH_3C_6H_4S(CH_2)_{14}CH_3$		(49)		73
	Benzalacetophenone	$p\text{-}CH_3C_6H_4SH$	β–Phenyl-β–p–tolylmercapto-propiophenone		(113)		107
C_{16}	11–Chloro–9,10–dihydro–9, 10– ethanoanthracene	$p\text{-}CH_3C_6H_4SH$		28	(158)		31

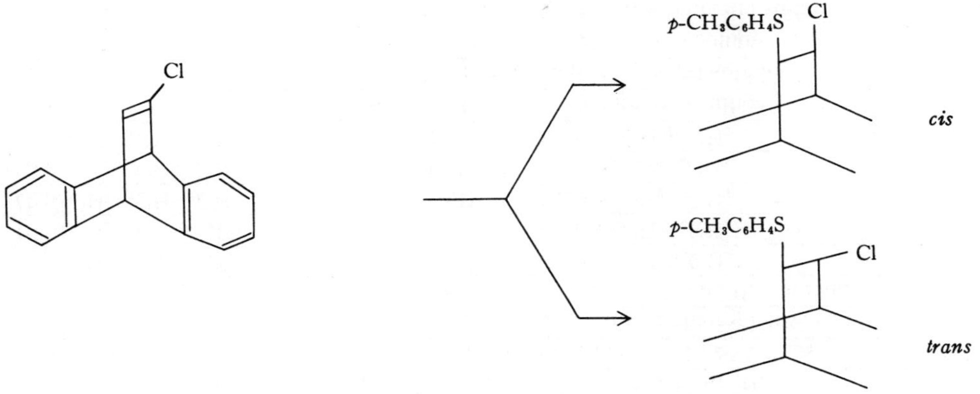

$p\text{-}CH_3C_6H_4S$ ... Cl   *cis* (194)

$p\text{-}CH_3C_6H_4S$ ... Cl   *trans*

Table 12. (cont.)   Addition of Thiophenols to Unsaturated Compounds

C_n	Unsaturated compound	Thiophenol	Product	% Yield	°C b.p./mm (m.p.)	n_D (°C)	Ref.
C_{17}	$CH_3(CH_2)_{14}CH{=}CH_2$	$p\text{-}CH_3C_6H_4SH$	$CH_3C_6H_4S(CH_2)_{16}CH_3$		(56)		73
C_{19}	$CH_3(CH_2)_{16}CH{=}CH_2$	$p\text{-}CH_3C_6H_4SH$	$CH_3C_6H_4S(CH_2)_{18}CH_3$		(60)		73
C_{20}	$(C_6H_5)_3SiCH{=}CH_2$	$p\text{-}CH_3C_6H_4SH$	$CH_3C_6H_4S(CH_2)_2Si(C_6H_5)_3$	57	(97)		51
C_9	Indene	$p\text{-}ClC_6H_4SH$	2–Indanyl-4-chlorophenyl sulfide	89	(90)		110
	Indene	$2\text{-}C_{10}H_7SH$	2–Indanyl-2-naphthyl sulfide	91	(99)		110
C_{11}	$CH_3(CH_2)_8CH{=}CH_2$	$\beta\text{-}C_{10}H_7SH$	$C_{10}H_7S(CH_2)_{10}CH_3$		(47)		73
C_{13}	$CH_3(CH_2)_{10}CH{=}CH_2$	$\beta\text{-}C_{10}H_7SH$	$C_{10}H_7S(CH_2)_{12}CH_3$		(55)		73
C_{15}	$CH_3(CH_2)_{12}CH{=}CH_2$	$\beta\text{-}C_{10}H_7SH$	$C_{10}H_7S(CH_2)_{14}CH_3$		(61)		73
C_{17}	$CH_3(CH_2)_{14}CH{=}CH_2$	$\beta\text{-}C_{10}H_7SH$	$C_{10}H_7S(CH_2)_{16}CH_3$		(66)		73
C_{19}	$CH_3(CH_2)_{16}CH{=}CH_2$	$\beta\text{-}C_{10}H_7SH$	$C_{10}H_7S(CH_2)_{18}CH_3$		(70)		73
C_6	Hexene–1	$p\text{-}C_6H_5C_6H_4SH$	Hexylbiphenyl sulfide		(75)		95
C_7	Heptene–1	$p\text{-}C_6H_5C_6H_4SH$	Heptylbiphenyl sulfide		(83)		95
C_8	Octene–1	$p\text{-}C_6H_5C_6H_4SH$	Octylbiphenyl sulfide		(82)		95
	Phenylethylene	$p\text{-}C_6H_5C_6H_4SH$	Phenylethylbiphenyl sulfide		(79)		95
C_9	Nonene–1	$p\text{-}C_6H_5C_6H_4SH$	Nonylbiphenyl sulfide		(88)		95
C_{10}	Decene–1	$p\text{-}C_6H_5C_6H_4SH$	Decylbiphenyl sulfide		(87)		95
C_{11}	Undecene–1	$p\text{-}C_6H_5C_6H_4SH$	Undecylbiphenyl sulfide		(92)		95
C_{12}	Dodecene–1	$p\text{-}C_6H_5C_6H_4SH$	Dodecylbiphenyl sulfide		(91)		95
C_{13}	Tridecene–1	$p\text{-}C_6H_5C_6H_4SH$	Tridecylbiphenyl sulfide		(96)		95
C_{14}	Tetradecene–1	$p\text{-}C_6H_5C_6H_4SH$	Tetradecylbiphenyl sulfide		(94)		95
C_{15}	Pentadecene–1	$p\text{-}C_6H_5C_6H_4SH$	Pentadecylbiphenyl sulfide		(98)		95
C_{16}	Hexadecene–1	$p\text{-}C_6H_5C_6H_4SH$	Hexadecylbiphenyl sulfide		(97)		95
C_{17}	Heptadecene–1	$p\text{-}C_6H_5C_6H_4SH$	Heptadecylbiphenyl sulfide		(100)		95

ADDITION OF BISULFITES TO UNSATURATED COMPOUNDS

Sodium bisulfite adds to olefins only in the presence of air, oxygen, peroxide, nitrite, or persulfate, to give alkyl sulfonates. The reaction is usually carried out in an aqueous medium. It is inhibited by hydroquinones and other antioxidants. The addition is abnormal; i.e., it does not proceed according to Markownikoff's rule and is a free radical process.

$$RR'C{=}CH_2 + NaHSO_3 \rightarrow RR'CHCH_2SO_3Na$$

The reaction can be performed by shaking the aqueous salt solution with an olefin in the presence of an initiator. It proceeds less readily in alcoholic solvent and more readily in ethylene diamine.[100] Depending on the starting materials, the reaction takes place at room or elevated (120°) temperature and at atmospheric or elevated pressure (90–350 psi).[12,88,155]

The reaction of sodium bisulfite with ethylene or propylene under pressure gives products of high molecular weight.[56,70] In the reaction of sodium bisulfite and ethylene, Kharasch and coworkers,[79] using nitrite or persulfate as initiator, obtained the 1:1 adduct (in 12% yield) in addition to the telomers. Under similar conditions, the reaction of sodium bisulfite with propylene, isobutylene, or cyclohexene forms the corresponding sulfonates.[79,100] In the presence of air, the reaction of sodium bisulfite with allyl alcohol forms sodium 1-hydroxypropane-3-sulfonate in 65% yield.[79] Some of these products are converted to the corresponding sulfonyl chloride and amide.

In the reaction of ammonium bisulfite with octene–1, decene–1, tetradecene–1, or hexadecene–1 at 120° for 2 hr in the presence of 2, 2–bis-(t-butylperoxy) butane, monomeric sulfonate is produced in high yield.[57]

Aqueous sodium bisulfite and tetrafluoroethylene at 120°, pH 7–10, and 350 psi react for 9 hr in the presence of benzoyl peroxide and give an adduct in 88% yield.[12] The reaction of sodium bisulfite with vinylidene fluoride at 90 psi oxygen and 120° for 8 hr produces a salt, m.p. 274°.[12] In the presence of benzoyl peroxide, sodium bisulfite condenses with perfluoroalkenes, such as perfluoropropene,[88] perfluoropentene–1,[88] perfluoroheptene–1,[88] 4, 4–dichlorohexafluorobut–1–ene,[60] and 4, 6, 6–trichlorononafluorohex–1–ene,[60] in 9 hr to the corresponding sodium sulfonate. The sulfonate can then be converted with oleum to the corresponding free acid.[60,88] The fluorinated sulfonic acids are viscous, hygroscopic, strongly acidic liquids and liberate hydrogen chloride from sodium chloride.[60,88] Aqueous sodium bisulfite and vinyl chloride react at 30° and 90 psi oxygen to form sodium 2-chloroethanesulfonate in 90% yield.[155]

In the presence of oxygen, sodium sulfite, ammonium sulfite, sodium bisulfite, or ammonium bisulfite reacts with styrene to give three different

Table 13. Addition of Bisulfites to Unsaturated Compounds

C_n	Unsaturated compound	Bisulfite	Product	% Yield	°C b.p./mm (m.p.)	n_D (°C)	Ref.
C_2	Ethylene	$NaHSO_3$	Sodium ethane sulfonate	12			79
	Vinyl chloride	$NaHSO_3$	Sodium 2–chloroethane sulfonate	90			155
	$CF_2=CF_2$	$NaHSO_3$	Tetrafluoroethane sulfonic acid·H_2O	88	110/3 (54)		12
C_3	Propylene	$NaHSO_3$	Sodium propane sulfonate	55			79
	Perfluoropropene	$NaHSO_3$	$CF_3CFHCF_2SO_3H$	64	112/20		88
	Allyl alcohol	$NaHSO_3$	Sodium 1–hydroxypropane–3–sulfonate	65			79
C_4	Isobutylene	$NaHSO_3$	Sodium–2–methylpropane–1–sulfonate	62			79
	4, 4–Dichlorohexafluorobut–1–ene	$NaHSO_3$	4, 4–Dichloro–1, 1, 2, 3, 3,–hexafluoro–butane sulfonic acid	69	119/3.5		60
C_5	Perfluoropentene–1	$NaHSO_3$	$C_3F_7CFHCF_2SO_3H$	79	119/14		88
C_6	Cyclohexene	$NaHSO_3$	Sodium cyclohexane sulfonate	80			100
	4, 6, 6–Trichlorononafluorohex–1–ene	$NaHSO_3$	4, 6, 6–Trichloro–1, 1, 2, 3, 3, 4, 5, 5, 6–nonafluorohexane sulfonic acid	57	130/0.1		60
C_7	Perfluoroheptene–1	$NaHSO_3$	$C_5F_{11}CFHCF_2SO_3H$	73	119/3		88
C_8	Octene–1	NH_4HSO_3	Ammonium octane sulfonate	97			57
C_{10}	Decene–1	NH_4HSO_3	Ammonium decane sulfonate	77			57
C_{12}	Dodecene–1	NH_4HSO_3	Ammonium dodecane sulfonate	73			57
C_{14}	Tetradecene–1	NH_4HSO_3	Ammonium tetradecane sulfonate	60			57
C_{16}	Hexadecene–1	NH_4HSO_3	Ammonium hexadecane sulfonate	22			57

compounds (I, II, III).[83] The relative proportions of the compounds depend on the type of cation in the reaction mixture, the oxygen pressure, the catalyst, and to some extent the pH. The products can be converted to the corresponding sulfonamides for comparison with authentic samples.

$$C_6H_5CH_2CH_2SO_3Na \qquad C_6H_5CH{=}CHSO_3Na \qquad C_6H_5CH(OH)CH_2SO_3Na$$

$$I \qquad\qquad\qquad II \qquad\qquad\qquad III$$

ADDITION OF SULFUR CHLORIDE PENTAFLUORIDE TO UNSATURATED COMPOUNDS

Sulfur chloride pentafluoride undergoes free radical addition reactions with acetylenes or olefins.[28,29,121] The reactions are carried out under the influence of heat, benzoyl peroxide, ultraviolet light, or a combination of these effects. The thermal reactions are carried out around 90–100°, and sometimes, as in the case of vinyl chloride, at 150° usually in an autoclave. Thus, sulfur chloride pentafluoride reacts with propene at 90° or in ultraviolet light, and 2–chloropropylsulfur pentafluoride is produced. Sulfur chloride pentafluoride reacts similarly with propyne, ethylene, butadiene, vinyl chloride, or cyclohexene.[28]

The thermal reactions of sulfur chloride pentafluoride with fluoroolefins must be catalyzed by a free radical initiator such as benzoyl peroxide.[29] The mechanism of these reactions is analogous to that of reactions of trifluoromethyl iodide with fluoroolefins. In reactions with unsymmetrical olefins the CF_3 radical and the SF_5 radical follow the same mode of attack.

$$SF_5Cl + CF_2{=}CF_2 \rightarrow SF_5CF_2CF_2Cl$$

$$SF_5Cl + CFH{=}CF_2 \rightarrow SF_5CFHCF_2Cl$$

$$SF_5Cl + CF_2{=}CClF \rightarrow SF_5CF_2CCl_2F$$

In photochemical reactions of sulfur chloride pentafluoride, dichloro compounds, $Cl(CF_2CF_2)_nCl$, are formed in addition to sulfur pentafluoro derivatives.[28,29,121] With acetylenes, addition of one molecule of sulfur chloride pentafluoride takes place.

$$SF_5Cl + CH{\equiv}CH \rightarrow SF_5CH{=}CHCl$$

$$SF_5Cl + CH_3C{\equiv}CH \rightarrow SF_5CH{=}CClCH_3$$

Table 14.   Addition of Sulfur Chloride Pentafluoride to Unsaturated Compounds

C_n	Unsaturated compound	Product	% Yield	°C b.p./mm	n_D (°C)	Ref.
C_2	CH≡CH	$SF_5CH=CHCl$		66		29
	$CH_2=CH_2$	$SF_5CH_2CH_2Cl+$	47	92	1.3590 (20)	28
		$SF_5(CH_2CH_2)_2Cl$		171	1.3900 (20)	
	$CH_2=CHCl$	$SF_5CH_2CHCl_2+$		108	1.3840 (20)	28
		$SF_5CH_2CHClCH_2CHCl_2$		72/9	1.4269 (20)	
	$CF_2=CF_2$	$SF_5CF_2CF_2Cl+$		47	1.3052 (20)	29
		$SF_5(CF_2CF_2)_2Cl+$		99	1.3079 (20)	
		$SF_5(CF_2CF_2)_3Cl$		142		
	$CF_2=CClF$	$SF_5CF_2CCl_2F$		80		29
C_3	$CH_3C≡CH$	$SF_5CH=CClCH_3$		92	1.3760 (20)	28
	$CH_3CH=CH_2$	$SF_5CH_2CHClCH_3$	78	109	1.3686 (20)	28
C_6	Cyclohexene	2-Chlorocyclohexyl sulfur pentafluoride		189	1.4320 (20)	28

REACTION OF SH-CONTAINING COMPOUNDS WITH HYDROCARBONS IN THE PRESENCE OF OXYGEN

A small amount of oxygen catalyzes the addition of thiols to olefins to form sulfides. However, in the presence of an equimolar amount of oxygen, the reaction of thiols and olefins is accompanied by oxidation and β–hydroxy sulfoxides (I) are isolated in some instances.[47,81,147]

$$RCH(OH)CH_2S(O)R'$$

I

For example, a mixture of n–propyl mercaptan and octene–1 reacts with oxygen even at room temperature, to form a racemic mixture of n–propyl–β–hydroxy–n–octyl sulfoxide, $CH_3(CH_2)_5CH(OH)CH_2S(O)$–$n$–$C_3H_7$.[81] Similarly, the addition of n–propyl mercaptan to styrene in the presence of oxygen produces racemic n–propyl–β–hydroxyphenethyl sulfoxide, $C_6H_5CH(OH)CH_2S(O)$–n–C_3H_7, in 60% yield.[81] p–Anisyl mercaptan and styrene react rapidly in the presence of oxygen, with evolution of heat, to give a solid, m.p. 128°, and an oil.[81]

In contrast, t–butyl mercaptan and styrene react slowly in the presence of oxygen.[81] The reaction can be accelerated by addition of cumene hydroperoxide and a catalytic amount of ferrous ions. Two racemic products are obtained. Kharasch and coworkers[81] suggested that this reaction proceeds by a radical mechanism: a hydroperoxide forms as an intermediate which rearranges itself under mild experimental conditions to give the observed β–hydroxy sulfoxides.

The existence of such an intermediate peroxide was demonstrated by Ford and co-workers.[47] A mixture of thiophenol and indene absorbed oxygen rapidly at room temperature and reacted completely in 85 min. Immediately after the oxygen was completely absorbed, the reaction mixture consisted of 77% hydroperoxide and only 7% sulfoxide. After 2 hr at room temperature the peroxide rearranged completely to a racemic mixture of sulfoxides, II and III, m.p. 155° and 99°, respectively.

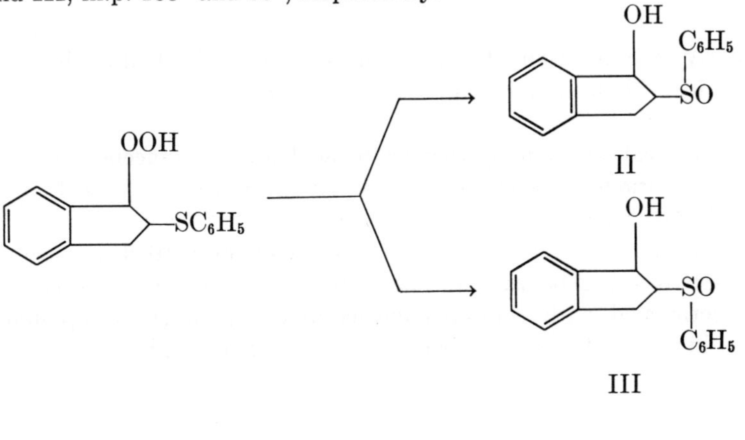

Oswald[109] isolated an intermediate hydroperoxide from a different reaction mixture. 2–Naphthalenethiol and α–methylstyrene reacted with oxygen to give a solid identified as 2–hydroperoxy–2–phenylpropyl–2–naphthyl sulfide, m.p. 10°. After 16 hr at 40° this solid rearranged to 2–hydroxy–2–phenylpropyl–2–naphthyl sulfoxide. Under similar conditions the reaction of 2–naphthalenethiol and indene produced the more stable 2–(2–naphthylmercapto)–1–indanyl hydroperoxide, m.p. 70°, which subsequently rearranged to the corresponding 2–(2–naphthylsulfinyl)–1–indanol.

Thiolacetic acid reacts in the presence of oxygen with various polycyclic aromatic compounds and with olefins containing aromatic substituents.[102,103] Dry oxygen is passed into the thiolacetic acid containing the hydrocarbon. Depending on the hydrocarbon, the duration of the reaction ranges from 20 min to several hours. When air is used instead of oxygen, the reaction time is prolonged appreciably. Thus, the reaction of thiolacetic acid and anthracene with oxygen produces a mixture of *cis*– and *trans*–9, 10–dithioacetoxy–9, 10–dihydroanthracene (IVa), m.p. 148° and 124°, respectively, in 68% yield; water and compound V, b.p. 85°/6 mm, are also formed.

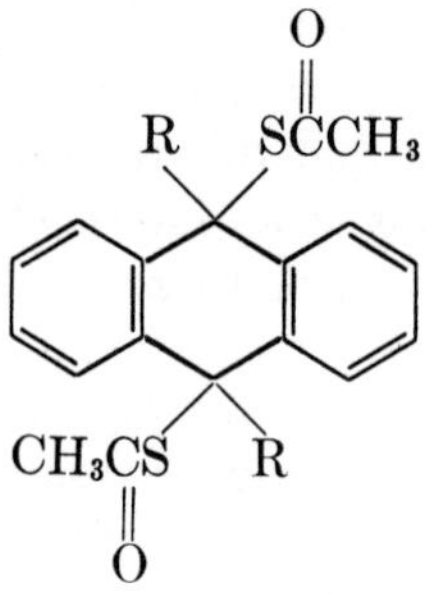

IVa R = H

IVb R = CH$_3$

IVc R = C$_2$H$_5$

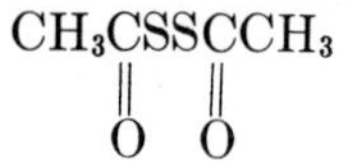

V

Similarly, the reaction of thiolacetic acid with 9, 10–dimethyl– or 9, 10–diethylanthracene forms IVb, m.p. 214°, and IVc, m.p. 161°, in good yield.

An ethereal solution of thiolacetic acid and anthracene reacts with oxygen to form 9–thioacetoxy–9, 10–dihydroanthracene, m.p. 151°, in 18% yield.[103] The reaction of thiolacetic acid and 1, 2–benzanthracene with oxygen forms a mixture of *cis* and *trans* isomers of 9, 10–di(thioacetoxy)–9, 10–dihydro–1, 2–benzanthracene, m.p. 193°.[103] Similarly, the reaction of thiolacetic acid with o–dibiphenyleneethylene produces compound VI, 9, 9–difluorenyl–9, 9'–di(thioacetate), m.p. 236°, and the reaction of

Table 15. Reaction of SH-Containing Compounds with Hydrocarbons in the Presence of Oxygen

C_n	Hydrocarbon	SH-containing compound	Product	% Yield	°C (m.p.)	Ref.
C_8	Octene–1	n–Propyl mercaptan	Two racemic products: n–Propyl-β-hydroxy-n-octyl sulfoxide	13	(39, 106)	81
	Styrene	n–Propyl mercaptan	Two racemic products: $C_6H_5CH(OH)CH_2S(O)-n-C_3H_7$	60	(69, 106)	81
C_9	Indene	Thiophenol	Mixture of: [indanol with OH, C6H5, SO — (150)] and [indanol with OH, SO, C6H5 — (99)]	70	(150), (99)	47
	Indene	2–Naphthalenethiol	2–(2–Naphthylsulfinyl)–1–indanol		(139)	109
C_{10}	α–Methylstyrene	2–Naphthalenethiol	2–Hydroxy–2–phenylpropyl–2–naphthyl sulfoxide		(116)	109
C_{14}	Anthracene	CH_3COSH	9–Thioacetoxy–9, 10–dihydro–anthracene	18	(151)	103
		CH_3COSH	cis– and trans–9, 10–dithioacetoxy–9, 10–dihydroanthracene	68	(148, 124)	102, 103
C_{16}	9, 10–Dimethylanthracene	CH_3COSH	9, 10–Dithioacetoxy–9, 10–dimethyl-dihydroanthracene	81	(214)	102, 103

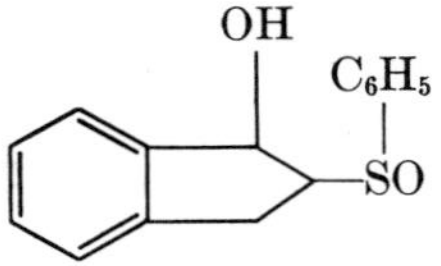

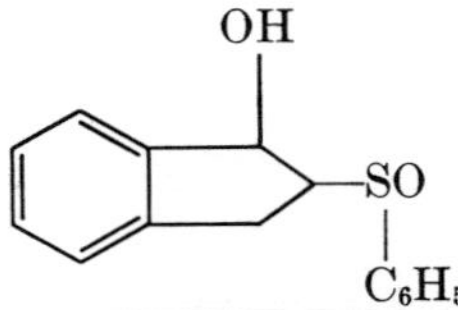

Table 15. (cont.)   Reaction of SH-Containing Compounds with Hydrocarbons in the Presence of Oxygen

C_n	Hydrocarbon	SH-containing compound	Product	% Yield	(m.p.) °C	Ref.
C_{18}	9, 10–Diethylanthracene	CH₃COSH	9, 10–Dithioacetoxy–9, 10–diethyl– dihydroanthracene		(161)	102, 103
	1, 2–Benzanthracene	CH₃COSH	9, 10–Di(thioacetoxy)–9, 10– dihydro–1, 2–benzanthracene		(193)	103
	1, 1, 2–Triphenylethylene	CH₃COSH	1, 1, 2–Triphenyl–1–hydroxy– 2–thioacetoxyethane	34	(201)	103
C_{20}	9–Benzylidenefluorene	CH₃COSH	9–(ω–thioacetoxybenzyl)–fluorenyl– 9–thioacetate	17	(170)	103
C_{26}	o–Dibiphenyleneethylene	CH₃COSH	9, 9′–Difluorenyl–9, 9′–di(thioacetate)		(236)	103

thiolacetic acid with 9–benzylidenefluorene produces compound VII, 9–(ω–thioacetoxybenzyl)fluorenyl 9–thioacetate, m.p. 170°, in 17% yield.[103]

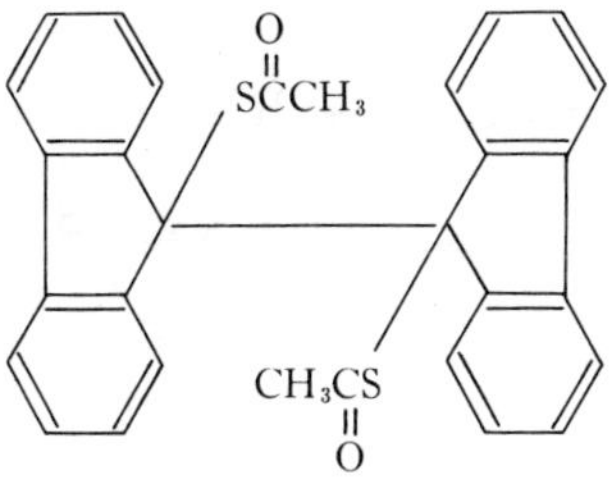

VI 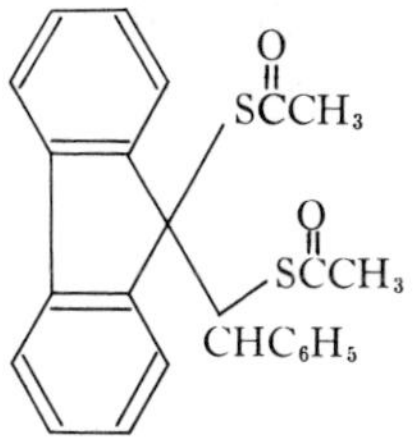   VII

The reaction of thiolacetic acid and 1, 1, 2–triphenylethylene with oxygen produces compound VIII, 1, 1, 2–triphenyl–1–hydroxy–2–thioacetoxy-ethane, m.p. 201°, in 34% yield.[103] When air is used instead of oxygen, 54% of VIII is obtained plus 1, 1, 2–triphenyl–2–thioacetoxyethane (IX), m.p. 171°.[103]

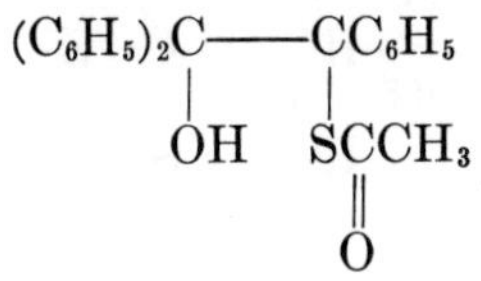

VIII 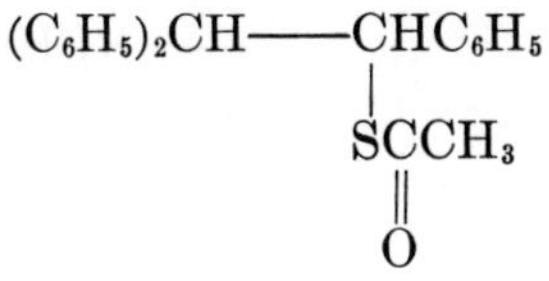   IX

REACTION OF ELEMENTAL SULFUR WITH UNSATURATED COMPOUNDS AND WITH THIOLS

Elemental sulfur is used in the vulcanization of rubber. Consequently there is an enormous amount of literature on its reaction with olefinic compounds. A critical review containing many pertinent references has been published by Walling.[153]

The reactions of elemental sulfur with unsaturated compounds are complex. Many are carried out at elevated temperatures, usually above 140°. Under these conditions sulfur abstracts hydrogen to form hydrogen sulfide, which reacts with the unsaturated compound to form mercaptans. The mercaptans, in turn, are capable of undergoing various reactions, including addition to olefins to produce sulfides.

This discussion is restricted to high-temperature reactions between sulfur and unsaturated compounds. The reaction products are an interesting class of heterocyclic compounds. These reactions are described in

German,[19-21,98] Russian,[23,152] French,[97,127] and American[93,94,142] literature. They involve heating an olefin of the general structure I or II with sulfur to 180–215° for 10–25 hr to produce a heterocyclic compound of structure III, often in high yield.

$$R'CH{=}C(R'')CH_3 \qquad R'CH_2C(R'')_2{=}CH_2 \qquad \begin{array}{c} 2(4)\ R''C\underset{\parallel}{\rule{1.5cm}{0.4pt}}C{=}S\ 1(3) \\ 3(5)\ R'C \qquad S \qquad 5(2) \\ \diagdown\ \diagup \\ S \\ 4(1) \end{array}$$

$$\qquad I \qquad\qquad\qquad II \qquad\qquad\qquad III$$

R′ = H, alkyl, aryl

R″ = H, alkyl, aryl

A radical mechanism with the following possible sequence is proposed for these reactions.[23,152]

$$RCH{=}CHCH_3 \xrightarrow[-H_2S]{+S} RCH{=}CHCH_2SH \xrightarrow[-H_2S]{+S} RCH{=}CHCH{=}S$$

$$\xrightarrow{S} RCH{=}CHC(SH){=}S \xrightarrow[-H_2S]{+S} \begin{array}{c} HC\underset{\parallel}{\rule{1.5cm}{0.4pt}}C{=}S \\ RC \qquad S \\ \diagdown\ \diagup \\ S \end{array}$$

German chemists refer to these heterocyclics as trithiones, whereas Russians call them 4, 5–disubstituted 1, 2–dithiol–2–thiones. The German and Russian numbering systems for heterocyclic compounds are also different; the German system is shown outside the parentheses and the Russian system in the parentheses in compound III. The unsubstituted member of the class, R′ = R″ = H, has been prepared from sulfur and propylene.

The history of these reactions up to about 1949 has been described by Lozac'h.[97] Schmitt and Lespagnol[127] reported briefly on condensations of p–methoxyisopropenylbenzene, p–methoxyisobutenylbenzene, p–methoxy-phenyl–3–phenylpropylene–2, ethyl p–methoxy–β–methyl cinnamate, p–methylisopropenylbenzene, and α–isopropenylnaphthalene. They[127] listed the melting points of the products but did not include yields. Broun and co-workers[23] reported on reactions with 2–methylbutene–2, pentene–2, and 2, 3–dimethylbutene–2. Voronkov and co-workers[152] conducted a detailed study with α– and β–methylstyrene, β, β–dimethylstyrene, α–methyl-stilbene, and allylbenzene.

Spindt[142] reacted sulfur with isobutylene and diisobutylene. After 1 hr at 165–170° in a steel bomb at 830-psi initial pressure and 200-psi final pressure, methyl–1, 2–dithia–4–cyclopentene–3–thione (IV) forms. Under similar conditions the reaction of sulfur with diisobutylene, which is a mixture of 2, 4, 4–trimethyl–1–pentene and –2–pentene, forms two products, V and VI.[142]

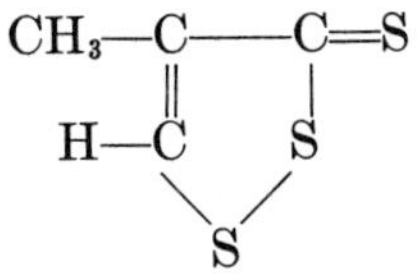

$$CH_3-C\text{——}C\text{=}S$$
$$H-C\quad S$$
$$\diagdown_S\diagup$$

IV

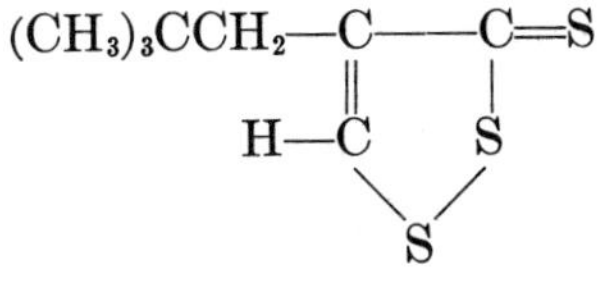

$$(CH_3)_3CCH_2-C\text{——}C\text{=}S$$
$$H-C\quad S$$
$$\diagdown_S\diagup$$

V

$$CH_3-C\text{——}C\text{=}S$$
$$(CH_3)_3C-C\quad S$$
$$\diagdown_S\diagup$$

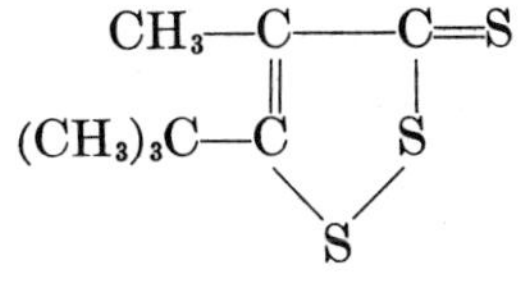

VI

When either the pentene–1 or the pentene–2 derivative is used, a mixture of products V (17–21%) and VI (10–11%) is obtained. This result shows that the position of the double bond in the original diisobutylene is unimportant in directing the distribution of the two isomers.

Under similar conditions the reaction of sulfur with triisobutylene, which is mainly a mixture of 2, 2, 4, 6, 6–pentamethylheptene–3 and 1, 1–diisopentylethylene, yields VII exclusively.[93]

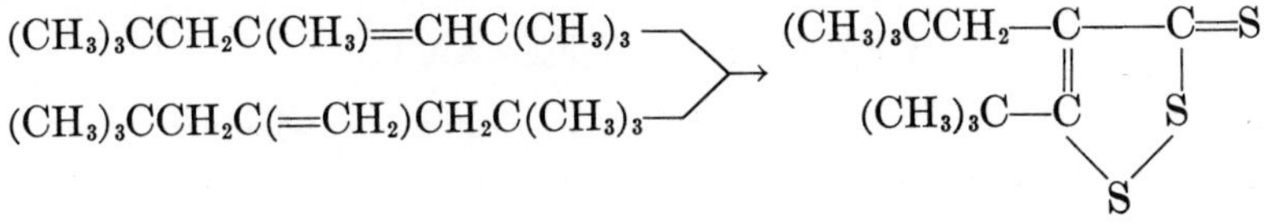

$$(CH_3)_3CCH_2C(CH_3)\text{=}CHC(CH_3)_3 \longrightarrow$$
$$(CH_3)_3CCH_2C(\text{=}CH_2)CH_2C(CH_3)_3 \longrightarrow$$

$$(CH_3)_3CCH_2-C\text{——}C\text{=}S$$
$$(CH_3)_3C-C\quad S$$
$$\diagdown_S\diagup$$

VII

Landis and Hamilton[93] concluded that only one product is observed because terminal olefins are isomerized to methyl compounds before the reaction with sulfur occurs. When the reaction is carried out by dissolving the sulfur in preformed compound VII, the yield of the product is higher because of better contact of the reactants.[93]

The interaction of sulfur with tertiary mercaptans is related to these condensations of sulfur with olefins. Sulfur reacts with tertiary thiols such as 2, 4, 4–trimethyl–2–pentanethiol and 2, 2, 4, 6, 6–pentamethyl–4–heptanethiol at 200° with evolution of hydrogen sulfide to give 1, 2–dithiol–3–thione compounds in high yield.[94] The reaction of sulfur with the pentanethiol results in a mixture of VIII, m.p. 80°, and IX, m.p. 85°; the mixture can be separated by fractional crystallization.

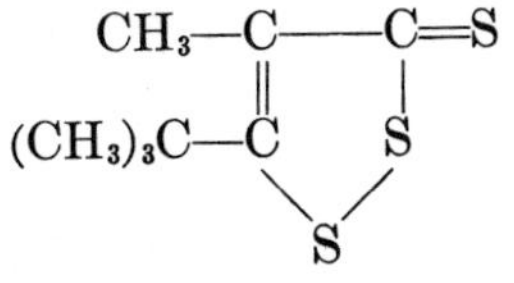

$$CH_3-C\text{——}C\text{=}S$$
$$(CH_3)_3C-C\quad S$$
$$\diagdown_S\diagup$$

VIII

$$(CH_3)_3CCH_2-C\text{——}C\text{=}S$$
$$H-C\quad S$$
$$\diagdown_S\diagup$$

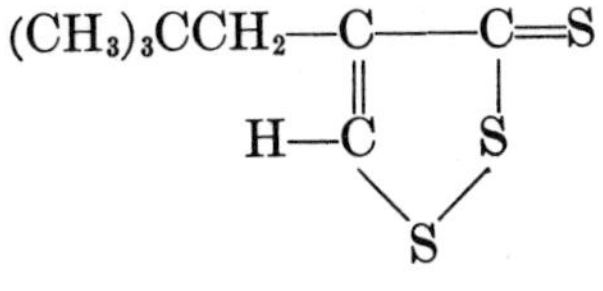

IX

The reaction of sulfur with the heptanethiol results in X, b.p. 150–170°/0.1–0.3 mm.

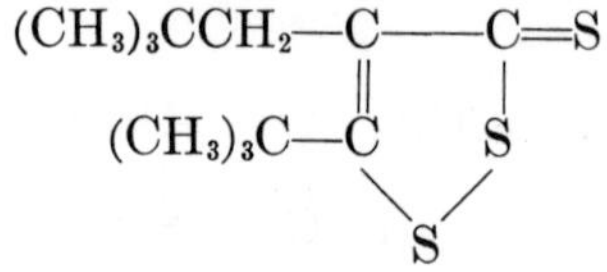

$$(CH_3)_3CCH_2-C----C=S$$
$$(CH_3)_3C-C \quad S$$
$$\diagdown S \diagup$$

X

Landis and Hamilton[94] assume that these reactions proceed through a dehydrosulfuration step to give an olefin, which then undergoes further reaction with sulfur.

The reaction of sulfur with bis(polyfluoroalkyl) acetylenes produces dithietenes in good yield.[89] Thus, a mixture of boiling sulfur and hexafluoro–2–butyne in an atmosphere of nitrogen gas or heated under pressure at 200° reacts to give 3, 4–bis(trifluoromethyl)–1, 2–dithietene, b.p. 93°, in 80% yield.

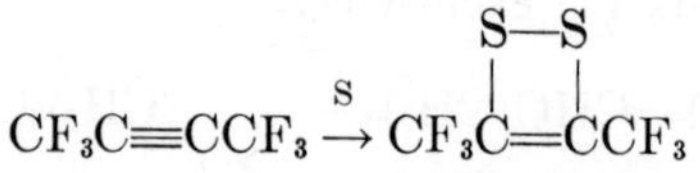

$$CF_3C\equiv CCF_3 \xrightarrow{S} CF_3\overset{\displaystyle S-S}{\overset{|\quad|}{C=C}}CF_3$$

The reaction of sulfur and 1, 12–dihydroeicosafluoro–6–dodecyne produces 3, 4–bis–(5–hydrodecafluoropentyl)–1, 2–dithietene, b.p. 103°/5 mm, in 41% yield.

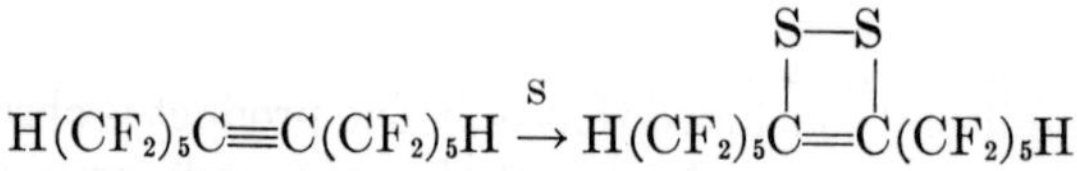

$$H(CF_2)_5C\equiv C(CF_2)_5H \xrightarrow{S} H(CF_2)_5\overset{\displaystyle S-S}{\overset{|\quad|}{C=C}}(CF_2)_5H$$

And the reaction of sulfur with 1, 6–dichlorooctafluoro–3–hexyne produces 3, 4–bis–(2–chlorotetrafluorethyl)–1, 2–dithietene, b.p. 98°/40 mm, in 82% yield.

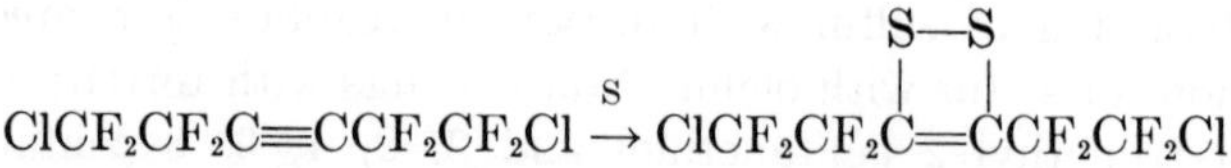

$$ClCF_2CF_2C\equiv CCF_2CF_2Cl \xrightarrow{S} ClCF_2CF_2\overset{\displaystyle S-S}{\overset{|\quad|}{C=C}}CCF_2CF_2Cl$$

These reactions proceed through a radical mechanism.[89]

Table 1. Reaction of Elemental Sulfur with Unsaturated Compounds

C_n	Unsaturated compound	Product	% Yield	°C b.p./mm (m.p.)	Ref.
C_4	Isobutylene	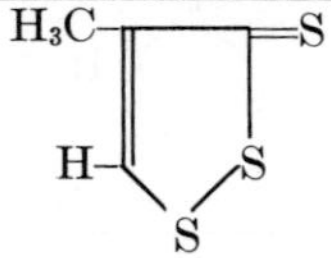 H_3C— [dithiole-thione] —H	39	111/1.7 (41)	142
C_8	Diisobutylene	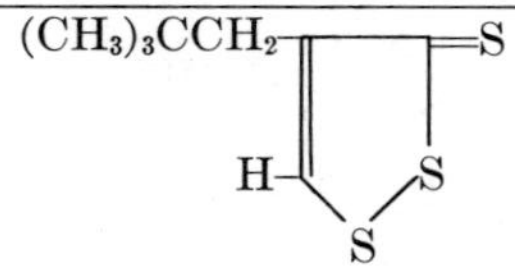 $(CH_3)_3CCH_2$— [dithiole-thione] —H		159/1.7 (87)	142
		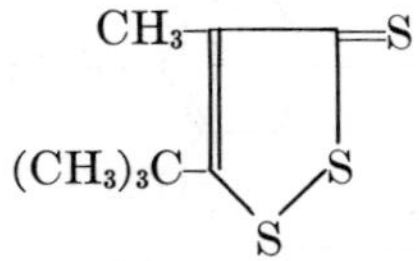 + CH_3— [dithiole-thione] —$C(CH_3)_3$		175/5 (81)	
C_9	2–Phenylpropene–1	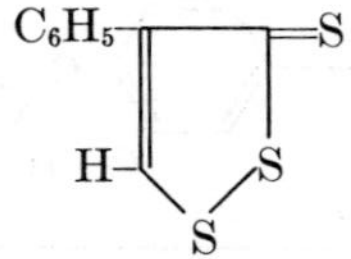 C_6H_5— [dithiole-thione] —H	42	(123)	21, 152
	1–Phenylpropene–1	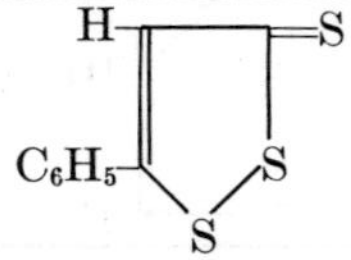 H— [dithiole-thione] —C_6H_5	30	(126)	21, 152
C_{10}	2–Methyl–1–phenylpropene–1	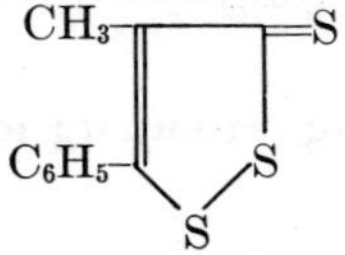 CH_3— [dithiole-thione] —C_6H_5	80	208/1.5 (105)	152

Table 16. (cont.) Reaction of Elemental Sulfur with Unsaturated Compounds

C_n	Unsaturated compound	Product	% Yield	°C b.p./mm (m.p.)	Ref.
	Anethol	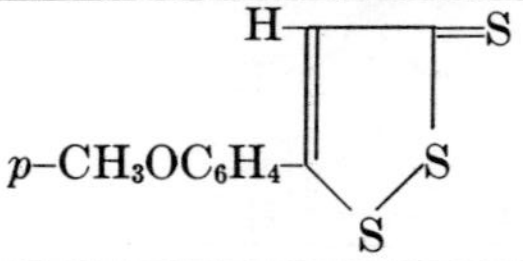 p–CH$_3$OC$_6$H$_4$ (dithiole-thione structure)	20–45	(111)	21
	Safrole or isosafrole	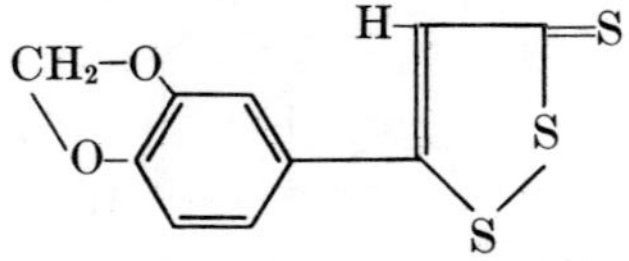 (dithiole-thione structure, CH$_2$O, O–CH$_2$)		(195)	97
C_{11}	Dimethoxy–3, 4, –allylbenzene or dimethoxy–3, 4, –propenylbenzene	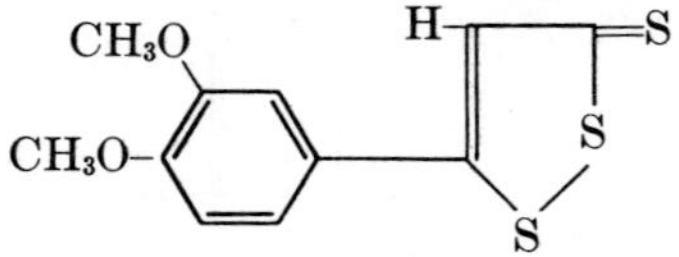 (dithiole-thione structure, CH$_3$O, CH$_3$O)	95	(127)	97
C_{12}	Triisobutylene	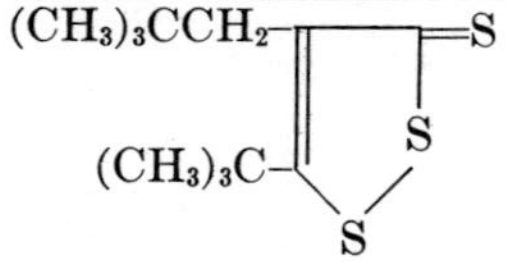 (CH$_3$)$_3$CCH$_2$, (CH$_3$)$_3$C (dithiole-thione structure)	93	152/1	93
C_{15}	1, 2–Diphenylpropene–1	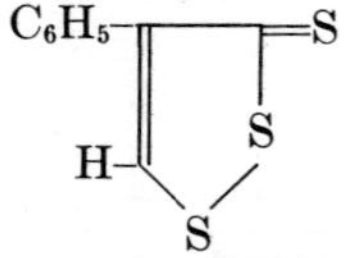 C$_6$H$_5$ (dithiole-thione structure)	80	(160)	152

REACTION OF SULFUR DIOXIDE WITH VARIOUS COMPOUNDS

Sulfur dioxide reacts with monoolefins such as ethylene, propylene, butene, vinyl chloride, allyl chloride, and trimethylethylene in the presence of peroxide or ultraviolet light to yield polysulfones.[76,84] This copolymerization has been discussed in detail by Walling.[153] Usually the reactions of sulfur dioxide with monoolefins under free radical conditions do not produce monomeric products.

Kharasch and Friedlander[76] have described a free radical reaction involving sulfur dioxide, an olefin, and bromotrichloromethane. Under irradiation with ultraviolet light, a mixture containing sulfur dioxide, octene–1, and bromotrichloromethane produces 1, 1, 1–trichloro–3–nonyl–2–bromooctyl sulfone (I), n_D 1.5028 (20°), in 12% yield.

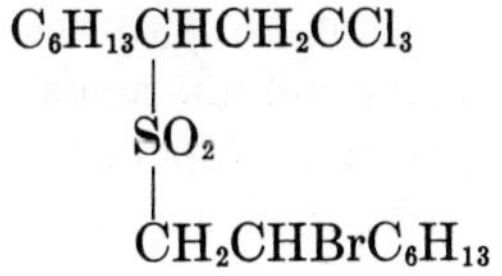

$$C_6H_{13}CHCH_2CCl_3$$
$$|$$
$$SO_2$$
$$|$$
$$CH_2CHBrC_6H_{13}$$

I

Sulfur dioxide reacts with some o-quinones under ultraviolet light to form cyclic esters of sulfuric acid.[126] For example, after 80 hr of irradiation of sulfur dioxide in a benzene solution of phenanthrenequinone, compound II, m.p. 202°, is formed in 86% yield.[126]

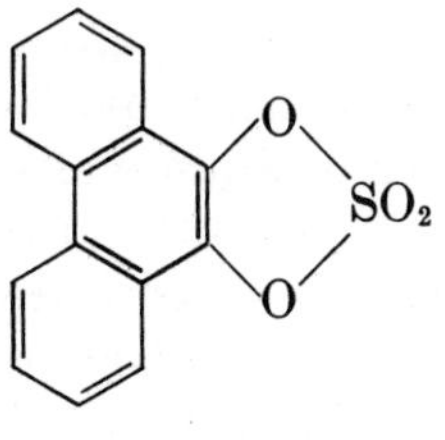

II

Tetrachloro–o–benzoquinone, 1, 2–naphthoquinone, 3–nitro–1, 2–naphthoquinone, 2–, 3–, and 4–nitrophenanthrenequinone, and chrysoquinone react with sulfur dioxide similarly; the reaction times range from 20 to 200 hr.[126] Most of these substances decompose on melting, with evolution of sulfur dioxide.

Under ultraviolet light sulfur dioxide reacts with short-chain aliphatic hydrocarbons, such as methane, ethane, propane, and butane, to give sulfinic acids.[37,38]

$$RH + SO_2 \rightarrow RSO_2H$$

This reaction is of limited preparative value. Much more attention has been given to the reaction of sulfur dioxide with long-chain aliphatic hydrocarbons in the presence of oxygen.

$$RH + SO_2 + \tfrac{1}{2}O_2 \rightarrow RSO_3H$$

This reaction is called sulfoxidation.

The sulfoxidation of paraffins was studied extensively during World War II, particularly by German chemists, and Orthner[108] has published a review of the patented processes. Sulfoxidation can be initiated by ultraviolet light,[41,42,53,144] peracids,[43] ozone,[44] azonitriles,[96] or chlorine with light.[74] In spite of some industrial importance, this type of reaction is also of limited preparative value. Like free radical chlorination and nitration, sulfoxidation of long-chain aliphatic hydrocarbons produces equimolar mixtures of isomers of secondary sulfonic acids.[4] Primary sulfonic acids are formed only in very small quantity. Topchiev and co-workers[144] found that sulfoxidation of n–heptane at 20° yields mainly the α–substituted product, III.

$$CH_3(CH_2)_4CHCH_3$$
$$|$$
$$SO_3H$$

III

The reaction of sulfur dioxide with cyclohexane in the presence of oxygen produces cyclohexane sulfonic acid in high yield.[22,41,53,54,74,96,128b] Laboratory procedures for this preparation are given in detail by Graf[53] and Schönberg.[128b] A 2:1 mixture of sulfur dioxide and oxygen is introduced into cyclohexane at room temperature under illumination by a mercury quartz lamp. The peracid, $C_6H_{11}SO_2O_2H$, is formed as an intermediate, but it cannot be isolated. In Graf's work[53] cyclohexane was sulfoxidized in acetic acid, and acetyl cyclohexane sulfonyl peroxide, $C_6H_{11}SO_2O_2COCH_3$, m.p. 35°, was obtained. This is a mixed anhydride of the peracid and the acetic acid. It can be used to initiate chlorination, sulfochlorination, carboxylation, and sulfoxidation. Even better results are obtained when acetic acid anhydride is used instead of acetic acid. When the sulfoxidation is carried out in methanol, monomethyl sulfate and cyclohexane sulfonic acid are produced. In the presence of phosphorus trichloride the anhydride of cyclohexane sulfonic acid, m.p. 106°, is formed.

Sulfur dioxide reacts with saturated hydrocarbons in the presence of chlorine and ultraviolet light to give sulfonyl chlorides. The process, known as sulfochlorination, was first reported by Reed.[120]

$$RH + SO_2 + Cl_2 \rightarrow RSO_2Cl + HCl$$

The reaction is not influenced by aluminum chloride, sulfur, or iodine. Temperature accelerates it, although not as much as light does.[117] This process was of technological importance in Germany during World War II, since synthetic detergents are produced by this method.[22] As a laboratory method[3,120,128a] it is much less important, because it often produces mixtures which are difficult to resolve into pure components. Sulfochlorination is carried out at the temperature of liquid sulfur dioxide or at room temperature. A 1.1:1 mixture of sulfur dioxide and chlorine is introduced into the hydrocarbon. The reaction mixture is usually illuminated with a mercury vapor lamp. Sometimes the gaseous hydrocarbon is introduced into a carbon tetrachloride solution of sulfur dioxide and chlorine.

The reaction of sulfur dioxide with ethane in the presence of chlorine produces ethane sulfonyl chloride, b.p. 71°/22 mm, in 26% yield.[120] The reaction with propane produces a mixture of two isomers, namely, propane–1–sulfonyl chloride and propane–2–sulfonyl chloride, b.p. 74–78°/15 mm, n_D 1.452 (20°), plus propane–1, 3–disulfonyl chloride, m.p. 48°.[3,120,128a] Propane–2–sulfonyl chloride is not further attacked by any of the reagents.[143] The reaction with butane produces a mixture of monosulfonyl chloride, b.p. 60–64.5°/1 mm, in 75% yield.[3,22] As in the case of propane, 1, 2 isomer is not obtained. The boiling points of the pure isomers are: butane–1–sulfonyl chloride, 94°/15 mm, and butane–2–sulfonyl chloride, 85°/15 mm.

The reaction of sulfur dioxide with isobutane in the presence of chlorine results in primary isobutanesulfonyl chloride, b.p. 87°/15 mm, in 75% yield, and a mixture of disubstituted products.[2,22] The reaction with 1–chloropropane produces dichloropropane and chloropropanesulfonyl chloride.[61] The latter are converted by heat into 1, 2– and 1, 3–dichloropropane.[61,143]

The reaction of sulfur dioxide with 1–chlorobutane in the presence of chlorine produces a dichlorobutane in 60% yield and an unresolvable mixture of chlorobutane sulfonyl chlorides.[61] The mixture can be converted by heat to the dichloro derivatives; it consists of the 1, 2, the 1, 3, and the 1, 4 isomers. The reaction with 1–chlorobutane can produce a 3:1 mixture of 4–chlorobutane–1–sulfochloride and 3–chlorobutane–1–sulfochloride, and no 1, 1 and 1, 2 isomers are formed.[143] The reaction with butane–2–sulfochloride results in a mixture of 3– and 4–chlorobutane–1–sulfonyl chlorides.[143] The yield in all these reactions is generally poor.

Table 17. Addition of Sulfur Dioxide to o–Quinones

C_n	o–Quinone	Product	% Yield	°C (m.p.)	Ref.
C_6	Tetrachloro–o–benzoquinone		57	(125)	126
C_{10}	o–Naphthoquinone		33	(73)	126
	3–Nitronaphthoquinone		45	(143)	126
C_{14}	Phenanthrenequinone		92	(202)	126
	2–Nitrophenanthrenequinone	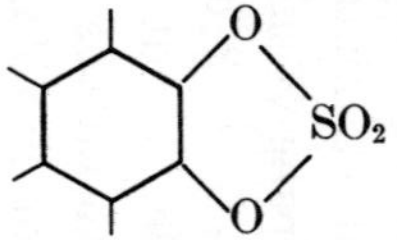	48	(205)	126
	3–Nitrophenanthrenequinone		17	(190)	126
	4–Nitrophenanthrenequinone		40	(185)	126
C_{18}	Chrysoquinone		27	(221)	126

REACTION OF SULFURYL CHLORIDE WITH VARIOUS COMPOUNDS

Sulfuryl chloride adds across the double bond of olefins. For example, sulfuryl chloride reacts with ethylene to give, besides the expected dichloroethane, β–chloroethylchlorosulfite in low yield.[156] Sulfuryl chloride also reacts with propylene to form 1–chloro–2–propylchlorosulfite in 45% yield.[156] These reactions are carried out at room or slightly elevated temperature (60°) in the presence of benzoyl peroxide, ultraviolet light, or other catalysts.[56,156]

Sulfuryl chloride also reacts with olefins to give sulfones. Thus, the reaction of sulfuryl chloride with hexene–1, heptene–1, octene–1, or decene–1 in the presence of benzoyl peroxide at 60° forms the β–chloro–n–hexyl, -heptyl, -octyl, and -decyl sulfones, respectively.[85] The products are purified by high-vacuum sublimation. The reactions are inhibited by p–t–butylcatechol.

Sulfuryl chloride reacts with saturated hydrocarbons in ultraviolet light to give sulfonyl chloride. The process is called sulfochlorination. In addition, the chlorinated derivative is formed.[75,82,128a]

$$RH + SO_2Cl_2 \rightarrow RSO_2Cl + HCl$$

A catalytic amount of a base such as pyridine, quinoline, or 2, 6–diaminopyridine facilitates the reaction.[22,30] Thus, the reaction of sulfuryl chloride with n–heptane, ethyl benzene, t–butyl benzene, cyclohexane, or methylcyclohexane gives a mixture of the chlorinated derivative and the sulfonyl chloride.[82] In the reaction of sulfuryl chloride with cyclohexane, 54% cyclohexanesulfonyl chloride and 9.4% cyclohexyl chloride are obtained.[22,82,128a]

Sulfuryl chloride also reacts with organosilicon compounds, producing sulfonyl chlorides.[30] The reactions are carried out at room temperature in the presence of a trace amount of pyridine under ultraviolet irradiation. Thus, the reaction of sulfuryl chloride with tetramethylsilane produces trimethylsilylmethanesulfonyl chloride, b.p. 57°/1 mm, n_D 1.4680 (20°), in 53% yield.[30] The reaction of sulfuryl chloride with trimethylchlorosilane produces dimethylchlorosilanylmethanesulfonyl chloride, b.p. 70°/1 mm, n_D 1.4780 (20°), in 17% yield.[30] The reaction of sulfuryl chloride with ethyltrichlorosilane or diethyldichlorosilane results in 16% of product, b.p. 69°/1 mm, m.p. 29°, and 22% of product, b.p. 85°/1 mm, n_D 1.4928 (20°), respectively; the structure of the products was not firmly established.[30] The reaction of sulfuryl chloride with octamethylcyclotetrasiloxane results in 20% of heptamethyl cyclotetrasiloxanylmethanesulfonyl chloride, b.p. 109°/1 mm, n_D 1.4350 (20°).[30]

Sulfuryl chloride chlorinates aliphatic carboxylic acids in the presence of peroxide. When ultraviolet light is used, the sulfonated derivatives are also obtained. The use of lower aliphatic acids results in cyclic sulfocarboxylic acid anhydrides in which the sulfo group appears in either the β or the β and γ positions in relation to the carboxylic group.[75]

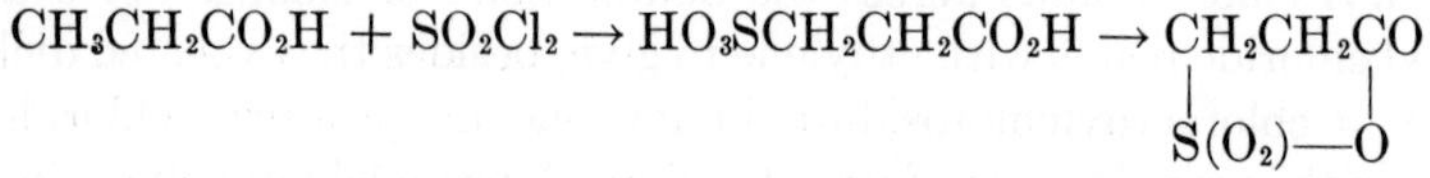

$$CH_3CH_2CO_2H + SO_2Cl_2 \rightarrow HO_3SCH_2CH_2CO_2H \rightarrow \underset{\underset{S(O_2)\!-\!\!-\!O}{|\qquad\quad|}}{CH_2CH_2CO}$$

α Derivatives are not obtained, but α chlorinated products are found as by-products. The general experimental procedure is to mix the organic acid with a slight excess of sulfuryl chloride and illuminate the mixture with a tungsten lamp at 37–67°. The reaction is complete when the evolution of gas ceases. Addition of a small amount of pyridine, which catalyzes the decomposition of sulfuryl chloride into sulfur dioxide and chlorine, has no effect upon the sulfonation of propionic and butyric acids but aids the sulfonation of higher acids.[75]

The reaction of sulfuryl chloride with n–propionic acid[75,128a] or with iso-butyric acid[75] produces the anhydrides Ia, m.p. 77°, in 66% yield and Ib, b.p. 135°/3 mm, in 42% yield (slight decomposition), respectively. Acetic acid cannot be sulfonated by this procedure, and the reactions with n–butyric and higher aliphatic acids result in a mixture of unresolvable products.[75]

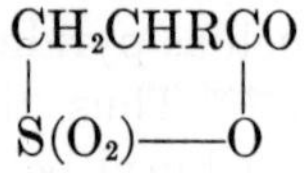

$$\underset{\underset{S(O_2)\!-\!\!-\!\!-\!O}{|\qquad\qquad|}}{CH_2CHRCO}$$

I

Ia R = H

Ib R = CH$_3$

Sulfopropionic acid anhydride (Ia) is transformed into β–sulfopropionic acid, m.p. 102°, by hydrogenation.[75] This anhydride also reacts with alcohols and amines to form the following products.[75]

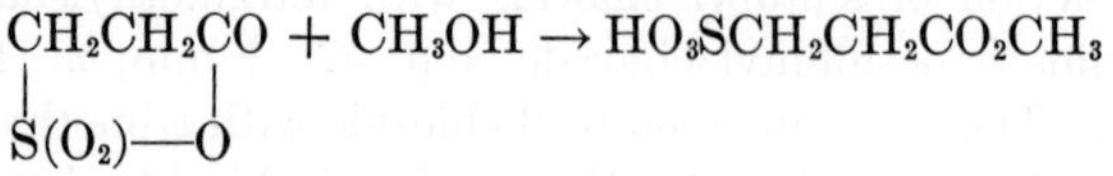

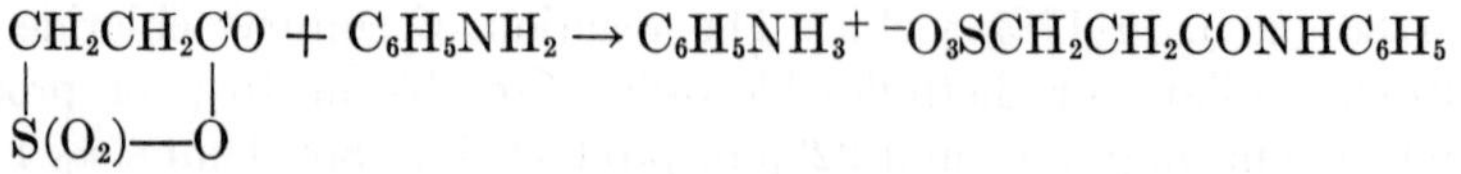

$$\underset{\underset{S(O_2)\!-\!\!-\!O}{|\qquad\quad|}}{CH_2CH_2CO} + CH_3OH \rightarrow HO_3SCH_2CH_2CO_2CH_3$$

$$\underset{\underset{S(O_2)\!-\!\!-\!O}{|\qquad\quad|}}{CH_2CH_2CO} + C_6H_5NH_2 \rightarrow C_6H_5NH_3{}^+\ {}^-O_3SCH_2CH_2CONHC_6H_5$$

Table 18. Addition of Sulfuryl Chloride to Unsaturated Compounds

C_n	Unsaturated compound	Product	% Yield	°C b.p./mm (m.p.)	n_D (°C)	Ref.
C_2	Ethylene	$ClCH_2CH_2Cl +$	73	83		156
		$ClCH_2CH_2SO_2Cl$	15	72/5	1.4992 (20)	
C_3	Propylene	1, 2–Dichloropropane+	98			156
		1–Chloro-2-propylchlorosulfite	45	90/28	1.4883 (20)	
C_6	Hexene–1	1, 2–Dichlorohexane+	79	62/14	1.4500 (20)	85
		$(n\text{-}C_4H_9CHClCH_2)_2SO_2$	13	(42)		
C_7	Heptene–1	1, 2–Dichloroheptane+	49	54/4	1.4503 (20)	85
		$(n\text{-}C_5H_{11}CHClCH_2)_2SO_2$	21	(58)		
C_8	Octene–1	1, 2–Dichlorooctane+	51	69/4	1.4531 (20)	85
		$(n\text{-}C_6H_{13}CHClCH_2)_2SO_2$	28	(57)		
C_{10}	Decene–1	1, 2–Dichlorodecane+	69	57/0.3	1.4564 (20)	85
		$(n\text{-}C_8H_{17}CHClCH_2)_2SO_2$	15	(68)		

REACTION OF SULFONYL HALIDES WITH UNSATURATED COMPOUNDS

Benzene sulfonyl iodide reacts with both the *cis* and *trans* isomers of butene–2.[138,139] At 0–26° under irradiation from a tungsten filament lamp the reaction is completed in 35 min. Essentially the same mixture of diastereomeric products is obtained from both isomers. The products can be dehydrohalogenated to give unsaturated sulfones. One isomer, m.p. 70°, can be isolated from the mixture and purified.

p–Chlorobenzenesulfonyl chloride reacts with allyl acetate at 78° in the presence of benzoyl peroxide.[90] The 1:1 adduct, p–ClC$_6$H$_4$SO$_2$CH$_2$CH(Cl)-CH$_2$OCOCH$_3$, n_D 1.5471 (20°), boiling over a wide temperature range, is obtained in 25% yield. p–Chlorobenzenesulfonyl chloride reacts with ethylene at 70° and 1500 psi in the presence of benzoyl peroxide.[91] A mixture of 1:1 (21%), 2:1 (32%), and 4:1 products is obtained; the individual fractions boil over a wide temperature range. p–Chlorobenzenesulfonyl chloride also reacts with isobutylene at 70° in the presence of benzoyl peroxide in an autoclave.[91] Solid 2–chloroisobutyl–p–chlorophenyl sulfone is obtained in high yield.

N–chlorosulfonyl phthalimide reacts rapidly (15–25 min) with octene–1 or decene–1 at 125–130° in the presence of benzoyl peroxide to give the corresponding N–(2–chloro–n–octyl)- and N–(2–chloro–n–decyl)sulfonyl phthalimides.[80]

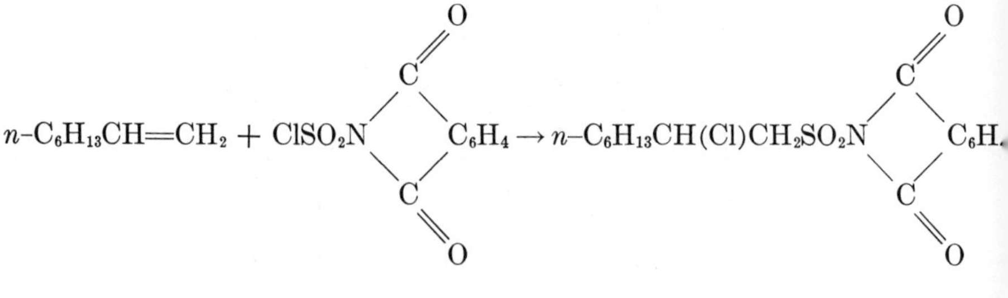

p–Toluenesulfonyl chloride adds across the double bond of norbornene in the presence of benzoyl peroxide at 75–90° or when irradiated with ultraviolet light for 8 hr at 120–130° to give the *trans* product without skeletal rearrangement or *cis-exo* addition.[34] *exo*–2–p–Toluenesulfonyl-*endo*–3–chloronorborane, m.p. 114°, is obtained in 64% yield.

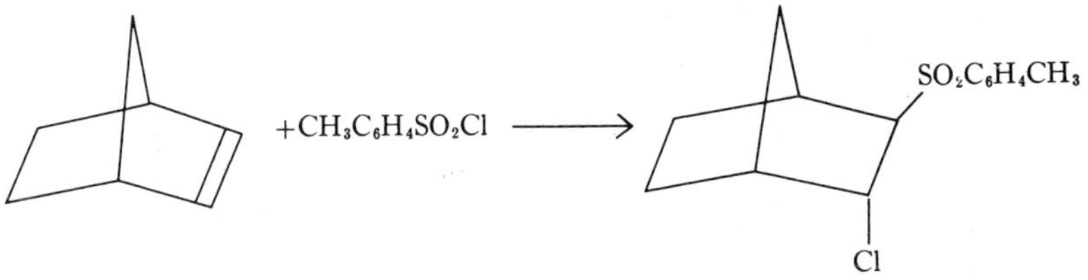

Addition of p–toluenesulfonyl chloride to aldrin proceeds similarly at 155° in the presence of di–t–butyl peroxide for 24 hr to form a *trans* addition product, m.p. 265°, in 13% yield.[34]

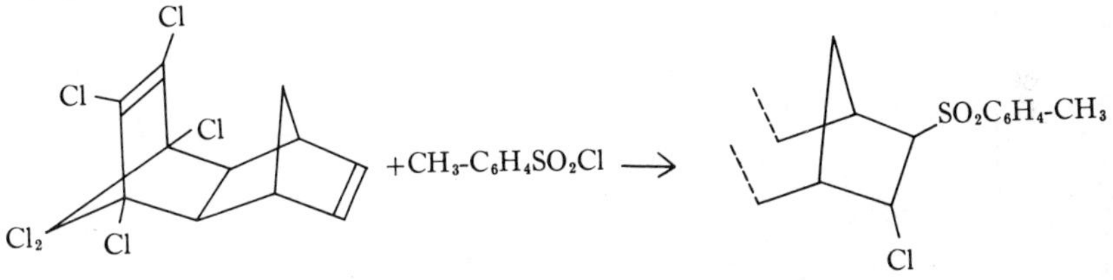

The addition of p–toluenesulfonyl chloride to norbornadiene, however, at 75–82° in the presence of benzoyl peroxide for 24 hr produces a rearranged product, m.p. 154°, in 42% yield.[34]

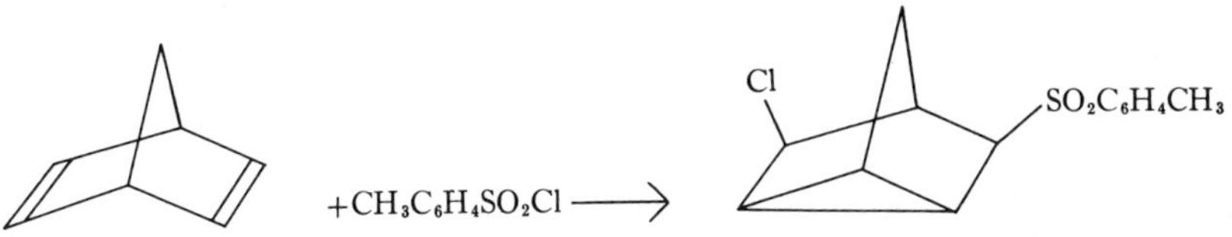

In the reaction of trichloromethanesulfonyl chloride with olefins, sulfur dioxide is lost and the elements of carbon tetrachloride add across the double bond.[92,141,145,146]

$$RCH{=}CH_2 + CCl_3SO_2Cl \rightarrow RCH(Cl)CH_2CCl_3 + SO_2$$

Since trichloromethanesulfonyl chloride can readily be prepared from the commercially available corresponding sulfenyl chloride,[141] this reaction may be useful for the preparation of various polychlorinated compounds. The production of polyhalogenated compounds from the corresponding olefins is described in patents.[92,145,146]

Table 19. Reaction of Sulfonyl Halides with Unsaturated Compounds

C_n	Unsaturated compound	Sulfonyl halide	Product	% Yield	°C b.p./mm (m.p.)	n_D (°C)	Ref.
C_2	Ethylene	CCl_3SO_2Cl	1,1,1,3–Tetrachloropropane		40/10	1.4825 (20)	145
C_3	Allyl alcohol	CCl_3SO_2Cl	2,4,4–Tetrachlorobutanol		61/0.5	1.5065 (20)	145
C_5	Isoprene	CCl_3SO_2Cl	1,1,1,5–Tetrachloro–3–methyl–2–pentene		97/6	1.5129 (20)	145
	Allyl acetate	CCl_3SO_2Cl	2,4,4,4–Tetrachlorobutyl acetate		66/0.3		145
C_8	Octene–1	CCl_3SO_2Cl	1,1,1,3–Tetrachlorononane	67	76/0.3	1.4771 (20)	145
	Styrene	CCl_3SO_2Cl	1,1,1,3–Tetrachloropropylbenzene	53	86/0.2	1.5557 (20)	92,146
C_4	Butene–2	$C_6H_5SO_2I$	$C_6H_5SO_2CH(CH_3)CH(CH_3)I$	80		1.582 (25)	138
	Isobutylene	p–$ClC_6H_4SO_2Cl$	2–Chloroisobutyl–p–chlorophenyl sulfone	75	(82)		91
C_8	Octene–1	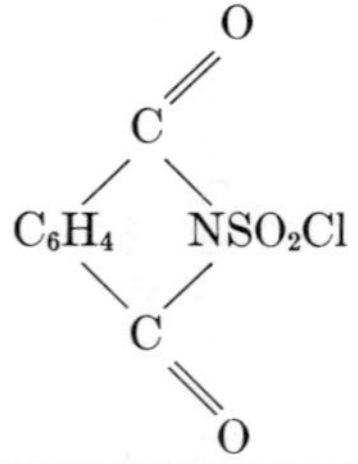 $C_6H_4(CO)_2N\!-\!SO_2Cl$	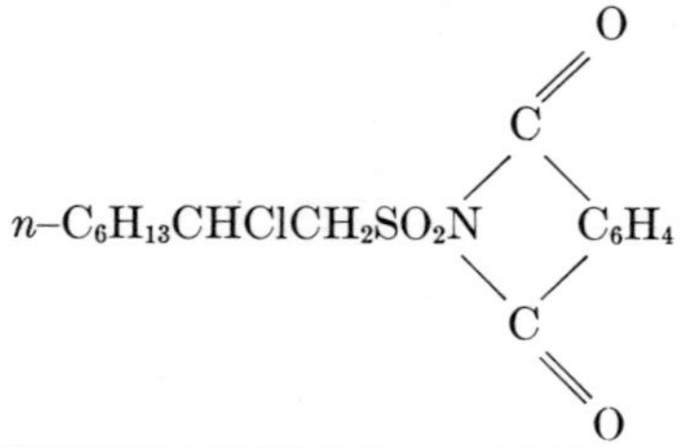 $C_6H_4(CO)_2N\!-\!SO_2CHClCH_2CHCl\text{-}n\text{-}C_6H_{13}$	48	(98)		80
C_{10}	Decene–1	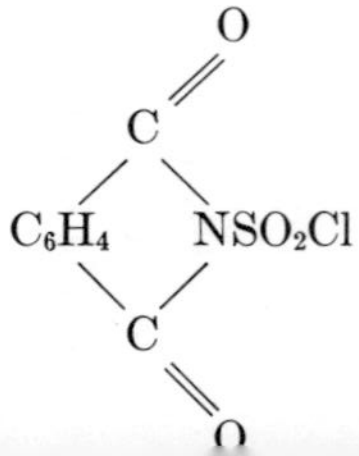 $C_6H_4(CO)_2N\!-\!SO_2Cl$	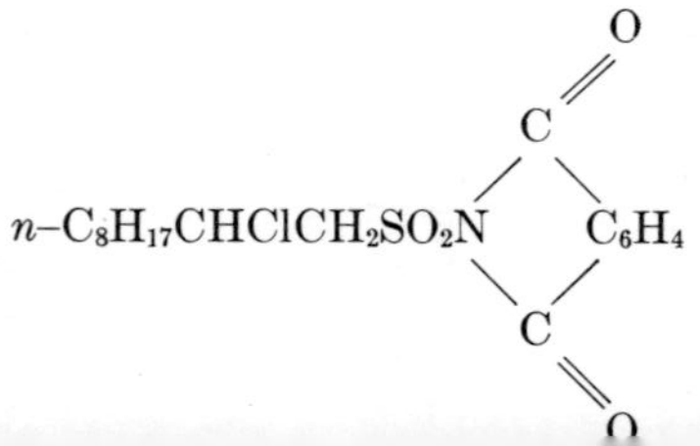 $C_6H_4(CO)_2N\!-\!SO_2CHClCH_2CHCl\text{-}n\text{-}C_8H_{17}$	64	(91)		80

REACTION OF THIOCYANIC ACID, THIOCYANOGEN, AND THIOCYANOGEN CHLORIDE WITH VARIOUS COMPOUNDS

The reactions of thiocyanic acid, thiocyanogen, and thiocyanogen chloride with organic compounds under free radical conditions have received little attention.

In one study thiocyanic acid was reacted with isobutylene, trimethylethylene, 2–pentene, styrene, and camphene.[78] The reaction with isobutylene resulted in a mixture of t–butyl thiocyanate and t–butyl isothiocyanate. No experimental details were reported.

Frederiksen[49] found that thiocyanogen cannot react with cholesterol or its esters in the absence of ultraviolet light. But when a chloroform solution of cholesterol or cholesteryl benzoate is irradiated, 7–thiocyano derivatives, m.p., 139° and 164°, respectively, are obtained in good yield.

Bacon, Guy, and Irwin[6-8] have studied the reaction of thiocyanogen and of thiocyanogen chloride with hydrocarbons. In organic solvents such as carbon tetrachloride, thiocyanogen undergoes homolysis when irradiated with a mercury vapor lamp.[8] The thiocyanogen radicals substitute the α–hydrogen atoms of arylalkyl hydrocarbons.

$$RCHR'R'' + (SCN)_2 \rightarrow RCR'R''SCN + HSCN$$

Thiocyanogen absorbs light between 400 and 280 mμ (maximum at 300 mμ). The reactions are carried out at 35° using a 250-watt lamp which has an intense radiation at 365 mμ. The reactions are complete in $\frac{1}{2}$–6 hr, and the yield of products varies between 10 and 90%.

Thus, the reaction of thiocyanogen with toluene, 2–methylnaphthalene, ethylbenzene, 2–ethylnaphthalene isobutylbenzene, or bibenzyl produces thiocyanates.[8] The reaction of thiocyanogen with isopropylbenzene or diphenylmethane produces thiocyanates, which rearrange to isothiocyanates during the isolation procedure.[8] The reaction of thiocyanogen with sec–butylbenzene, triphenylmethane, 2–isopropylnaphthalene, or retene produces isothiocyanates only.[8]

A reaction also occurs between thiocyanogen chloride and arylalkyl hydrocarbons, with the replacement of an α–hydrogen atom by the thiocyanogen radical.[6,7]

$$RH + ClSCN \rightarrow RSCN + HCl$$

Thiocyanogen chloride reacts with toluene, ethylbenzene, m–xylene, 2–methylnaphthalene, 2–ethylnaphthalene, isopropylbenzene, isopropylnaphthalene, diphenylmethane, or triphenylmethane. The last four substrates form isothiocyanates instead of thiocyanates. Polar solvents and polar groups in the hydrocarbon molecule can also cause competitive nuclear thiocyanation.[6,7]

Table 20. Reaction of Thiocyanogen or Thiocyanogen Chloride with Arylalkyl Hydrocarbons

C_n	Hydrocarbon	(SCN)₂ or NCSCl	Product	% Yield	°C b.p./mm (m.p.)	n_D (°C)	Ref.
C_7	Toluene	(SCN)₂	Benzyl thiocyanate	49	(40)		8
	Toluene	NCSCl	Benzyl thiocyanate	63	(40)		6
C_8	Ethylbenzene	(SCN)₂	1'-Thiocyanatoethylbenzene	89	138/11	1.5615 (25)	8
	Ethylbenzene	NCSCl	1'-Thiocyanatoethylbenzene	68	136/11	1.5610 (25)	6
	m-Xylene	NCSCl	3-Methylbenzylthiocyanate	69	145/10	1.5657 (25)	6
C_9	Isopropylbenzene	(SCN)₂	2-Isothiocyanato-2-phenylpropane	82	72/0.2	1.5682 (25)	8
	Cumene	NCSCl	2-Isothiocyanato-2-phenylpropane	14	80/0.2		6
C_{10}	Isobutylbenzene	(SCN)₂	2-Methyl-1-phenyl-1-thiocyanatopropane	70	77/0.1		8
	sec-Butylbenzene	(SCN)₂	2-Isothiocyanato-2-phenylbutane	58	82/0.07		8
C_{11}	1-Methylnapthalene	NCSCl	1-Thiocyanatomethylnaphthalene	65	(89)		7
	2-Methylnaphthalene	(SCN)₂	2-Thiocyanatomethylnaphthalene	25	(101)		8
	2-Methylnaphthalene	NCSCl	2-Thiocyanatomethylnaphthalene	25	(101)		7
C_{12}	2-Ethylnaphthalene	(SCN)₂	2-1'-Thiocyanatoethylnaphthalene	51	(52)		8
	2-Ethylnaphthalene	NCSCl	2-1'-Thiocyanatoethylnaphthalene	33	(52)		7
C_{13}	2-Isopropylnaphthalene	(SCN)₂	2-Isothiocyanato-2, 2'-naphthylpropane	5	(46)		8
	2-Isopropylnaphthalene	NCSCl	2-Isothiocyanato-2, 2'-naphthylpropane	10	(45)		7

Table 20. (cont.) Reaction of Thiocyanogen or Thiocyanogen Chloride with Arylalkyl Hydrocarbons

C_n	Hydrocarbon	$(SCN)_2$ or NCSCl	Product	% Yield	°C b.p./mm (m.p.)	n_D (°C)	Ref.
	Diphenylmethane	$(SCN)_2$	Diphenylmethyl isothiocyanate	49	(57)		8
	Diphenylmethane	NCSCl	Diphenylmethyl isothiocyanate	9	(57)		6
C_{14}	Bibenzyl	$(SCN)_2$	1, 2-Diphenylethyl thiocyanate	61	$27/4 \times 10^{-3}$ (35)		8
C_{18}	Retene	$(SCN)_2$	2-Isothiocyanato-2-1'-methyl-7'-phenanthrylpropane	15	(106)		8
C_{19}	Triphenylmethane	$(SCN)_2$	Triphenylmethyl isothiocyanate	77	(138)		8
	Triphenylmethane	NCSCl	Triphenylmethyl isothiocyanate	71	(137)		6

REFERENCES

[1] Akabori and Kaneko, *Bull. Chem. Soc. Japan*, **14**, 1 (1939).

[2] Asinger and Ebeneder, *Chem. Ber.*, **75**, 344 (1942).

[3] Asinger, Ebeneder, and Bock, *Chem. Ber.*, **75**, 42 (1942).

[4] Asinger, Geiseler, and Eckoldt, *Chem. Ber.*, **89**, 1037 (1956).

[5] Ashworth and Burkhardt, *J. Chem. Soc.*, **1928**, 1791.

[6] Bacon and Guy, *J. Chem. Soc.*, **1961**, 2428.

[7] Bacon, Guy, and Irwin, *J. Chem. Soc.*, **1961**, 2436.

[8] Bacon and Irwin, *J. Chem. Soc.*, **1961**, 2447.

[9] Bacon and LeSuer, *J. Am. Chem. Soc.*, **76**, 670 (1954).

[10] Bader, *J. Chem. Soc.*, **1956**, 116.

[11] Bader, *et al.*, *J. Chem. Soc.*, **1949**, 619.

[12] Barrick, U.S. 2,403,207 (1946).

[13] Behringer, *Ann. Chem.*, **564**, 219 (1949).

[14] Berson and Jones, *J. Am. Chem. Soc.*, **78**, 6045 (1956).

[15] Blomquist and Wolinsky, *J. Org. Chem.*, **23**, 551 (1958).

[16] Bordwell, Chapman, and McKellin, *J. Am. Chem. Soc.*, **76**, 3637 (1954).

[17] Bordwell and Hewett, *Ang. Chem.*, **67**, 280 (1955).

[18] Bordwell and Hewett, *J. Am. Chem. Soc.*, **79**, 3493 (1957).

[19] Böttcher and Bauer, *Ann. Chem.*, **568**, 218 (1950).

[20] Böttcher and Bauer, *Ann. Chem.*, **568**, 227 (1950).

[21] Böttcher and Lüttringhaus, *Ann. Chem.*, **557**, 89 (1947).

[22] Brooks, *et al.*, *The Chemistry of Petroleum Hydrocarbons*, vol. 3, p. 101, Reinhold, New York (1955).

[23] Broun, Varonkov, and Katkova, *Zh. Obsh. Khim.*, **20**, 726 (1950).

[24] Brown, Jones, and Pinder, *J. Chem. Soc.*, **1951**, 2123.

[25] Burkhard, *J. Am. Chem. Soc.*, **72**, 1078 (1950).

[26] Cairns and Sauer, U.S. 2,776,995 (1957).

[27] Carother, *J. Am. Chem. Soc.*, **55**, 2008 (1955).

[28] Case, Ray, and Roberts, *J. Chem. Soc.*, **1961**, 2066.

[29] Case, Ray, and Roberts, *J. Chem. Soc.*, **1961**, 2070.

[30] Cooper, *J. Org. Chem.*, **21**, 1214 (1956).

[31] Cristol and Arganbright, *J. Am. Chem. Soc.*, **79**, 6039 (1957).

[32] Cristol and Brindell, *J. Am. Chem. Soc.*, **76**, 5699 (1954).

[33] Cristol, Brindell, and Reeder, *J. Am. Chem. Soc.*, **80**, 635 (1958).

[34] Cristol and Reeder, *J. Org. Chem.*, **26**, 2182 (1961).

[35] Cunneen, *J. Chem. Soc.*, **1947**, 36.

[36] Cunneen, *J. Chem. Soc.*, **1947**, 134.

[37] Dainton and Ivin, *Trans. Faraday Soc.*, **46**, 374 (1950).

[38] Dainton and Ivin, *Trans. Faraday Soc.*, **46**, 382 (1950).

[39] Evans, Vaughan, and Rust, U.S. 2,376,675 (1944).

[40] Evans, Vaughan, and Rust, U.S. 2,411,961 (1946).

[41] I. G. Farbenindustrie A. G., German 735,096 (1940).

[42] I. G. Farbenindustrie A. G., Belg. 443,658 (1942).

[43] I. G. Farbenindustrie A. G., Belg. 445,312 (1942).

[44] I. G. Farbenindustrie A. G., Belg. 445,349 (1942).

[45] Fields, *J. Org. Chem.*, **21**, 497 (1956).

[46] Fife, Brit. 532,676 (1941).

[47] Ford, Pitkethly, and Young, *Tetrahedron*, **4**, 325 (1958).
[48] Foster, *et al.*, *J. Am. Chem. Soc.*, **78**, 5606 (1956).
[49] Frederiksen and Liisberg, *Chem. Ber.*, **88**, 684 (1955).
[50] Fuson and Ziegler, *J. Org. Chem.*, **11**, 510 (1946).
[51] Gilman, Cason, and Brooks, *J. Am. Chem. Soc.*, **75**, 3760 (1953).
[52] Goering, Relyea, and Larson, *J. Am. Chem. Soc.*, **78**, 348 (1956).
[53] Graf, *Ann. Chem.*, **578**, 50 (1952).
[54] Graf, German 917,427 (1954).
[55] Hackmann and Berkenbosch, *Rec. trav. chim.*, **80**, 745 (1949).
[56] Hanford, U.S. 2,398,426 (1946).
[57] Harman, U.S. 2,504,411 (1950).
[58] Harmon, U.S. 2,390,099 (1945).
[59] Harris and Stacey, *J. Am. Chem. Soc.*, **83**, 840 (1961).
[60] Haszeldine, *J. Chem. Soc.*, **1955**, 4291.
[61] Helberger, Manecke, and Fischer, *Ann. Chem.*, **562**, 23 (1949).
[62] Hoeffelmann and Berkenbosch, U.S. 2,352,435 (1944).
[63] Holmberg, Swedish 94,913 (1937).
[64] Holmberg, *Ark. Kemi. Min. Geol.*, **12B**, 1 (1938).
[65] Holmberg, *Chem. Z.*, **II**, 4354 (1939).
[66] Holmberg and Schjånberg, *Ark. Kemi. Min. Geol.*, **14A**, 1 (1940).
[67] Holmberg and Schjånberg, *Chem. Ber.*, **74**, 1751 (1941).
[68] Hoshino and Yamagishi, Jap. 6480 (1953).
[69] Hoshino, Yamagishi, and Ichikawa, *J. Chem. Soc. Japan*, **74**, 510 (1953).
[70] Imperial Chemical Industry, Ltd., Brit. 583,118 (1946).
[71] Ipatieff and Friedman, *J. Am. Chem. Soc.*, **61**, 71 (1939).
[72] Ipatieff, Pines, and Friedman, *J. Am. Chem. Soc.*, **60**, 2731 (1938).
[73] Jones and Reid, *J. Am. Chem. Soc.*, **60**, 2452 (1938).
[74] Kennedy, Brit. 703,474 (1954).
[75] Kharasch, Chao, and Brown, *J. Am. Chem. Soc.*, **62**, 2393 (1940).
[76] Kharasch and Friedlander, *J. Org. Chem.*, **13**, 882 (1948).
[77] Kharasch and Fuchs, *J. Org. Chem.*, **13**, 97 (1948).
[78] Kharasch, May, and Mayo, *J. Am. Chem. Soc.*, **59**, 1580 (1937).
[79] Kharasch, May, and Mayo, *J. Org. Chem.*, **3**, 175 (1938).
[80] Kharasch and Mosher, *J. Org. Chem.*, **17**, 453 (1952).
[81] Kharasch, Nudenberg, and Mantell, *J. Org. Chem.*, **16**, 524 (1951).
[82] Kharasch and Read, *J. Am. Chem. Soc.*, **61**, 3089 (1939).
[83] Kharasch, Schenk, and Mayo, *J. Am. Chem. Soc.*, **61**, 3092 (1939).
[84] Kharasch and Sternfeld, *J. Am. Chem. Soc.*, **62**, 2559 (1940).
[85] Kharasch and Zavist, *J. Am. Chem. Soc.*, **73**, 964 (1951).
[86] Koenig and Swern, *J. Am. Chem. Soc.*, **79**, 362 (1957).
[87] Kohler and Potter, *J. Am. Chem. Soc.*, **57**, 1316 (1935).
[88] Koshar, Trott, and LaZerte, *J. Am. Chem. Soc.*, **75**, 4595 (1953).
[89] Krespan, *J. Am. Chem. Soc.*, **83**, 3434 (1961).
[90] Ladd, U.S. 2,521,068 (1950).
[91] Ladd, U.S. 2,573,580 (1951).
[92] Ladd and Kiley, U.S. 2,606,213 (1952).
[93] Landis and Hamilton, *J. Org. Chem.*, **25**, 1742 (1960).
[94] Landis and Hamilton, *J. Org. Chem.*, **26**, 274 (1961).
[95] Lester, Rodgers, and Reid, *J. Am. Chem. Soc.*, **66**, 1674 (1944).
[96] Lockwood, U.S. 2,503,280 (1950).
[97] Lozac'h, *Bull. soc. chim. France*, **1949**, 840.
[98] Luttringhaus, König, and Böttcher, *Ann. Chem.*, **560**, 201 (1948).

118 FREE RADICAL REACTIONS

[99] Matteson, *J. Am. Chem. Soc.*, **82**, 4228 (1960).

[100] Mayo and Walling, *Chem. Revs.*, **27**, 351 (1940).

[101] Melnikov and Shvetsova-Shilovskaya, *Dok. Akad. Nauk*, **86**, 543 (1952).

[102] Mikhailov and Blokhina, *Dok. Akad. Nauk*, **80**, 373 (1951).

[103] Mikhailov and Blokhina, Akad. Nauk Ukr. S.S.R. Otdel Fiz.-Mat. i Khim. Nauk, **1952**, 215.

[104] Miles and Owne, *J. Chem. Soc.*, **1952**, 817.

[105] Nesmeyanov, *et al.*, *Dok. Akad. Nauk*, **127**, 575 (1959).

[106] Neureiter and Bordwell, *J. Am. Chem. Soc.*, **82**, 5354 (1960).

[107] Nicolet, *J. Am. Chem. Soc.*, **57**, 1098 (1935).

[108] Orthner, *Ang. Chem.*, **62**, 302 (1950).

[109] Oswald, *J. Org. Chem.*, **24**, 443 (1959).

[110] Oswald, *J. Org. Chem.*, **25**, 467 (1960).

[111] Overberger, Mulvaney, and Beringer, *J. Org. Chem.*, **21**, 1311 (1956).

[112] Owen and Sultanbawa, *J. Chem. Soc.*, **1949**, 3109.

[113] Perklev, *Svensk Kem. Tidskr.*, **65**, 216 (1953).

[114] Petrov, Mironov, and Glukhovtsev, *Dok. Akad. Nauk*, **93**, 499 (1953).

[115] Pinkney, U.S. 2,551,813 (1951).

[116] Posner, *Chem. Ber.*, **38**, 646 (1905).

[117] Povenz, *Z. Elek.*, **56**, 746 (1952).

[118] Prileshaeva, Shapiro, and Shostakovskii, *Izvest. Akad. Nauk*, **1951**, 438.

[119] Prileshaeva, Shapiro, and Shostakovskii, *Izvest. Akad. Nauk*, **1951**, 560.

[120] Reed, U.S. 2,174,492 (1939).

[121] Roberts, *Quart. Revs.*, **15**, 30 (1961).

[122] Rueggeberg and Cook, U.S. 2,810,687 (1957).

[123] Rueggeberg, Cook, and Reid, *J. Org. Chem.*, **13**, 110 (1948).

[124] Rueggeberg, *et al.*, *J. Am. Chem. Soc.*, **70**, 2292 (1948).

[125] Sauer, *J. Am. Chem. Soc.*, **79**, 5314 (1957).

[126] Schenck and Schmidt-Thomée, *Ann. Chem.*, **584**, 199 (1953).

[127] Schmitt and Lespagnol, *C.r.* **230**, 551 (1950).

[128] Schönberg, *Präparative Organische Photochemie*, Springer Verlag, Berlin (1958).
   a. p. 201.
   b. p. 205.

[129] Shostakovskii and Prileshaeva, *Izvest. Akad. Nauk*, **1954**, 517.

[130] Shostakovskii, Prileshaeva, and Shapiro, *Izvest. Akad. Nauk*, **1953**, 357.

[131] Shostakovskii, Prileshaeva, and Shapiro, *Izvest. Akad. Nauk*, **1954**, 292.

[132] Shostakovskii, Prileshaeva, and Shapiro, *Izvest. Akad. Nauk*, **1954**, 303.

[133] Shostakovskii, Prileshaeva, and Uvarova, *Izvest. Akad. Nauk*, **1954**, 527.

[134] Shostakovskii, Prileshaeva, and Uvarova, *Izvest. Akad. Nauk*, **1955**, 906.

[135] Shostakovskii, Shapiro, and Sidelkovskaya, *Izvest. Akad. Nauk*, **1958**, 68.

[136] Sjoberg, *Chem. Ber.*, **74**, 64 (1941).

[137] Skell and Allen, *J. Am. Chem. Soc.*, **82**, 1511 (1960).

[138] Skell and McNamara, *J. Am. Chem. Soc.*, **79**, 85 (1957).

[139] Skell, Woodworth, and McNamara, *J. Am. Chem. Soc.*, **79**, 1253 (1957).

[140] Smith and Hernestam, *Acta chim. Scand.*, **8**, 1111 (1954).

[141] Sosnovsky, *Chem. Revs.*, **58**, 509 (1952).

[142] Spindt, Stevens, and Baldwin, *J. Am. Chem. Soc.*, **73**, 3693 (1951).

[143] Terentev and Gershenovich, *Zh. Obsh. Khim.*, **23**, 208 (1953).

[144] Topchiev, Tsiguro, and Gryaznov, *Dok. Akad. Nauk*, **113**, 1302 (1957).

[145] United States Rubber Co., Brit. 649,555 (1951).

[146] United States Rubber Co., Brit. 650,204 (1951).

[147] Vaughan and Rust, *J. Org. Chem.*, **7**, 472 (1942).
[148] Vaughan and Rust, U.S. 2,392,294 (1946).
[149] Vaughan and Rust, U.S. 2,398,479 (1946).
[150] Vaughan and Rust, U.S. 2,398,480 (1946).
[151] Vaughan and Rust, U.S. 2,398,481 (1946).
[152] Voronkov, Broun, and Karpenko, *Zh. Obsh. Khim.*, **19**, 1927 (1949).
[153] Walling, *Free Radicals in Solution*, p. 223, John Wiley, New York (1957).
[154] Weinstock and Lewis, *J. Am. Chem. Soc.*, **79**, 6243 (1957).
[155] Wicklatz, U.S. 2,600,287 (1952).
[156] Yakubovich and Zinovev, *Zh. Obsh. Khim.*, **17**, 2028 (1947).
[157] Yamagishi and Nakazina, *Nippon Kagaku Zasshi*, **75**, 1086 (1954).
[158] Yamagishi, Tanaka, and Hoshino, *Bull. Chem. Soc. Japan*, **29**, 447 (1956).

CHAPTER IV

Addition-type Reaction of Water, Hydrogen Peroxide, Alcohols, Acetals, Ethers, Carbonyl Compounds, and Saturated Compounds with Unsaturated Compounds

REACTION OF WATER AND HYDROGEN PEROXIDE

The reaction of water with unsaturated compounds, in particular under the influence of solar energy, probably plays an important role in biological systems.[48] However, only a few of these reactions are of interest from a preparative point of view.

Water reacts with crotonic acid or its sodium salt under the influence of ultraviolet light to give β–hydroxybutyric acid in 10–24% yield,[54,57] and it reacts with 1, 3–dimethyluracil under the influence of ultraviolet light to give 1, 3–dimethyl–5, 6–dihydrouracil, m.p. 105°, in 60–75% yield.[54,68]

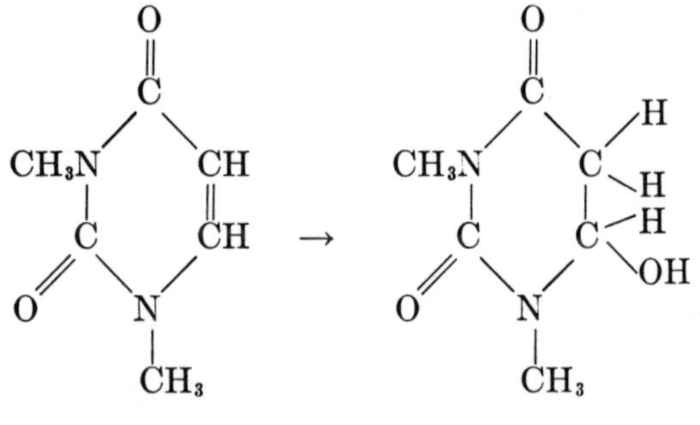

The photochemically catalyzed addition of water to various ergot alkaloids takes place at the double bond Δ9.10 of the D ring.[11,54,58] Depending on the position of the hydroxy group, two stereoisomers are formed from each starting material. The name of the product is formed by attaching the prefix "lumi" to the name of the starting material. The *trans* or *cis* products are differentiated by the Roman numerals I and II[58] or by the Greek letters α and β.[11] The addition is also facilitated by electrolytes.[11]

Aqueous hydrogen peroxide reacts very slowly with unsaturated systems. The reaction is accelerated in the presence of various metal ions or under ultraviolet light. Hydrogen peroxide absorbs strongly below 3100 A, and it has been suggested that hydroxyl radicals are formed in the primary process.[70]

$$H_2O_2 + h\nu \rightarrow 2HO\cdot$$

The production of hydroxyl radicals has also been proposed for the reactions catalyzed by a metal ion.[7,69] Thus, in the presence of osmium, vanadium, or chromium compounds or in ultraviolet light, the hydroxyl radical adds to allyl alcohol to give glycerin in 43% yield.[25,54] The reaction of hydrogen peroxide with crotonic acid in ultraviolet light produces dihydroxybutyric acid in 30% yield.[25] Hydrogen peroxide reacts with maleic acid or its diethyl ester to give *meso*-tartaric acid and its ester, respectively.[25] The products are obtained in 9–22% yield. These reactions seem to be of limited preparative value at present.

Table 21.   Addition of Water to Ergot Alkaloids

Starting material	Product	°C (m.p.)	$[\alpha]_D^{20}$ (Pyridine)	Ref.
Ergotamine	Lumiergotamine I+	(247)	+14	58, 11
	Lumiergotamine II	(192)	+2	
Ergotaminine	Lumiergotaminine I+	(217)	+68	58
	Lumiergotaminine II	(228)	−12	
Ergobasine	Lumiergobasine	(161)	−28	58
Ergometrine	α–Lumiergometrine+	(193–197) decomp.	+24	11
	β–Lumiergometrine	(125–35)	+18	
Ergocristine	β–Lumiergocristine	(179–81)	+17	11
Ergocristinine	α–Lumiergocristinine+	(235)	+116	11
	β–Lumiergocristinine	(171)	+0	
Lysergic acid diethylamide	Lumilysergic acid diethyl- amide I+	(223)	−29	58
	Lumilysergic acid diethylamide II	(256)	−75	

REACTION OF ALCOHOLS

The addition of alcohols to olefins under free radical conditions can proceed by two routes. In one case (a) the functional group of the alcohol adds to a double bond. In the other case (b) the mobile α–hydrogen atoms participate in the reaction.

$$\begin{array}{c} \diagup \\ C=C \\ \diagup \end{array} + HOR \rightarrow H{-}\overset{|}{\underset{|}{C}}{-}\overset{|}{\underset{|}{C}}{-}OR \qquad (a)$$

$$\begin{array}{c} \diagup \\ C=C \\ \diagup \end{array} + H{-}\overset{H}{\underset{OH}{\underset{|}{C}}}{-}R \rightarrow H{-}\overset{H}{\underset{|}{C}}{-}\overset{|}{\underset{OH}{\underset{|}{C}}}{-}\overset{H}{\underset{|}{C}}{-}R \qquad (b)$$

Despite its probable biological significance, the addition involving the functional group (a) is of little preparative value to date. When methanol and crotonic acid or ethanol and crotonic acid are irradiated by ultraviolet light for 4 weeks, β–methoxybutyric acid, b.p. 117°/20 mm, in 7% yield, and β–ethoxybutyric acid, b.p. 113°/14 mm, respectively, are obtained.[54,57]

Considerably greater importance is attributed to the second method (b) of addition of alcohols to olefins. Methanol, ethanol, or isopropanol reacts with ethylene under pressure in the presence of dialkyl peroxides to give telomers and 1:1 adducts.[1,17] Under the most favorable conditions the methanol reaction produces the 1:1 adduct in only 5% yield, whereas the ethanol and isopropanol reactions produce the 1:1 adduct in 40% and 80% yield, respectively.[17] The reactions are carried out at 135–145° in about 16 hr. Precise control of ethylene pressure (60 psig) seems to be important for achieving optimum yields. Di–t–butyl peroxide is the preferred catalyst. In the case of isopropanol 0.1 mole of the peroxide per 6.7 moles of alcohol is used. Benzoyl peroxide, cumyl hydroperoxide, and azobisisobutyronitrile are ineffective in this series of condensations.[17]

Under similar conditions or in ultraviolet light at 30–35°, methanol, ethanol, propanol, butanol–1, butanol–2, or cyclohexanol reacts with hexene–1, octene–1, or dodecene–1 to give a moderate yield of 1:1 adduct.[61,62] The formation of a 1:1 adduct is favored by a high alcohol:olefin ratio. Acyl peroxides are ineffective. Methanol, ethanol, or isopropanol reacts with tetrafluoroethylene at 175° in the presence of a radical initiator such as azonitrile or peroxide to give a 1:1 adduct in 8–10 hr.[14] Perfluoropropylene or higher fluorinated homologues react with methanol, ethanol, or isopropanol for 15 hr in the presence of benzoyl peroxide at 100° to give fluorinated alcohols in excellent yield.[23]

The photochemical reactions of ethanol, isopropanol, butanol–2, or octanol–2 with maleic acid in the presence of benzophenone or anthraquinone as the photosensitizer for 25 hr yield γ–methylparaconic acid (I),[6] terebic acid (II),[49] γ–ethyl–γ–methylparaconic acid (III),[49] and γ–hexyl–γ–methylparaconic acid (IV),[6] respectively, and water.

I   R = H
II   R = CH$_3$
III   R = C$_2$H$_5$
IV   R = n–C$_6$H$_{13}$

The reaction of isopropanol with crotonic acid under similar conditions produces β, γ–dimethyl–γ–valerolactone (V) in 38% yield.[6]

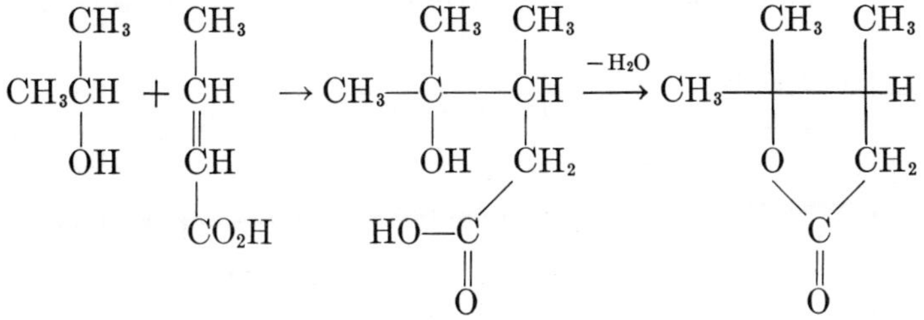

V

The benzophenone-photosensitized condensation of 2 moles of isopropanol with acetylene dicarboxylic acid leads to the formation of compounds VI and VII.[50]

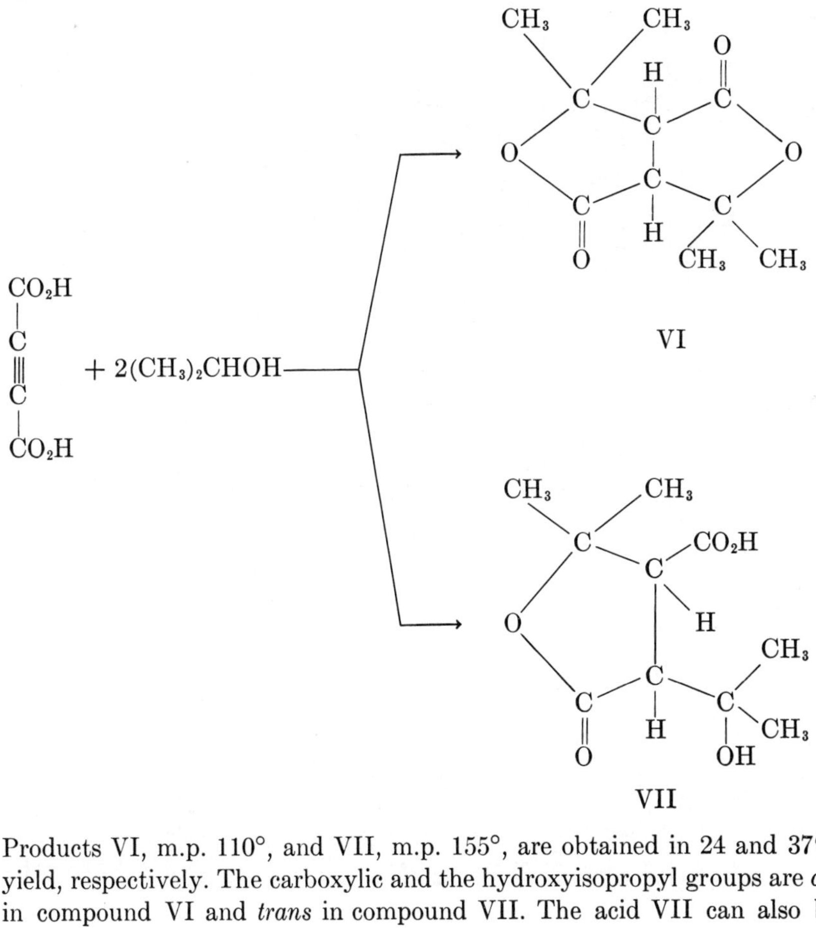

VI

VII

Products VI, m.p. 110°, and VII, m.p. 155°, are obtained in 24 and 37% yield, respectively. The carboxylic and the hydroxyisopropyl groups are *cis* in compound VI and *trans* in compound VII. The acid VII can also be

Table 22.   Reaction of Alcohols with Unsaturated Compounds

C_n	Unsaturated compound	Alcohol	Product	% Yield	°C b.p./mm (m.p.)	n_D (°C)	Ref.
C_3	$CF_3CF{=}CF_2$	Methanol	$CF_3CHFCF_2CH_2OH$	90	114	1.3115 (25)	23
C_4	$C_2F_5CF{=}CF_2$	Methanol	$C_2F_5CHFCF_2CH_2OH$	76	124	1.3083 (25)	23
C_5	$C_2F_5CF{=}CFCF_3$	Methanol	$C_2F_5CHFCF(CH_2OH)CF_3$	70	118	1.3118 (25)	23
	$C_3F_7CF{=}CF_2$	Methanol	$C_3F_7CHFCF_2CH_2OH$	85	138	1.3098 (25)	23
C_7	$C_5F_{11}CF{=}CF_2$	Methanol	$C_5F_{11}CHFCF_2CH_2OH$	90	170 (39)		23
C_8	Octene-1	Methanol	Nonanol-1	16	110/20	1.4342 (20)	61, 62
C_9	$C_7F_{15}CF{=}CF_2$	Methanol	$C_7F_{15}CHFCF_2CH_2OH$	90	210 (80)		23
C_4	$C_2F_5CF{=}CF_2$	Ethanol	$C_2F_5CHFCF_2CHOHCH_3$	66	130	1.3202 (25)	23
	Maleic acid	Ethanol	γ-Methylparaconic acid	18	(80)		6
C_5	$C_3F_7CF{=}CF_2$	Ethanol	$C_3F_7CHFCF_2CHOHCH_3$	60	145	1.3183 (25)	23
C_6	Hexene-1	Ethanol	Octanol-2	13	97/38	1.4290 (20)	61, 62
C_8	Octene-1	Ethanol	Decanol-2	28	53/1	1.4358 (20)	61, 62
C_8	Octene-1	Propanol-2	2-Methyldecanol-2	46	50/0.2	1.4359 (20)	61, 62
C_{12}	Dodecene-1	Propanol-2	2-Methyltetradecanol-2	51	115/0.2	1.4437 (20)	61, 62
	Maleic (fumaric acid)	Isopropanol	Terebic acid	96	(176)		49
	Crotonic acid	Isopropanol	γ, β-Dimethyl-γ-valerolactone	38	34/0.05 (12)		6
C_5	$C_3F_7CF{=}CF_2$	Isopropanol	$C_3F_7CHFCF_2COH(CH_3)_2$	55	152	1.3291 (25)	23
	Maleic acid	Butanol-2	γ-Ethyl-γ-methylparaconic acid	57	(131)		49
C_8	Octene-1	Butanol-1	Dodecanol-4	37	83/1	1.4409 (20)	61, 62
	Octene-1	Butanol-2	3-Methylhendecanol-3	37	59/0.1	1.4418 (20)	61, 62
C_6	Hexene-1	Cyclohexanol	1-n-Hexylcyclohexanol	42	115/7	1.4645 (20)	61, 62
	Maleic acid	Octanol-2	γ-Hexyl-γ-methylparaconic acid	23	(183)		6

obtained from the reaction of isopropanol and terebilenic acid (VIII) in the presence of benzophenone and ultraviolet light.[50]

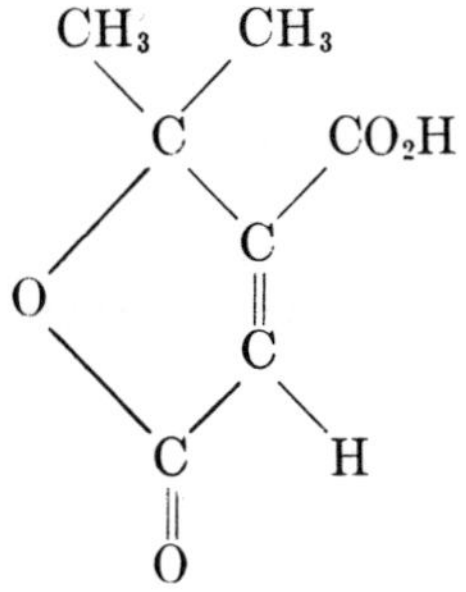

$$+ (CH_3)_2CHOH \rightarrow \text{Compound VII}$$

VIII

REACTION OF ALDEHYDES

Aldehydes react with acetylenes or olefins in the presence of free radical initiators to give the corresponding ketones.

$$RCH{=}CH_2 + HCR' \rightarrow RCH_2CH_2CR'$$
$$\quad\quad\quad\quad\quad \underset{O}{\|} \quad\quad\quad\quad \underset{O}{\|}$$

$$CH{\equiv}CH + HCR' \rightarrow CH_2{=}CHCR'$$
$$\quad\quad\quad\quad \underset{O}{\|} \quad\quad\quad\quad \underset{O}{\|}$$

$$CH_2{=}CHCR' + HCR' \rightarrow R'CCH_2CH_2CR'$$
$$\quad\quad\quad \underset{O}{\|} \quad\quad \underset{O}{\|} \quad\quad \underset{O}{\|} \quad\quad \underset{O}{\|}$$

Depending on the nature of the catalyst, the temperature of the addition reaction ranges from 25° to 100°. The reaction is carried out at room temperature when ultraviolet illumination is used.[16,38,51] A higher temperature is used when the reaction is catalyzed by peroxide, such as acetyl, benzoyl,[12,13,16,18−23,31,35,36,39,41,44,51,55,56,63−66,67] or di-t-butyl peroxide,[47] or by azonitrile.[26] Reaction of aldehydes with olefins can also be induced by high-energy radiation.[59,71] The radiation-induced reactions follow predominantly the same course as that observed in reactions initiated by the customary free radical catalysts; ketones are produced by a chain process.[59,71]

Aldehydes condense with esters of maleic, fumaric, or acetylene dicarboxylic acids when a γ-radiation source (Co[60]) is used.[71] Thus, butyro-, isobutyro-, or benzaldehyde reacts with maleic or fumaric acid esters at a total dose level of 17.4–27.6 megarep. The yield of adduct ranges from 14% for benzaldehyde to 27% for isobutyroaldehyde to 84% for butyroaldehyde.

Addition of the same aldehydes to esters of acetylenic acid at a total dose level of 10.4–10.8 megarep results in lower yield, 9–31%.[71]

With highly volatile unsaturated compounds, such as acetylene, ethylene, and propylene, and with low-boiling aldehydes, such as acetaldehyde, the reaction is best performed in a sealed reaction vessel such as a steel autoclave.[38,56,65,66] Excess aldehyde is recommended to repress telomer formation.[16] Best results are obtained with long straight-chain olefins containing terminal unsaturation. Most work reported to date involves aliphatic aldehydes.

Occasionally difficulties are experienced in condensation of aldehydes with olefinic systems. Butyroaldehyde fails to react with methylvinyl ketone, isopropenylmethyl ketone, isophorone, benzalacetone, benzoquinone, or 4–acetoxy–3–penten–2–one.[39] The reactions with benzaldehyde usually give a low yield of adduct,[38] and the reaction of butanal with styrene does not give a 1:1 adduct.[16,63] Formaldehyde, paraformaldehyde, trioxane, chloral, crotonaldehyde, or furfural cannot be condensed with unsaturated dicarboxylic acid esters.[38]

At 4–12 atm and 0–60°, aldehyde reacts with acetylene in the presence of benzoyl peroxide to form acetonyl acetone in 20% yield.[51]

$$HC{\equiv}CH + 2CH_3CHO \rightarrow CH_3COCH_2CH_2COCH_3$$

Acetaldehyde and ethylene at 80 and 800 psi after 20 hr produce methylethyl ketone, b.p. 80°/760 mm, in low yield, methyl–n–butyl ketone, b.p. 128°/760 mm, and methyl–n–hexyl ketone, b.p. 172°/760 mm.[56,66] In the reaction of n–butylaldehyde with ethylene, n–propylethyl ketone and n–butylpropyl ketone are obtained.[56,66] Acetaldehyde and propylene react to give methylpropyl ketone in low yield.[18,67]

Various aldehydes react with perhalogenated olefins in the presence of benzoyl peroxide.[28] 1, 2–Dichloro–1, 2–difluoroethylene or 1, 1–dichloro–2, 2–difluoroethylene condenses with acet-, proprio-, butyro-, or isobutyroaldehyde in a stainless steel autoclave.[28] The mixture is maintained at 105–110° for approximately 20 hr.

$$CClF{=}CClF + HCOR \rightarrow CHFClCFClCOR$$

$$CF_2{=}CCl_2 + HCOR \rightarrow CHCl_2CF_2COR$$

The yields range from 15 to 43%. However, isobutyroaldehyde reacts with 1, 2–dichloro–1, 2–difluoroethylene to give the 1:1 adduct in very low yield, 3%.[28] Instead, 1, 2–dichloro–1, 2–difluoro–3–methylbutane, b.p. 73°/100 mm, n_D 1.4099 (20°), is isolated in 15% yield. The reaction of isobutyroaldehyde and 1, 1–dichloro–2, 2–difluoroethylene produces a 1:1 adduct in 15% yield and 1, 1–dichloro–2, 2–difluoro–3–methylbutane, b.p. 77°/100 mm, n_D 1.4090 (20°), in 26% yield. Butyro- or acetaldehyde reacts with perfluoropropene–1 or perfluorobutene–1 to give the corresponding adduct in excellent yield.[23]

Various aldehydes condense with unsaturated aliphatic acids,[12,21,36,65] nitriles,[36] esters,[12,19,21,31,35,36,38,64,65,71] ketones,[22,39] ethers,[19,64] or acetals[19,64] to give 1:1 products in moderate to excellent yield. For example, acetaldehyde adds to acroleindiethyl acetal at 80° in the presence of azobisisobutyronitrile or benzoyl peroxide to give an adduct which can be hydrolyzed to levulinic aldehyde (I), with an over-all yield of 53%.[26]

$$H_2C{=}CH{-}CH(OC_2H_5)_2 + CH_3CHO \rightarrow CH_3COCH_2CH_2CH(OC_2H_5)_2$$
$$\xrightarrow[H^+]{H_2O} CH_3COCH_2CH_2CHO$$

I

The reaction of acetaldehyde with esters of unsaturated dicarboxylic acid generally results in a 1:1 product in high yield, 76–80%.[12,21,31,35,38,65,71] However, n–butyroaldehyde and diethyl itaconate condense to give an ill-defined adduct.[41] The reaction of acetaldhyde with vinyl esters such as vinyl formate and acetate produces only gummy and resinous materials.[24] Condensation of butyroaldehyde with trimethylvinylsilane produces 7, 7–dimethyl–7–silaoctane–4–one (II), b.p. 53°/4 mm, n_D 1.4294 (20°), in an unspecified yield.[55]

$$(CH_3)_3Si(CH_2)_2COC_3H_7$$

II

However, butyroaldehyde condenses with triethylvinylsilane to give a product in 45% yield.[44] Benzaldehyde also adds to this silane at 156–177° in the presence of benzoyl peroxide.[44]

An interesting study of addition of aldehyde to β, β–dimethylacrylic acid and its derivatives was conducted in an effort to determine the relative stabilizing influence of substituents on free alkyl radicals.[13] The reactions of butyroaldehyde with β, β–dimethyl acrylate (IIIa) forms two isomers, IV and V, in a ratio of 3:1, in good yield.

$(CH_3)_2C{=}CHR$ $(CH_3)_2CCH_2CO_2C_2H_5$ $(CH_3)_2CHCHCO_2C_2H_5$

                        $\overset{|}{C}OC_3H_7\text{–}n$ $\overset{|}{C}OC_3H_7\text{–}n$

IIIa R = CO₂C₂H₅   IV   V

IIIb R = CO₂H

IIIc R = CN

The reaction of butyroaldehyde with the acid IIIb also results in two products, VI and VII.

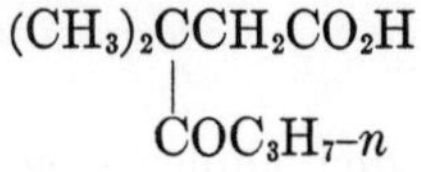

$(CH_3)_2CCH_2CO_2H$
|
COC_3H_7-n

VI

$(CH_3)_2CHCH_2COC_3H_7-n$

VII

The latter is formed from the corresponding 1:1 adduct through loss of carbon dioxide. However, the reaction of butyroaldehyde with the corresponding nitrile, IIIc, produces only one adduct, VIII.

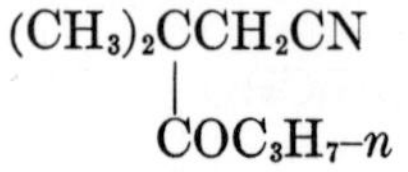

$(CH_3)_2CCH_2CN$
|
COC_3H_7-n

VIII

Heptanal reacts with IIIb to give IX and X as the final products.

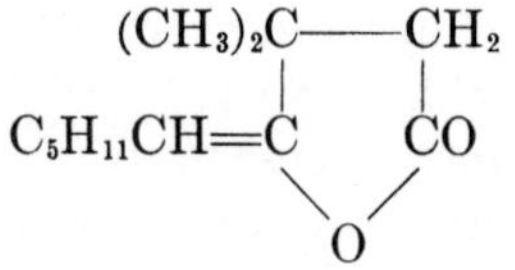

$(CH_3)_2C$——CH_2
| |
$C_5H_{11}CH{=}C$ CO
\   /
O

IX

$(CH_3)_2CHCH_2COC_6H_{13}$

X

These products are probably formed from the corresponding adducts, XI and XII, respectively.

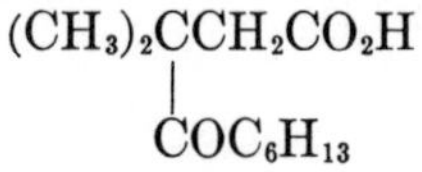

$(CH_3)_2CCH_2CO_2H$
|
COC_6H_{13}

XI

$(CH_3)_2CHCHCO_2H$
|
COC_6H_{13}

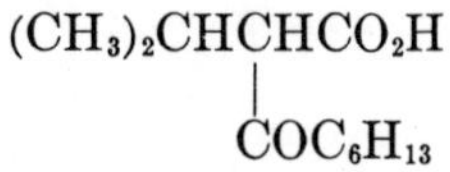

XII

An interesting reaction occurs between an aldehyde, oxygen, and an olefin.[8] The reaction is promoted by ultraviolet light in conjunction with a photosensitizer such as eosine, chlorophyll, hemin, or hematoporphyrine or with an oxidation promoter such as cobalt acetate, ferric salt, vanadium, or platinum oxide. If equimolar quantities of aldehyde and unsaturated compound are used, the reaction proceeds to the glycol monoester stage.

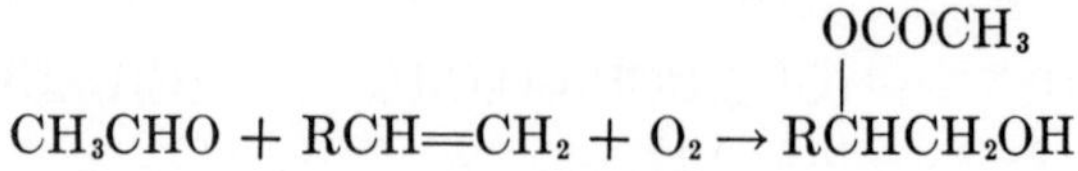

$$CH_3CHO + RCH{=}CH_2 + O_2 \rightarrow R\overset{\displaystyle OCOCH_3}{\overset{|}{C}}HCH_2OH$$

With large proportions of aldehyde, the product is a diester.

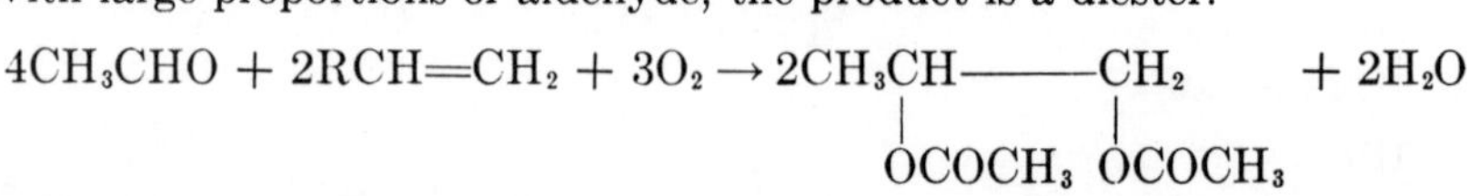

$$4CH_3CHO + 2RCH{=}CH_2 + 3O_2 \rightarrow 2CH_3CH\underset{OCOCH_3}{\underset{|}{}}\!\!-\!\!-\!\!-CH_2\underset{OCOCH_3}{\underset{|}{}} + 2H_2O$$

The best reaction temperature is $-20°$ to $10°$. The pressure is not critical. Under the conditions described, acetaldehyde reacts with diisobutene to give

Table 23. Addition of Aldehydes to Unsaturated Compounds

C_n	Unsaturated compound	Aldehyde	Product	% Yield	°C b.p./mm (m.p.)	n_D (°C)	Ref.
C_2	C_2H_2	CH_3CHO	$CH_3COCH_2CH_3COCH_3$	20	77/13		51
C_4	Perfluorobutene-1	CH_3CHO	$C_2F_5CHFCF_2COCH_3$	76	91/140	1.2988 (25)	23
	$CH_2{=}CHCH_2CN$	CH_3CHO	$CH_3CO(CH_2)_3CN$		85/5	1.4805 (22)	36
C_5	Allyl acetate	CH_3CHO	3-Acetylpropyl acetate	51	67/3	1.4305 (10)	19, 36, 64
C_6	Mesityl oxide	CH_3CHO	3,3-Dimethyl-2,5-hexanedione	31	93/20	1.4363 (25)	39
	1,5-Hexadiene	CH_3CHO	Hexenylmethyl ketone	22	67/14	1.4313 (20)	18
	Dimethylacetylene dicarboxylate	CH_3CHO	Dimethyl 2,3-diacetyl succinate	31	(148)		71
C_7	Acroleindiethyl acetal	CH_3CHO	$CH_3COCH_2CH_2CH(OC_2H_5)_2$	50	87/11	1.4232 (17)	26
C_8	Octene-1	CH_3CHO	2-Decanone	64	117/37	1.4267 (20)	16, 18, 67
	Diethyl maleate	CH_3CHO	Diethyl α-acetyl succinate		90/0.5	1.4360 (25)	38
	Diethyl acetylene dicarboxylate	CH_3CHO	Diethyl 2,3-diacetyl succinate	26	(90)		71
C_{11}	Undecylenic acid	CH_3CHO	12-Ketotridecanoic acid	14	(71)		21, 65
C_{12}	Methylundecylenate	CH_3CHO	12-Ketotridecanoate	30	122-133/0.1		21, 65
	Dodecene-1	CH_3CHO	Methyldodecyl ketone	23	104-118/1.7		18, 67
C_2	CClF=CClF	CH_3CHO	$CHFClCFClCOCH_3$	20	95/300	1.4062 (20)	28
	$CF_2{=}CCl_2$	CH_3CHO	$CHCl_2CF_2COCH_3$	38	96/300	1.4028 (20)	28
	CClF=CClF	CH_3CH_2CHO	$CHFClCFClCOC_2H_5$	15	100/200	1.4122 (20)	28
	$CF_2{=}CCl_2$	CH_3CH_2CHO	$CHCl_2CF_2COC_2H_5$	42	101/200	1.4088 (20)	28
C_6	Hexene-1	CH_3CH_2CHO	Ethylhexyl ketone		189/769	1.4213 (20)	47
	Dimethyl maleate	CH_3CH_2CHO	Dimethyl propionyl succinate	71	130/15		31
C_8	Octene-1	CH_3CH_2CHO	Octylethyl ketone	64	227/760	1.4296 (20)	47

Table 23. (cont.)   Addition of Aldehydes to Unsaturated Compounds

C_n	Unsaturated compound	Aldehyde	Product	% Yield	°C b.p./mm (m.p.)	n_D (°C)	Ref.
	Diethyl maleate	$CH_3OCH_2CH_2CHO$	$CH_3OCH_2CH_2C$—$CHCO_2C_2H_5$ / O $CH_2CO_2C_2H_5$	17	115/0.5	1.4410 (25)	38
C_2	$ClCF{=}CClF$	$CH_3CH_2CH_2CHO$	$CHFClCFClCOC_3H_7\text{-}n$	17	101/100	1.4159 (20)	28
	$CF_2{=}CCl_2$	$CH_3CH_2CH_2CHO$	$CHCl_2CF_2COC_3H_7\text{-}n$	43	100/100	1.4136 (20)	28
C_3	Perfluoropropene	$CH_3CH_2CH_2CHO$	$CF_3CHFCF_2COC_3H_7$	70	111/738	1.3268 (25)	23
C_4	Methyl acrylate	$CH_3CH_2CH_2CHO$	Methyl 4-ketoheptanoate	11	97/9	1.4410 (20)	21, 65
	$CH_3CH{=}CHCO_2H$	$CH_3CH_2CH_2CHO$	3-Methyl-4-oxoheptanoic acid	83	91/0.5		12
	$CH_2{=}CHCH_2CN$	$CH_3CH_2CH_2CHO$	$C_3H_7CO(CH_2)_3CN$		96/6		36
	$CH_2{=}CHCH_2CO_2H$	$CH_3CH_2CH_2CHO$	$C_3H_7CO(CH_2)_3CO_2H$		(32)		36
C_5	Allyl acetate	$CH_3CH_2CH_2CHO$	3-Butyrylpropyl acetate	41	112/11	1.4311 (20)	19, 36, 64
	$CH_2{=}C(CH_3)CO_2C_2H_5$	$CH_3CH_2CH_2CHO$	$C_3H_7COCH(CH_3)CO_2CH_3$	11	95/5	1.4340 (15)	35
	$(CH_3)_3SiCH{=}CH_2$	$CH_3CH_2CH_2CHO$	$(CH_3)_3SiCH_2CH_2COC_3H_7$		53/4	1.4294 (20)	55
	3-Penten-2-one	$CH_3CH_2CH_2CHO$	4-Methyl-2, 5-octanedione	64	107/20	1.4303 (25)	39
C_6	Methylisopropenyl ketone	$CH_3CH_2CH_2CHO$	3-Methyl-2, 5-octanedione		93/3.5	1.4380 (20)	22
	Mesityl oxide	$CH_3CH_2CH_2CHO$	4, 4-Dimethyl-2, 5-octanedione + 3-Isopropyl-2, 4-heptanedione	88 / 9	112/20 / 105/20	1.4371 (25) / 1.4350 (25)	39
	Diallyl ether	$CH_3CH_2CH_2CHO$	3-Butyrylpropylallyl ether	17	97/6	1.4539 (20)	19, 64
	Ethyl crotonate	$CH_3CH_2CH_2CHO$	Ethyl 3-methyl-4-oxoheptanoate	77	82/2	1.4271 (22)	12, 35
	Ethyl hydrogen maleate	$CH_3CH_2CH_2CHO$	Ethyl 4-oxoheptanoate	49	52/1	1.4278 (23)	12
C_9	Phorone	$CH_3CH_2CH_2CHO$	2, 6, 6-Trimethyl-2-decene-4, 7-dione + 5, 5, 9, 9-tetramethyl-4, 7, 10-tridecanetrione	80 / 10	103/2 / 131/1	1.4651 (25) / 1.4620 (25)	39

Table 23. (cont.) Addition of Aldehydes to Unsaturated Compounds

C_n	Unsaturated compound	Aldehyde	Product	% Yield	°C b.p./mm (m.p.)	n_D (°C)	Ref.
C_{10}	3-Decene-2-one	$CH_3CH_2CH_2CHO$	4-Hexyl-2, 5-octanedione	42	98/0.6	1.4421 (25)	39
	Crotonophenone	$CH_3CH_2CH_2CHO$	3-Methyl-1-phenyl-1, 4-heptanedione	24	125/1	1.5168 (25)	39
C_{16}	Dihexyl maleate	$CH_3CH_2CH_2CHO$	Dihexyl α-butyryl succinate		160/0.4	1.4440 (25)	38
	Dicyclohexyl maleate	$CH_3CH_2CH_2CHO$	Dicyclohexyl α-butyryl succinate		180/1	1.4728 (25)	38
	Dibenzyl maleate	$CH_3CH_2CH_2CHO$	Dibenzyl α-butyryl succinate		212/1	1.5268 (25)	38
C_{20}	Di-2-ethylhexyl maleate	$CH_3CH_2CH_2CHO$	Di-2-ethylhexyl-α-butyryl succinate		183/0.5	1.4492 (25)	38
C_{32}	Ditetradecyl maleate	$CH_3CH_2CH_2CHO$	Ditetradecyl α-butyryl succinate	15	263/0.5	1.4563 (25)	38
C_2	$CF_2=CCl_2$	$(CH_3)_2CHCHO$	$CHCl_2CF_2COC_3H_7$-i		92/100	1.4087 (20)	28
C_8	Diethyl maleate	$(CH_3)_2CHCHO$	Diethyl 2-isobutyryl succinate	27	99/2		71
	Diethylacetylene dicarboxylate	$(CH_3)_2CHCHO$	Diethyl 2, 3-diisobutyryl succinate	9	112/1		71
C_5	Octene-1	$(CH_3)_3CCHO$	2, 2-Dimethyldecane	25	64/5	1.4199 (20)	20
	$(CH_3)_2C=CHCN$	Heptanal	3, 3-Dimethyl-4-oxoheptano-nitrile	52	72/2	1.4398 (21)	13
C_6	Mesityl oxide	Heptanal (enanth aldehyde)	4, 4-Dimethyl-2, 5-undecane-dione	61	92/1	1.4447 (20)	39
C_7	Ethyl β-acetyl acrylate	Heptanal	Ethyl 2, 5-dioxoundecane-4-carboxylate	42	120/1	1.4481 (24)	13
C_8	Octene-1	Heptanal	7-Pentadecanone	77	67/0.1 (32)		16, 18, 67
	Diethyl maleate	Heptanal	Diethyl α-heptyryl succinate		132/0.5	1.4392 (25)	38
C_{20}	Di-2-ethylhexyl maleate	Heptanal	Di-2-ethylhexyl α-heptyryl succinate		200/0.7	1.4511 (25)	38

Table 23. (cont.) Addition of Aldehydes to Unsaturated Compounds

C_n	Unsaturated compound	Aldehyde	Product	% Yield	°C b.p./mm (m.p.)	n_D (°C)	Ref.
C_8	$(C_2H_5)_3SiCH=CH_2$	C_6H_5CHO	$(C_2H_5)_3SiCH_2CH_2COC_6H_5$	35	169/5	1.5155 (20)	44
	Diethyl maleate	C_6H_5CHO	Diethyl 2-benzoyl succinate	14	159/1	1.5012 (27)	38, 71
	Diethyl maleate	$CH_3CH_2CH_2CH(C_2H_5)CHO$	$CH_3CH_2CH_2CH_2CH(C_2H_5)CH$—$C$—$CHCO_2C_2H_5$, $\|$O, $CH_2CO_2C_2H_5$	38	117/0.5	1.4400 (25)	38
	Dimethyl acetylene dicarboxylate	$CH_3CH_2CH_2CHO$	Dimethyl 2, 3-dibutyryl succinate	23	172/2 (111)		71
C_7	3-Butenylmethyl ketone	$CH_3CH_2CH_2CHO$	2, 7-Decanedione	70	72/0.15		22
	Ethyl β-acetyl acrylate	$CH_3CH_2CH_2CHO$	Ethyl 2, 5-dioxooctane-4-carboxylate	54	90/0.5	1.4445 (23)	12
	Heptene-1	$CH_3CH_2CH_2CHO$	Heptylpropyl ketone	85			47
	Acroleindiethyl acetal	$CH_3CH_2CH_2CHO$	$CH_3(CH_2)_2CO(CH_2)_2CH(OC_2H_5)_2$	28	102/6	1.4325 (20)	19, 64
	Diallyl formal	$CH_3CH_2CH_2CHO$	3-Butyrylpropyl allyloxy-methyl ether	7	80/1	1.4447 (20)	19, 64
C_8	Octene-1	$CH_3CH_2CH_2CHO$	4-Dodecanone	55	65/0.25	1.4313 (20)	16, 18, 47, 67
	Vinylcyclohexene	$CH_3CH_2CH_2CHO$	Propylcyclohexenylethyl ketone	34	102/6	1.4759 (20)	18
	$(C_2H_5)_3SiCH=CH_2$	$CH_3CH_2CH_2CHO$	$(C_2H_5)_3SiCH_2CH_2COC_3H_7$	60	104/3	1.4560 (20)	44
	2-Acetoxymethylallyl acetate	$CH_3CH_2CH_2CHO$	2-Acetoxymethyl-3-butyryl-propyl acetate	37	157/7		19, 64
	Diethyl maleate	$CH_3CH_2CH_2CHO$	Diethyl α-butyryl succinate	84	113/1 121/1-2 103/1	1.4412 (15) 1.4344 (25) 1.4392 (20)	35, 38 71 21, 65

2, 4, 4–trimethylpentane–2, 4 diacetate, which on saponification forms the corresponding 2, 4, 4–trimethylpentanediol, m.p. 63°. Acetaldehyde also reacts with 2–methylpentene–2 to give 2–methylpentane diacetate–2, 3, which on saponification forms 2–methylpentanediol–2, 3, m.p. 184°, in 76% yield.

ADDITION OF KETONES

The radical reaction of ketones involving their α–hydrogen atoms with unsaturated compounds was first reported by Kharasch, Kuderna, and Nudenberg.[15] In their work cyclohexanone and octene–1 were irradiated with ultraviolet light to give 5–hexenal, b.p. 118°, n_D 1.4109 (20°), cis– and trans–2–octene, high-boiling products, and the 1:1 adduct in 18% yield.

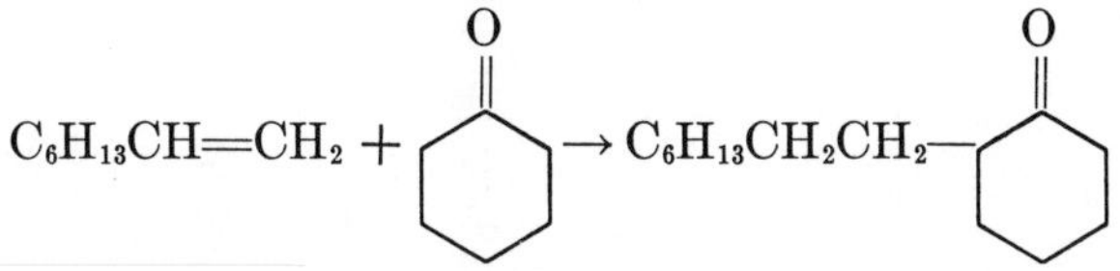

$$C_6H_{13}CH{=}CH_2 + \underset{\text{(cyclohexanone)}}{\overset{O}{\bigcirc}} \rightarrow C_6H_{13}CH_2CH_2{-}\overset{O}{\bigcirc}$$

The reaction is carried out by using an 8:1 ratio of olefin to ketone. The temperature is maintained at 40° for 48–73 hr. Cyclopentanone does not react with the olefin under these conditions; allylacetaldehyde is obtained as the reaction product.

This reaction was extended by Nikishin, Somov, and Petrov[32,33] to include other olefinic substrates. These workers used di–t–butyl peroxide as the initiator instead of ultraviolet light. Thus, cyclopentanone or cyclohexanone reacts with undecylenic acid at 130° and 152°, respectively. Approximately a 10:1 ratio of ketone to acid is used, and the reaction time is about 8.5 hr. A good yield of the 1:1 products is obtained.[32]

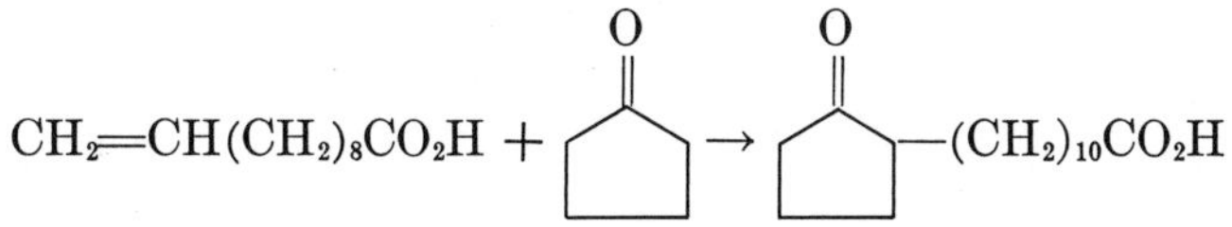

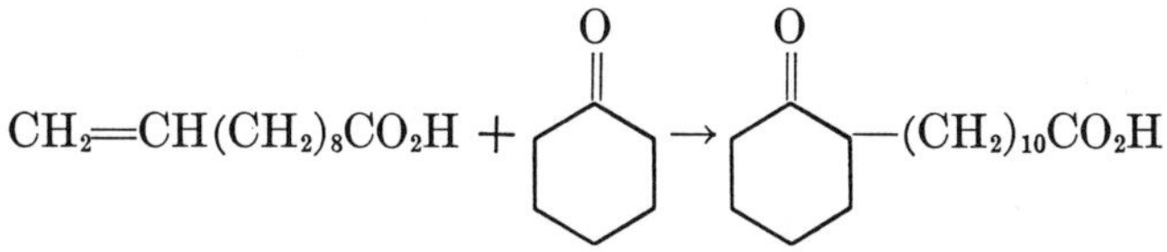

$$CH_2{=}CH(CH_2)_8CO_2H + \overset{O}{\bigcirc} \rightarrow \overset{O}{\bigcirc}{-}(CH_2)_{10}CO_2H$$

$$CH_2{=}CH(CH_2)_8CO_2H + \overset{O}{\bigcirc} \rightarrow \overset{O}{\bigcirc}{-}(CH_2)_{10}CO_2H$$

Cyclopentanone condenses with octene–1, decene–1, 4–methyldecene–1, allyloctyl ether, or allyldecyl ether.[33] Cyclohexanone also reacts smoothly with octene–1, decene–1, 4–methyldecene–1, allyloctyl ether, or monoallyl

Table 24. Addition of Ketones to Unsaturated Compounds

C_n	Unsaturated compound	Ketone	Product	% Yield	°C b.p./mm (m.p.)	n_D (°C)	Ref.
C_8	Octene-1	Cyclopentanone	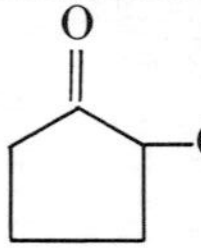 $\overset{O}{\diagup}$—C_8H_{17}	57	96/1.5	1.4530 (20)	33
C_{10}	Decene-1	Cyclopentanone	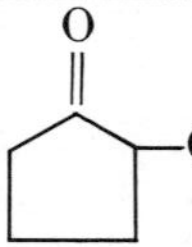 $\overset{O}{\diagup}$—C_8H_{17}	71	107/1	1.4558 (20)	33
C_{11}	4-Methyldecene-1	Cyclopentanone	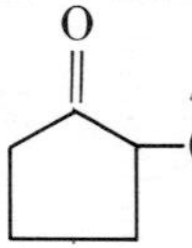 $(CH_2)_3CH(CH_3)C_6H_{13}$	62	129/1	1.4580 (20)	33
	Undecylenic acid	Cyclopentanone	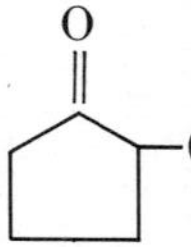 $(CH_2)_{10}CO_2H$	70	213–20/2 (52)		32
	Allyloctyl ether	Cyclopentanone	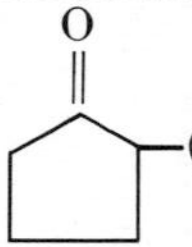 $(CH_2)_3OC_8H_{17}$	53	136/1	1.4560 (20)	33

Table 24. (cont.)   Addition of Ketones to Unsaturated Compounds

C_n	Unsaturated compound	Ketone	Product	% Yield	°C b.p./mm (m.p.)	n_D (°C)	Ref.
C_{13}	Allyldecyl ether	Cyclopentanone	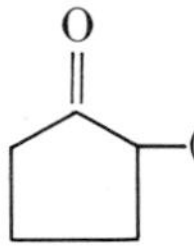 O=⟨cyclopentane⟩—$(CH_2)_3OC_{10}H_{21}$	45	154/1	1.4574 (20)	33
C_5	Monoallyl ether of ethylene glycol	Cyclohexanone	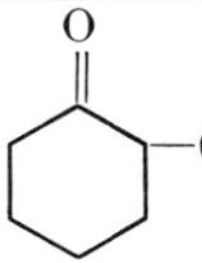 O=⟨cyclohexane⟩—$(CH_2)_3OCH_2CH_2OH$	30	131/1	1.4789 (20)	33
C_8	Octene–1	Cyclohexanone	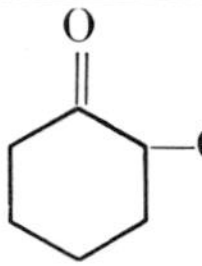 O=⟨cyclohexane⟩—C_8H_{17}	59	100/1.5	1.4605 (20)	15, 33
C_{10}	Decene–1	Cyclohexanone	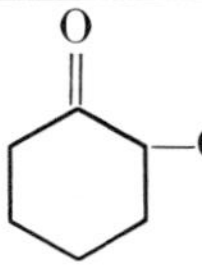 O=⟨cyclohexane⟩—$C_{10}H_{21}$	62	119/1	1.4606 (20)	33
C_{11}	4–Methyldecene–1	Cyclohexanone	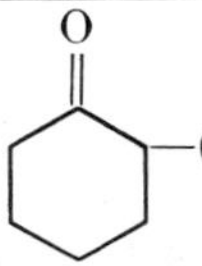 O=⟨cyclohexane⟩—$(CH_2)_3CH(CH_3)C_6H_{13}$	61	122/1	1.4625 (20)	33

Table 24. (cont.) Addition of Ketones to Unsaturated Compounds

C_n	Unsaturated compound	Ketone	Product	% Yield	°C b.p./mm (m.p.)	n_D (°C)	Ref.
	Undecylenic acid	Cyclohexanone	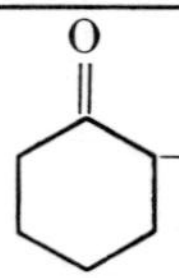 (cyclohexanone ring)—$(CH_2)_{10}CO_2H$	50	(64)		32
	Allyloctyl ether	Cyclohexanone	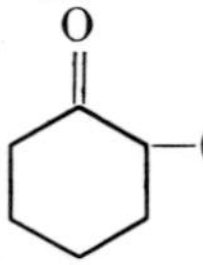 (cyclohexanone ring)—$(CH_2)_3OC_8H_{17}$	57	176/2.5	1.4603 (20)	33

ether of ethylene glycol.[33] The ratio of ketone to olefin is usually 10:1. The temperature varies between 127° and 153°, and the reaction time is 4–6 hr. The initiator is di–t–butyl peroxide, and the yield is 50–70%.

A stereospecific photochemical addition of acetone to norbornylene occurs.[46] When a boiling 8% solution of norbornylene in acetone is irradiated for 48 hr, a 45% yield of 2–exo–acetonylnorbornane, b.p. 95°/12 mm, is obtained. No reaction occurs in the dark.

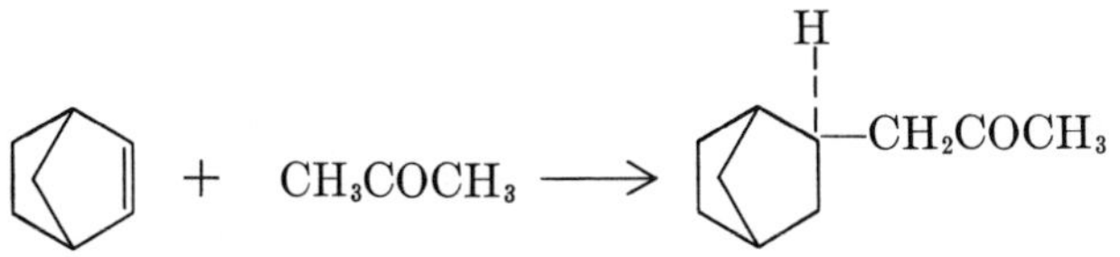

ADDITION OF ALIPHATIC ACIDS AND ESTERS

Various aliphatic acids and esters containing a mobile α-hydrogen atom react with olefins under free radical conditions.

$$RCH{=}CH_2 + CH_2R'COOH \rightarrow RCH_2CH_2CH(R')CO_2H$$

To date, the best results have been obtained with olefins containing six or more carbon atoms. Carboxylic acids also react with lower olefins, however.

Thus, acetic acid reacts with ethylene in the presence of di–t–butyl peroxide at 800–1000 psi in 1–4 hr at 145–170° to produce a mixture of four acids (I–IV), in 75% yield, plus high-boiling products.[2]

$$CH_3CH_2CH_2CH_2CO_2H \qquad\qquad C_6H_{13}CO_2H$$
I   II

$$C_8H_{17}CO_2H \qquad\qquad C_{10}H_{21}CO_2H$$
III   IV

When butyric acid reacts with ethylene under the same conditions, a mixture of the following acids is obtained: V, b.p. 174°, VI and VII, b.p. 107–114°/12 mm, VIII, b.p. 186°, and IX, b.p. 221°.[2]

$$C_2H_5CH(CH_3)CO_2H \qquad\qquad (C_2H_5)_2C(CH_3)CO_2H$$
V   VI

$$C_4H_9CH(CH_3)CO_2H \qquad\qquad C_2H_5C(CH_3)_2CO_2H$$
VII   VIII

$$C_4H_9C(CH_3)_2CO_2H$$
IX

Isobutyric acid and ethylene react in the presence of oxygen at about 250° and 850–980 atm of pressure to form 2, 2–dimethylbutanoic acid (X), b.p. 184°, in 6–13% yield, plus higher adducts.[5]

$$CH_3CH_2C(CH_3)_2COOH$$

X

Methyl formate reacts with ethylene in the presence of di–t–butyl peroxide to form a complex mixture of telomeric esters.[60] Methyl formate and hexene–1 react to form methyl enanthate plus a 2:1 adduct.[60] A complex reaction occurs between ethyl orthoformate and diethyl maleate in the presence of benzoyl peroxide.[29,30] The main products are acetyl succinic acid ester, phenyl succinic acid ester, and tetralintetracarboxylic acid ester, all obtained in poor yield.

The condensation of acids with olefins containing six or more carbon atoms is usually carried out at 135–180° in the presence of di–t–butyl peroxide with a 5- to 8-fold excess of the acid or the ester over the olefin.[45] With sufficiently high-boiling starting materials, the reaction is carried out at atmospheric pressure; whereas with more volatile substances, such as gaseous olefins, low-boiling acids, and methyl esters of propionic, butyric, and isobutyric acid, the reaction is carried out in an autoclave under pressure. After a reaction time of 5–24 hr the products are obtained in 36–69% yield.

Aliphatic acids containing three to six carbon atoms react with hexene or octene under ultraviolet light of 2000–3000 A as the initiator.[27] In addition to a 2:1 adduct, a 1:1 adduct is obtained in good yield. Isolation and characterization of the products appear to be incomplete. The low yield, 12%, in the preparation of n–$C_6H_{13}C(CH_3)_2COOH$ is attributed to the low reaction temperature, 120–130°.[45]

Table 25. Addition of Aliphatic Acids and Esters to Unsaturated Compounds

C_n	Olefin	Acid or ester	Product	% Yield	°C b.p./mm (m.p.)	n_D (°C)	Ref.
C_{13}	Tridecene-1	$CH_3CH_2CO_2H$	$n\text{-}C_{13}H_{27}CH(CH_3)CO_2H$	38	173/3 (37)		45
C_6	Hexene-1	$CH_3CH_2CO_2CH_3$	$n\text{-}C_6H_{13}CH(CH_3)CO_2CH_3$	31	61/5	1.4210 (20)	45
C_{10}	Decene-1	$CH_3CH_2CO_2CH_3$	$n\text{-}C_{10}H_{21}CH(CH_3)CO_2CH_3$	31	88/1	1.4332 (20)	45
C_6	Hexene-1	$n\text{-}C_3H_7CO_2H$	$n\text{-}C_6H_{13}CH(C_2H_5)CO_2H$	69	107/4	1.4344 (20)	45
	Hexene-1	$n\text{-}C_3H_7CO_2CH_3$	$n\text{-}C_6H_{13}CH(C_2H_5)CO_2CH_3$	34	70/6	1.4248 (20)	45
	Hexene-1	$(CH_3)_2CHCO_2H$	$n\text{-}C_6H_{13}C(CH_3)_2CO_2H$	12	102/3.5	1.4350 (20)	45
C_{10}	Decene-1	$(CH_3)_2CHCO_2H$	$n\text{-}C_{10}H_{21}C(CH_3)_2CO_2H$	36	144/3 (26)		45
	Decene-1	$(CH_3)_2CHCO_2CH_3$	$n\text{-}C_{10}H_{21}C(CH_3)_2CO_2CH_3$	26	97/3	1.4378 (20)	45
C_8	Octene-1	$n\text{-}C_6H_{13}CO_2H$	$n\text{-}C_8H_{17}CH(C_5H_{11})CO_2H$	65	170/4	1.4457 (20)	45
	Octene-1	$n\text{-}C_6H_{13}CO_2CH_3$	$n\text{-}C_8H_{17}CH(C_5H_{11})CO_2CH_3$	57	95/1	1.4370 (20)	45
	Octene-1	$n\text{-}C_9H_{19}CO_2CH_3$	$n\text{-}(C_8H_{17})_2CHCO_2CH_3$	54	150/4	1.4422 (20)	45

REACTIONS OF ETHERS AND ACETALS

Most of the condensations of olefins with ethers and with acetals are reported in the patent literature. The products described may have useful commercial applications, but the reactions are of limited value for the preparation of well-defined products. For example, various ethers and acetals react with tetrafluoroethylene in the presence of benzoyl peroxide at 110° and 350–1000 psi to give a mixture of telomers.[9] A reaction occurs between tetrafluoroethylene and dioxane, 1, 3–dioxolane, sym–dimethoxyethane, acetal, metylal, ethylene oxide, diethyl ether, dimethyl ether of tetraethylene glycol, or 2–methyl–2–chloromethyl–1, 3–dioxolane.[9]

The reaction of 1, 1–diethoxyethane and diethyl maleate at 102° with benzoyl peroxide results in telomers which are not well defined.[43] The reaction of a boiling mixture of diethylformal and dimethyl maleate in the presence of benzoyl peroxide produces a methyl ester of α–acetylsuccinic acid, in low yield, by a complicated reaction path.[30] Likewise, the reaction of di–n–propyl formal and diethyl maleate in the presence of benzoyl peroxide is complicated.[29] After hydrolysis, β–formylpropionic, acetylsuccinic, and levulinic acids are formed. Methylal, $CH_2(OCH_3)_2$, reacts with maleic acid anhydride in the presence of peroxide at 120° to give telomers and dimethoxymethylsuccinic anhydride (I), b.p. 116°/12 mm, n_D 1.4460 (25°), in 34% yield.[40]

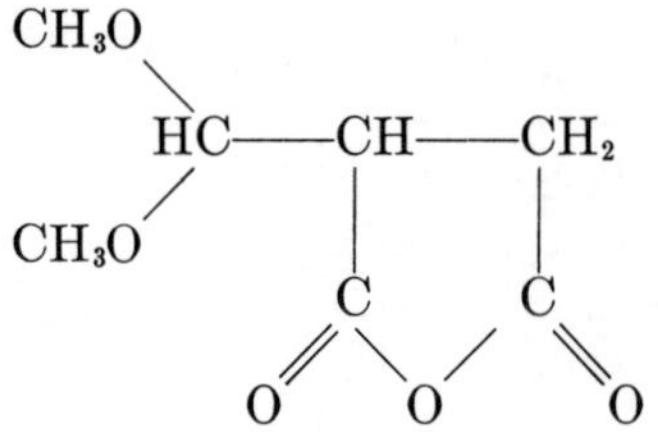

$$CH_3O$$
$$CH_3O$$
$$HC---CH---CH_2$$
$$C \qquad C$$
$$O \quad O \quad O$$

I

The reaction of 1, 3–dioxolane and diethyl maleate at 80–100° in the presence of benzoyl peroxide after 17 hr produces diethyl 2–(1, 3–dioxolanyl)-succinate, b.p. 122°/1 mm, n_D 1.4457 (25°), in 25% yield.[42]

REACTION OF SATURATED HYDROCARBONS

Generally, hydrocarbon radicals react readily and rapidly with unsaturated compounds. These reactions usually result in a complex mixture which is difficult to separate into individual components.[34] However, it is possible to prepare monomeric products from hydrocarbons and olefins.

$$\underset{CH_3}{RCH{=}CH_2} + \underset{CH_3}{CH_2R'} \rightarrow \underset{CH_3}{RCH_2CH_2CH_2R'}$$

Thus, toluene, ethylbenzene, xylene, cumene, or 1–methylnaphthalene reacts at 150–160° in the presence of di–t–butyl peroxide with hexene–1, heptene–1, octene–1, nonene–1, or undecene–1 to give a 1:1 adduct in 10–15% yield.[34]

Saturated hydrocarbons such as propane, isobutane, n–pentane, cyclopentane, 2, 2– and 2, 3–dimethylbutane, cyclohexane, or methylcyclohexane condense with cis– or $trans$–dichloroethylene, trichloroethylene, or tetrachloroethylene in the presence of a radical chain initiator.[52] Instead of the expected addition reaction, chlorovinylation occurs with the elimination of hydrogen chloride; and the products are unsaturated compounds containing one chlorine atom less than the starting haloolefin.

$$RH + ClCH{=}CHCl \rightarrow RCH{=}CHCl + HCl$$

$$RH + CHCl{=}CCl_2 \rightarrow RCH{=}CCl_2 + HCl$$

$$RH + CCl_2{=}CCl_2 \rightarrow RCCl{=}CCl_2 + HCl$$

Both cis– and $trans$–dichloroethylene show little difference in reactivity. The reactions are carried out at approximately 135° with di–t–butyl peroxide as the initiator. Gaseous reactants are enclosed at $-78°$ in an autoclave under nitrogen gas of 50 atm. The reaction mixture is heated for several hours. The cooled reaction mixture is then washed with a sodium carbonate solution and with water, dried, and fractionated.

Aromatic hydrocarbons containing a side chain undergo reaction with dichloro-, trichloro-, or tetrachloroethylene to give products which are chlorovinylated in the side chain.[53] In the reaction of benzene with trichloroethylene, however, only the dimer of the polyhaloethylene is obtained.[53] Toluene shows little reactivity with dibromoethylene.[53]

CYCLOADDITION OF CARBONYL COMPOUNDS

An interesting reaction, though until recently of limited preparative utility, is the photochemical reaction of Paterno and Chieffi[37]: aldehydes or ketones react with acetylenes or olefins under the influence of ultraviolet rays to give trimethylene oxide derivatives. In recent years the reaction has been studied extensively by Büchi and his associates.[3,4] For example, benzaldehyde and 2–methylbutene–2 react under ultraviolet light to give

Table 26.   Reaction of Saturated Hydrocarbons with Unsaturated Compounds

C_n	Unsaturated compound	Hydrocarbon	Product	% Yield	°C b.p./mm	n_D (°C)	Ref.
C_7	Heptene-1	$C_6H_5CH_3$	$CH_3(CH_2)_7C_6H_5$		135/18	1.4865 (20)	34
C_{11}	Undecene-1	$C_6H_5CH_3$	$CH_3(CH_2)_{11}C_6H_5$		133/2	1.4795 (20)	34
C_6	Hexene-1	$C_6H_5CH_2CH_3$	$CH_3(CH_2)_5CH(CH_3)C_6H_5$		110/5	1.4860 (20)	34
C_7	Heptene-1	$C_6H_5CH_2CH_3$	$CH_3(CH_2)_6CH(CH_3)C_6H_5$		121/15	1.4850 (20)	34
C_6	Hexene-1	p-Xylene	$p\text{-}CH_3(CH_2)_6C_6H_4CH_3$	29	130/7	1.4887 (20)	34
C_9	Nonene-1	p-Xylene	$p\text{-}CH_3(CH_2)_9C_6H_5CH_3$		140/7	1.4870 (20)	34
C_8	Octene-1	Cumene	$CH_3(CH_2)_7C(CH_3)_2C_6H_5$		176/6	1.4817 (20)	34
C_7	Heptene-1	$1\text{-}CH_3C_{10}H_7$	$1\text{-}CH_3(CH_2)_7C_{10}H_7$		143/0.5	1.5547 (20)	34
C_3	cis-trans-1, 2-Dichloro-ethylene	C_3H_8	$C_3H_7CH=CHCl$	10	87/726	1.4229 (20)	52
C_4	cis-1, 2-Dichloroethylene	$i\text{-}C_4H_{10}$	$(CH_3)_3CCH=CHCl$	35	105/750	1.4280 (20)	52
	trans-1, 2-Dichloroethylene	$i\text{-}C_4H_{10}$	$(CH_3)_3CCH=CHCl$	38	105/750	1.4280 (20)	52
C_5	cis-trans-1, 2-Dichloro-ethylene	$n\text{-}C_5H_{12}$	$C_5H_{11}CH=CHCl$	7	61/61	1.4333 (20)	52
	trans-1, 2-Dichloroethylene	Cyclo-C_5H_{10}	Cyclo-$C_5H_9CH=CHCl$ + Cyclo-$C_5H_9CHClCHCl$-$CH=CHCl$	17 / 10	63/29 / 54/2	1.4740 (20) / 1.4912 (20)	52 / 52
C_6	cis-trans-1, 2-Dichloro-ethylene	Cyclo-C_6H_{12}	Cyclo-$C_6H_{11}CH=CHCl$	19	70/21	1.4778 (20)	52
C_7	trans-1, 2-Dichloroethylene	$C_6H_5CH_3$	$C_6H_5CH_2CH=CHCl$	18	53/2	1.5385 (20)	53
C_8	Dichloroethylene	$C_6H_5CH_2CH_3$	$C_6H_5CH(CH_3)CH=CHCl$	18	73/3	1.5329 (20)	53
C_9	Dichloroethylene	Indan	$C_9H_9CH=CHCl$	18	87/1.7	1.5532 (20)	53
C_3	Trichloroethylene	C_3H_8	$(CH_3)_2CHCH=CCl_2$	31	58/96	1.4452 (20)	52
C_4	Trichloroethylene	$i\text{-}C_4H_{10}$	$(CH_3)_3CCH=CCl_2$	46	134/726	1.4550 (20)	52

Table 26. (cont.) Reaction of Saturated Hydrocarbons with Unsaturated Compounds

C_n	Unsaturated compound	Hydrocarbon	Product	% Yield	°C b.p./mm	n_D (°C)	Ref.
C_6	Trichloroethylene	2,2-Dimethyl-butane	$C_6H_{13}CH=CCl_2$	6	30/2	1.4650 (20)	52
	Trichloroethylene	2,3-Dimethyl-butane	$C_6H_{13}CH=CCl_2$	13	28/1	1.4688 (20)	52
	Trichloroethylene	Cyclo-C_6H_{12}	Cyclo-$C_6H_{11}CH=CCl_2$	23	38/1.5	1.4970 (20)	52
C_7	Trichloroethylene	Methylcyclohexane	Cyclo-$C_6H_{10}(CH_3)CH=CCl_2$	32	75/3	1.4928 (20)	52
	Trichloroethylene	$C_6H_5CH_3$	$C_6H_5CH_2CH=CCl_2$	23	87/3.5	1.5491 (20)	53
C_8	Trichloroethylene	$C_6H_5CH_2CH_3$	$C_6H_5CH(CH_3)CH=CCl_2$	30	95/4	1.5392 (20)	53
C_9	Trichloroethylene	Indan	$C_9H_9CH=CCl_2$	13	102/1.5	1.5685 (20)	53
C_3	Tetrachloroethylene	C_3H_8	$(CH_3)_2CHCHCl=CCl_2$	27	150/756	1.4783 (20)	52
C_4	Tetrachloroethylene	i-C_4H_{10}	$(CH_3)_3CCCl=CCl_2$	7	48/4	1.4878 (20)	52
C_7	Tetrachloroethylene	$C_6H_5CH_3$	$C_6H_5CH_2CCl=CCl_2$	45	90/1.8	1.5635 (20)	53

1, 2, 2–trimethyl–3–phenyltrimethylene oxide (I), b.p. 44°/0.2 mm, in 10% yield.[3]

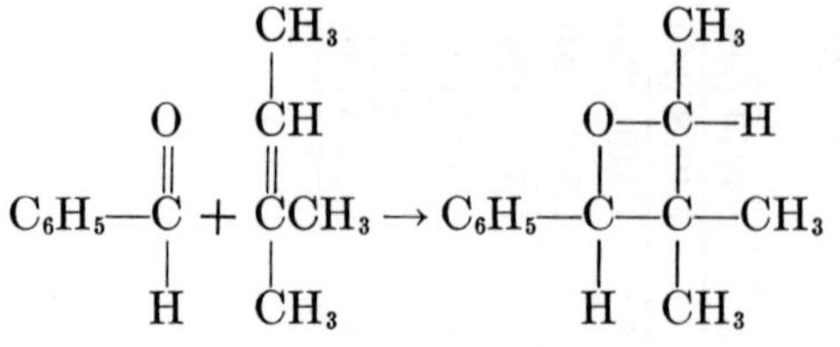

$$
\begin{array}{cc}
& CH_3 \\
O & CH \\
\| & \| \\
C_6H_5-C & + CCH_3 \\
| & | \\
H & CH_3
\end{array}
\rightarrow
\begin{array}{c}
CH_3 \\
| \\
O-C-H \\
| \quad | \\
C_6H_5-C-C-CH_3 \\
| \quad | \\
H \quad CH_3
\end{array}
$$

I

However, benzaldehyde or acetophenone reacts with decyne–5 to give the rearranged products 6–benzylidene–5–decanone (IIa), b.p. 110°/0.1 mm, and 2–phenyl–3–n–butyl–2–octene–4–one (IIb), b.p. 122°/0.35 mm, respectively.

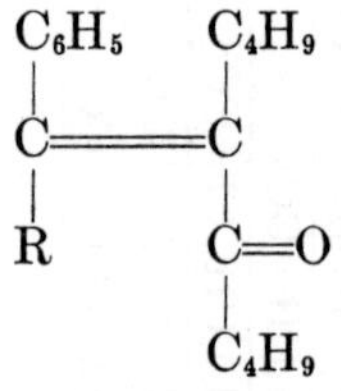

$$
\begin{array}{cc}
C_6H_5 & C_4H_9 \\
| & | \\
C & \!\!=\!\! & C \\
| & | \\
R & C\!\!=\!\!O \\
& | \\
& C_4H_9
\end{array}
$$

IIa R = H
IIb R = CH₃

Recently Harris and Coffman showed that many fluoroaldehydes, fluoroketones, and fluoroacyl fluorides react with fluoroolefins under ultraviolet irradiation to give polyfluorooxetanes.[10]

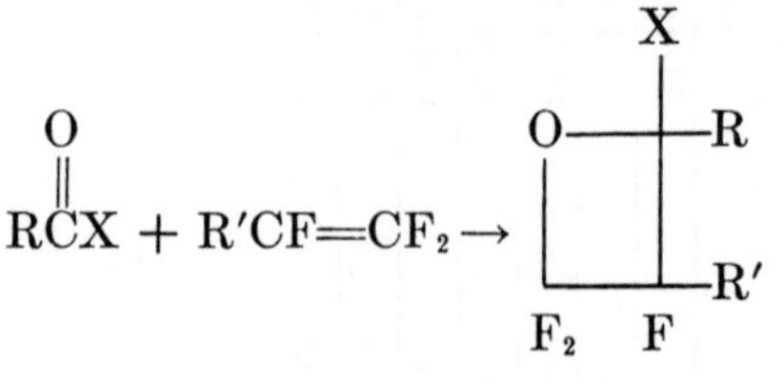

$$
\begin{array}{c}
O \\
\| \\
R\overset{\|}{C}X + R'CF\!\!=\!\!CF_2 \rightarrow
\end{array}
\qquad
\begin{array}{cc}
& X \\
O & \!\!-\!\! R \\
& \\
& R' \\
F_2 & F
\end{array}
$$

X = H, F, R
R' = R, Cl

Depending on the materials, the duration of irradiation varies between 1 and 12 days. All the products are colorless oils which can be purified by fractionation.

The reaction of hexafluoroglutaryl fluoride with hexafluoropropene results in the 1:1 product and the 2:1 product (III), b.p. 154°.[10]

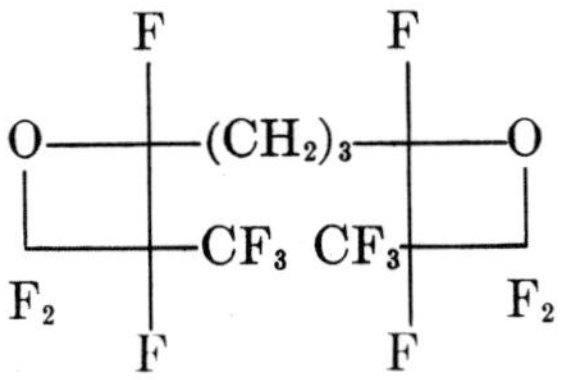

$$
\begin{array}{c}
\quad\;\; F \qquad\qquad F \\
\mathrm{O} \!-\!\!-\!\!-\!(\mathrm{CH_2})_3\!-\!\!-\!\!-\mathrm{O} \\
\quad\;\; \mathrm{CF_3 \;\; CF_3} \\
F_2 \qquad\qquad\qquad F_2 \\
\quad\;\; F \qquad\qquad F
\end{array}
$$

III

sym–Dichlorotetrafluoroacetone and hexafluoropropene react to form the cyclic ether in 12% yield and a number of other products.[10] The more important are compound IV, b.p. 91°, n_D 1.3135 (25°), in 15% yield; compound V, b.p. 150°, n_D 1.3271 (25°), in 15% yield; and *sym*–tetrafluorodichloroethane, in 20% yield.

$$\mathrm{ClCF_2CF_2CF(CF_3)CF_2Cl} \qquad\qquad \mathrm{ClCF_2[CF_2CF(CF_3)]_2CF_2Cl}$$

IV   V

Table 27. Cycloaddition of Polyfluorocarbonyl Compounds to Polyfluoroolefins

C_n	Unsaturated compound	Carbonyl compound	Product	% Yield	°C b.p./mm	n_D (°C)	Ref.
	Aldehydes						
C_2	$CF_2{=}CFCF_3$	CF_3CHO	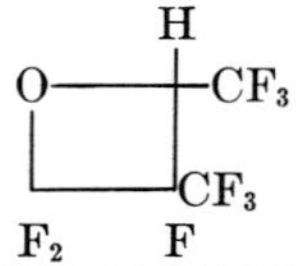 oxetane: H, CF_3; F, CF_3; F_2	32	*trans* 38; *cis* 41		10
	$CF_2{=}CFCl$	CF_3CHO	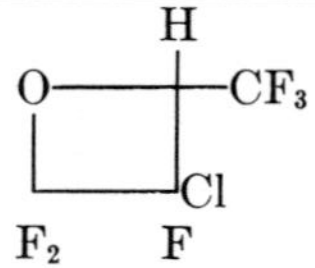 oxetane: H, CF_3; F, Cl; F_2	14	53		10
	$CF_2{=}CF(CF_2)_2H$	CF_3CHO	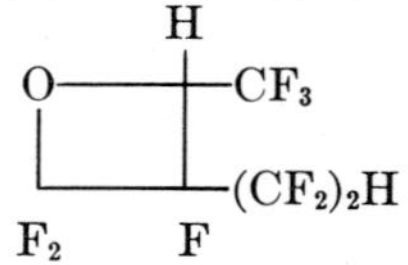 oxetane: H, CF_3; F, $(CF_2)_2H$; F_2	66	*trans* 72; *cis* 89		10
C_4	$CF_2{=}CFCF_3$	C_3F_7CHO	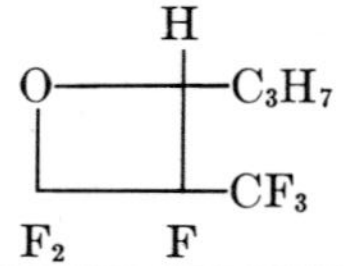 oxetane: H, C_3H_7; F, CF_3; F_2	37	*trans* 83; *cis* 86		10
C_5	$CF_2{=}CFCl$	$H(CF_2)_4CHO$	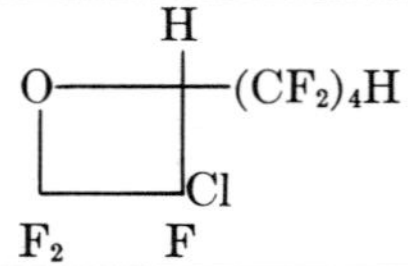 oxetane: H, $(CF_2)_4H$; F, Cl; F_2	15	136	1.3204 (25)	10

Table 27. (cont.) Cycloaddition of Polyfluorocarbonyl Compounds to Polyfluoroolefins

C_n	Unsaturated compound	Carbonyl compound	Product	% Yield	°C b.p./mm	n_D (°C)	Ref.
		Aldehydes (cont.)					
	$CF_2=CFCF_3$	$H(CF_2)_4CHO$	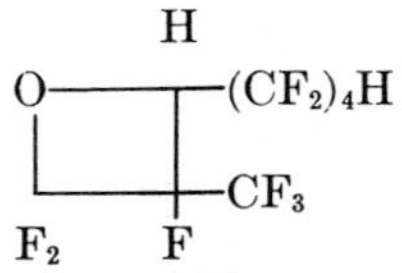 oxetane: O–$C(H)((CF_2)_4H)$–$C(CF_3)(F)$–CF_2	59	trans 124 / cis 128		10
		Ketones					
C_3	$CF_2=CFCF_3$	CF_3COCF_3	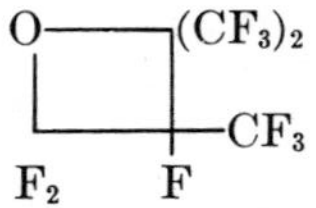 oxetane: O–$C(CF_3)_2$–$C(CF_3)(F)$–CF_2	50	51		10
	$CF_2=CFCl$	$ClCF_2COCF_2Cl$	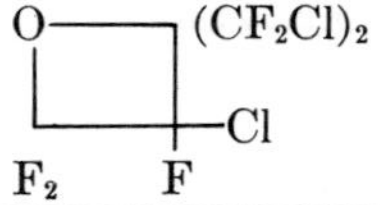 oxetane: O–$C(CF_2Cl)_2$–$C(Cl)(F)$–CF_2	11	120	1.3613 (24)	10
	$CF_2=CFCF_3$	$ClCF_2COCF_2Cl$	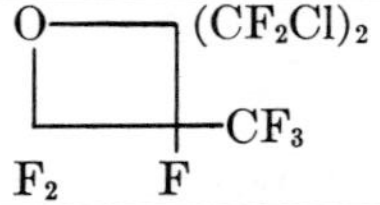 oxetane: O–$C(CF_2Cl)_2$–$C(CF_3)(F)$–CF_2	56	107.5	1.3259 (26)	10
	$CF_2=CFC_5F_{11}$	$ClCF_2COCF_2Cl$	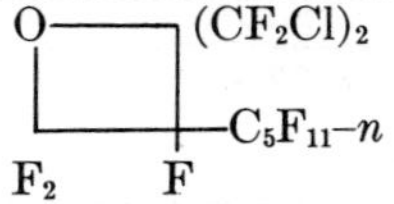 oxetane: O–$C(CF_2Cl)_2$–$C(C_5F_{11}\text{-}n)(F)$–CF_2	47	183	1.3255 (25)	10

Table 27. (cont.) Cycloaddition of Polyfluorocarbonyl Compounds to Polyfluoroolefins

C_n	Unsaturated compound	Carbonyl compound	Product	% Yield	°C b.p./mm	n_D (°C)	Ref.
		Ketones (cont.)					
	$CF_2{=}CFCF_3$	$Cl_2CFCOCFCl_2$	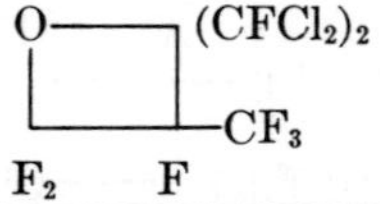 $O{-}(CFCl_2)_2$, CF_3, F, F_2 (oxetane ring)	39	171	1.3869	10
C_4	$CF_2{=}CFCF_3$	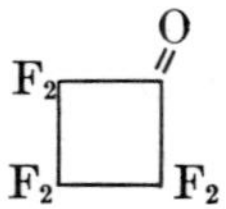 (cyclic: F_2, F_2, $O{=}$, F_2)	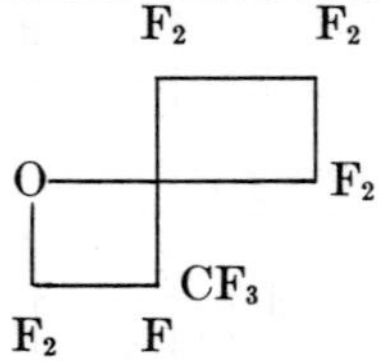 $O{-}$ ring, F_2, CF_3, F, F_2, F_2	33	68		10
C_5	$CF_2{=}CFCF_3$	$C_2F_5COC_2F_5$	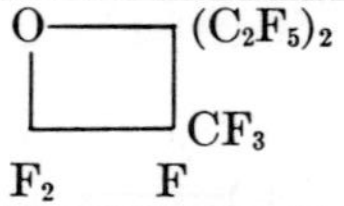 $O{-}(C_2F_5)_2$, CF_3, F, F_2 (oxetane ring)	46	97		10
C_7	$CF_2{=}CFCF_3$	$C_3F_7COC_3F_7$	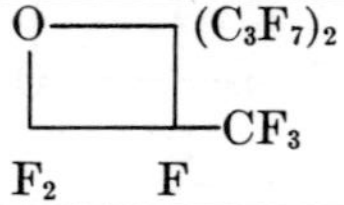 $O{-}(C_3F_7)_2$, CF_3, F, F_2 (oxetane ring)	62	136		10
C_7	$CF_2{=}CFC_5F_{11}$	$C_3F_7COC_3F_7$	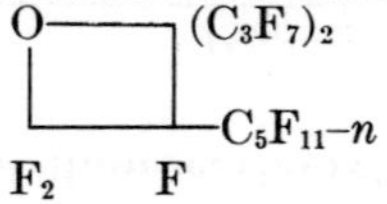 $O{-}(C_3F_7)_2$, $C_5F_{11}{-}n$, F, F_2 (oxetane ring)	32	200		10

Table 27. (cont.) Cycloaddition of Polyfluorocarbonyl Compounds to Polyfluoroolefins

C_n	Unsaturated compound	Carbonyl compound	Product	% Yield	°C b.p./mm	n_D (°C)	Ref.
		Acyl fluorides					
C_2	$CF_2=CFCF_3$	CF_3COF	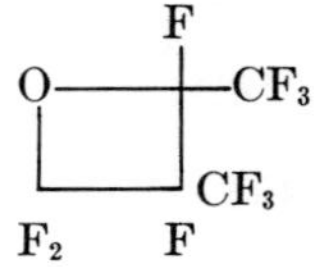 F, CF_3, CF_3, O, F_2, F	38	25		10
C_4	$CF_2=CFCF_3$	C_3F_7COF	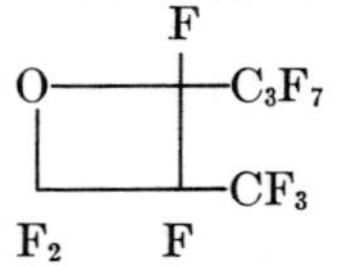 F, C_3F_7, CF_3, O, F, F_2	73	79		10
	$CF_2=CF(CF_2)_2H$	C_3F_7COF	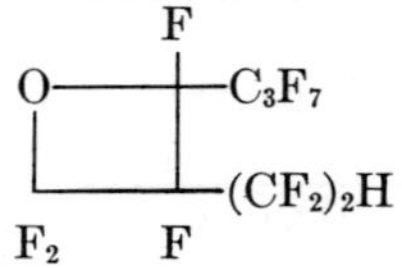 F, C_3F_7, $(CF_2)_2H$, O, F, F_2	35	109–115		10
C_5	$CF_2=CFCF_3$	$H(CF_2)_4COF$	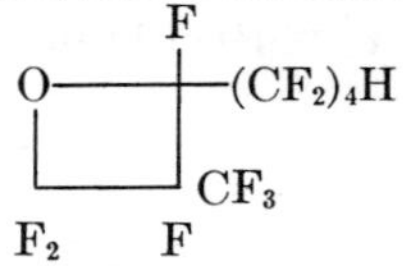 F, $(CF_2)_4H$, CF_3, O, F, F_2	48	111–118.5		10

Table 27. (cont.) Cycloaddition of Polyfluorocarbonyl Compounds to Polyfluoroolefins

C_n	Unsaturated compound	Carbonyl compound	Product	% Yield	°C b.p./mm	n_D (°C)	Ref.
		Acyl fluorides (cont.)					
	$CF_2{=}CFCF_3$	$FOC(CF_2)_3COF$	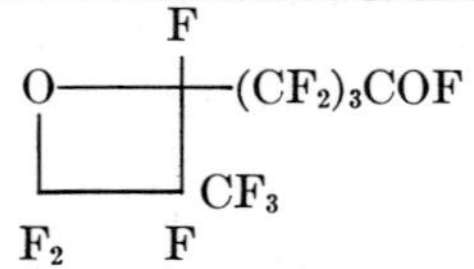 oxetane ring: F and $(CF_2)_3COF$; O—; F_2 and CF_3, F	34	103		10
	$CF_2{=}CF(CF_2)_2H$	$H(CF_2)_4COF$	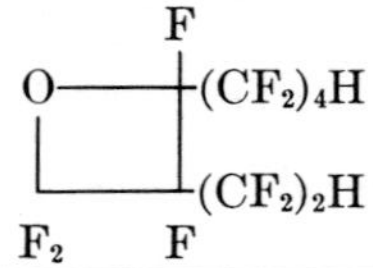 oxetane ring: F and $(CF_2)_4H$; O—$(CF_2)_2H$; F_2, F	61	79–94/98		10
C_8	$CF_2{=}CFCF_3$	$C_7F_{15}COF$	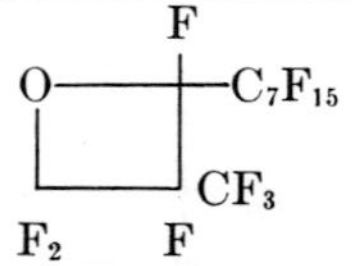 oxetane ring: F and C_7F_{15}; O—; F_2 and CF_3, F	91	161		10

REFERENCES

[1] Banes and Fitzgerald, U.S. 2,671,121 (1954).
[2] Banes, Fitzgerald, and Nelson, U.S. 2,585,723 (1952).
[3] Büchi, Inman, and Lipinsky, *J. Am. Chem. Soc.*, **76,** 4327 (1954).
[4] Büchi, *et al.*, *J. Am. Chem. Soc.*, **78,** 876 (1956).
[5] Coffman and Roland, *J. Am. Chem. Soc.*, **72,** 3392 (1950).
[6] Dulon, Vilkas, and Pfau, *C.r.* **249,** 429 (1959).
[7] Evans, *Inst. intern. chim. Solvay, 8e conseil chim. Univ. Bruxelles, Mecanisme de oxydation, Rapp. et disc., Bruxelles,* **1950,** 13.
[8] Hackmann, U.S. 2,600,054 (1952).
[9] Hanford, U.S. 2,433,844 (1948).
[10] Harris and Coffman, *J. Am. Chem. Soc.*, **84,** 1553 (1962).
[11] Hellberg, *Acta chim. Scand.*, **11, 219** (1957).
[12] Huang, *J. Chem. Soc.*, **1956,** 1749.
[13] Huang, *J. Chem. Soc.*, **1957,** 1342.
[14] Joyce, U.S. 2,559,628 (1951).
[15] Kharasch, Kuderna, and Nudenberg, *J. Org. Chem.*, **18,** 1225 (1953).
[16] Kharasch, Urry, and Kuderna, *J. Org. Chem.*, **14,** 248 (1949).
[17] Kirkland, *Ind. Eng. Chem.*, **52,** 397 (1960).
[18] Ladd, U.S. 2,517,684 (1950).
[19] Ladd, U.S. 2,533,944 (1950).
[20] Ladd, U.S. 2,552,980 (1951).
[21] Ladd, U.S. 2,577,133 (1951).
[22] Ladd, U.S. 2,621,212 (1952).
[23] La Zerte and Koshar, *J. Am. Chem. Soc.*, **77,** 910 (1955).
[24] Matheson and Skirrow, U.S. 1,725,362 (1929).
[25] Milas, Kurz, and Anslow, *J. Am. Chem. Soc.*, **59,** 543 (1937).
[26] Mondon, *Ang. Chem.*, **64,** 224 (1952).
[27] Moote and Steitz, U.S. 2,823,216 (1958).
[28] Muramatsu and Inukai, *J. Org. Chem.*, **27,** 1572 (1962).
[29] Nagasaka, Nakamura, and Oda, *Bull. Inst. Chem. Res. Kyoto Univ.*, **33,** 85 (1955).
[30] Nagasaka and Oda, *Bull. Inst. Chem. Res. Kyoto Univ.*, **32,** 238 (1954).
[31] Nagasaka and Oda, *Kogyo Kagaku Zasshi*, **59,** 1024 (1956).
[32] Nikishin, Somov, and Petrov, *Dok. Akad. Nauk*, **136,** 1099 (1961).
[33] Nikishin, Somov, and Petrov, *Izvest. Akad. Nauk*, **1961,** 2065.
[34] Nikishin, Vorobev, and Petrov, *Dok. Akad. Nauk*, **130,** 1256 (1960).
[35] Okawara, *J. Chem. Soc. Japan,* Ind. Chem. Sect., **57,** 760 (1954).
[36] Okawara, Komeda, and Imoto, *J. Chem. Soc. Japan,* Ind. Chem. Sect., **58,** 705 (1955).
[37] Paterno and Chieffi, *Gazz. chim. ital.*, **39 (II),** 341 (1909).
[38] Patrick, *J. Org. Chem.*, **17,** 1009 (1952).
[39] Patrick, *J. Org. Chem.*, **17,** 1269 (1952).
[40] Patrick, U.S. 2,628,238 (1953).
[41] Patrick, U.S. 2,665,304 (1954).
[42] Patrick, U.S. 2,684,373 (1954).
[43] Patrick, U.S. 2,716,660 (1955).
[44] Petrov, Chernyshev, and Bisku, *Izvest. Akad. Nauk*, **1956,** 1445.
[45] Petrov, Nikishin, and Ogibin, *Dok. Akad. Nauk*, **131,** 580 (1960).
[46] Reusch, *J. Org. Chem.*, **27,** 1883 (1962).
[47] Rust and Vaughan, U.S. 2,650,253 (1953).

[48] Schauenstein, *Naturw.*, **43**, 372 (1956).
[49] Schenck, Koltzenburg, and Grossmann, *Ang. Chem.*, **69**, 177 (1957).
[50] Schenck and Steinmetz, *Naturw.*, **47**, 514 (1960).
[51] Schlubach, Franzen, and Dahl, *Ann. Chem.*, **587**, 124 (1954).
[52] Schmerling and West, *J. Am. Chem. Soc.*, **71**, 2015 (1949).
[53] Schmerling and West, *J. Am. Chem. Soc.*, **75**, 6216 (1953).
[54] Schönberg, *Präparative Organische Photochemie*, pp. 73–76, Springer, Berlin, (1958).
[55] Sommer, *et al.*, *J. Am. Chem. Soc.*, **76**, 1613 (1954).
[56] Stiteler and Little, U.S. 2,517,732 (1950).
[57] Stoermer and Stockmann, *Chem. Ber.*, **47**, 1786 (1914).
[58] Stoll and Schlietz, *Helv. chim. Acta*, **38**, 585 (1955).
[59] Stoops and Furrow, *J. Org. Chem.*, **26**, 3264 (1961).
[60] Urry and Huyser, *J. Am. Chem. Soc.*, **75**, 4876 (1953).
[61] Urry, *et al.*, *J. Am. Chem. Soc.*, **75**, 250 (1953).
[62] Urry, *et al.*, *J. Am. Chem. Soc.*, **76**, 450 (1954).
[63] U.S. Rubber Co., Brit. 634,959 (1950).
[64] U.S. Rubber Co., Brit. 635,934 (1950).
[65] U.S. Rubber Co., Brit. 636,287 (1950).
[66] U.S. Rubber Co., Brit. 640,479 (1950).
[67] U.S. Rubber Co., Brit. 640,537 (1950).
[68] Wang, Apicella, and Stone, *J. Am. Chem. Soc.*, **78**, 4180 (1956).
[69] Waters, *Inst. intern. chim. Solvay, 8e conseil chim. Univ. Bruxelles, Mechanisme de oxydation, Rapp. et disc., Bruxelles*, **1950**, 63.
[70] Weiss, *Advances in Catalysis*, vol. IV, p. 343, Academic Press, Inc., New York (1952).
[71] Wiley and Harrell, *J. Org. Chem.*, **25**, 903 (1960).

CHAPTER V

Reactions of Phosphorus Compounds

ADDITION OF PHOSPHINES TO UNSATURATED COMPOUNDS

Phosphine itself and primary and secondary phosphines add to various unsaturated compounds. The reactions are initiated by peroxide, azonitrile, ultraviolet light, or x rays.

$$RCH{=}CH_2 + PH_3 \rightarrow RCH_2CH_2PH_2$$

$$RCH{=}CH_2 + R'PH_2 \rightarrow RCH_2CH_2PR'H$$

The reaction of phosphine itself with unsaturated compounds usually produces a mixture of primary, secondary, and tertiary phosphines. The ratio of the products depends largely on the ratio of the reactants.[58,66] Peroxide-initiated reactions are usually carried out at about 120°. Photochemical reactions can proceed at room temperature;[46] light below 2300 A should be used. Light of higher wavelength can be used in the presence of photosensitizers such as acetone.[66] Di-*t*-butyl peroxide is most commonly employed to initiate the reactions. However, a number of other commercially available peroxides can be used.[46]

The scope and various factors of the free radical-initiated addition reaction of phosphines have been investigated by Rauhut and co-workers.[58] The reactions were initiated by di-*t*-butyl peroxide, α, α'-azobisisobutyronitrile, or x radiation. The general procedure was to react the phosphine with the unsaturated compound in a stainless-steel autoclave. The reactions were carried out under a pressure of 200–600 psig. Reactions initiated by x rays were carried out in heavy-walled glass ampules. Most reactions were carried out at 75–85°, although some were conducted at room temperature and some at elevated temperatures up to 140°.

The products of all phosphine reactions are usually isolated by fractionation in a nitrogen atmosphere.[46,58,66]

Several of the phosphine addition reactions warrant comment. Bis–(2–cyanoethyl)phosphine reacts with acetylene at 80–85° in the presence of azobisisobutyronitrile, but no products have been isolated.[58] The same phosphine with heptyne–1 or octyne–1 produce, respectively, bis–(2–cyanoethyl)–1–heptenylphosphine, b.p. 170°/0.4 mm, n_D 1.5008 (25°), in 27% yield, and bis–(2–cyanoethyl)–1–octenylphosphine, b.p. 187°/0.6 mm, n_D 1.5000 (28°), in 30% yield.[58]

The reaction of 2–cyanoethylphosphine with heptyne–1 results in the 1:1 product 2–cyanoethylbis–(1–heptenyl)phosphine, b.p. 140°/0.25 mm, n_D 1.4930 (25°), in 26% yield.[58] Dibutylphosphine and 1, 3–butadiene react to produce dibutyl–2–*trans*–butenylphosphine (I), b.p. 118°/13 mm, n_D 1.4725 (25°), in 51% yield, plus a 2:1 product (II), b.p. 144°/0.07 mm, n_D 1.4895 (25°).[58]

$$(C_4H_9)_2PCH_2CH{=}CHCH_3 \qquad\qquad (C_4H_9)_2PCH_2CH_2CH_2CH_2P(C_4H_9)_2$$

$$\text{I} \qquad\qquad\qquad\qquad\qquad\qquad \text{II}$$

Similarly, bis–(2–carbethoxyethyl)phosphine and diethyl–α–methylene glutarate react to form bis–(2–carbethoxyethyl)–2, 4–dicarbethoxybutyl-phosphine (III), b.p. 196–201°/0.2 mm, n_D 1.4730 (25°).[58]

$$
\begin{array}{c}
CH_2 \\
\parallel \\
C_2H_5OCCCH_2CH_2COC_2H_5 + (C_2H_5OCCH_2CH_2)_2PH \\
\end{array}
$$

$$
\rightarrow (C_2H_5OCCH_2CH_2)_2PCH_2CHCOC_2H_5
$$

$$\text{III}$$

In the presence of dibutyl peroxide, 2–carbethoxyethylphosphine reacts with octene–1 to give 2–carbethoxyethyloctylphosphine, b.p. 106°/0.25 mm, n_D 1.4620 (25°), in 32% yield, and 2–carbethoxyethyldioctylphos-phine, b.p. 165°/0.2 mm, n_D 1.4655 (25°), in 60% yield.[58]

Under ultraviolet radiation phosphine and allyl chloride react to form 3–chloropropylphosphine, b.p. 125°.[67] Under similar conditions phosphine and methyl acrylate react to form 2–methylcarboxyethylphosphine, b.p. 74°/56 mm, and bis–(2–methylcarboxyethyl)phosphine, b.p. 95°/6 mm.[67] The reaction of phosphine with methyl vinyl ether produces three products: 2–methoxyethylphosphine, bis– and tris–(2–methoxyethyl)phosphine.[67]

At 80° in the presence of azobisisobutyronitrile, 2, 4, 6–triisopropyl–1, 3,

5–dioxaphosphorinane (IV) adds to methyl vinyl ketone to give the 1:1 adduct (V), b.p. 122°/0.4 mm, n_D 1.4749 (25°).[58]

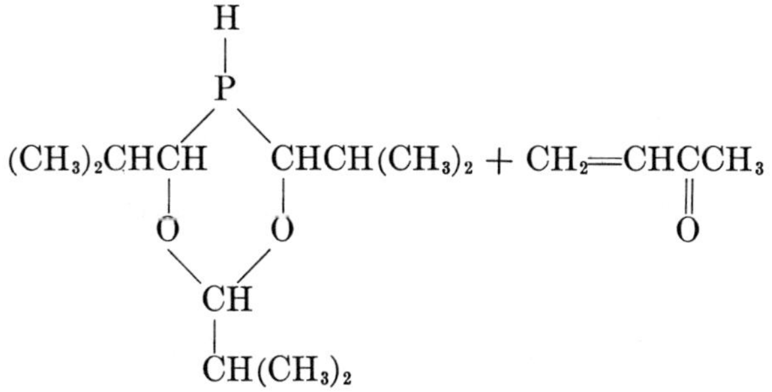

$$(CH_3)_2CHCH \underset{\overset{|}{O}}{\overbrace{}} P \overset{H}{\underset{\overset{|}{O}}{}} CHCH(CH_3)_2 + CH_2\!\!=\!\!CHCCH_3$$

(CH₃)₂CHCH / P\ CHCH(CH₃)₂ + CH₂=CHCCH₃

O   O   O
\CH/
CH(CH₃)₂

IV

$$\rightarrow (CH_3)_2CHCH \underset{\overset{|}{O}}{} \overset{\overset{\displaystyle O}{\|}}{\underset{\underset{P}{|}}{CH_2CH_2CCH_3}} CHCH(CH_3)_2$$

→ (CH₃)₂CHCH / P\ CHCH(CH₃)₂

with P bearing CH₂CH₂CCH₃ (C=O)

O   O
\CH/
CH(CH₃)₂

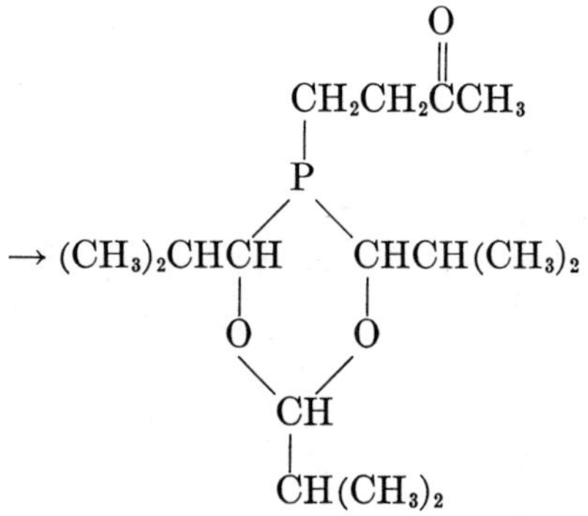

V

Thermal reactions of phosphines can take place in the absence of a catalyst at 120–150°.[1,42,49] Although the mechanism of the reactions is uncertain, the reaction pattern points to a free radical process. For example, the addition of phenyl- or diphenylphosphine to vinyl cyanide is not affected by acetic acid, whereas a basic catalyst decreases the yield of the products.[42]

Table 28.   Addition of Phosphines to Unsaturated Compounds

C_n	Unsaturated compound	Phosphine	Ratio of phosphine to unsaturated compound	Product	% Yield	°C b.p./mm (m.p.)	n_D (°C)	Ref.
C_2	$CF_2=CF_2$	PH_3		$HCF_2CF_2PH_2$	53	21		49
	$CClF=CF_2$	PH_3		$HCClFCF_2PH_2$	54	67		49
	$CCl_2=CF_2$	PH_3		$HCCl_2CF_2PH_2$	30	110		49
C_3	Allyl alcohol	PH_3	1	3-Hydroxypropyl-phosphine	26	82/32		66, 67
	Allyl chloride	PH_3		3-Chloropropylphosphine		125		67
	Allylamine	PH_3	5	3-Aminopropyl-phosphine + Bis-(β-aminopropyl-phosphine)	28 / 20	60/52 / 165/36		66, 67
	$CF_3CF=CF_2$	PH_3		$CF_3CF(PH_2)CF_2H$	36	46		49
	Methyl acrylate	PH_3		$CH_3CO_2CH_2CH_2PH_2$ + $(CH_3CO_2CH_2CH_2)_2PH$	38	74/56 / 95/6		67
	Methyl vinyl ether	PH_3		$CH_3OCH_2CH_2PH_2$ + $(CH_3OCH_2CH_2)_2PH$ + $(CH_3OCH_2CH_2)_3P$		82 / 119/51 / 164/51		67
C_4	Butene–1	PH_3	1	Butylphosphine + Dibutylphosphine + Tributylphosphine	38	87 / 183 / 241	1.4477 (20) / 1.4572 (20) / 1.4634 (20)	66, 67
	Butene–1	PH_3	3.2	Tributylphosphine	67	150/50		66, 67
	Isobutylene	PH_3	1	$(CH_3)_2CHCH_2PH_2$ + $((CH_3)_2CHCH_2)_2PH$ + $((CH_3)_2CHCH_2)_3P$	18 / 52 / 21	77 / 47/8 / 85/7	1.4308 (25) / 1.4487 (25) / 1.4530 (25)	58, 67

Table 28. (cont.)   Addition of Phosphines to Unsaturated Compounds

C_n	Unsaturated compound	Phosphine	Ratio of phosphine to unsaturated compound	Product	% Yield	°C b.p./mm (m.p.)	n_D (°C)	Ref.
C_5	Ethyl acrylate	PH$_3$	1	$C_2H_5O_2CCH_2CH_2PH_2+$ $(C_2H_5O_2CCH_2CH_2)_2PH+$ $(C_2H_5O_2CCH_2CH_2)_3P$	21 20 23	52/9 109/0.2 193/1	1.4552 (25) 1.4668 (25) 1.4748 (25)	58
C_6	Cyclohexene	PH$_3$	1.5	$C_6H_{11}PH_2+$ $(C_6H_{11})_2PH$	49 29	145 129/8	1.4822 (25) 1.5142 (25)	58, 66, 67
	Vinyl butyl ether	PH$_3$	1.9	$n\text{-}C_4H_9OCH_2CH_2PH_2+$ $(n\text{-}C_4H_9OCH_2CH_2)_2PH+$ $(n\text{-}C_4H_9OCH_2CH_2)_3P$	45 30 10	47/9 139/9 150/0.25	1.4478 (25) 1.4570 (25) 1.4617 (25)	58
C_8	1-Octene	PH$_3$	1.1	$C_8H_{17}PH_2+$ $(C_8H_{17})_2PH+$ $(C_8H_{17})_3P$	23 28 22	67/7 137/0.25 176/0.3	1.4539 (25) 1.4666 (25)	58
	1-Octene	PH$_3$	0.33	$(C_8H_{17})_3P$	83			58
	1-Octene	PH$_3$	3.6	$C_8H_{17}PH_2+$ $(C_8H_{17})_2PH+$ $(C_8H_{17})_3P$	65 18 4			58
C_{12}	1-Dodene	PH$_3$	1.2	$(n\text{-}C_{12}H_{25})PH_2+$ $(n\text{-}C_{12}H_{25})_2PH$	23 20	80/0.1 198/0.35	1.4585 (25)	58
C_3	Allylamine	CNCH$_2$CH$_2$PH$_2$	0.5	$\begin{array}{l} CNCH_2CH_2 \\ \diagdown \\ PH+ \\ \diagup \\ NH_2CH_2CH_2CH_2 \end{array}$	18	90/0.4		58
				$\begin{array}{l} CNCH_2CH_2 \\ \diagdown \\ P \\ \diagup \diagup \\ (NH_2CH_2CH_2CH_2)_2 \end{array}$	56	165/0.5	1.5250 (25)	

Table 28. (cont.) Addition of Phosphines to Unsaturated Compounds

C_n	Unsaturated compound	Phosphine	Ratio of phosphine to unsaturated compound	Product	% Yield	°C b.p./mm (m.p.)	n_D (°C)	Ref.
	Allyl alcohol	CNCH₂CH₂PH₂	1	CNCH₂CH₂ PH+ / HOCH₂CH₂CH₂	31	133/0.2	1.5090 (25)	58
				CNCH₂CH₂ P= / (HOCH₂CH₂CH₂)₂	17	193/0.7	1.5230 (25)	
	Allyl alcohol	CNCH₂CH₂PH₂	0.45	CNCH₂CH₂ P= / (HOCH₂CH₂CH₂)₂	76			58
C_6	CH₃COCH= C(CH₃)₂	CNCH₂CH₂PH₂	0.5	CNCH₂CH₂ PH / CH₃COCH₂C(CH₃)₂	8	127/0.8		58
	Cyclohexene	CNCH₂CH₂PH₂	1	CNCH₂CH₂ PH / C₆H₁₁	65	97/0.3	1.5088 (25)	58

Table 28. (cont.) Addition of Phosphines to Unsaturated Compounds

C_n	Unsaturated compound	Phosphine	Ratio of phosphine to unsaturated compound	Product	% Yield	°C b.p./mm (m.p.)	n_D (°C)	Ref.
C_8	1–Octene	$CNCH_2CH_2PH_2$	1	$CNCH_2CH_2$—PH+ C_8H_{17}	39	118/0.4	1.4745 (25)	58
				$(CNCH_2CH_2)_2$=P C_8H_{17}	25	184/0.2	1.4885 (25)	
	1–Octene	$CNCH_2CH_2PH_2$	0.45	$(CNCH_2CH_2)_2$=P C_8H_{17}	93			58
	2, 4–Trimethyl-pentene–1	$CNCH_2CH_2PH_2$	0.45	$CNCH_2CH_2$—PH+ C_3H_{17}	70	102/0.3	1.4735 (25)	58
				$(CNCH_2CH_2)_2$=P C_8H_{17}	15	157/0.15	1.4920 (25)	

Table 28. (cont.)   Addition of Phosphines to Unsaturated Compounds

C_n	Unsaturated compound	Phosphine	Ratio of phosphine to unsaturated compound	Product	% Yield	°C b.p./mm (m.p.)	n_D (°C)	Ref.
C_3	Allyl alcohol	$(CNCH_2CH_2)_2PH$	1	$(CNCH_2CH_2)_2P$—$CH_2CH_2CH_2OH$	78	228/0.5	1.5202 (25)	58
	Acrylonitrile	$(CNCH_2CH_2)_2PH$	1	$(CNCH_2CH_2)_3P$	92	(85–92)		58
C_6	Cyclohexene	$(CNCH_2CH_2)_2PH$	0.9	$(CNCH_2CH_2)_2P$—C_6H_{11}	55	185/0.4	1.5241 (25)	58
C_8	1–Octene	$(NCCH_2CH_2)_2PH$	1	$(CNCH_2CH_2)_2P$—C_8H_{17}	66	184/0.2	1.4885 (25)	58
	2, 4, 4–Trimethyl-pentene	$(CNCH_2CH_2)_2PH$	0.9	$(CNCH_2CH_2)_2P$—C_8H_{17}	13	157/0.15	1.4920 (25)	58
	Styrene	$(CNCH_2CH_2)_2PH$	0.9	$(CNCH_2CH_2)_2P$—$C_6H_5CH_2CH_2$	47	212/0.6	1.5580 (25)	58

Table 28. (cont.)   Addition of Phosphines to Unsaturated Compounds

C_n	Unsaturated compound	Phosphine	Ratio of phosphine to unsaturated compound	Product	% Yield	°C b.p./mm (m.p.)	n_D (°C)	Ref.
C_{10}	Vinyl 2-ethylhexyl ether	$(CNCH_2CH_2)_2PH$	1	$(CNCH_2CH_2)_2$=P–$C_8H_{17}OCH_2CH_2$	90	206/0.2	1.4860 (25)	58
C_2	CF_2=CF_2	$C_6H_5PH_2$		$CF_2HCF_2P(C_6H_5)H$	45	28 (0.5)	1.4758 (25)	49
C_3	CH_2=$CHCH_2OH$	$C_6H_5PH_2$		$HOCH_2CH_2CH_2)_2$-PC_6H_5	56	175/1	1.5740 (20)	1
	CH_2=$CHCN$	$C_6H_5PH_2$		$C_6H_5P(CH_2CH_2CN)_2+$	49	177/0.5 (70)	1.5672 (20)	1, 42
				$C_6H_5PHCH_2CH_2CN$	8	104/0.5	1.5649	
C_4	CH_2=$CHCO_2CH_3$	$C_6H_5PH_2$		$C_5H_5P(CH_2CH_2CO_2CH_3)$	56	150/1	1.5361 (20)	1
C_5	CH_2=$C(CH_3)CO_2$-CH_3	$C_6H_5PH_2$		$C_6H_5P(CH_2CH(CH_3)$-$CO_2CH_3)_2$	57	140/1	1.5242 (20)	1
C_6	CH_2=$C(CH_3)CO_2$-C_2H_5	$C_6H_5PH_2$		$C_6H_5P(CH_2CH(CH_3)$-$CO_2C_2H_5)_2$	58	150/1	1.5172 (20)	1
C_7	CH_2=$C(CH_3)CO_2$-C_3H_7	$C_6H_5PH_2$		$C_6H_5P(CH_2CH(CH_3)$-$CO_2C_3H_7)_2$	65	170/1	1.5061 (20)	1
	CH_2=$C(CH_3)CO_2$-C_3H_7-i	$C_6H_5PH_2$		$C_6H_5P(CH_2CH(CH_3)$-$CO_2C_3H_7$-$i)_2$	66	152/1	1.5038 (20)	1
C_8	CH_2=$C(CH_3)CO_2$-C_4H_9	$C_6H_5PH_2$		$C_6H_5P(CH_2CH(CH_3)CO_2$-$C_4H_9)_2$	67	186/1	1.5038 (20)	1
	CH_2=$C(CH_3)CO_2$-C_4H_9-i	$C_6H_5PH_2$		$C_6H_5P(CH_2CH(CH_3)CO_2$-C_4H_9-i	76	178/1	1.5001 (20)	1
C_3	CH_2=$CHCN$	$(C_6H_5)_2NH$		$(C_6H_5)_2PCH_2CH_2CN$	71	(64)		42

ADDITION OF HYPOPHOSPHOROUS ACID AND HYPOPHOSPHITES TO UNSATURATED COMPOUNDS

Aqueous hypophosphorous acid (50%) reacts with olefins in the presence of peroxide to give dialkyl acids.

$$2RCH{=}CH_2 + H_2P(O)OH \rightarrow (RCH_2CH_2)_2P(O)OH$$

Depending on the olefin, the reaction is carried out at temperatures ranging from 67° (hexene) to 175° (decene). At lower reaction temperatures benzoyl peroxide is used as a catalyst, and at higher temperatures di–t–butyl peroxide is used. In all the reactions the olefin is used in two- to threefold excess of the hypophosphorous acid. The reaction time varies between 11 and 24 hr. The reactions of hypophosphorous acid with hexene, octene, decene, dodecene, tetradecene, hexadecene, or octadecene produce di–n–alkyl phosphinic acid.[75]

Sodium hypophosphite reacts with hexene–1, octene–1, or tetradecene–1 to give sodium n–hexane–1–phosphinate (plus di(n–hexane–1–phosphinate)), sodium octane–1–phosphinate, or sodium tetradecane–1–phosphinate, respectively, in high yield.[45,47,65] The reactions are carried out at 120° in a pressure vessel in the presence of 2, 2–bis(t–butylperoxy)butane. The reactions of ammonium hypophosphite with vinyl disulfide and of sodium hypophosphite with diallyl sulfide each result in a mixture of 1:1 and 2:1 products.[47]

Table 29.   Addition of Hypophosphorous Acid to Unsaturated Compounds

C_n	Unsaturated compound	Product	% Yield	°C (m.p.)	Ref.
C_6	Hexene	(Hexyl)$_2$P(O)OH	9	(78)	75
C_8	Octene	(Octyl)$_2$P(O)OH	32	(85)	75
C_{10}	Decene	(Decyl)$_2$P(O)OH	19	(88)	75
C_{12}	Dodecene	(Dodecyl)$_2$P(O)OH	22	(94)	75
C_{14}	Tetradecene	(Tetradecyl)$_2$P(O)OH	16	(97)	75
C_{16}	Hexadecene	(Hexadecyl)$_2$P(O)OH	24	(103)	75
C_{18}	Octadecene	(Octadecyl)$_2$P(O)OH	40	(106)	75

ADDITION OF PHOSPHOROUS ACID TO UNSATURATED COMPOUNDS

Phosphorous acid adds to olefins to give alkyl phosphonic acids.

$$RCH{=}CH_2 + HP(O)(OH)_2 \rightarrow RCH_2CH_2P(O)(OH)_2$$

The reaction can be carried out in solvents such as dioxane or acetic acid and is initiated by benzoyl peroxide, di–t–butyl peroxide, or ultraviolet light. During the reaction, which takes 4–6 hr, the temperature is maintained around 90°. In the absence of an initiator no reaction occurs. In most cases the products are obtained in 20–30% yield.

Phosphorous acid reacts with cyclohexene, octene–1, indene, or decene–1 to form the 1:1 adduct mainly and the 2:1 product in lesser yield.[13,14] The products can be identified independently by the peroxide-initiated reaction of diethyl phosphonate and the corresponding olefin, followed by acidic hydrolysis.[13]

$$RCH_2CH_2CR'{=}CH_2 + HP(O)(OC_2H_5)_2$$
$$\rightarrow RCH_2CH_2CHR'CH_2P(O)(OC_2H_5)_2$$
$$\xrightarrow{H^+} RCH_2CH_2CHR'CH_2P(O)(OH)_2$$

Table 30.   Addition of Phosphorous Acid to Unsaturated Compounds

C_n	Unsaturated compound	Product	% Yield	°C (m.p.)	Ref.
C_6	Hexene–1	n–Hexyl–P(O)(OH)$_2$+	23	(105)	13
		2–Butyloctyl–P(O)(OH)$_2$	8	(99)	
	Cyclohexene	Cyclohexyl–P(O)(OH)$_2$+	20	(166)	13, 14
		2–Cyclohexylcyclohexyl–P(O)(OH)$_2$	9	(99)	
C_8	n–Octene–1	n–Octyl–P(O)(OH)$_2$	23	(100)	14
C_9	Indene	2–Indanyl–P(O)(OH)$_2$	20	(196)	14
C_{10}	Decene	n–Decyl–P(O)(OH)$_2$+	18	(102)	13
		2–Octyldodecyl–P(O)(OH)$_2$	6	(94)	

ADDITION OF DIALKYL PHOSPHITES TO UNSATURATED COMPOUNDS

Dialkyl phosphites react with unsaturated compounds in the presence of peroxide or ultraviolet light to give phosphonates in fair to good yield.

$$RCH{=}CH_2 + (RO)_2P(O)H \rightarrow RCH_2CH_2P(O)(OR)_2$$

With peroxides such as benzoyl peroxide, di–t–butyl peroxide, or t–butyl perbenzoate and with 2, 2′–azobisisobutyronitrile, the reaction is carried out between 80° and 170°. The photochemical reactions are usually carried out at 100–110°.[59] With highly volatile olefins the reactions are performed in a pressure vessel.[2,15,68] The duration of the condensation ranges from 1 to 36 hr.[68]

Among the condensations of various dialkyl phosphites with olefins, summarized in Table 31, only a few reactions warrant comment. Diethyl phosphite and ethylene react in the presence of benzoyl peroxide to give diethylethane phosphonate in 41% yield,[15] whereas diethyl phosphite reacts with tetrafluoroethylene to give a mixture of telomers.[2] Diethyl phosphite reacts with unsaturated ethers such as allyldodecyl ether at 80° in the presence of benzoyl peroxide to give diethyl 3–dodecyloxypropane–1–phosphonate in 33% yield.[39,69] When diethyl phosphite is heated with an enol ester such as isopropenyl acetate in the presence of benzoyl peroxide, β–acetoxypropyl phosphonate is produced in high yield.[50] To avoid 2:1 products, the phosphite should be used in excess.

$$CH_3C{=}CH_2 + H(O)(OC_2H_5)_2 \rightarrow CH_3CHCH_2P(O)(OC_2H_5)_2$$
$$\underset{OCOCH_3}{|} \qquad\qquad\qquad \underset{OCOCH_3}{|}$$

On hydrolysis, β–hydroxypropylphosphonic acid (I) is obtained.[50]

$$CH_3CH(OH)CH_2PO(OH)_2$$

I

The reaction of dibutyl phosphite with diallyl ether gives a mixture of two products.[47] Dibutyl phosphite and ethyl crotonate also react to give two isomers.[47]

Vinylsilanes such as triethoxyvinylsilane and diethoxymethylvinylsilane condense with diethyl or dimethyl hydrogen phosphite in the presence of 2, 2′–azobisisobutyronitrile at 120–130°.[41] Diethyl phosphite also condenses with cyclohexene.[51] On hydrolysis, the product forms cyclohexylphosphonic acid, m.p. 159°.

Trialkyl ω–phosphonoundecanoates are prepared in 53–66% yield by condensing a dialkyl phosphite with an alkyl undecanoate at 100–110° for 6 hr in the presence of t-butyl perbenzoate or ultraviolet light.[59]

$$CH_2=CH(CH_2)_8CO_2R + (R'O)_2P(O)H \rightarrow (R'O)_2P(O)(CH_2)_{10}CO_2R$$

R, R′ = alkyl

Dialkyl 2–acyloxyethyl phosphonates are prepared in 45–61% yield by condensing dialkyl phosphites with various vinyl esters.[59]

$$RCOCH=CH_2 + (R'O)_2P(O)H \rightarrow RCOCH_2CH_2(O)P(R')_2$$

with carbonyl $\overset{\|}{O}$ below RCOCH and below RCOCH$_2$CH$_2$(O)P(R′)$_2$

R, R′ = alkyl

The addition of dialkyl phosphites to various alkyl oleates in the presence of t-butyl perbenzoate at 100–110° results in trialkyl–9, 10–phosphonostearates in 66–77% yield.[59] Ultraviolet light does not promote the reaction. The product is a mixture of two isomers which are thermally stable colorless oils.

$$CH_3(CH)_7CH=CH(CH_2)_7CO_2R + (R'O)_2P(O)H$$

$$\rightarrow CH_3(CH_2)_7CH(CH_2)_8CO_2R + CH_3(CH_2)_8CH(CH_2)_7CO_2R$$

$$\underset{(R'O)_2P(O)}{|} \qquad \qquad \underset{(R'O)_2P(O)}{|}$$

R, R′ = CH₃, C₂H₅, n-C₄H₉, 2–ethylhexyl; R = C₂H₅, R′ = n-C₄H₉; R = n-C₄H₉, R′ = C₂H₅;

R = 2–ethylhexyl, R′ = C₂H₅

Table 31.   Addition of Dialkyl Phosphites to Unsaturated Compounds

C_n	Unsaturated compound	$(RO)_2P(O)H$	Product, $(RO)_2P(O)R'$	% Yield	°C b.p./mm (m.p.)	n_D (°C)	Ref.
		R = CH$_3$	R' = CH$_2$CH$_2$CO$_2$C$_2$H$_5$				
C$_5$	CH$_2$=CHCO$_2$C$_2$H$_5$	CH$_3$	CH$_2$CH$_2$CO$_2$C$_2$H$_5$	61	96/0.15	1.4316 (30)	59
C$_6$	CH$_2$=CHCO$_2$(CH$_2$)$_2$CH$_3$	CH$_3$	CH$_2$CH$_2$CO$_2$(CH$_2$)$_2$CH$_3$	65	93/0.01	1.4328 (30)	59
C$_7$	Heptene-1	CH$_3$	Heptyl	55	144/15.5	1.4330 (20)	51
	(C$_2$H$_5$O)$_2$CH$_3$SiCH=CH$_2$	CH$_3$	(CH$_3$O)$_2$CH$_3$SiCH$_2$CH$_2$		146/1		41
C$_8$	Octene-1	CH$_3$	Octyl	55	156/14	1.4350 (20)	51
C$_9$	Nonene-1	CH$_3$	Nonyl	52	171/16	1.4393 (20)	51
C$_{10}$	Decene-1	CH$_3$	Decyl	26	182/16	1.4388 (20)	51
C$_{11}$	Undecene-1	CH$_3$	Undecyl	45	192/20	1.4438 (20)	51
	CH$_2$=CHCO$_2$(CH$_2$)$_7$CH$_3$	CH$_3$	CH$_2$CH$_2$CO$_2$(CH$_2$)$_7$CH$_3$	55	125/0.02	1.4407 (30)	59
C$_{12}$	CH$_2$=CH(CH$_2$)$_8$CO$_2$CH$_3$	CH$_3$	(CH$_2$)$_{10}$CO$_2$CH$_3$	60	154/0.06	1.4456 (30)	59
C$_{14}$	Tetradecene-1	CH$_3$	Tetradecyl	61	142 mol. dist.	1.4478 (20)	68
C$_{16}$	CH$_2$=CHCO$_2$(CH$_2$)$_{12}$	CH$_3$	CH$_2$CH$_2$CO$_2$(CH$_2$)$_{12}$	49	120/0.002	1.4477 (30)	59
C$_{20}$	CH$_2$=CHCO$_2$(CH$_2$)$_{16}$	CH$_3$	CH$_2$CH$_2$CO$_2$(CH$_2$)$_{16}$	45	150/0.002 mol. dist.	1.4434 (50)	59
C$_2$	Ethylene	C$_2$H$_5$	C$_2$H$_5$	41	92/28	1.4322	15
C$_4$	Vinyl acetate	C$_2$H$_5$	2-Acetoxyethyl	14	96/0.7	1.4322	43
C$_5$	CH$_2$=CHCO$_2$C$_2$H$_5$	C$_2$H$_5$	CH$_2$CH$_2$CO$_2$C$_2$H$_5$	55	103/0.06	1.4291 (30)	59
	Isopropenyl acetate	C$_2$H$_5$	CH$_3$CH(OCOCH$_3$)CH$_2$	72	91/0.5	1.4301 (25)	50
C$_6$	Hexene-1	C$_2$H$_5$	Hexyl	29	126/10	1.4297 (20) 1.4545 (20)	47, 68 51
C$_7$	CH$_2$=CHCO$_2$(CH$_2$)$_2$CH$_3$	C$_2$H$_5$	CH$_2$CH$_2$CO$_2$(CH$_2$)$_2$CH$_3$	45	98/0.01	1.4300 (30)	59
	(C$_2$H$_5$)$_2$(CH$_3$)SiCH=CH$_2$	C$_2$H$_5$	(C$_2$H$_5$O)$_2$CH$_3$SiCH$_2$CH$_2$		170/3		41
C$_8$	Octene-1	C$_2$H$_5$	Octyl	60	105/0.8	1.4341 (20)	51, 69

Table 31. (cont.) Addition of Dialkyl Phosphites to Unsaturated Compounds

C_n	Unsaturated compound	$(RO)_2P(O)H$	Product, $(RO)_2P(O)R'$	% Yield	°C b.p./mm (m.p.)	n_D (°C)	Ref.
C_9	Nonene-1	$R = C_2H_5$	$R' = $ Nonyl	50	175/14	1.4360 (20)	51
C_{10}	Decene-1	C_2H_5	Decyl	37	184/12	1.4397 (20)	51
C_{11}	$CH_2{=}CHCO_2(CH_2)_7CH_3$	C_2H_5	$CH_2CH_2CO_2(CH_2)_7CH_3$	50	80/0.001 mol. dist.	1.4373 (30)	59
C_{12}	Dodecene-1	C_2H_5	Dodecyl		142/0.6		69
	$C_6H_{13}C(C_4H_9){=}CH_2$	C_2H_5	$C_6H_{13}CH(C_4H_9)CH_2$	17	100 mol. dist.	1.4466 (20)	47
C_{13}	$CH_2{=}CH(CH_2)_8CO_2C_2H_5$	C_2H_5	$(CH_2)_{10}CO_2C_2H_5$	58	161/0.1	1.4410 (30)	59
C_{15}	Allyldodecyl ether	C_2H_5	3-Dodecyloxypropyl		192/0.9		59
C_{16}	$CH_2{=}CHCO_2(CH_2)_{12}CH_3$	C_2H_5	$CH_2CH_2CO_2(CH_2)_{12}CH_3$	57	130/0.001	1.4450 (30)	59
C_{19}	$CH_2{=}CH(CH_2)_8CO_2$–2-ethylhexyl	C_2H_5	$(CH_2)_{10}CO_2$–2-ethylhexyl	53	140/0.001 mol. dist.	1.4472 (30)	59
C_{20}	$CH_2{=}CHCO_2(CH_2)_{16}CH_3$	C_2H_5	$CH_2CH_2CO_2(CH_2)_{16}CH_3$	49	160/0.001 mol. dist. (45)	1.4410 (50)	59
C_3	Allyl alcohol	C_3H_7	C_3H_7	30	80/1	1.4360 (20)	47
C_8	Octene-1	C_3H_7	C_3H_7	69	184/15		51
C_3	Allyl alcohol	C_4H_9	$CH_2CH_2CH_2OH$	30	70/1	1.4478 (20)	45, 47
C_4	Butene-2	C_4H_9	sec–C_4H_9	77	144/13	1.4322 (20)	68
C_5	$CH_2{=}CHCO_2C_2H_5$	C_4H_9	$CH_2CH_2CO_2C_2H_5$	45	127/0.01	1.4340 (30)	59
C_6	Cyclohexene	C_4H_9	Cyclohexyl	52	133/1	1.4544 (20)	45, 47, 68
C_6	$CH_2{=}CHCO_2(CH_2)_2CH_3$	C_4H_9	$CH_2CH_2CO_2(CH_2)_2CH_3$	58	142/0.13	1.4346 (30)	59

Table 31. (cont.)   Addition of Dialkyl Phosphites to Unsaturated Compounds

C_n	Unsaturated compound	$(RO)_2P(O)H$	Product, $(RO)_2P(O)R'$	% Yield	°C b.p./mm (m.p.)	n_D (°C)	Ref.
C_8	Octene–1	$R = C_4H_9$	$R' =$ Octyl	55	149/1	1.4396 (20)	47, 68
					201/15	1.4410 (20)	51
	Diisobutylene	C_4H_9	Isooctyl	42	116/1	1.4377 (20)	68
	$(C_2H_5O)_3SiCH=CH_2$	C_4H_9	$(C_2H_5O)_3SiCH_2CH_2$	25	149/1	1.4426 (20)	41
C_{10}	Decene–1	C_4H_9	Decyl	45	157/1	1.4400 (30)	47, 68
C_{11}	$CH_2=CHCO_2(CH_2)_7CH_3$	C_4H_9	$CH_2CH_2CO_2(CH_2)_7CH_3$	66	95/0.001 mol. dist.		59
C_{15}	$CH_2=CH(CH_2)_8CO_2-n-C_4H_9$	C_4H_9	$(CH_2)_{10}CO_2-n-C_4H_9$	21	150/0.001 mol. dist.	1.4458 (30)	59
C_{16}	C_8H_{17} $\quad\quad C=CH_2$ C_6H_{13}	C_4H_9	$C_8H_{17}CH(C_6H_{13})CH_2$	60	100 mol. dist.	1.4463 (20)	47
C_{20}	$CH_2=CHCO_2(CH_2)_{12}CH_3$	C_4H_9	$CH_2CH_2CO_2(CH_2)_{12}CH_3$	25	145/0.001	1.4462 (30)	59
	$C_{10}H_{21}$ $\quad\quad C=CH_2$ C_8H_{17}	C_4H_9	$C_{10}H_{21}CH(C_8H_{17})CH_2$	47	155 mol. dist.	1.4533 (20)	47
	$CH_2=CHCO_2(CH_2)_{16}CH_3$	C_4H_9	$CH_2CH_2CO_2(CH_2)_{16}CH_3$		175/0.001 mol. dist. (47)		59
C_5	$CH_2=CHCO_2C_2H_5$	2-Ethyl-hexyl	$CH_2CH_2CO_2C_2H_5$	45	110/0.001 mol. dist.	1.4437 (30)	59

Table 31. (cont.) Addition of Dialkyl Phosphites to Unsaturated Compounds

C_n	Unsaturated compound	$(RO)_2P(O)H$	Product, $(RO)_2P(O)R'$	% Yield	°C b.p./mm (m.p.)	n_D (°C)	Ref.
C_6	$CH_2=CHCO_2(CH_2)_2CH_3$	R = 2-Ethyl-hexyl	R' = $CH_2CH_2CO_2(CH_2)_2CH_3$	52	120/0.001 mol. dist.	1.4440 (30)	59
C_{11}	$CH_2=CHCO_2(CH_2)_7CH_3$	2-Ethyl-hexyl	$CH_2CH_2CO_2(CH_2)_7CH_3$	49	150/0.001 mol. dist.	1.4472 (30)	59
C_{13}	$CH_2=CH(CH_2)_8CO_2C_2H_5$	2-Ethyl-hexyl	$(CH_2)_{10}CO_2C_2H_5$	53	160/0.001	1.4500 (30)	59
C_{16}	$CH_2=CHCO_2(CH_2)_{12}CH_3$	2-Ethyl-hexyl	$CH_2CH_2CO_2(CH_2)_{12}CH_3$	49	170/0.001	1.4517 (30)	59
C_{19}	$CH_2=CH(CH_2)_8CO_2$-2-ethylhexyl	2-Ethyl-hexyl	$(CH_2)_{10}CO_2$-2-ethylhexyl	61	200/0.002 mol. dist.	1.4534 (30)	59
C_{20}	$CH_2=CHCO_2(CH_2)_{16}CH_3$	2-Ethyl-hexyl	$CH_2CH_2CO_2(CH_2)_{16}CH_3$	46	205/0.003 mol. dist.		59

REACTION OF PHOSPHORUS TRICHLORIDE WITH UNSATURATED COMPOUNDS

Phosphorus trichloride does not react with olefins or acetylenes in the absence of oxygen or a peroxide. In the presence of a large amount of oxygen the following reactions take place.[5,61,63,78,79]

$$HC\equiv CH + PCl_3 + \tfrac{1}{2}O_2 \rightarrow HCCl = CHPOCl_2$$

$$H_2C = CH_2 + PCl_3 + \tfrac{1}{2}O_2 \rightarrow H_2CClCH_2POCl_2$$

The reactions are carried out at temperatures between $-15°$ and $25°$. In most cases phosphorus trichloride is mixed with the unsaturated compound and oxygen is introduced to the mixture. In reactions with gaseous unsaturated compounds the 1:1 mixture of oxygen and the unsaturated compound can be combined with the phosphorus trichloride.[61,63,78]

Phosphorus trichloride and octene–1 react at $85°$ in the absence of oxygen but in the presence of acetyl peroxide to give a 1:1 adduct, b.p. $86°/0.5$ mm, in 52% yield.[33,34]

$$C_6H_{13}CH = CH_2 + ClPCl_2 \rightarrow C_6H_{13}CHClCH_2PCl_2$$

Phosphorus trichloride reacts with vinyl chloride in the presence of oxygen to give a liquid, b.p. $209°/750$ mm, n_D 1.4998 $(20°)$, in 68% yield, which is a mixture of two products.[63]

$$CH_2 = CHCl + 2PCl_3 + O_2 \begin{cases} \rightarrow CHCl_2CH_2POCl_2 \ (30\text{–}35\%) \\ \rightarrow CH_2ClCHClPOCl_2 \ (65\text{–}70\%) \end{cases} + POCl_3$$

The reaction of phosphorus trichloride with allyl chloride produces a product, b.p. $105°/34$ mm, n_D 1.5073 $(20°)$, in 79% yield, which is probably a mixture of two compounds.[63]

$$CH_2 = CHCH_2Cl + 2PCl_3 + O_2 \begin{cases} \rightarrow CH_2ClCHClCH_2POCl_2 \\ \rightarrow (CH_2Cl)_2CHPOCl_2 \end{cases} + POCl_3$$

The reaction of phosphorus trichloride with vinyltriethylsilane results in a product in low yield.[5]

$$(C_2H_5)_3SiCH = CH_2 + 2PCl_3 + O_2 \rightarrow (C_2H_5)_3SiCHClCH_2POCl_2 + POCl_3$$

This product is unstable and decomposes rapidly on standing.

Table 32. Reaction of Phosphorus Trichloride with Unsaturated Compounds in the Presence of Oxygen

C_n	Unsaturated compound	Product	% Yield	°C b.p./mm (m.p.)	n_D (°C)	Ref.
C_2	C_2H_2	$HCCl=CHPOCl_2$		60/1	1.5065 (20)	78
	C_2H_4	$CH_2ClCH_2POCl_2$		86/2	1.4998 (20)	61
C_3	Propylene	$C_3H_6ClPOCl_2$		86/2	1.4930 (20)	61
C_4	Vinyl acetylene	$CH_2=CHCCl=CHPOCl_2$		72/4	1.5291 (20)	78
	Butene	$C_4H_8ClPOCl_2$		86/5	1.4900 (20)	61
C_6	Hexyne-1	$CH_3(CH_2)_3CHCl=CHPOCl_2$		94/2	1.5059 (20)	78
C_8	Phenyl acetylene	$C_6H_5CHCl=CHPOCl_2$	24	122/2.5 (58)		78
	$(C_2H_5)_3SiCH=CH_2$	$(C_2H_5)_3SiCHClCH_2POCl_2$		130/5	1.4948 (20)	5

REACTIONS OF PHOSPHORUS TRICHLORIDE AND ALKYL AND ARYL PHOSPHORUS DICHLORIDES WITH SATURATED COMPOUNDS

Phosphorus trichloride as well as alkyl and aryl phosphorus dichloride do not react with saturated hydrocarbons in the absence of oxygen. In the presence of oxygen these phosphorus compounds react readily with a number of hydrocarbons as follows.

$$RH + 2PCl_3 + O_2 \rightarrow RPOCl_2 + POCl_3 + HCl$$

$$RH + 2R'PCl_2 + O_2 \rightarrow RR'P(O)Cl + R'OCl_2 + HCl$$

The rate of the reaction is governed largely by the speed at which the oxygen is dissolved in the reaction mixture.[20] When air is used instead of oxygen, the rate of the reaction decreases appreciably.

The reactions are usually carried out between 0° and 70°. However, the yield of the products is not influenced by the temperature. In reactions with highly volatile hydrocarbons a mixture of the hydrocarbon and oxygen is bubbled through the phosphorus compound.[61] The reactions are sensitive to impurities. Iron powder or boron trifluoride inhibit the reactions,[20] and manganese compounds, ferric chloride, anthracene, and sulfur dioxide lower the yield.[40] The reactions are not affected by ultraviolet radiation.[7,61] In reactions with hydrocarbons in which all hydrogen atoms are identical in reactivity, single products are obtained. Otherwise, mixtures of isomers are usually obtained. The phosphorus-carbon linkage is formed most readily with the tertiary carbon atom, next with the secondary, and least readily with the primary.[62]

Phosphorus trichloride, oxygen, and ethane react to yield only one product (I).[11]

$$C_2H_5POCl_2$$

I

The reaction of phosphorus trichloride and oxygen with propane produces two isomers in 30% yield: compound II, b.p. 72°/11 mm, n_D 1.4750 (20°), and III, b.p. 76°/11 mm, n_D 1.4630 (20°).[62]

$$(CH_3)_2CHPOCl_2 \qquad CH_3CH_2CH_2POCl_2$$

II   III

The reaction of phosphorus trichloride and oxygen with butane produces IV, b.p. 69°/3.5 mm, in 45% yield;[11] and the reaction with 3–methylpentane produces V, b.p. 110°/16 mm.[7]

$$C_4H_9POCl_2 \qquad\qquad C_6H_{13}POCl_2$$

IV   V

The reaction of phosphorus trichloride and oxygen with methylcyclo-pentane produces VI, b.p. 99°/5 mm, in 30% yield.[20]

$$C_6H_{11}POCl_2$$

VI

Similarly, the reaction with methylcyclohexane produces VII, b.p. 122°/7 mm, in 26% yield;[20] and the reaction with n–heptane results in VIII, b.p. 107°/10 mm.[7]

$$C_7H_{13}POCl_2 \qquad\qquad C_7H_{15}POCl_2$$

VII   VIII

All these products are most likely a mixture of isomers. Neopentane phosphonic acid, m.p. 140°, is obtained in 22% yield by hydrolysis of the product from the reaction with neopentane.[23]

Phosphorus trichloride and oxygen react with 2, 3–dimethylbutane to give mainly IX, b.p. 82°/2 mm, n_D 1.4728 (20°), plus some X, b.p. 86°/2 mm, n_D 1.4720 (20°).[62]

$$(CH_3)_2CHC(POCl_2)(CH_3)_2 \qquad\qquad (CH_3)_2CHCH(CH_3)CH_2POCl_2$$

IX   X

The reaction of phosphorus trichloride and oxygen with trimethylmethane yields mainly XI, b.p. 79°/15 mm, m.p. 116°, plus XII, b.p. 61°/2 mm, n_D 1.4676 (20°).[62]

$$(CH_3)_3CPOCl_2 \qquad\qquad (CH_3)_2CHCH_2POCl_2$$

XI   XII

The reaction of phosphorus trichloride and oxygen with cyclopropane results in γ–chloropropylphosphonyl dichloride, b.p. 88°/2 mm, n_D 1.4928 (20°), in low yield.[20] Phosphorus trichloride and oxygen do not react with nitrocyclohexane,[20] isopropylbenzene,[20] or triphenylmethane.[23] Hydrolysis of the product of the reactions with toluene and ethylbenzene produces phenylmethanephosphonic acid, m.p. 168°, in 12% yield, and β–phenyl-ethanephosphonic acid, m.p. 136°, in 11% yield, respectively.[23]

Phosphorus chloride and oxygen react with aliphatic chlorides analo-gously to their reaction with hydrocarbons and yield the corresponding phosphonyl dichlorides, isolated as mixtures of possible isomers.[62] Phos-phorus chloride and oxygen react with propyl chloride, isopropyl chloride,

XIII, and XIV to yield mixtures of isomers boiling over a wide temperature range.[62]

$$(CH_3)_2CHCH_2Cl \qquad CH_3(CH_2)_6CH_2Cl$$

XIII   XIV

The products from the butyl chloride reaction can be fractionated to give four possible isomers: XV, b.p. 95°/2 mm, n_D 1.4963 (20°); XVI, b.p. 110°/2 mm, n_D 1.4950 (20°); XVII, b.p. 84°/2 mm, n_D 1.4946 (20°); and XVIII, b.p. 78°/2 mm, n_D 1.4886 (20°).[62]

$$ClCH_2CH_2CH(POCl_2)CH_3 \qquad Cl(CH_2)_4POCl_2$$

XV   XVI

$$ClCH_2CH(POCl_2)C_2H_5 \qquad ClCH(POCl_2)C_3H_7$$

XVII   XVIII

The reaction of phosphorus trichloride and oxygen with alkyl chlorosilanes such as XIX,[6] XX,[6] XXI,[6] XXII,[5] XXIII,[5] XXIV,[5] or XXV[5] produces phosphonyl chlorides.

$$C_2H_5SiCl_3 \qquad (C_2H_5)_2SiCl_2 \qquad (C_2H_5)_3SiCl$$

XIX   XX   XXI

$$n-C_3H_7SiCl_3 \qquad n-C_3H_7SiCH_3Cl_2 \qquad CH_3CHClSiCl_3 \qquad ClCH_2CH_2SiCl_3$$

XXII   XXIII   XXIV   XXV

When the yields are calculated on the basis of the reacted silane, they range between 24 and 72%. When they are calculated on the basis of the starting materials, however, the yields are low, 1.8–12.8%. Most of the products are unstable and decompose rapidly on standing.

The reaction of phosphorus trichloride and oxygen with tetraethylsilane results in the expected product, XXVI.[6]

$$(C_2H_5)_3SiC_2H_4POCl_2$$

XXVI

Through scission of the Si–O bond, the reaction of phosphorus trichloride and oxygen with hexaethyldisiloxane forms triethylchlorosilane in good yield.[6] This reaction takes place also in the absence of oxygen. Phosphorus tribromide reacts similarly with silanes to give triethylbromosilane.[6] Silanes such as XXVII and XXVIII ignite when brought in contact with phosphorus trichloride.[6]

Table 33. Reaction of Phosphorus Trichloride, Alkyl Phosphorus Chlorides, and Aryl Phosphorus Chlorides with Saturated Compounds in the Presence of Oxygen

C_n	Hydrocarbon	Phosphorus chloride	Product	% Yield	°C b.p./mm (m.p.)	n_D (°C)	Ref.
C_2	Ethane	PCl_3	$C_2H_5POCl_2$		181/760		11
	$C_2H_5SiCl_3$	PCl_3	$Cl_3SiCH_2CH_2POCl_2$	42	130/8 (44)		6
	$CH_3CHClSiCl_3$	PCl_3	$Cl_3SiC_2H_3ClPOCl_2$		138/4.5	1.5068 (20)	5
	$ClCH_2CH_2SiCl_3$	PCl_3	$Cl_3SiC_2H_3ClPOCl_2$		143/4	1.5125 (20)	5
C_3	n-$C_3H_7SiCl_3$	PCl_3	$SiC_3H_6POCl_2$		138/4	1.5003 (20)	5
C_4	Isobutane	PCl_3	i-$C_4H_9POCl_2$	55	56/2	1.4660 (20)	61
	$(C_2H_5)_2SiCl_2$	PCl_3	$Cl_2Si(C_2H_5)C_2H_4POCl_2$	53	144/8	1.4960 (20)	6
	n-$C_3H_7Si(CH_3)Cl_2$	PCl_3	$Cl_2Si(CH_3)C_3H_6POCl_2$		141/4	1.4978 (20)	5
C_5	n-Pentane	PCl_3	$C_5H_{11}POCl_2$	55	68/2	1.4694 (20)	61
	Cyclopentane	PCl_3	$C_5H_9POCl_2$	35	98/6	1.4973 (20)	20
	2-Methylbutane	PCl_3	i-$C_5H_{11}POCl_2$	55	65/2	1.4708 (20)	61
C_6	Cyclohexane	PCl_3	$C_6H_{11}POCl_2$	50	127/15 (39)		7, 11, 20, 22, 40, 70
C_7	n-Heptane	PCl_3	$C_7H_{15}POCl_2$	55	97/2	1.4830 (20)	61
	2, 2, 4-Trimethylpentane	PCl_3	i-$C_8H_{17}POCl_2$	55	81/2	1.4707 (20)	61
C_6	n-Hexane	PCl_3	$C_6H_{13}POCl_2$	55	83/3		61
	2, 3-Dimethylbutane	PCl_3	i-$C_6H_{13}POCl_2$	55	75/2	1.4715 (20)	61, 62
	$(C_2H_5)_3SiCl$	PCl_3	$ClSi(C_2H_5)_2C_2H_4POCl_2$	56	145/8	1.4910	6
C_8	$(C_2H_5)_4Si$	PCl_3	$(C_2H_5)_3SiC_2H_4POCl_2$	62	143/8	1.4895	6

Table 33. (cont.) **Reaction of Phosphorus Trichloride, Alkyl Phosphorus Chlorides, and Aryl Phosphorus Chlorides with Saturated Compounds in the Presence of Oxygen**

C_n	Hydrocarbon	Phosphorus chloride	Product	% Yield	°C b.p./mm (m.p.)	n_D (°C)	Ref.
C_3	Propane	CH_3PCl_2	CH_3—POCl—C_3H_7	25	79/4	1.4628 (20)	60
C_6	Cyclohexane	CH_3PCl_2	CH_3—POCl—C_6H_{11}	44	101/3 (26)	1.4988 (20)	60
	Cyclohexane	$C_2H_5PCl_2$	C_2H_5—POCl—C_6H_{11}	68	118/3	1.5002 (20)	60
	Cyclohexane	$C_6H_5PCl_2$	C_6H_5—POCl—C_6H_{11}	36	192/6	1.5560 (20)	79

$$CH_3SiHCl_2 \qquad\qquad C_2H_5SiHCl_2$$

$$\text{XXVII} \qquad\qquad \text{XXVIII}$$

Acetyl chloride fails to react with phosphorus trichloride and oxygen.[20] Also, no reaction occurs between phosphorus tribromide and cyclohexane.[7]

Only a few reactions of alkyl or aryl phosphorus dichloride with saturated compounds are reported.[60,79]

REACTIONS OF TRIALKYL PHOSPHITES AND RELATED COMPOUNDS WITH HALOMETHANES

Trialkyl phosphites react readily with carbon tetrachloride at 80° to give dialkyl trichloromethane phosphonates in good yield.[3,12,24,29-31,38,48]

$$(RO)_3P + Cl_3CCl \rightarrow (RO)_2P(O)CCl_3 + RCl$$

Phosphites with different alkyl groups give dialkyl esters of trichloromethylphosphonic acid with either two identical alkyl groups or two different alkyl groups. The lighter alkyl radical is eliminated in preference to the heavier alkyl radical as a rule, and therefore the nature of the product depends largely on the nature of the phosphite used in the reaction.[30,31]

$$C_2H_5OP(OCH_3)_2 + Cl_3CCl \rightarrow Cl_3CP(O)(OCH_3)(OC_2H_5) + CH_3Cl$$

$$C_2H_5OP(O-n-C_3H_7)_2 + Cl_3CCl \rightarrow Cl_3CP(O)(O-n-C_3H_7)_2 + C_2H_5Cl$$

Although these reactions are usually carried out in the absence of free radical initiators, such initiators influence the course of the reactions. Benzoyl peroxide at 80° causes an increase in the rate of the reaction of triethyl phosphite with carbon tetrachloride.[3,12] In the dark at room temperature no reaction occurs.[3] In ultraviolet light the same reactants produce diethyl trichloromethane phosphonate in 80% yield.[12] Addition of hydroquinone to the reaction mixture inhibits the reaction.[12] Such results are consistent with the free radical nature of these processes.[3,12,31]

Dialkyl esters of aryl phosphorous acids (I) react with carbon tetrachloride to give esters of trichloromethylarylphosphinic acids (II).[25,26,35]

$$RP(OR')_2 + Cl_3CCl \rightarrow \begin{array}{c} R \\ \diagdown \\ Cl_3C \diagup \end{array} P(O)OR' + R'Cl$$

$$\text{I} \qquad\qquad\qquad \text{II}$$

$$R = C_6H_5,\ CH_3C_6H_4,\ CH_3OC_6H_4$$

$$R' = CH_3,\ C_2H_5,\ n\text{-}C_3H_7,\ i\text{-}C_3H_7,\ n\text{-}C_4H_9,\ i\text{-}C_4H_9$$

Alkyl esters of diphenyl phosphinous acid (III) react with carbon tetrachloride to give diphenyltrichlorophenylphosphine oxide (IV), the alkyl radical being eliminated as alkyl chloride.[26]

$$(C_6H_5)_2POR'' \rightarrow (C_6H_5)_2P(O)CCl_3 + R''Cl$$

III   IV

R'' $= C_2H_5$, i-C_3H_7

Bromotrichloromethane reacts similarly to carbon tetrachloride. For instance, in the reaction of bromotrichloromethane with triethyl phosphite, compound V is obtained in 88% yield.[12,28] In the reaction with VI, product VII, b.p. 147°/1 mm, m.p. 79°, is obtained in 80% yield.[25]

$(C_2H_5O)_2P(O)CCl_3$ $C_6H_5P(OC_2H_5)_2$ $C_6H_5P(O)(OC_2H_5)CCl_3$

V   VI   VII

Trialkyl phosphites also react with other halomethanes, such as carbon tetrabromide,[25] bromoform,[28] iodoform,[28] fluorotrichloromethane,[28] and chloropicrin.[28] However, these reactions seem to be more complex and are of no preparative utility to date. The reaction between phosphites containing vinyl groups and carbon tetrachloride has received little attention.[4]

The reaction of alkyl esters of pyrophosphoric acid with carbon tetrachloride proceeds through a rupture of the phosphorus-oxygen bonds of the ester, in accordance with the following scheme[27]:

$$(RO)_2PO \mid P(OR)_2 \rightarrow CCl_3P(OR)_2 + (RO)_2PCl$$
$$Cl_3C \mid Cl \qquad\qquad\qquad \overset{\|}{O}$$

$$(RO)_2P \mid OP(OR)_2 \rightarrow (RO)_2PCl + Cl_3CP(OR)_2$$
$$Cl_3C \mid Cl \qquad\qquad\qquad\quad \overset{\|}{O}$$

Thus, the reaction with the ethyl ester produces VIII, b.p. 50°/14 mm, IX, b.p. 88°/15 mm, and X, b.p. 123°/12 mm, n_D 1.4589 (20°).[27]

$(C_2H_5O)_2PCl$ $(C_2H_5O)_2P(O)Cl$ $CCl_3P(O)(OC_2H_5)_2$

VIII   IX   X

Similarly, the reaction with the n–propyl ester yields XI, b.p. 69°/12 mm, n_D 1.4409 (20°), XII, b.p. 106°/12 mm, and XIII, b.p. 144°/12 mm, n_D 1.4591 (20°).[27]

$(n–C_3H_7O)_2PCl$ $(n–C_3H_7O)_2P(O)Cl$ $CCl_3P(O)(O–n–C_3H_7)_2$

XI   XII   XIII

The reaction with the n–butyl ester yields only one product, XIV, b.p. 151°/10 mm, n_D 1.4523 (20°).[27]

$$CCl_3P(O)(O–n–C_4H_9)_2$$

XIV

These processes appear to be free radical in nature.

MISCELLANEOUS REACTIONS OF PHOSPHORUS COMPOUNDS

There are a number of reactions which involve various phosphorus compounds and which proceed by a free radical mechanism.

One such reaction is the interaction of trivalent phosphorus halides with diazonium salts. Phosphorus trichloride reacts with aryl diazonium fluoroborates in the presence of copper halides in dry solvents, and after hydrolysis and steam distillation of the reaction mixture aryl phosphoric acids (I) are obtained.[8]

$$RP(O)(OH)_2$$

I

R = aryl

The occurrence of an induction period in this reaction points to a radical mechanism. However, the formation of the products can be explained by an ionic mechanism equally well.

Another reaction of trivalent phosphorus compounds which most probably proceeds through a free radical mechanism is one which leads to the preparation of tetraarylphosphonium halides.[9,17–19,74] The Dodonow-Medox reaction utilizes arylphosphines, arylmagnesium halide, and oxygen.[9,17,74] In Horner and Hoffmann's method an aromatic or an aromatic-aliphatic phosphine is reacted with an aryl halogenide in the presence of an aryl or alkyl Grignard reagent and cobaltous chloride.[17,19] The Grignard reagent does not supply the radical for the formation of the product; it merely acts as a reducing agent for the transition halide, since the reaction of an arylphosphine with an aryl halogenide in the presence of an alkyl Grignard reagent produces only the arylphosphonium halide.[19] The mechanism of this reaction and the Dodonow-Medox reaction is somewhat obscure.

Table 34. Reaction of Phosphites with Carbon Tetrachloride

C_n	Alkyl phosphite	Product	% Yield	°C b.p./mm (m.p.)	n_D (°C)	Ref.
C_3	$(CH_3O)_3P$	$CCl_3P(O)(OCH_3)_2$	50	111/9	1.4580 (14)	24, 29
C_6	$(C_2H_5O)_3P$	$CCl_3P(O)(OC_2H_5)_2$	94	122/12	1.4612 (21) 1.4582 (25)	3, 12, 24 29, 38, 48
C_9	$(C_3H_5O)_3P$	$CCl_3P(O)(OC_3H_5)_2$	50	137/10	1.4552 (20)	24, 29
	$(n\text{-}C_3H_7O)_3P$	$CCl_3P(O)(O\text{-}n\text{-}C_3H_7)_2$	50	144/12	1.4582 (15)	24, 29
	$(i\text{-}C_3H_7O)_3P$	$CCl_3P(O)(O\text{-}i\text{-}C_3H_7)_2$	50	130/12	1.4478 (20)	24, 29
C_{12}	$(n\text{-}C_4H_9O)_3P$	$CCl_3P(O)(O\text{-}n\text{-}C_4H_9)_2$	25	145/7	1.4521 (18) 1.4490 (20)	24, 29 38, 48
	$(i\text{-}C_4H_9O)_3P$	$CCl_3P(O)(O\text{-}i\text{-}C_4H_9)_2$	50	145/9	1.4487 (17)	24, 29, 38
C_4	$C_2H_5OP(OCH_3)_2$	$CCl_3P(O)(OCH_3)(OC_2H_5)$	60	117/10	1.4620 (20)	31
C_8	$C_2H_5OP(O\text{-}i\text{-}C_3H_7)_2$	$CCl_3P(O)(O\text{-}i\text{-}C_3H_7)_2$	95	95/4	1.4560 (20)	31
	$C_2H_5OP(O\text{-}n\text{-}C_3H_7)_2$	$CCl_3P(O)(O\text{-}n\text{-}C_3H_7)_2$	36	124/7	1.4625 (20)	31
C_{10}	$C_2H_5OP(O\text{-}n\text{-}C_4H_9)_2$	$CCl_3P(O)(O\text{-}n\text{-}C_4H_9)_2$	45	152/10	1.4600 (20)	31
	$C_2H_5OP(O\text{-}i\text{-}C_4H_9)_2$	$CCl_3P(O)(O\text{-}i\text{-}C_4H_9)_2$	70	142/10	1.4585 (20)	31
C_{11}	$C_6H_5CH_2OP(OC_2H_5)_2$	$CCl_3P(O)(OC_2H_5)_2$				3
C_{12}	$C_2H_5OP(O\text{-}i\text{-}C_5H_{11})_2$	$CCl_3P(O)(O\text{-}i\text{-}C_5H_{11})_2$	45	134/3	1.4615 (20)	31
C_6	$n\text{-}C_4H_9OP(OCH_3)_2$	$CCl_3P(O)(OCH_3)(O\text{-}n\text{-}C_4H_9)$	31	125/7	1.4625 (20)	31
C_8	$n\text{-}C_4H_9OP(OC_2H_5)_2$	$CCl_3P(O)(OC_2H_5)(O\text{-}n\text{-}C_4H_9)$	45	106/5	1.4602 (20)	31
C_{10}	$(C_2H_5O)_2POC_6H_5$	$CCl_3P(O)(OC_2H_5)(OC_6H_5)$	44	155/8	1.5163 (20)	30
C_{12}	$n\text{-}C_4H_9OP(O\text{-}i\text{-}C_4H_9)_2$	$CCl_3P(O)(O\text{-}n\text{-}C_4H_9)(O\text{-}i\text{-}C_4H_9)_2$	50	107/3	1.4545 (20)	31
C_{14}	$n\text{-}C_4H_9OP(O\text{-}i\text{-}C_5H_{11})_2$	$CCl_3P(O)(O\text{-}n\text{-}C_4H_9)(O\text{-}i\text{-}C_5H_{11})_2$	84	150/11	1.4575 (20)	31

Table 34. (cont.) Reaction of Phosphites with Carbon Tetrachloride

C_n	Alkyl phosphite	Product	% Yield	°C b.p./mm (m.p.)	n_D (°C)	Ref.
C_8	$C_6H_5P(OCH_3)_2$	C_6H_5—P(O)OCH$_3$, CCl$_3$	61	(108)		24, 25
C_{10}	$C_6H_5P(OC_2H_5)_2$	C_6H_5—P(O)OC$_2$H$_5$, CCl$_3$	66	147/1 (79)		24, 25
C_{12}	$C_6H_5P(O-n-C_3H_7)_2$	C_6H_5—P(O)O-n-C$_3$H$_7$, CCl$_3$	70	151/1	1.4945 (19)	24, 25
C_{14}	$C_6H_5P(O-i-C_4H_9)_2$	C_6H_5—P(O)O-i-C$_4$H$_9$, CCl$_3$	58	155/1	1.4993 (18)	24, 25
C_9	p-CH$_3$C$_6$H$_4$P(OCH$_3$)$_2$	C_7H_7—P(O)OCH$_3$, CCl$_3$		129/2	1.5312 (20)	35

Table 34. (cont.)   Reaction of Phosphites with Carbon Tetrachloride

C_n	Alkyl phosphite	Product	% Yield	°C b.p./mm (m.p.)	n_D (°C)	Ref.
C_{11}	p–$CH_3C_6H_4P(OC_2H_5)_2$	C_7H_7–P(O)OC$_2$H$_5$ / CCl$_3$		157/2	1.5428 (16)	35
C_{13}	p–$CH_3C_6H_4P(O$-n-$C_3H_7)_2$	C_7H_7–P(O)O-n-C$_3$H$_7$ / CCl$_3$		169/2	1.5370 (16)	35
C_{15}	p–$CH_3C_6H_4P(O$-n-$C_4H_9)_2$	C_7H_7–P(O)O-n-C$_4$H$_9$ / CCl$_3$		180/2	1.5267 (16)	35
	p–$CH_3C_6H_4P(O$-i-$C_4H_9)_2$	C_7H_7–P(O)O-i-C$_4$H$_9$ / CCl$_3$		179/2	1.5294 (16)	35
C_{11}	p–$CH_3OC_6H_4P(OC_2H_5)_2$	p–CH$_3$OC$_6$H$_4$–P(O)OC$_2$H$_5$ / CCl$_3$		146/4		26
C_{14}	$(C_6H_5)_2POC_2H_5$	$(C_6H_5)_2P(O)CCl_3$		(138)		26
C_{15}	$(C_6H_5)_2POCH(CH_3)_2$	$(C_6H_5)_2P(O)CCl_3$		(138)		26

In a third method for the preparation of quaternary phosphonium halides, Horner and Hoffmann use diazonium salts and arylphosphines.[18]

$$Ar[N\!\!=\!\!N]X + (C_6H_5)_3P \rightarrow [ArN\!\!=\!\!NP(C_6H_5)_3]X$$
$$\rightarrow [ArP(C_6H_5)_3]X + N_2$$

The success of this method depends on the pH of the solution. The diazonium solution must be well buffered with sodium acetate, because the reaction takes an entirely different course in an acid medium. The arylphosphine solution is added to the diazonium solution, and after the evolution of nitrogen has ceased the quaternary salt is isolated from the aqueous phase. The yield is usually between 40 and 80%.[18] A number of quaternary salts are listed in Table 35.

Another reaction of diazonium compounds which seems to involve free radical species is the reduction of diazonium salts with hypophosphorous acid to give the corresponding hydrocarbon.[36,37]

$$RNH_2 + HNO_2 \rightarrow RN_2^+X^- \xrightarrow{H_3PO_2} RH + N_2$$

Since the conversion of primary aromatic amines to the corresponding diazonium compounds and the reduction with hypophosphorous acid are both easy to perform, this deamination reaction is a useful preparative method. Kornblum and co-workers found that traces of oxidizing compounds of iron, copper, chromium, or manganese accelerate the reaction, whereas benzoquinone retards or inhibits the reaction.[36,37] They concluded that the reaction is a free radical chain process.

Diazonium salts can also be reduced with phosphorous acid.[32] The reaction of p–methoxybenzene diazonium chloride in the presence of phosphorous acid at room temperature for 30 days produces anisol in only 35% yield. Ether peroxide accelerates the reaction to give anisol in yields almost as high as those obtained with hypophosphorous acid. This catalysis suggests a possible free radical chain mechanism in which the phosphorus-hydrogen bond of phosphorous acid is involved.

The reactions of trialkylphosphines and -phosphites with sulfur compounds are radical processes. For example, tri–n–butylphosphine reacts at 60° with isobutyl or n–butyl mercaptan in the presence of azonitrile or ultraviolet light to give tributylphosphine sulfide (II), in high yield.[71-73]

$$(n\text{–}C_4H_9)_3PS$$

II

Triethyl phosphite and octyl mercaptan after 6 hr under ultraviolet light produce triethylthionophosphate, b.p. 45°/0.5 mm, n_D 1.4461 (20°), in 92% yield, and octane, in 88% yield.[16] With benzyl mercaptan, triethylthionophosphate plus toluene are obtained.[16]

Similar results are obtained with trialkyl phosphites and a disulfide.[71-73] Triethyl phosphite reacts with ethyl disulfide, butyl disulfide, or isobutyl disulfide either on exposure to ultraviolet light at 55–65° or in the presence of di–t–butyl peroxide at 120° to give triethylphosphorothionate, b.p. 103°/11 mm, n_D 1.4455 (25°), in nearly quantitative yield.[73] A mixture of triethyl phosphite, butane–1–thiol, and carbon tetrachloride boiled for 12 hr in the presence of benzoyl peroxide forms triethylphosphorothionate, in 18% yield, diethyltrichloromethylphosphonate, in 22% yield, and S–butyldiethylphosphorothioate, $(C_2H_5)_2P(O)SC_4H_9$, in 60% yield.[3] Triethyl phosphite, n–dibutyl disulfide, and di–t–butyl peroxide react at 120° under 325 atm of carbon monoxide to form n–butylthiovalerate, b.p. 219°, n_D 1.4608 (25°), in 99% yield.[71] The reaction is carried out in a glass-lined hydrogenation bomb.

Triphenylphosphine reacts with bromoform at 150° in the absence of a catalyst, or at 80° in the presence of benzoyl peroxide, or at room temperature in ultraviolet light to give triphenyl(dibromomethyl)phosphonium bromide, $[(C_6H_5)_3P^+CHBr_2]Br^-$, m.p. 235°.[53]

The reaction of dialkyl phosphites with chloranil to give substituted dialkyl–(4–hydroxy–2, 3, 5, 6–tetrachlorophenyl) phosphates is markedly influenced by ultraviolet light and probably involves free radical intermediates.[52]

IIIa　R = CH₃

IIIb　R = C₂H₅

In the dark at room temperature, IIIa, m.p. 237°, and IIIb, m.p. 180°, are each obtained in about 25% yield. Under ultraviolet exposure the yield increases to about 65%.

Another interesting free radical reaction occurs between diethyl or diaryl phosphites and aldehydes and ketones.[64] The reactions are catalyzed by di–t–butyl peroxide or ultraviolet light. The peroxide-catalyzed reactions are carried out around 130° and those catalyzed by ultraviolet light around 80°. The products are dialkyl α–hydroxy phosphonates, which are reportedly purified by distillation. Thus, dipropyl phosphite and methylethyl ketone react in the presence of di–t–butyl peroxide for 24 hr to form dipropyl 2–hydroxybutane–2–phosphonate, n_D 1.4518 (20°). Dibutyl phosphite and heptaldehyde react to form dibutyl 1–hydroxyheptane–1–phosphonate, n_D 1.4416 (20°), in 80% yield. Dipropyl phosphite and benzaldehyde react to form dipropylphenylhydroxymethane phosphonate, n_D 1.4908 (20°), in 54% yield. Dipropyl phosphite and acetophenone form 1–hydroxy–1–phenylethane–1–phosphonate, n_D 1.4751 (20°). And diphenyl phosphite and isovaleryl aldehyde react in ultraviolet light to form diphenyl 1–hydroxy–3–methylbutane–1–phosphonate.

The thermal decomposition of pentaphenyl phosphorus or its decomposition under the influence of ultraviolet radiation takes place through a free radical process.[76,77] In benzene, diphenyl and triphenylphosphine are formed.[76,77] In chloroform,[54,55] carbon tetrachloride,[54,55] and pentachloroethane, tetraphenylphosphonium chloride is formed.

$$(C_6H_5)_5 + CHCl_3 \rightarrow (C_6H_5)_4PCl + C_6H_6$$

$$(C_6H_5)_5 + CCl_4 \rightarrow (C_6H_5)_4PCl + C_6H_5Cl$$

In methyl iodide, tetraphenylphosphonium iodide, m.p. 315°, is produced in nearly quantitative yield.[56] The mechanism of this last reaction is complex, since benzene, toluene, diphenylmethane, ethane, and iodobenzene are all formed. Pentaphenyl phosphorus reacts with a large amount of mercury to form phenylmercuric chloride in quantitative yield.[54] The free radical reactions of pentavalent phosphorus are of very limited preparative value at present.

Air oxidation of secondary phosphines can be utilized for the preparation of the corresponding phosphine oxides.[57]

$$2R_2PH + O_2 \rightarrow R_2PH \atop \downarrow \atop O$$

The reaction probably proceeds through intermediate peroxide formation and is a free radical process. Oxidation is inhibited by hydroquinone. Interestingly, the reaction does not take place in benzene. The reaction is carried out by dissolving the phosphine in isopropanol and passing dry air at 45–50° through the solution. In another method a thin layer of phosphine is exposed to air at room temperature. Under these conditions no phosphinic acids are formed. These reactions are listed in Table 36.

The phosphonation of aromatic compounds is also a free radical reaction. Diethyl phosphite reacts with methyl benzoate in the presence of di–t–butyl peroxide when boiled for 24 hr to give diethylisobutyl phosphonate, b.p. 83°/3 mm, in 45% yield, and p–carboxyphenylphosphonic acid ester (IV), in high yield.[10]

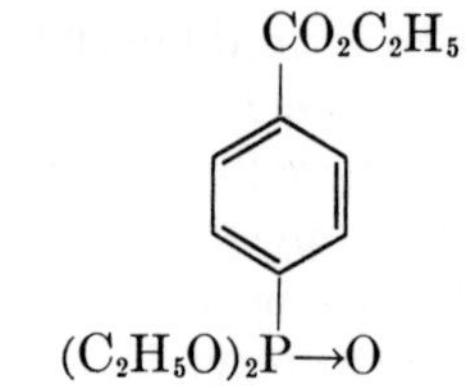

$$CO_2C_2H_5$$

$$(C_2H_5O)_2P{\rightarrow}O$$

IV

On hydrolysis, the corresponding acid, m.p. 378°, is formed.

This interesting reaction has recently been extended to include polycyclic aromatic and heterocyclic compounds.[21] Thus, naphthalene, anthracene, phenanthrene, dibenzofuran, or carbazole reacts with diethyl phosphite in the presence of di–t–butyl peroxide to give a phosphonic acid derivative in 51–96% yield. The reaction with anthracene or phenanthrene forms mainly the 9–isomer, whereas the reaction with naphthalene, dibenzofuran, or carbazole forms a mixture of isomers. Ferrocene and pyridine do not react under these conditions. A by-product of these reactions is diethylisobutyl phosphonate, which is probably formed from diethyl phosphite and t–butoxy radical. The reaction product of anthracene and diethyl phosphite hydrolyzed with ethanolic hydrogen chloride results in anthracene–9–phosphonic acid, m.p. 282° (decomp.). Similarly, the reaction product of phenanthrene and diethyl phosphite yields phenanthrene–9–phosphonic acid, m.p. 227°, on hydrolysis.

Compounds of the general formula V react with a variety of unsaturated compounds in the presence of a free radical initiator such as benzoyl peroxide, azonitrile, or ultraviolet light.[44]

$$RPCl_2$$

V

R = alkyl, aryl, or aralkyl

Unfortunately, no monomeric products have been isolated. The addition products are converted directly to polymers by hydrolysis.

Table 35. Preparation of Phosphonium Halides

Reagents used in addition to phosphine	Phosphonium halide, [R'R''R'''R''''P] X	°C (m.p.)	Ref.
Grignard + O$_2$	R', R'', R''', R'''' = C$_6$H$_5$; X = Br	(287)	9
Grignard + CoCl$_2$	R', R'', R''', R'''' = C$_6$H$_5$; X = Br		19
Diazonium salt	R', R'', R''', R'''' = C$_6$H$_5$; X = I	(337)	18
Diazonium salt	R', R'', R''' = C$_6$H$_5$; R'''' = p-CH$_3$C$_6$H$_4$; X = I	(208)	18
Diazonium salt	R', R'', R''' = C$_6$H$_5$; R'''' = m-CH$_3$C$_6$H$_4$; X = I	(188)	18
Diazonium salt	R', R'', R''' = C$_6$H$_5$; R'''' = o-ClC$_6$H$_4$; X = I	(243)	18
Diazonium salt	R', R'', R''' = C$_6$H$_5$; R'''' = p-ClC$_6$H$_4$; X = I	(217)	18
Diazonium salt	R', R'', R''' = C$_6$H$_5$; R'''' = p-BrC$_6$H$_4$; X = I	(211)	18
Diazonium salt	R', R'', R''' = C$_6$H$_5$; R'''' = o-NO$_2$C$_6$H$_4$; X = I	(230, decomp.)	18
Diazonium salt	R', R'', R''' = C$_6$H$_5$; R'''' = p-NO$_2$C$_6$H$_4$; X = I	(228, decomp.)	18
Diazonium salt	R', R'', R''' = C$_6$H$_5$; R'''' = m-NO$_2$C$_6$H$_4$; X = I	(215, decomp.)	18
Grignard + CoCl$_2$	R', R'', R''' = C$_6$H$_5$; R'''' = p-CH$_3$OC$_6$H$_4$; X = I	(209)	19
Grignard + CoCl$_2$	R', R'', R''' = C$_6$H$_5$; R'''' = m-CH$_3$OC$_6$H$_4$; X = I	(204)	19
Diazonium salt	R', R'', R''' = C$_6$H$_5$; R'''' = p-C$_2$H$_5$O$_2$CC$_6$H$_4$; X = I	(204, decomp.)	18
Grignard + CoCl$_2$	R', R'', R''' = C$_6$H$_5$; R'''' = 2, 5-(CH$_3$O)$_2$C$_6$H$_3$; X = I	(202)	19
Grignard + CoCl$_2$	R', R'', R''' = C$_6$H$_5$; R'''' = α-pyridyl; X = I	(253, decomp.)	19
Diazonium salt	R', R'', R''' = C$_6$H$_5$; R'''' = α-naphthyl; X = I	(278)	18
Diazonium salt	R', R'', R''' = C$_6$H$_5$; R'''' = β-naphthyl; X = I	(256)	18
Grignard + CoCl$_2$	R', R'', R''' = C$_6$H$_5$; R'''' = p-C$_6$H$_5$C$_6$H$_4$; X = I	(242)	19
Diazonium salt	R', R'', R''' = p-CH$_3$C$_6$H$_4$; R'''' = C$_6$H$_5$; X = I	(196)	18
Grignard + CoCl$_2$	R', R'' = C$_6$H$_5$; R''', R'''' = C$_2$H$_5$; X = I	(206)	19
Diazonium salt	R', R'' = C$_6$H$_5$; R''', R'''' = p-CH$_3$C$_6$H$_4$; X = I	(201)	18
Diazonium salt	R', R'' = p-CH$_3$C$_6$H$_4$; R''' = C$_6$H$_5$; R'''' = p-NO$_2$C$_6$H$_4$; X = I	(143)	18

Table 36.   Air Oxidation of Secondary Phosphines to Phosphine Oxides

Phosphine	Product	% Yield	°C (m.p.)	Ref.
$(n\text{-}C_4H_9)_2PH$	$(n\text{-}C_4H_9)_2P(O)H$	47	66	57
$(i\text{-}C_4H_9)_2PH$	$(i\text{-}C_4H_9)_2P(O)H$			57
$(n\text{-}C_8H_{17})_2PH$	$(n\text{-}C_8H_{17})_2P(O)H$	88	85	57
$(n\text{-}C_{12}H_{25})_2PH$	$(n\text{-}C_{12}H_{25})_2P(O)H$	71	99	57
$(C_6H_5CH_2CH_2)_2PH$	$(C_6H_5CH_2CH_2)_2P(O)H$	81	70	57
$(NCCH_2CH_2)_2PH$	$(NCCH_2CH_2)_2P(O)H$	90	98	57
$NCCH_2CH_2$ $\diagdown$ PH $\diagup$ $n\text{-}C_8H_{17}$	$NCCH_2CH_2$ $\diagdown$ P(O)H $\diagup$ $n\text{-}C_8H_{17}$		68	57
$C_2H_5O_2CCH_2CH_2$ $\diagdown$ PH $\diagup$ $n\text{-}C_8H_{17}$	$C_2H_5O_2CCH_2CH_2$ $\diagdown$ P(O)H $\diagup$ $n\text{-}C_8H_{17}$	80	51	57
$(C_6H_5)_2PH$	$(C_6H_5)_2P(O)H$	85	54	57

REFERENCES

1 Arbuzov, Vinokurova, and Perfileeva, *Dok. Akad. Nauk,* **127,** 1217 (1959).
2 Bittles and Joyce, U.S. 2,559,754 (1951).
3. Cadogan and Foster, *J. Chem. Soc.,* **1961,** 3071.
4 Chadaeva and Kamai, *Zh. Obsh. Khim.,* **20,** 1487 (1950).
5 Chernyshev, *Izvest. Akad. Nauk,* **1958,** 96.
6 Chernyshev and Petrov, *Dok. Akad. Nauk,* **105,** 282 (1955).
7 Clayton and Jensen, *J. Am. Chem. Soc.,* **70,** 3880 (1948).
8 Crofts, *Quart. Revs.* **12,** 341 (1958).
9 Dodonow and Medox, *Chem. Ber.,* **61,** 907 (1928).
10 Fields and Rolih, *Chem. Ind.,* **1960,** 999.
11 Graf, *Chem. Ber.,* **85,** 9 (1952).
12 Griffin, *Chem. Ind.,* **1958,** 415.
13 Griffin, *J. Org. Chem.,* **25,** 665 (1960).
14 Griffin and Wells, *J. Org. Chem.,* **24,** 2049 (1959).
15 Hanford and Joyce, U.S. 2,478,390 (1949).
16 Hoffmann, *et al., J. Am. Chem. Soc.,* **78,** 6414 (1956).
17 Horner and Hoffmann, *Ang. Chem.,* **68,** 473 (1956).
18 Horner and Hoffmann, *Chem. Ber.,* **91,** 45 (1958).
19 Horner and Hoffmann, *Chem. Ber.,* **91,** 50 (1958).
20 Isbell and Wadsworth, *J. Am. Chem. Soc.,* **78,** 6042 (1956).
21 Jason and Fields, *J. Org. Chem.,* **27,** 1402 (1962).
22 Jensen and Clayton, U.S. 2,683,168 (1954).
23 Jensen and Noller, *J. Am. Chem. Soc.,* **71,** 2384 (1949).
24 Kamai, *C.r. acad. Sci. USSR,* **55,** 219 (1947).
25 Kamai, *Zh. Obsh. Khim.,* **18,** 443 (1948).
26 Kamai, *Dok. Akad. Nauk,* **66,** 389 (1949).
27 Kamai, *Dok. Akad. Nauk,* **70,** 233 (1950).
28 Kamai, *Dok. Akad. Nauk,* **79,** 795 (1951).
29 Kamai and Egorova, *Zh. Obsh. Khim.,* **16,** 1521 (1946).
30 Kamai and Kharrasova, Trudy Kazan Khem. Teknol. Inst. Emeny S. M. Kirova, **23,** 122 (1957).
31 Kamai and Kharrasova, *Zh. Obsh. Khim.,* **27,** 953 (1957).
32 Kelley, Univ. Mich. Ann Arbor Microfilm, Publ. No. 19415.
33 Kharasch, U.S. 2,489,091 (1949).
34 Kharasch, Jensen, and Urry, *J. Am. Chem. Soc.,* **67,** 1864 (1945).
35 Khisamova and Kamai, *Zh. Obsh. Khim.,* **20,** 1162 (1950).
36 Kornblum, in *Organic Reactions,* edited by Adams, vol. II, p. 277, John Wiley and Sons, New York (1944).
37 Kornblum, Cooper, and Taylor, *J. Am. Chem. Soc.,* **72,** 3013 (1950).
38 Kosolapoff, *J. Am. Chem. Soc.,* **69,** 1002 (1947).
39 Ladd and Harvey, U.S. 2,664,438 (1953).
40 Lesfauries and Rumpf, *Bull. soc. chim. France,* **1950,** 542.
41 Linville, U.S. 2,843,615 (1958).
42 Mann and Miller, *J. Chem. Soc.,* **1952,** 4453.
43 McConnell and Coover, *J. Am. Chem. Soc.,* **79,** 1961 (1957).
44 McCormack, U.S. 2,671,077–80 (1954).
45 N. V. de Bataafsche Petroleum Maatschappij, Brit. 660,918 (1951).
46 N. V. de Bataafsche Petroleum Maatschappij, Brit. 673,451 (1952).

[47] N. V. de Bataafsche Petroleum Maatschappij, Dutch 69,357 (1952).
[48] N. V. de Bataafsche Petroleum Maatschappij, Brit. 692,261 (1953).
[49] Parshall, England, and Lindsey, *J. Am. Chem. Soc.*, **81**, 4801 (1959).
[50] Preis, Myers, and Jensen, *J. Am. Chem. Soc.*, **77**, 6225 (1955).
[51] Pudovik, Moshkina, and Konovalova, *Zh. Obsh. Khim.*, **29**, 3342 (1959).
[52] Ramirez and Dershowitz, *J. Org. Chem.*, **22**, 1282 (1957).
[53] Ramirez and McKelvie, *J. Am. Chem. Soc.*, **79**, 5829 (1957).
[54] Rasuvaev and Osanova, *Dok. Akad. Nauk*, **104**, 552 (1955).
[55] Rasuvaev and Osanova, *Zh. Obsh. Khim.*, **26**, 2531 (1956).
[56] Rasuvaev, Osanova, and Shlyapnikova, *Zh. Obsh. Khim.*, **27**, 1466 (1957).
[57] Rauhut and Currier, *J. Org. Chem.*, **26**, 4626 (1961).
[58] Rauhut, *et al.*, *J. Org. Chem.*, **26**, 5138 (1961).
[59] Sasin, *et al.*, *J. Am. Chem. Soc.*, **81**, 6275 (1959).
[60] Soborovskii and Zinovev, *Zh. Obsh. Khim.*, **24**, 516 (1954).
[61] Soborovskii, Zinovev, and Englin, *Dok. Akad. Nauk*, **67**, 293 (1949).
[62] Soborovskii, Zinovev, and Englin, *Dok. Akad. Nauk*, **73**, 333 (1950).
[63] Soborovskii, Zinovev, and Muler, *Dok. Akad. Nauk*, **109**, 98 (1956).
[64] Stiles, U.S. 2,593,213 (1952).
[65] Stiles and Rust, U.S. 2,724,718 (1955).
[66] Stiles, Rust, and Vaughan, *J. Am. Chem. Soc.*, **74**, 3282 (1952).
[67] Stiles, Rust, and Vaughan, U.S. 2,803,597 (1957).
[68] Stiles, Vaughan, and Rust, *J. Am. Chem. Soc.*, **80**, 714 (1958).
[69] U.S. Rubber Co., Brit. 694,772 (1953).
[70] Viout, *J. recherches centre natl. recherches sci. Labs. Bellevue (Paris)*, No. 28, 15 (1954).
[71] Walling, Basedow, and Savas, *J. Am. Chem. Soc.*, **82**, 2181 (1960).
[72] Walling and Rabinowitz, *J. Am. Chem. Soc.*, **79**, 5326 (1957).
[73] Walling and Rabinowitz, *J. Am. Chem. Soc.*, **81**, 1243 (1959).
[74] Willard, Perkins, and Blicke, *J. Am. Chem. Soc.*, **70**, 737 (1948).
[75] Williams and Hamilton, *J. Am. Chem. Soc.*, **77**, 3411 (1955).
[76] Wittig and Rieber, *Ann. Chem.*, **562**, 187 (1949).
[77] Wittig and Geissler, *Ann. Chem.*, **580**, 44 (1953).
[78] Zinovev, Muler, and Soborovskii, *Zh. Obsh. Khim.*, **24**, 381 (1954).
[79] Zinovev and Soborovskii, *Zh. Obsh. Khim.*, **26**, 3030 (1956).

CHAPTER VI

Addition of Silicon and Germanium Compounds to Unsaturated Compounds

ADDITION OF SILANES

Many silanes react under free radical conditions with a variety of unsaturated compounds to give 1:1 adducts. These silanes include dimethylsilane,[31] amylsilane,[63] triethylsilane,[26] triethoxysilane,[26] phenylsilane,[46,47,58,60] methylphenylsilane,[63] triphenylsilane,[27,28,45] trichlorosilane,[1,2,6−11,14−25,31,33−35,] [37,40,41,43,44,47,50,52,56−58,62,64,66−69] methylphenylchlorosilane,[2−4] tribromosilane, [2,5,47,59,63−65] dichlorosilane,[31] methyldichlorosilane,[2−4,10,21,30,31,33,44,56,64] diethylchlorosilane,[12,13] phenyldichlorosilane,[2−4] diphenylchlorosilane,[2] methyldiethoxysilane,[31] tetrachlorodisilanemethane,[65] dichlorodi−(3, 3, 3−trifluoropropyl)silane,[31] and dimethyl−1, 1, 2, 2−tetrafluoroethylsilane.[29] Silane (SiH_4) itself condenses with acetylene, ethylene, or vinylsilane at high temperature in ultraviolet light. However, the methods required may not be easily adaptable to routine laboratory preparation.[70,71]

The addition of silanes to unsaturated compounds containing a terminal double bond proceeds in a non-Markownikoff fashion:

$$RCH{=}CH_2 + HSiR'R''R''' \rightarrow RCH_2CH_2SiR'R''R'''$$

The reaction of silanes with unsaturated compounds containing a nonterminal double bond produces a mixture of products.

$$CH_3CH_2CH{=}CHCH_3 + SiHCl_3 \rightarrow CH_3CH_2CH_2CH(SiCl_3)CH_3$$
$$+ CH_3CH_2CH(SiCl_3)CH_2CH_3$$

The reactions of silanes are initiated by ultraviolet light,[10,12−15,17−19,25,29,31,] [34,35,41,43,44,57,65] azonitrile,[40,62] peroxide,[1,6−11,16,18−20,28,33,37,38,43−47,49,50,52,56,57,62−64,66] heat,[2−5,68] or iron pentacarbonyl.[26] Peroxide-initiated reactions seem to give the most reliable results, in particular with halogenated olefins.[44] The most widely used peroxides are acetyl peroxide, benzoyl peroxide, di–t–butyl peroxide, t–butyl peracetate, and t–butyl perbenzoate. The reactions are carried out at 80–150°. The photochemical reactions are performed either at room temperature or at 90–110°.[65] The condensation reactions are commonly performed in an atmosphere of nitrogen gas. Reactions involving gaseous compounds such as acetylene[10,70] and ethylene[3–5,40,68,70] are performed in an autoclave.

The reaction of trichlorosilane with acetylene in a high-pressure autoclave produces bis(trichlorosilyl)ethane.[10] Trichlorosilane or methyldichlorosilane can be condensed with a number of olefins by irradiation with γ rays as the initiator. The reactions are carried out in 40–60 hr at room temperature by using γ rays from a 3.0-kilocurie Co^{60} source. The following olefins can be used: butene–2, isobutylene, 2–methyl–2–butene, cyclopentene, cyclohexene, 1–methylcyclohexene, allyl chloride, allyl acetate, allyl cyanide, cis–1, 2–dichloroethylene, 3, 3, 4, 4, 4–pentafluoro–1–pentene, and 2–methyl–3, 3, 4, 4, 5, 5, 5–heptafluoro–1–pentene. With styrene and α–methylstyrene, high-boiling polymers are produced.[21] In most cases good yields of products are obtained.

Silanes can be condensed with unsaturated chloro and fluoro compounds under free radical conditions. The reaction of trichlorosilane with dichloroacetylene in the presence of benzoyl peroxide at 70–80° for 65 hr yields the adduct I. This adduct can add another mole of silane, yielding a saturated product.[1]

$$ClC{\equiv}CCl + HSiCl_3 \rightarrow Cl_3SiCCl{=}CHCl$$

I

$$I + HSiCl_3 \rightarrow Cl_3SiCHClCHClSiCl_3$$

The reaction of trichlorosilane with trichloroethylene results in a low yield of product.[1]

The reaction of trichlorosilane with tetrachloroethylene in ultraviolet light results in a low yield (7%) of trichlorovinyltrichlorosilane, b.p. 68°/6.5 mm. This addition reaction is accompanied by dehydrochlorination.[43] The same product can be obtained in 12% yield when the reaction is carried out at 125° in the presence of t–butyl peroxide.[43] The reaction of trichlorosilane[34] or dimethylsilane[29] with tetrafluoroethylene in ultraviolet light results in 1:1 products in 44 and 83% yield, respectively. The product of the trichlorosilane reaction can be further condensed to give dimethyldi–(1, 1, 2, 2–tetrafluoroethyl)silane (II) in high yield.[29]

$$CF_2{=}CF_2 + (CH_3)_2SiHCF_2CF_2H \rightarrow (CH_3)_2Si(CF_2CF_2H)_2$$

II

Trichlorosilane and chlorotrifluoroethylene react at 125° in the presence of t–butyl peroxide to form compound III in 38% yield.[35,44]

$$CF_2{=}CClF + HSiCl_3 \rightarrow Cl_3SiCF_2CClFH$$

III

Trichlorosilane or methyldichlorosilane each react with trifluoropropene or 2, 3, 3, 4, 4, 4–hexafluorobutene to form 1:1 adducts.[44] The reactions can be catalyzed with t–butyl peroxide at 125° or ultraviolet light. The reactions are carried out in an atmosphere of nitrogen in a glass-lined autoclave, since stainless steel seems to retard the reactions. A nickel autoclave can be used but is less satisfactory. Under similar conditions, the reaction of trichlorosilane with perfluoropropene or perfluoroisobutylene yields a negligible amount of products.[44]

In an interesting method of condensation of silanes with unsaturated compounds, a catalytic amount of peroxide is used with tin, stannous chloride or oxide, or stannic chloride or oxide; the addition of tin or tin compounds increases the reaction rate substantially.[69] For example, 0.02 mole of t–butyl peracetate or t–butyl perbenzoate per mole of α–olefin such as pentene–1 produces no adduct with trichlorosilane after 20 hr at room temperature, whereas the same reactants in the presence of 2 wt. % of tin for 1.5 hr form a 1:1 addition product in 67% yield.[69] Similar effects are observed with methyldichlorosilane and phenyldichlorosilane. Under similar conditions trichlorosilane can be condensed with allyl acetate, cyclohexene, bicyclo [2, 2, 1] hept–5–ene–2–carbonyl chloride (IV), and diethyl bicyclo-[2, 2, 1] hept–5–ene–2, 3–dicarboxylate (V).[69]

VI   V

Azonitriles and peroxides are sometimes ineffective for reactions carried out in steel autoclaves because the material of the autoclaves tends to act as an inhibitor.[26] However, the reactions of silanes with olefins in the presence of iron pentacarbonyl can be carried out successfully in steel autoclaves at 100–130° to give adducts in 60–85% yield.[26] Thus, triethylsilane or triethoxysilane reacts with ethylene to give tetraethylsilane and triethoxyethylsilane, respectively. In the reaction with triethylsilane a by-product, $[(C_2H_5)_3SiCH_2-]_2$, b.p. 117°/8 mm, n_D 1.4592 (20°), is formed. A surprising result is obtained in the reaction of triethylsilane with ethyl vinyl ether: β–ethoxyvinyltriethylsilane, b.p. 79°/10 mm, is formed. The addition reactions of silanes with olefins in the presence of iron pentacarbonyl are explained by a free radical mechanism.[26]

Trichlorosilane reacts with alkyl vinyl and alkyl allyl ethers in ultraviolet light to give 1:1 adducts in good yield.[15,67] Trichlorosilane reacts with acrylonitrile in the presence of benzoyl peroxide at 160° to give $Cl_3SiCH_2-CH_2CN$ in 46% yield.[50]

Phenylsilane reacts with methyl cyclohexene carboxylate (VI) at 90° in the presence of t–butyl perbenzoate to give a mixture of isomers.[58,63] Trichlorosilane or methyldichlorosilane reacts with compound VII to give 1:1 adducts which are probably mixtures of isomers.[58]

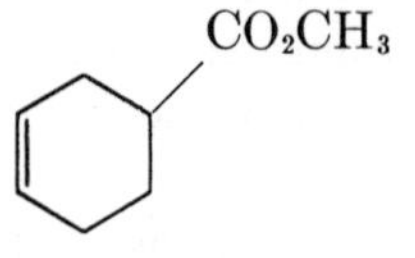

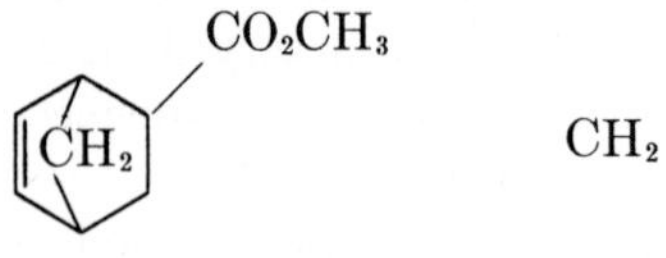

VI   VII

Trichlorosilane or methyldibromosilane reacts with compounds VIII and IX to give the adducts X and XI, respectively.[58]

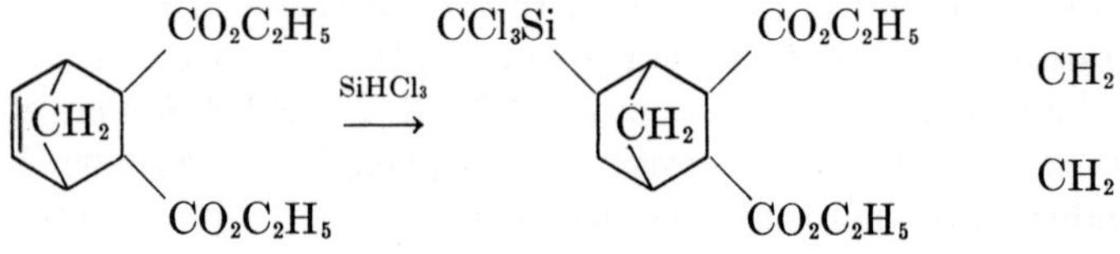

VIII   X

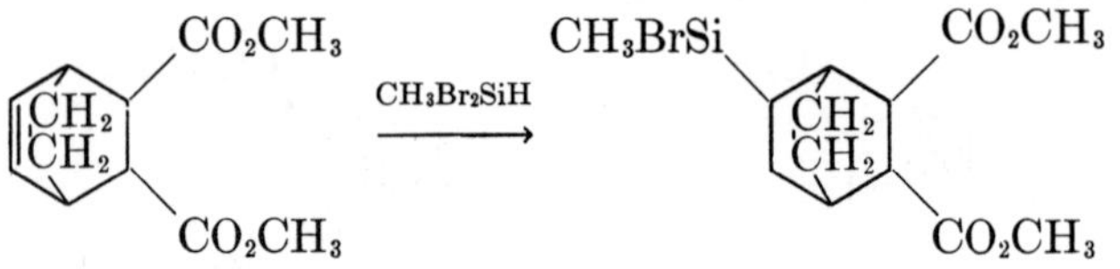

IX   XI

Trichlorosilane reacts with methyl undecylenate (XII) in the presence of acetyl peroxide to give methyl 11–trichlorosilyl undecanoate in 75% yield.[11,13,20]

$$Cl_3SiH + H_2C{=}CH(CH_2)_8CO_2CH_3 \rightarrow Cl_3SiCH_2CH_2(CH_2)_8CO_2CH_3$$

XII

Ethyldichlorosilane or diethylchlorosilane in ultraviolet light adds to 10–undecylenate to give $C_2H_5SiCl_2(CH_2)_{10}CO_2CH_3$ and $(C_2H_5)_2SiCl(CH_2)_{10}$–$CO_2CH_3$, respectively.[12,13] The yields depend largely on the duration of illumination. In 96 hr 32 and 40%, respectively, of 1:1 adduct are obtained. Ultraviolet irradiation of a mixture of trichlorosilane and undecenoyl chloride results in the expected linear 1:1 adduct, $Cl_3Si(CH_2)_{10}COCl$, in 93% yield.[14] Triphenylsilane and compound XII react at 90° in the presence of t–butyl perbenzoate to form methyl 11–(phenylsilyl) undecanoate in 98% yield.[46,58] Triphenylsilane reacts with methyl 4–cyclohexene carboxylate at

106° in the presence of t–butyl perbenzoate to give an adduct in 66% yield; the adduct is most likely a mixture of isomers.[46,58,63]

The values for the physical constants listed in the patent literature[47,59] and the *Journal of the American Chemical Society*[63] for the 1:1 adducts of phenylsilane with allyl acetate and with N–allylhexamethyldisilazane differ. The correct data for $C_6H_5SiH_2(CH_2)_3OCOCH_3$ and $C_6H_5SiH_2(CH_2)_3N$-$(SiCH_3)_3$ are b.p. 156°/25 mm and n_D 1.5040–1.5050 (25°) and b.p. 184°/25 mm and n_D 1.4900 (25°), respectively.[61]

Trichlorosilane reacts smoothly in ultraviolet light with methyl oleate to form an adduct, b.p. 200°/1 mm, n_D 1.4672 (20°), which is probably a mixture of isomers.[12] Phenylsilane and methyl oleate in the presence of t–butyl peroxide at 90° produce $C_6H_5SiH_2C_{17}H_{34}COOCH_3$, n_D 1.4896 (25°), in 100% yield.[58,63] Trichlorosilane[16,18,24,25,33] or methyldichlorosilane[33] reacts with β–pinene in the presence of acetyl peroxide or benzoyl peroxide at 55–95° or in ultraviolet light to give 1:1 products, b.p. 95°/2 mm[16,18,24,33] and 110°/8 mm,[33] respectively. The trichlorosilane adduct has an n_D of 1.4905 (15°) and an $[\alpha]_D$ of $-66.4°$.[16,18,24] This addition reaction is accompanied by a rearrangement.[16,18,24,25]

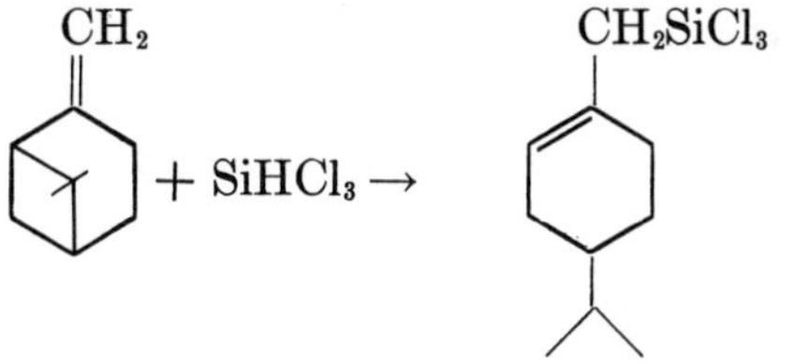

XIII

After prolonged exposure to ultraviolet light another mole of trichlorosilane can be added to XIII to give bis(trichlorosilyl)–2, 7–paramenthane (XIV), b.p. 131°/1 mm, n_D 1.5022 (20°), $[\alpha]_D$ +1.5°.[17]

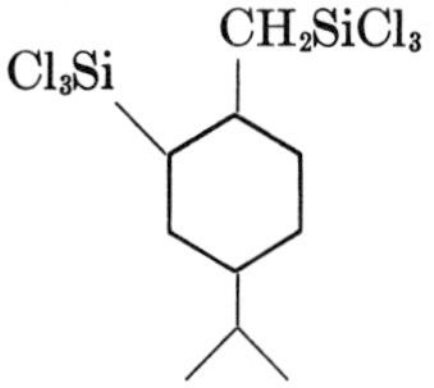

XIV

Trichlorosilane and limonene ($[\alpha]_D$ +118.7°) react to give the adduct XV, b.p. 98°/2 mm, n_D 1.4940 (20°), $[\alpha]_D$ +34.4°, which in the presence of a large excess of trichlorosilane forms bis(trichlorosilyl)–2, 9–menthane (XVI) b.p. 146°/2 mm, n_D 1.5059 (20°), $[\alpha]_D$ +5.4°.[19]

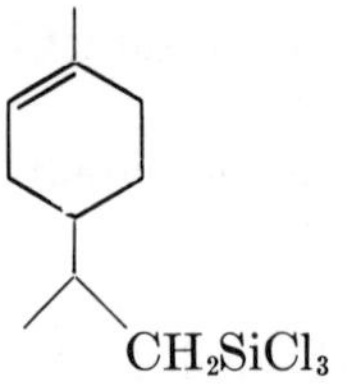

XV 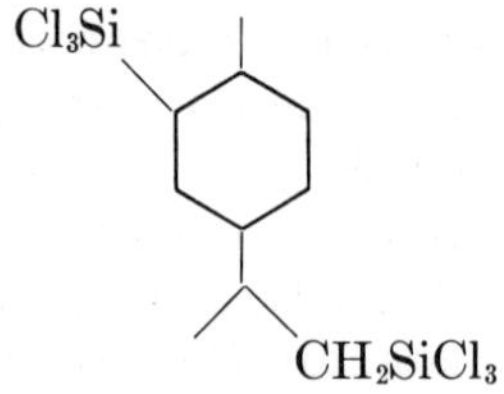   XVI

Trichlorosilane adds to α–pinene, camphene, or dipentene to give adducts, b.p. 101°/1 mm, 104°/4 mm, and 98°/2 mm, respectively.[33] Methyldichlorosilane and α–pinene also form a product, b.p. 104°/1 mm.[33] These condensation products are not yet completely characterized.

Some unusual, highly chlorinated silanes have been condensed with olefins under free radical conditions. Tetrachlorodisilanemethane (XVII) and pentachlorodisilanemethane (XVIII) react with hexene–1 and heptene–1 at 75–120° in the presence of benzoyl peroxide to give 1:1 and 1:2 adducts.[49,65] The products of the reaction of XVII with hexene–1 are hexyltetrachlorodisilanemethane, b.p. 114°/2 mm,[49] and dihexyltetrachlorodisilanemethane, b.p. 170°/1.5 mm,[49,65] in a combined yield of 55%. The product of the reaction of XVIII with hexene–1 is hexylpentachlorodisilanemethane, b.p. 124°/3 mm; and the product of the reaction of XVIII with heptene–1 is heptylpentachlorodisilanemethane, b.p. 136°/3 mm.

$$Cl_2HSiCH_2SiHCl_2 \qquad\qquad Cl_3SiCH_2SiHCl_2$$

XVII   XVIII

While the structure of these products is not firmly established, it is probable that linear condensation products are formed in accordance with the following scheme.

$$RCH{=}CH_2 + Cl_2HSiCH_2SiHCl_2 \rightarrow RCH_2CH_2Si(Cl_2)CH_2SiHCl_2$$

$$RCH{=}CH_2 + RCH_2CH_2Si(Cl_2)CH_2SiHCl_2 \rightarrow (RCH_2CH_2SiCl_2)_2CH_2$$

Recently the steroechemistry of addition of trichlorosilane to 1–pentyne, 1–hexyne, 1–heptyne, 3–methyl–1–butyne, and 3, 3–dimethyl–1–butyne was investigated.[6,7] With benzoyl peroxide as the catalyst, stereo selective *trans* addition occurs. The *cis*-to-*trans* isomer distribution is 79:21, 77:23, 75:25, and 72:28, respectively. In the reaction of trichlorosilane with *t*–butyl acetylene, a mixture of *cis-trans* adducts is obtained, the *trans* isomer predominating.

Table 37.   Addition of Silanes to Unsaturated Compounds

C_n	Unsaturated compound	Silane	Product	% Yield	°C b.p./mm (m.p.)	n_D (°C)	Ref.
C_2	$CH_2=CH_2$	Cl_3SiH	Ethyltrichlorosilane	50	97/737		5, 38, 40, 68
	$CH_2=CHCl$	Cl_3SiH	β-Chloroethyltrichlorosilane	49	150		68
	Vinyltrichlorosilane	Cl_3SiH	1,2-Bis(trichlorosilyl)ethane	19	199		8, 10
	$ClC≡CCl$	Cl_3SiH	$ClHC=CClSiCl_3$	28	90/55	1.4988 (20)	1
	$ClCH=CClSiCl_3$	Cl_3SiH	$Cl_3SiCHClCHClSiCl_3$	40	100/4	1.5158 (20)	1
	cis-$CHCl=CHCl$	Cl_3SiH	$CH_2ClCHClSiCl_3$	27	63/13	1.4762 (20)	21
	$CF_2=CF_2$	Cl_3SiH	$Cl_3SiCF_2CHF_2$	44	85	1.367 (18)	34
	$CF_2=CFCl$	Cl_3SiH	$CClFHCF_2SiCl_3$	38	117/746		35, 44
C_3	$CH_3CH=CH_2$	Cl_3SiH	n-Propyltrichlorosilane	38	122/740		5
	$CH_3CH=CH_2$	Br_3SiH	n-Propyltribromosilane	70	182/746		2, 5
	Allyl chloride	Cl_3SiH	$Cl(CH_2)_3SiCl_3$	40	59/8	1.4646 (20)	21
	Allyltrichlorosilane	Cl_3SiH	1,3-Bis(trichlorosilyl)-propane	83	111/20 (29)		8, 66
	3,3,3-Trifluoropropene	Cl_3SiH	3,3,3-Trifluoropropyltri-chlorosilane	72	113		31, 44
C_4	Acrylonitrile	Cl_3SiH	$Cl_3SiCH_2CH_2CN$	46	117/41 (35)		50
	Butene-1	Cl_3SiH	n-Butyltrichlorosilane		150		5
	Butene-2	Cl_3SiH	$CH_3CH_2CH(CH_3)SiCl_3$	95	146/736	1.4403 (25)	2, 5, 21
	Isobutylene	Cl_3SiH	$(CH_3)_2CHCH_2SiCl_3$	95	141/760	1.4346 (25)	21
	Butyne-1	Cl_3SiH	n-Butenyltrichlorosilane	8	64/40		2
	Allyl cyanide	Cl_3SiH	$CN(CH_2)_3SiCl_3$	8	93/8	1.4654 (20)	21
	$(CH_3)_2Si(CH=CH_2)_2$	Cl_3SiH	Bis-(β-trichlorosilylethyl)-dimethylsilane	72	120/3	1.4838 (20)	37

Table 37. (cont.)   Addition of Silanes to Unsaturated Compounds

C_n	Unsaturated compound	Silane	Product	% Yield	°C b.p./mm (m.p.)	n_D (°C)	Ref.
	3,3,4,4-Pentafluoro-butene-1	Cl_3SiH	$C_2F_5(CH_2)_2SiCl_3$	40	120	1.3705 (20)	21
	$CH_2=CHOC_2H_5$	Cl_3SiH	$Cl_3SiCH_2CH_2OC_2H_5$	53	146/764	1.4310 (20)	15
	$CH_2=CHCH_2OCH_3$	Cl_3SiH	$Cl_3Si(CH_2)_3OCH_3$		159/756	1.4420 (20)	15, 67
	2,3,3,4,4,4-Hexafluoro-butene	Cl_3SiH	$CF_3CF_2HCFCH_2SiCl_3$	52	127/758		44
C_5	Pentyne-1	Cl_3SiH	1-Trichlorosilyl-1-pentene	38	82/45		6, 9, 41
	Pentene-1	Cl_3SiH	n-Pentyltrichlorosilane	82	171/742	1.4379 (25)	10, 62, 68, 69
	3-Methyl-1-butyne	Cl_3SiH	1-Trichlorosilyl-3-methyl-1-butene	37	56/20		7
	Cyclopentene	Cl_3SiH	$C_5H_9SiCl_3$	96	70/19	1.4688 (20)	21
	Trimethylvinylsilane	Cl_3SiH	β-Trimethylsilylethyl-trichlorosilane	71	82/25	1.4473 (20)	37, 56
	2-Methyl-3,3,4,4,4-pentafluoro-1-butene	Cl_3SiH	$C_2F_5CH(CH_3)CH_2SiCl_3$	9	65/28	1.3812 (20)	21
	Allyl acetate	Cl_3SiH	3-Trichlorosilylpropyl-acetate + $H(CH_3CO_2CH_2CHCH_2)_2$-$SiCl_3$	22, 71	143/70, 120/24	1.4477 (25), 1.4380 (20), 1.4474 (20)	47, 69; 21; 21
	Allyl acetate	Br_3SiH	$Br_3Si(CH_2)_3OCOCH_3$		109/4		47
	$CH_2=CHCH_2OC_2H_5$	Cl_3SiH	$Cl_3Si(CH_2)_3OC_2H_5$	84	178/760	1.4402 (20)	15
	3,3,4,4,5,5,5-Hepta-fluoro-1-pentene	Cl_3SiH	$C_3F_7(CH_2)_2SiCl_3$	52	63/49	1.3626 (20)	21
C_6	3,3-Dimethyl-1-butyne	Cl_3SiH	1-Trichlorosilyl-3,3-dimethyl-1-butene	68	80/35		7
	Hexyne-1	Cl_3SiH	1-Trichlorosilyl-1-hexene	36	94/27		6

Table 37. (cont.) Addition of Silanes to Unsaturated Compounds

C_n	Unsaturated compound	Silane	Product	% Yield	°C b.p./mm (m.p.)	n_D (°C)	Ref.
	2, 3–Dimethyl–2–butene	Cl_3SiH	$CH_3CH(CH_3)C(CH_3)_2SiCl_3$	59	186/728	1.4631 (20)	52
	$CH_3CH_2CH_2C=CH_2$ │ CH_3	Cl_3SiH	2–Methylpentyltrichloro-silane		98/50		2
	Hexene–1	Br_3SiH	Hexyltribromosilane	71	119/15		65
	Methylcyclopentene–1	Br_3SiH	Methylcyclopentyltri-bromosilane	70	140/9		65
	Cyclohexene	Cl_3SiH	Cyclohexyltrichlorosilane	64	199/760	1.4773 (25)	10, 21, 22, 38, 68
	Cyclohexene	Br_3SiH	Cyclohexyltribromosilane	70	113/4		65
	1, 5–Hexadiene	Cl_3SiH	Bis(trichlorosilyl)hexane		150/10		2
	2–Methyl–3, 3, 4, 4, 5, 5, 5–heptafluoro–1–pentene	Cl_3SiH	$C_3F_7CH(CH_3)CH_2SiCl_3$	11	53/24	1.3722 (20)	21
C_7	Heptene–1	Br_3SiH	Heptyltribromosilane	75	132/14		65
	Heptyne–1	Cl_3SiH	1–Trichlorosilyl–1–heptene	47	103/24		6
C_8	n–Octene–1	Cl_3SiH	$CH_3(CH_2)_7SiCl_3$	99	231/728	1.4480 (20) 1.4453 (25)	5, 40, 52, 57 21
	2, 4, 4–Trimethyl-pentene–1	Cl_3SiH	2, 4, 4–Trimethylpentyl-trichlorosilane	30	40/2		40
	2, 4, 4–Trimethylpentene–2	Cl_3SiH	3–(2, 2, 4–Trimethylpen-tyl)trichlorosilane		95/20		2
	$(C_2H_5)_3SiCH=CH_2$	Cl_3SiH	β–Trichlorosilylethyltri-ethylsilane	42	123/18	1.4632 (20)	37
	4–Vinylcyclohexene	Cl_3SiH	Trichlorosilyl–(trichloro-silylethyl)cyclohexane		161/6		2

Table 37. (cont.)   Addition of Silanes to Unsaturated Compounds

C_n	Unsaturated compound	Silane	Product	% Yield	°C b.p./mm (m.p.)	n_D (°C)	Ref.
	2-Methyl-1-heptene	Cl_3SiH	$CH_3(CH_2)_5CH(CH_3)CH_2$–$SiCl_3$	70	221/736	1.4500 (20)	52
	Methyl cis-bicyclo [2, 2, 1]-hept-5-ene-2-carboxylate	Br_3SiH	Methyl tribromosilylbicyclo [2, 2, 1] heptyl carboxylate	82	151/2	1.5430 (25)	63
	Bicyclo [2, 2, 1] hept-5-ene-2-carbonyl chloride	Cl_3SiH	5–Trichlorosilylbicyclo [2, 2, 1] heptane-2-carbonyl chloride	69	125/1.6	1.5108 (25)	69
C_9	$(C_2H_5)_3SiCH_2CH=CH_2$	Cl_3SiH	$(C_2H_5)_3SiCH_2CH_2CH_2SiCl_3$	10	99/5	1.4673 (20)	66
	Nonene-1	Cl_3SiH	Nonyltrichlorosilane	61	122/5	1.4498 (20)	64
	Nonene-1	Br_3SiH	Nonyltribromosilane	79	155/5	1.4764 (20)	64
	Methyl bicyclo-2, 2, 1-heptene carboxylate	Cl_3SiH	Methyl trichlorosilylbicyclo [2, 2, 1] heptyl carboxylate		122/2	1.4937 (25)	58
C_{10}	n–Decene-1	Cl_3SiH	n–Decyltrichlorosilane	88	137/10	1.4528 (20)	5, 64
	n–Decene-1	Br_3SiH	Decyltribromosilane	74	167/5	1.4692 (20)	64
C_{11}	$C_6H_5(CH_3)_2SiCH=CH_2$	Cl_3SiH	$C_6H_5(CH_3)_2SiCH_2CH_2SiCl_3$	24	138/10	1.5112 (20)	37
	$C_6H_5(CH_3)_2SiCH_2CH=CH_2$	Cl_3SiH	$C_6H_5(CH_3)_2Si(CH_2)_3SiCl_3$	22	174/7	1.5117 (20)	66
	$CH_2=CH(CH_2)_8COCl$	Cl_3SiH	$Cl_3SiCH_2CH_2(CH_2)_8COCl$	93	192/16	1.4712 (20)	14
	β–Pinene	Cl_3SiH	CH_2SiCl_3 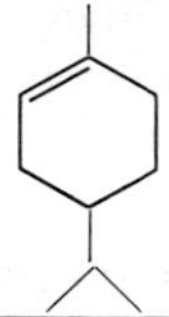	80	133/20	1.4905 (15)	16, 18, 24, 33

Table 37. (cont.) Addition of Silanes to Unsaturated Compounds

C_n	Unsaturated compound	Silane	Product	% Yield	°C b.p./mm (m.p.)	n_D (°C)	Ref.
C_{12}	Methyl undecylenate	Cl_3SiH	11-Trichlorosilyl-undecanoate	75	193/15	1.4622 (15)	11, 12, 20
	Dodecene-1	Cl_3SiH	Dodecyltrichlorosilane	84	156/10		5
C_{13}	Diethyl bicyclo-2, 2, 1-hept-5-ene-2, 3-dicarboxylate	Cl_3SiH	Diethyl 5-trichlorosilyl-bicyclo-2, 2, 1-heptane-2, 3-dicarboxylate		164/2	1.4835 (25)	58, 69
C_{14}	Tetradecene-1	Cl_3SiH	Tetradecyltrichlorosilane	13	147-158/3.0		5
C_{15}	$(Butyl)_3SiCH_2CH=CH_2$	Cl_3SiH	$(Butyl)_3Si(CH_2)_3SiCl_3$	13	190/7	1.4803 (20)	66
C_{16}	n-Hexadecene-1	Cl_3SiH	n-Hexadecyltrichlorosilane	29	195/7.5		2, 64
C_{18}	Octadecene-1	Cl_3SiH	Octadecyltrichlorosilane	88	270/50		2, 5
C_3	3, 3, 3-Trifluoropropene	Cl_2SiH_2	Dichloro-3, 3, 3-trifluoro-propylsilane	83	90		31
	3, 3, 3-Trifluoropropene	$CF_3CH_2CH_2-SiHCl_2$	Dichlorodi (3, 3, 3-trifluoro-propyl) silane	85	162		31
C_2	Ethylene	CH_3SiHCl_2	Ethylmethyldichlorosilane		100/744		2-4
	$CF_2=CF_2$	CH_3SiHCl_2	Methyl-1, 1, 2, 2-tetrafluoroethyldichlorosilane	98	96/770		30
C_3	Propylene	CH_3SiHCl_2	Methylpropyldichloro-silane	72	123/747		2-4
	3, 3, 3-Trifluoropropene	CH_3SiHCl_2	$CF_3CH_2CH_2Si(CH_3)Cl_2$	70	121/737		31, 44
C_4	n-Butene-1	CH_3SiHCl_2	n-Butylmethyldichloro-silane		147/744		2
	Butene-2	CH_3SiHCl_2	$CH_3CH_2CH(CH_3)Si-(CH_3)Cl_2$	57	45/20	1.4343 (25)	21

Table 37. (cont.) Addition of Silanes to Unsaturated Compounds

C_n	Unsaturated compound	Silane	Product	% Yield	°C b.p./mm (m.p.)	n_D (°C)	Ref.
	3, 3, 3–Trifluoro–2–methylpropene	CH_3SiHCl_2	Methyl–3, 3, 3–trifluoro–2–methylpropyldichlorosilane	63	139		31
	2, 3, 3, 4, 4, 4–Hexafluorobutene	CH_3SiHCl_2	$CF_3CF_2HCFCH_2Si(CH_3)Cl_2$	46	128/746		44
C_5	n–Pentene–1	CH_3SiHCl_2	1–Pentylmethyldichlorosilane	37	166		10, 38, 69
	n–Pentene–2	CH_3SiHCl_2	2–Pentylmethyldichlorosilane	71	100/100		10
	Cyclopentene	CH_3SiHCl_2	$C_5H_9Si(CH_3)Cl_2$	20	75/23	1.4627 (25)	21
	Allyl acetate	CH_3SiHCl_2	$CH_3C(O)O(CH_2)_3Si(CH_3)Cl_2$	47	121/30	1.4437 (25)	21
	3, 3, 4, 4, 5, 5, 5–Heptafluoro–1–pentene	CH_3SiHCl_2	$C_3F_7(CH_2)_2Si(CH_3)Cl_2$	23	54/33	1.3707 (25)	21
	Trimethylvinylsilane	CH_3SiHCl_2	Methyl–(β–methylsilylethyl)dichlorosilane	74	76/18		56
	3, 3, 4, 4, 5, 5, 5–Heptafluoropentene	CH_3SiHCl_2	Dichloro–3, 3, 4, 4, 5, 5, 5–heptafluoropentylmethylsilane	73	72/70		31
C_6	n–Hexene	CH_3SiHCl_2	n–Hexylmethyldichlorosilane	45	192/743		2
	Cyclohexene	CH_3SiHCl_2	Cyclohexylmethyldichlorosilane	45	204/745	1.4711 (25)	2, 21
	Methyl bicyclo [2, 2, 1]–heptene carboxylate	CH_3SiHCl_2	Methyl methyldichlorosilylbicyclo [2, 2, 1]–heptyl carboxylate		105/2	1.4862 (25)	58

Table 37. (cont.)   Addition of Silanes to Unsaturated Compounds

C_n	Unsaturated compound	Silane	Product	% Yield	°C b.p./mm (m.p.)	n_D (°C)	Ref.
C_8	n–Octene–1	CH_3SiHCl_2	$CH_3(CH_2)_7SiCH_3Cl_2$	55	113/20	1.4422 (25)	2–4, 21
C_9	Nonene–1	CH_3SiHCl_2	Nonyl methyldichlorosilane	21	116/5	1.4548 (20)	64
C_{10}	Decene–1	CH_3SiHCl_2	Decyl methyldichlorosilane	38	127/5	1.4542 (20)	64
C_{18}	n–Octadecene	CH_3SiHCl_2	Methyloctadecyldichlorosilane		205/6		2–4
C_2	$CF_2=CF_2$	$(CH_3)_2SiH_2$	Dimethyl–(1, 1, 2, 2–tetrafluoroethyl)silane	83	63		29
	$CH_2=CH_2$	$(C_2H_5)_3SiH$	$(C_2H_5)_4Si$	81	151	1.4250 (20)	26
	$CH_2=CH_2$	$(C_2H_5O)_3SiH$	$(C_2H_5O)_3SiC_2H_5$	65	80/40	1.3935 (20)	26
	$CF_2=CF_2$	$(CH_3)_2SiH-CF_2CF_2H$	Dimethyldi–(1, 1, 2, 2–tetrafluoroethyl)silane	90	120		31
C_6	Hexene–1	Tetrachlorodisilane methane	$(C_6H_{13}SiCl_2)_2CH_2$	22	222/5		49, 65
C_8	n–Octene–1	$C_5H_{11}SiH_3$	Amyloctylsilane	60	141/25	1.4400 (25)	63
C_5	Allyl acetate	$C_6H_5SiH_3$	Phenylsilylpropyl acetate	77	156/25	1.5040 (25)	47, 61, 63
C_6	Allyloxytrimethylsilane	$C_6H_5SiH_3$	Phenylsilylpropoxytrimethylsilane	67	130/25	1.4886 (25)	47, 63
	Diallyl ether	$C_6H_5SiH_3$	Phenylsilylpropylallyl ether	60	162/25	1.4984 (25)	63
	Cyclohexene	$C_6H_5SiH_3$	Cyclohexylphenylsilane	26	135/20	1.5255 (26)	63
C_7	Allylidene diacetate	$C_6H_5SiH_3$	Phenylsilylpropyl–1, 1–diacetate		152/2	1.4948 (25)	63
	Acrolein diethyl acetal	$C_6H_5SiH_3$	(1, 1–Diethoxypropyl)–phenylsilane	54	162/25	1.4872 (25)	60, 63

Table 37. (cont.) Addition of Silanes to Unsaturated Compounds

C_n	Unsaturated compound	Silane	Product	% Yield	°C b.p./mm (m.p.)	n_D (°C)	Ref.
C_8	Octene-1	$C_6H_5SiH_3$	Octylphenylsilane	70	161/21	1.495 (25)	63
	cis-4-Cyclohexene-1,2-dicarboxylic anhydride	$C_6H_5SiH_3$	1:1 Adduct	95		1.549 (25)	63
	Methyl 3-cyclohexene carboxylate	$C_6H_5SiH_3$	Phenylsilylcyclohexyl carboxylate	66	159/5	1.5238 (25)	63
				66	158/4.5		46, 58
C_9	N-Allylhexamethyldisilazane, $[(CH_3)_3Si]_2NC_3H_5$	$C_6H_5SiH_3$	N-(Phenylsilylpropyl)hexamethyldisilazane	70	184/25	1.4900 (25)	59, 61, 63
	o-Allylphenyl acetate	$C_6H_5SiH_3$	o-(Phenylsilylpropyl)-phenyl acetate	50	188/3.5	1.5472 (25)	63
C_{12}	6-Acetoxy-3a, 4, 5, 6, 7, 7a-hexahydro-4, 7-methanoindene	$(C_6H_5)_3SiH$	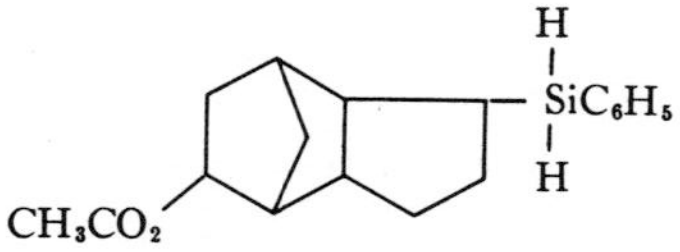	78	>175/5	1.5395 (25)	47
C_{14}	N-trimethylsilylundecenyl amine	$C_6H_5SiH_3$	$C_6H_5SiH_2C_{11}H_{22}NHSi(CH_3)_3$			1.4952 (25)	59
C_{15}	$(C_2H_5O)_2CH(CH_2)_8$-$CH{=}CH_2$	$C_6H_5SiH_3$	$(C_2H_5O)_2CH(CH_2)_{10}Si(C_6H_5)H_2$	100		1.4972 (25)	60
C_5	Allyl acetate	$CH_3C_6H_5SiH_2$	Methylphenylsilylpropyl acetate	43	158/25	1.5000 (25)	63
C_{12}	$CH_2{=}CH(CH_2)_8CO_2CH_3$	$C_2H_5SiHCl_2$	$C_2H_5SiCl_2(CH_2)_{10}CO_2CH_3$	32	150/0.7	1.4611 (20)	13
C_3	Propylene	$(C_2H_5)_2SiHCl$	Diethylpropylchlorosilane		165/742		2–4

Table 37. (cont.)   Addition of Silanes to Unsaturated Compounds

C_n	Unsaturated compound	Silane	Product	% Yield	°C b.p./mm (m.p.)	n_D (°C)	Ref.
C_{12}	$CH_2=CH(CH_2)_8CO_2CH_3$	$(C_2H_5)_2SiHCl$	$(C_2H_5)_2SiCl(CH_2)_{10}CO_2CH_3$	40	155/1	1.4585 (20)	12, 13
	Propylene	$CH_3C_6H_5SiHCl$	Methylphenylpropyl-chlorosilane		125/30		2-4
	Propylene	$C_6H_5SiHCl_2$	Phenylpropyldichloro-silane		142/45		2-4
	Propylene	$(C_6H_5)_2SiHCl$	Diphenylpropylchloro-silane		176/10		2
C_2	Ethylene	$C_6H_5SiHCl_2$	$C_6H_5C_2H_5SiCl_2$		135/50		3, 4
C_5	3, 3, 4, 4, 5, 5, 5–Hepta-fluoropentene	$CH_3(C_2H_5O)_2-SiH$	$C_3F_7CH_2CH_2Si(OC_2H_5)_2CH_3$	79	82/28		31
C_8	Octene-1	$(C_6H_5)_3SiH$	Triphenyl-1-octylsilane	54	182/0.5 (72)		27
C_{11}	9-Undecylenic acid	$(C_6H_5)_3SiH$	Triphenylsilylundecylenic acid	96	mol. dist. (59)		28
C_{12}	n–Dodecene	$(C_6H_5)_3SiH$	n–Dodecyltriphenylsilane	46	(64)		45
C_{14}	n–Tetradecene	$(C_6H_5)_3SiH$	n–Tetradecyltriphenyl-silane	52	(66)		45
C_{16}	n–Hexadecene	$(C_6H_5)_3SiH$	n–Hexadecyltriphenyl-silane	45	(69)		45
C_{17}	n–Heptadecene	$(C_6H_5)_3SiH$	n–Heptadecyltriphenyl-silane		(71)		45
C_{18}	n–Octadecene	$(C_6H_5)_3SiH$	n–Octadecyltriphenyl-silane	40	(72)		45
C_{21}	$(C_6H_5)_3SiCH_2CH=CH_2$	$(C_6H_5)_3SiH$	$(C_6H_5)_3Si(CH_2)_3Si(C_6H_5)_3$	36	(210)		66

ADDITION OF GERMANES

Compared with silanes, only a few reactions of germanes with olefins have been reported in the literature. The reactions are initiated with peroxide or ultraviolet light. Reactions without an initiator have also been reported. Two recent surveys include the reactions of organogermanium compounds.[54,55]

The reaction of a mixture of germanium trichloride (70%) and germanium tetrachloride (30%) with hexene–1 in the presence of benzoyl peroxide results in addition of trichloride and yields only hexyltrichlorogermane.[23] The reaction of triphenylgermane with olefins in ultraviolet light at room temperature or 75° in the presence of benzoyl peroxide produces triphenyl–1–octylgermane in excellent yield,[27] whereas the reaction of triphenylgermane with cyclohexene under similar conditions produces triphenylcyclohexylgermane, m.p. 149°, in much lower yield.[27]

Trichlorogermane reacts readily with acetylene and a number of olefins in the absence of a catalyst, and heat is evolved.[48,51]

$$CH_2{=}CHCl + Cl_3GeH \rightarrow ClCH_2CH_2GeCl_3$$

In the reaction of triphenylgermane with unsaturated compounds in the absence of a catalyst, 1:1 adducts are obtained in moderate yield. n–Octene, styrene, cyclohexene, and phenyl acetylene condense with triphenylgermane at 110–135°. Vinyl acetate, methyl acrylate, acrylonitrile, acrylamide, methylvinyl ketone, 4–pentene–1–ol, and 2–methyl–3–butyn–2–ol condense with triphenylgermane at 50–70°.[36]

Triethyl-, tripropyl-, tributyl-, or triamylgermane combines with acrylic acid, its esters, and its nitrile at 140° without a catalyst.[39] When these germanes are condensed with acrolein or allyl alcohol in the presence of benzoyl peroxide, 1:1 products are obtained in 60% yield.[39]

While the mechanism of the uncatalyzed condensations is not established, the general pattern (anti-Markownikoff) suggests a free radical mechanism.

Table 38. Addition of Germanes to Unsaturated Compounds

C_n	Unsaturated compound	Germane	Initiator	Product	% Yield	°C b.p./mm (m.p.)	n_D (°C)	Ref.
C_2	CH≡CH	Cl_3GeH	None	$Cl_3GeCH_2CH_2GeCl_3$	90	130/12		51
	$CH_2=CH_2$	Cl_3GeH	None	$C_2H_5GeCl_3$	55	142/761		51
	$CH_2=CHCl$	Cl_3GeH	None	$ClCH_2CH_2GeCl_3$	33	75/15	1.5092 (20)	48
	trans-$ClCH=CHCl$	Cl_3GeH	None	$ClCH_2CHClGeCl_3$	62	88/12	1.5240 (20)	48
	$Cl_2C=CHCl$	Cl_3GeH	None	$Cl_3GeC_2H_2Cl_3$	55	92/9	1.5341 (20)	48
	$Cl_2C=CCl_2$	Cl_3GeH	None	$Cl_2CHCl_2CGeCl_3$	48	123/25	1.5378 (20)	48
	$Cl_3SiCH=CH_2$	Cl_3GeH	None	$Cl_3SiCH_2CH_2GeCl_3$	83	120/15		51
C_3	$CH_2=CHCN$	Cl_3GeH	None	$Cl_3GeCH_2CH_2CN$	53	135/22		51
	Allyl chloride	Cl_3GeH	None	$Cl_3Ge(CH_2)_3Cl$	77	105/20		51
C_4	Methallyl chloride	Cl_3GeH	None	$Cl_3GeCH_2CH(CH_3)CH_2Cl$	58	91/11		51
C_5	Pentene-1	Cl_3GeH	Peroxide	$Cl_3Ge(CH_2)_4CH_3$	21	102/40		53
	4-Chloropentene-1	Cl_3GeH	Peroxide	$Cl_3Ge(CH_2)_3CHClCH_3$	10	80/0.4		53
	Allyl acetate	Cl_3GeH	None	$Cl_3Ge(CH_2)_3CO_2CH_3$	41	127/12		51
C_6	Hexene-1	Cl_3GeH	Bz_2O_2	$CH_3(CH_2)_5GeCl_3$	22	97/14	1.4719 (25)	23, 53
	Heptene-1	Cl_3GeH	Peroxide	$Cl_3Ge(CH_2)_6CH_3$	18	102/10		53
C_3	$CH_2=CHCHO$	$(C_2H_5)_3GeH$	Bz_2O_2	$(C_2H_5)_3GeCH_2CH_2CHO$		130/17		39
	$CH_2=CHCN$	$(C_2H_5)_3GeH$	None	$(C_2H_5)_3GeCH_2CH_2CN$		226/760		39
	$CH_2=CHCO_2H$	$(C_2H_5)_3GeH$	None	$(C_2H_5)_3GeCH_2CH_2CO_2H$		159/10		39
C_8	$(C_2H_5)_3GeCH=CH_2$	$(C_2H_5)_3GeH$	None	$(C_2H_5)_3Ge(CH_2)_2Ge(C_2H_5)_3$		126/1.5	1.4773 (20)	42
C_9	$(C_2H_5)_3GeCH_2-CH=CH_2$	$(C_2H_5)_3GeH$	None	$(C_2H_5)_3Ge(CH_2)_3Ge(C_2H_5)_3$		128/1.4	1.4759 (20)	42
C_3	$CH_2=CHCH_2OH$	$(n-Propyl)GeH$	Bz_2O_2	$(n-C_3H_7)_3GeCH_2CH_2CH_2OH$		177/20		39
C_4	$CH_2=CHCO_2CH_3$	$(n-C_3H_7)_3GeH$	None	$(n-C_3H_7)_3GeCH_2CH_2CO_2CH_3$		152/18		39
C_3	$CH_2=CHCH_2OH$	$(n-Butyl)_3GeH$	Bz_2O_2	$(n-Butyl)_3GeCH_2CH_2CH_2OH$		154/3		39

Table 38. (cont.)   Addition of Germanes to Unsaturated Compounds

C_n	Unsaturated compound	Germane	Initiator	Product	% Yield	°C b.p./mm (m.p.)	n_D (°C)	Ref.
C_3	$CH_2=CHCHO$	$(n-Butyl)_3GeH$	Bz_2O_2	$(n-Butyl)_3GeCH_2CH_2CHO$		126/1		39
	$CH_2=CHCN$	$(n-Butyl)_3GeH$	None	$(n-Butyl)_3GeCH_2CH_2CN$		168/11		39
C_5	$CH_2=CHCO_2C_2H_5$	$(n-Butyl)_3GeH$	None	$(n-Butyl)_3GeCH_2CH_2CO_2C_2H_5$		123/0.5		39
C_3	$CH_2=CHCN$	$(n-Amyl)_3GeH$	None	$(n-Amyl)_3GeCH_2CH_2CN$		193/11		39
	Acrylonitrile	$(C_6H_5)_3GeH$	None	$(C_6H_5)_3GeCH_2CH_2CN$	83	(128)		36
	Acrylamide	$(C_6H_5)_3GeH$	None	$(C_6H_5)_3GeCH_2CH_2CONH_2$		(177)		36
C_4	Vinyl acetate	$(C_6H_5)_3GeH$	None	$(C_6H_5)_3GeCH_2CH_2OOCCH_3$	54	(62)		36
	Methyl acrylate	$(C_6H_5)_3GeH$	None	$(C_6H_5)_3GeCH_2CH_2CO_2CH_3$	50	(61)		36
	Methylvinyl ketone	$(C_6H_5)_3GeH$	None	$(C_6H_5)_3GeCH_2CH_2COCH_3$	53	(145)		36
C_5	4–Penten–1–ol	$(C_6H_5)_3GeH$	None	$(C_6H_5)_3Ge(CH_2)_4CH_2OH$	41	(60)		36
	2–Methyl–3–butyn–2–ol	$(C_6H_5)_3GeH$	None	$(C_6H_5)_3GeCH=CHC(OH)(CH_3)_2$	49	(91)		36
C_6	Cyclohexene	$(C_6H_5)_3GeH$	None or UV or Bz_2O_2	$(C_6H_5)_3GeCH(CH_2)_4CH_2$	39	(146)		27, 36
C_8	Octene–1	$(C_6H_5)_3GeH$	None or UV or Bz_2O_2	$(C_6H_5)_3GeCH_2CH_2C_6H_{13}$	91	194/0.25 (70)		27, 36, 53
	Styrene	$(C_6H_5)_3GeH$	None	$(C_6H_5)_3GeCH_2CH_2C_6H_5$	40	(145)		36
	Phenyl acetylene	$(C_6H_5)_3GeH$	None	$(C_6H_5)_3GeCH=CHC_6H_5$	12	(147)		36
C_{18}	Octadecene–1	$(C_6H_5)_3GeH$	Bz_2O_2	Triphenyl–n–octadecyl-germane	67	(76)		32
C_{21}	$(C_6H_5)_3GeCH_2CH=CH_2$	$(C_6H_5)_3GeH$	Bz_2O_2	1,3–Bis(triphenylgermyl)-propane	87	(135)		32

REFERENCES

[1] Agre, *J. Am. Chem. Soc.*, **71**, 300 (1949).
[2] Barry, *et al.*, *J. Am. Chem. Soc.*, **69**, 2916 (1947).
[3] Barry, De Pree, and Hook, U.S. 2,626,268 (1953).
[4] Barry, De Pree, and Hook, Brit. 632,824 (1949).
[5] Barry, Hook, and De Pree, U.S. 2,626,271 (1953).
[6] Benkeser and Hickner, *J. Am. Chem. Soc.*, **80**, 5298 (1958).
[7] Benkeser, *et al.*, *J. Am. Chem. Soc.*, **83**, 4385 (1961).
[8] The British Thomson-Houston Co., Ltd., Brit. 661,094 (1951).
[9] Burkhard, *J. Am. Chem. Soc.*, **72**, 1402 (1950).
[10] Burkhard and Krieble, *J. Am. Chem. Soc.*, **69**, 2687 (1947).
[11] Calas and Duffaut, *Oléagineux*, **8**, 21 (1953).
[12] Calas and Duffaut, *Bull. soc. chim. France*, **1953**, 792.
[13] Calas and Duffaut, *Bull. mens. inform. ITERG*, **7**, 438 (1953).
[14] Calas and Duffaut, *Rev. franc. Corps Gras*, **3**, 5 (1956).
[15] Calas, Duffaut, and Valade, *Bull. soc. chim. France*, **1955**, 790.
[16] Calas and Frainnet, *Bull. soc. chim. France*, **1952**, 241.
[17] Calas and Frainnet, *Bull. soc. chim. France*, **1953**, 792.
[18] Calas and Frainnet, *C.r.* **243**, 595 (1956).
[19] Calas, Frainnet, and Valade, *Bull. soc. chim. France*, **1953**, 793.
[20] Duffaut and Calas, *Bull. soc. chim. France*, **1952**, 241.
[21] El Abbady and Anderson, *J. Am. Chem. Soc.*, **80**, 1737 (1958).
[22] Ernsberger and Lipscomb, U.S. 2,570,463 (1951).
[23] Fisher, West, and Rochow, *J. Am. Chem. Soc.*, **76**, 5878 (1954).
[24] Frainnet, *Bull. soc. chim. France*, **1953**, 792.
[25] Frainnet and Calas, *C.r.* **240**, 203 (1955).
[26] Freidlina, Chukovskaya, and Tsao, *Dok. Akad. Nauk*, **127**, 352 (1959).
[27] Fuchs and Gilman, *J. Org. Chem.*, **22**, 1009 (1957).
[28] Gadsby, *Res.*, **3**, 338 (1950).
[29] Geyer and Haszeldine, *J. Chem. Soc.*, **1957**, 1038.
[30] Geyer and Haszeldine, *J. Chem. Soc.*, **1957**, 3925.
[31] Geyer, *et al.*, *J. Chem. Soc.*, **1957**, 4472.
[32] Gilman and Gerow, *J. Am. Chem. Soc.*, **79**, 342 (1957).
[33] Goldblatt and Oldroyd, U.S. 2,533,240 (1950).
[34] Haszeldine and Marklow, *J. Chem. Soc.*, **1956**, 962.
[35] Haszeldine and Young, *J. Chem. Soc.*, **1959**, 394.
[36] Henry and Downey, *J. Chem. Soc.*, **26**, 2299 (1961).
[37] Kanazashi, *Bull. Chem. Soc. Japan*, **26**, 493 (1953).
[38] Krieble, U.S. 2,524,529 (1950).
[39] Lesbre and Satgé, *C.r.*, **247**, 471 (1958).
[40] Lipscomb, U.S. 2,570,462 (1951).
[41] MacKenzie, Spialter, and Schoffmann, Brit. 684,597 (1952).
[42] Mazerolles and Lesbre, *C.r.*, **248**, 2018 (1959).
[43] McBee, Roberts, and Puerckhauer, *J. Am. Chem. Soc.*, **79**, 2326 (1957).
[44] McBee, Roberts, and Puerckhauer, *J. Am. Chem. Soc.*, **79**, 2329 (1957).
[45] Merten and Gilman, *J. Am. Chem. Soc.*, **76**, 5798 (1954).
[46] Midland Silicones, Ltd., Brit. 769,496 (1957).
[47] Midland Silicones, Ltd., Brit. 769,497 (1957).

[48] Mironov, Dzurinskaya, and Petrov, *Dok. Akad. Nauk*, **131,** 98 (1960).

[49] Nametkin, Topchiev, and Solovova, *Dok. Akad. Nauk*, **93,** 285 (1953).

[50] Nozakura and Konotsune, *Bull. Chem. Soc. Japan*, **29,** 322 (1956).

[51] Petrov, Mironov, and Dzurinskaya, *Dok. Akad. Nauk*, **128,** 302 (1959).

[52] Pietrusza, Sommer, and Whitmore, *J. Am. Chem. Soc.*, **70,** 484 (1948).

[53] Riemschneider, Menge, and Klang, *Z. Naturforsch.*, **11,** 115 (1956).

[54] Rijkens, *Organogermanium Compounds*, Germanium Research Committee. Utrecht (1960).

[55] Satgé, *Ann. chim. Paris*, **6,** 519 (1961).

[56] Seyferth and Rochow, *J. Org. Chem.*, **20,** 250 (1955).

[57] Sommer, Pietrusza, and Whitmore, *J. Am. Chem. Soc.*, **69,** 188 (1947).

[58] Speier, U.S. 2,723,987 (1955).

[59] Speier, U.S. 2,762,823 (1956).

[60] Speier, U.S. 2,803,637 (1957).

[61] Speier, Private communication (1961).

[62] Speier and Webster, *J. Org. Chem.*, **21,** 1044 (1956).

[63] Speier, Zimmerman, and Webster, *J. Am. Chem. Soc.*, **78,** 2278 (1956).

[64] Topchiev, Nametkin, and Chernysheva, *Dok. Akad. Nauk*, **115,** 326 (1957).

[65] Topchiev, Nametkin, and Solovova, *Dok. Akad. Nauk*, **86,** 965 (1952).

[66] Topchiev, *et al.*, *Dok. Akad. Nauk*, **110,** 97 (1956).

[67] Valade and Calas, *C.r. France*, **243,** 386 (1956).

[68] Wagner and Strother, U.S. 2,632,013 (1953).

[69] Webster, U.S. 2,894,968 (1959).

[70] White and Rochow, *J. Am. Chem. Soc.*, **76,** 3897 (1954).

[71] Wolfe and Cook, U.S. 2,786,862 (1957).

CHAPTER VII

Reactions of Nitrogen Oxides
and Related Compounds

The literature dealing with the reactions of nitrogen oxides and related compounds is extensive. The chemistry of nitroparaffins, mainly vapor-phase nitrations, has been reviewed by Hass and Riley.[76] Topchiev's review deals mainly with the mechanism of vapor-phase nitration of paraffins.[219] Topchiev also describes ionic and radical nitrations of hydrocarbons and other organic compounds.[220] Titov has reviewed nitration of aromatic and unsaturated compounds[211] and the theory of nitration of hydrocarbons and side chains of arylparaffins.[212] Others have described the chemistry and technology of nitroalkanes, historical developments, plant operations, vapor- and liquid-phase nitrations, physical constants of some aliphatic nitroalkanes, and addition of nitrogen dioxide to olefins.[53,54,57,171,222] The addition of dinitrogen trioxide and dinitrogen tetroxide to acetylenes and olefins has been reviewed by Riebsomer.[169] Addition of nitrogen oxides to olefins has been reviewed by Levy and Rose.[107] The nitration of fluoroolefins with nitrogen dioxide is discussed by Knunyants and Fokin.[89] The reactions of nitric oxide, dinitrogen trioxide, dinitrogen tetroxide, nitrosyl chloride, and nitryl chloride with olefins and the nitration of hydrocarbons with nitrogen dioxide and diluted nitric acid are described in *Chemistry of Petroleum Hydrocarbons*.[35] The preparation, structure, and properties of C–nitroso compounds and the addition of nitrosyl chloride and dinitrogen trioxide to olefins have been reviewed by Gowenlock and Lüttke.[70] The photochemical reactions of nitric oxide and rearrangements of nitro compounds are described by Schönberg.[181a,b]

Despite the large number of publications dealing with nitrogen oxides and nitrogen oxyhalides, comparatively little is known about the mechanism of these reactions. This lack of information made it difficult to select reactions for inclusion in the present work. In the past, reactions involving nitrogen oxide and nitrogen oxychlorides were interpreted as ionic reactions. Recently, however, evidence has accumulated in favor of a radical nature of most of these processes. It is certain that the photochemical reactions of nitric oxide proceed by radical mechanisms. These reactions include the reactions of nitric oxide in the presence of halogens,[130,136,138-140] the reaction of nitrosyl chloride with hydrocarbons,[4,14,50,83,113-115,123,142,149,196] the reaction of nitric oxide with fluorinated iodoalkanes,[16-19,79,80,85] the reaction of nitric oxide with cyclohexanone peroxide in the presence of ferrous ion,[40] the reaction of nitric oxide with saturated hydrocarbons,[142,143] the photochemical reduction of chloronitroso compounds,[141] the reaction of nitric oxide with fluoroolefins,[160] the reaction of nitric oxide or nitrosyl chloride with fluoroolefins in the presence of ferric chloride,[158,159] the decomposition of nitrites,[25,26,43,103,150-152] and the rearrangement of nitro compounds.[181a,b]

Many difficulties in interpreting the earlier results of reactions of dinitrogen trioxide with unsaturated compounds are now attributed to the use of impure starting materials. Dinitrogen trioxide, which is produced from nitric acid and arsenic trioxide or from sodium nitrite and sulfuric acid, contains varying amounts of other nitrogen oxides, such as nitric oxide and nitrogen dioxide. Thus, in many cases the combining of such a mixture with unsaturated compounds gave complex and ill-defined products.

Recently it was shown that the addition of dinitrogen trioxide to unsaturated compounds is independent of the electronic demands of groups attached to the unsaturated system and that the nitro group adds to the terminal carbon atoms of the unsaturated system.[184,185] The nitro group adds to the terminal carbon atoms when the unsaturated compound is reacted stepwise first with nitrous oxide and then with nitrogen dioxide.[20] For example, styrene reacts in such a manner to yield the corresponding pseudonitrosite.[20] This result suggests a radical rather than an ionic mechanism for the reactions of dinitrogen trioxide.[20,182]

In the past, difficulties were also experienced in interpreting the reactions of dinitrogen tetroxide with olefins. In most cases, the reactions with unsubstituted olefins yielded ill-defined, oily products and the reactions with substituted olefins yielded well-defined products. Levy and associates concluded that many difficulties can be overcome by employing pure starting materials, by using solvents, by working at low temperatures, and by carrying out the reaction in an atmosphere of oxygen to prevent the formation of lower nitrogen oxides.[15,108-111] The single fact that oxygen is present indicates that free radical intermediates might be involved in these reactions.

Recently it was suggested that addition of nitrogen dioxide to olefins proceeds by a free radical path.[33,34,182,183,192,193] This conclusion is not surprising in view of the fact that nitrogen dioxide is paramagnetic and shows other free radical properties. The free radical nature of nitrogen dioxide addition to olefins has been demonstrated by the following reactions: addition of nitrogen dioxide to the terminal position of methyl methacrylate,[182] simultaneous incorporation of oxygen and nitrogen dioxide into the styrene molecule,[20] the reaction of cyclohexene with nitrogen dioxide in the presence of bromoform to form 2–bromonitrocyclohexane,[20] the reaction of cyclohexene with nitrogen dioxide in bromotrichloromethane,[33,34] and the reaction of dinitrogen tetroxide with stilbene.[64]

The reaction of nitrogen dioxide with olefins in the presence of halogens is almost certainly a free radical process.[13,195] The reaction of nitrogen dioxide with fluoroolefins is also a radical reaction,[88,89] as is the addition of nitrosyl chloride[159] and nitryl chloride[185] to terminal olefins. The addition of nitryl chloride to some acetylenes is probably a radical process also.[60,173]

Nitration of paraffins and of side chains of aralkyl compounds in the liquid phase with dilute nitric acid or with nitrogen dioxide is most likely a radical process.[201,204,205,211,212,216] Nitric acid does not act as such but is the source of nitrogen dioxide.[211,212] Substitution nitration of olefins with nitric acid is likewise free radical in nature. In general, liquid-phase nitration with nitrogen dioxide or nitric acid resembles gas-phase nitration, which is undoubtedly a radical process.[205-208,211,212,219,220] Nitration of aromatic hydrocarbons with dilute nitric acid, nitrogen dioxide, or nitrogen pentoxide may well be a radical process.[21,32,199,202,206,210,213,218]

The reaction of mercury paraffins with dilute nitric acid or nitrogen dioxide may also be a radical process.[217] The reaction of nitric oxide, nitrogen dioxide, or nitroso compounds with α, α'–azobisisobutyronitrile is undoubtedly a radical process,[66,67,197,198] as are the reactions of triphenylmethyl[172] and tetraphenylsuccinonitrile[248] with nitrogen dioxide.

On the basis of these results, it is concluded that many addition and substitution reactions involving nitrogen oxide and related compounds probably proceed by a radical path. This chapter therefore includes many reactions despite the inadequate knowledge of their reaction mechanism. It is hoped that the inclusion of these reactions will stimulate present and future investigations in this area.

NITRATION OF AROMATIC AND SATURATED COMPOUNDS

The nitration reactions of hydrocarbons can be conveniently divided into two major classes: (1) the nitration of aromatic hydrocarbons; (2) the nitration of paraffins, cycloparaffins, and side chains of aromatic compounds.

Aromatic Compounds

Industrially, aromatic nitro compounds are more important than nitroparaffins. Most nitrations of aromatic hydrocarbons are carried out at relatively low temperatures with concentrated nitric acid in the presence of sulfuric, phosphoric, hydrofluoric, or acetic acid. Since these nitrations proceed through ionic intermediates, they are outside the scope of the present work. For details on this subject see the review by McKinney.[128]

However, some aromatic nuclear nitrations may be free radical processes. In such nitrations with dilute nitric acid, the nitric acid serves only as a source of nitrogen dioxide radical. Titov showed that nitric acid by itself, in the absence of nitrogen oxides, does not attack hydrocarbons.[202,205,210-214] Under conditions which facilitate the decomposition of nitric acid, nitration commences immediately.

For example, the nitration of benzene produces nitrobenzene, p–dinitrobenzene, 2, 4–dinitrophenol, and sym–trinitrophenol.[210,213] The nitration of toluene yields o–nitrotoluene, p–nitrotoluene, dinitro–p–cresol, trinitro–m–cresol, and dinitro–p–cresol;[210] oxygen accelerates these reactions. Similarly, naphthalene is not affected by dilute nitric acid (sp. gr. 1.357) in the absence of nitrogen dioxide.[202] In the presence of nitrogen oxides at 100°, α–nitronaphthalene, m.p. 52°, is formed.[202] Titov proposed radical intermediates for this reaction also,[202] and the nitrations of anthracene and derivatives probably belong in the same category.

Dinitrogen tetroxide reacts with anthracene in chloroform to give dihydrodinitroanthracene (I), m.p. 194°.[129] Treatment of this compound with a base converts it to nitroanthracene, m.p. 146°.

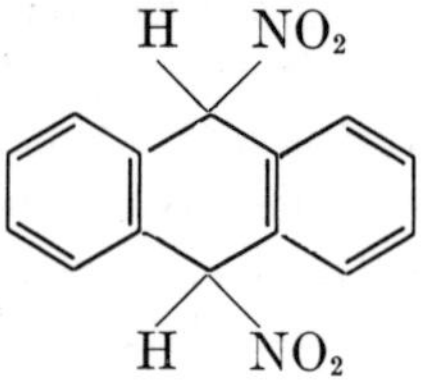

I

Dinitrogen tetroxide reacts with nitroanthracene in chloroform to give a trinitro derivative, m.p. 140°, which on treatment with a base is converted to dinitroanthracene (II), m.p. 294°.[129]

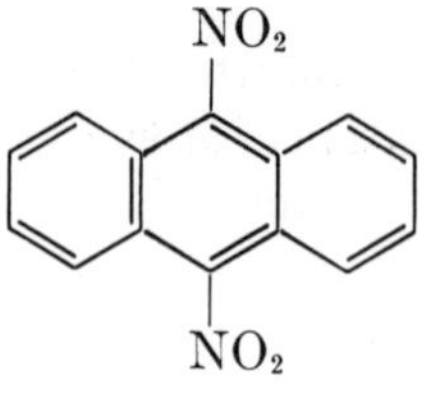

II

In all likelihood the nitration of aromatic compounds by dinitrogen pentoxide also proceeds by a radical mechanism. In a nonpolar solvent and at elevated temperature (70–100°) dissociation of dinitrogen pentoxide into radical species may occur to some extent.

$$N_2O_5 \rightarrow NO_3\cdot + NO_2\cdot$$

The nitration of an aromatic compound probably commences by addition of the NO_3 radical to the π bond of the aromatic substrate. Then the reaction with the NO_2 radical follows.

The nitrations of benzene, chlorobenzene, and toluene each yield a complex mixture of products.[21,211,212] As yet these reactions have little preparative value. They are mentioned merely to alert the reader to the interesting free radical nitrations of aromatic systems.

Saturated Compounds

The second group of nitrations of hydrocarbons—the nitration of paraffins, cycloparaffins, and aralkyls—is carried out either in the gas phase or the liquid phase. At present the gas-phase reactions are more important commercially and have been thoroughly investigated.[6–9,11,12,53,54,57,74–77,126,171,186,219,220,222] They are carried out at 410–425° with dilute nitric acid or nitrogen dioxide. There is no doubt that these processes are of a free radical nature.[12,35,126] Thus, in the nitrations of propane and butane, a small amount of oxygen facilitates the conversion of the hydrocarbons to the nitro products.[7,8] Bromine has a beneficial effect upon both the yield and the conversion,[9] and a small amount of oxygen augments the effectiveness of bromine.[9] Similarly, the addition of a small amount of oxygen to chlorine facilitates the nitration of paraffins.[6,11] Tetraethyl lead also promotes the nitration of paraffins.[126] However, a large amount of oxygen, halogen, or nitric oxide retards nitration processes.[12]

The ease with which gas-phase nitration occurs also depends upon the nature of the hydrocarbon. The hydrocarbons which more readily yield radicals are usually the ones which are most easily nitrated. For example, methane is more difficult to nitrate than ethane, while propane yields a mixture of nitromethane, nitroethane, and 1– and 2–nitropropane.[6]

The formation of nitroalkanes with a lower number of carbon atoms than the number present in the starting alkane cannot be explained by thermal rupture of the carbon-carbon bond or by cleavage of this bond caused by NO_2 radical attack. The fragmentation of the molecules can be explained as follows.[12] Nitrogen dioxide exists in two resonance forms, A and B. Thus, the odd electron is located either on a nitrogen or an oxygen atom.

$$O\dot{N}O \leftrightarrow ON\dot{O}$$

A   B

If the alkyl radical reacts with A, the product is a nitroparaffin. If it reacts with B, the product is an alkyl nitrite. The nitrites are unstable at elevated temperatures and may decompose to give, among other products, alkanes and aldehydes with fewer carbon atoms than those present in the initial alkane.[12]

It is well established that in nitration processes the active species is the NO_2 radical. It was first believed that nitric acid dissociates to give the NO_2 radical.[12,126]

$$HNO_3 \rightarrow HO\cdot + NO_2\cdot$$

$$RH + HO\cdot \rightarrow R\cdot + H_2O$$

$$R\cdot + HONO_2 \rightarrow RNO_2 + HO\cdot \text{ , etc.}$$

However, this assumption was criticized by Titov, who proposed a different mechanism which does not involve hydroxy radicals.[211]

$$RH + \cdot NO_2 \rightarrow R\cdot + HNO_2$$

$$HNO_2 + HNO_3 \rightleftharpoons 2NO_2 + H_2O$$

or

$$2HNO_3 + NO \rightleftharpoons 3NO_2 + H_2O$$

$$R\cdot + NO_2 \Big\langle {\longrightarrow RNO_2 \atop \longrightarrow RONO}$$

The nitro product is a stable compound, while the nitrite may enter into the following equilibrium.

$$RONO + H_2O \rightleftharpoons ROH + HNO_2$$

Although Markownikoff's, Konowalov's, and Nametkin's pioneering investigations of liquid-phase nitrations with nitric acid were carried out around the turn of the century, the mechanism of these nitrations was not understood until the extensive studies by Titov.[211,212,220] The results of these studies are apparently little known outside Russia. Despite the sustained interest of the Russian investigators, liquid-phase nitrations with dilute nitric acid, dinitrogen tetroxide (nitrogen dioxide), and dinitrogen pentoxide are of limited preparative value to date. The reactions of dinitrogen pentoxide are primarily of theoretical interest.

In most work with nitric acid the specific gravity of the acid varies from 1.025 to 1.5. The majority of reactions are carried out at 100–130°. The pioneering work was done in small batches in sealed tubes. This procedure often gave poor reproducibility. Later, Titov showed that these nitrations can be performed conveniently in open reaction vessels.[205]

In nitrations with dinitrogen tetroxide, particularly in those at elevated temperature, the reagent is dissociated into the nitrogen dioxide radical, which is the active species. As in the case of vapor-phase nitrations, the nitric acid does not react as such with the hydrocarbons but rather is a source of NO_2 radicals.[201,211,212] For example, neither n–heptane nor 2, 7–dimethyloctane reacts with nitric acid even during prolonged storage if nitrogen dioxide is absent.[209] Similarly, in the absence of nitrogen dioxide, cyclohexane can be stored with dilute nitric acid for prolonged periods of time without any reaction, but nitrogen dioxide reacts with cyclohexane slowly at room temperature and rapidly at 100°.[215]

Nitrations with nitrogen dioxide and with dilute nitric acid give the same mixture of products. When nitric acid is added to a mixture of cyclohexane and nitrogen dioxide, the oxidizing and nitrating effect of nitrogen dioxide is lowered.[215] An increase in the nitrogen dioxide concentration increases the yield of products of oxidation and at the same time lowers the yield of the nitro compounds.[215] The nitration of cyclohexane was first investigated by Markownikoff.[116]

Liquid-phase nitration, like gas-phase nitration, is retarded by nitric oxide. As in the vapor-phase processes, the reaction of nitrogen dioxide with a hydrocarbon in the liquid phase produces either a nitro product or an alkyl nitrite. As in the vapor-phase reactions, the first step in the nitration in solution is abstraction of the hydrogen atom of the substrate by nitrogen dioxide.

$$RH + NO_2 \rightarrow R\cdot + HNO_2$$

The hydrocarbon radical R· reacts with nitrogen dioxide to give a nitro compound and a nitrite.

$$R\cdot \overset{ONO}{\underset{}{\diagup\diagdown}} \begin{matrix} RNO_2 \\ RONO \end{matrix}$$

The nitro product is stable and can be isolated as such. The nitrite, on the other hand, may react with water in an equilibrium reaction[215]:

$$RONO + H_2O \rightleftharpoons ROH + HNO_2$$

For example, the nitration of cyclohexane with nitric acid forms nitro-cyclohexane and cyclohexyl nitrite initially.[116,144,216] The latter, being un-stable, hydrolyzes to cyclohexanol, which in turn transforms into adipic acid and other products.[215] Cyclohexyl nitrite also decomposes on standing, to give a mixture of cyclohexanol, adipic acid, and mono- and dicyclohexyl adipate.[215] Nitrogen dioxide reacts with cyclohexane for 1 hr in a sealed vessel at 100° to give 50% of nitrocyclohexane, 8% of cyclohexyl nitrite, 8% of cyclohexanol, 20% of adipic acid, and 14% of various esters of cyclo-hexanol such as cyclohexyl nitrate, b.p. 97°/40 mm, and dicyclohexyl adipate, m.p. 36°.[51,215]

In liquid-phase nitrations the order of reactivity of the hydrogen atoms of the substrate is the same as that observed with other free radical systems; namely, tertiary hydrogen atoms are substituted more easily than second-ary, which in turn are more readily substituted than primary.[32] For example, the nitration of methylcyclopentane with nitric acid at 115° yields a mix-ture of the tertiary (III) and secondary (IV) nitro compounds in a 2:1 ratio.[118,146]

III   IV

The nitration of n–hexane with dilute nitric acid (sp. gr. 1.075) at 130–140° was carried out in a sealed tube by Konowalov, and he assigned the structure of 2–nitrohexane on the basis of reduction experiments.[90,91] Worstall used stronger nitric acid (sp. gr. 1.42–1.52) and obtained a mono-nitro compound and a dinitro compound.[249] On the basis of his results Worstall assigned the structures of primary mononitro compound and 1, 1–dinitro compound. Similar results were obtained by Worstall with n–hep-tane, n–octane, n–nonane, n–decane, dodecane, and hendecane.[249,250] Re-cently the nitration of dodecane was investigated thoroughly.[5,65,72] All these nitrations are undoubtedly free radical processes. The structures assigned by Worstall are questionable, however. Titov[209] obtained 2–nitroheptane from n–heptane and nitric acid containing nitrogen dioxide at 100°; this result is in agreement with Konowalov's[90,91] interpretation.

The nitration of isopentane with nitric acid (sp. gr. 1.42) at 60° produces a mixture of β–nitro–β–methylbutane, β, γ–dinitro–β–methylbutane, and β, γ, δ–trinitro–β–methylbutane.[164] The nitration of isohexane, isoheptane, or diisobutyl with fuming nitric acid produces trinitro derivatives, m.p. 86°, 194° , and 91°, respectively.[59] A mixture of isooctane and nitric acid (sp. gr. 1.075) heated in a sealed tube for 20 hr produces secondary and tertiary mononitro derivatives, the dinitro derivative, acetone, nitromethane, 2, 2–dimethylpentanone–4, and 2, 2, 4–trimethylpentanone–3.[148]

$(CH_3)_3CCH_2CH(CH_3)_2 \rightarrow (CH_3)_3CCH(NO_2)CH(CH_3)_2$
$+ (CH_3)_3CCH_2C(NO_2)(CH_3)_2 + (CH_3)_3CCH(NO_2)C(NO_2)(CH_3)_2$
$+ CH_3NO_2 + CH_3COCH_3 + (CH_3)_3CCH_2COCH_3$
$+ (CH_3)_3CCOCH(CH_3)_2$

Trimethylethylmethane reacts with nitric acid (sp. gr. 1.235) at 100° to give the mononitro product (V).[117]

$$(CH_3)_3CCH(NO_2)CH_3$$

V

Similarly, trimethylpropylmethane reacts with dilute nitric acid (sp. gr. 1.235) at 110–115° to give compound VI.[119]

$$(CH_3)_3CCH(NO_2)C_2H_5$$

VI

More concentrated acid is not effective.[119] Nitration of diisopropyl yields β–nitro–β,γ–dimethylbutane and β,γ–dinitro–β,γ–dimethylbutane.[95,96] Nitration of diisobutyl yields a β–nitro derivative, which can be further nitrated to β, ε–dinitro–β, ε–dimethylhexane.[92,95-97] In addition, a 17% yield of a mixture of α– and γ–mononitro derivatives is obtained. In nitration of diisopropylmethane both tertiary hydrogen atoms are substituted to give the mono and dinitro derivatives.[95,96] Nitration of diisoamyl produces a 60% yield of nitro products: α–nitro–β, η–dimethyloctane, b.p. 126°/17 mm, n_D 1.4426 (20°); β–nitro–β, η–dimethyloctane, b.p. 125°/22.5 mm, n_D 1.4357; and β, η–dinitro–β, η–dimethyloctane.[92,95-97]

Nitration of cumene at 100° with nitric acid (sp. gr. 1.075) produces 2–nitro–2–phenylpropane.[92] Nitration of α, β–diphenylpropane with nitric acid yields γ–nitro–α, β–diphenylpropane.[99]

A radical mechanism has been proposed for the nitration of diphenylmethane with dinitrogen tetroxide.[207] The reaction is carried out in carbon tetrachloride solution at 20 or 70°. At the lower temperature a 22% yield of mononitro derivative, isolated either as the potassium salt or as the bromine derivative, m.p. 44°, is obtained. A 28% yield of the dinitro compound, m.p. 79°, is isolated from the mother liquor. At the higher temperature a higher yield of nitrodiphenylmethane is obtained. The reaction was first studied by Konowalov and Jatzewitch.[100]

The reaction of nitric acid (sp. gr. 1.075 or 1.1) with menthane at 115° results in a mixture of crystalline nitro products, one of which is believed to be compound VII, m.p. 108°.[98,101]

$$NO_2 \quad CH_2-CH_2$$
$$\diagdown \diagup \qquad \diagdown$$
$$C \qquad\qquad CHC(CH_3)_2NO_2$$
$$\diagup \diagdown \qquad \diagup$$
$$CH_3 \quad CH_2-CH_2$$

VII

The reaction of dilute nitric acid with triethylmenthane at 120° produces a 57% yield of a product which consists of the tertiary nitro derivative, b.p. 190°/743 mm, and a mixture of primary and secondary nitro compounds, b.p. 196°/750 mm.[102]

The reaction of nitric acid (sp. gr. 1.075) with dimethylethylcyclohexane at 125° yields a secondary nitro compound, b.p. 148°/40 mm, n_D 1.4529 (20°), and a tertiary nitro compound, b.p. 146°/40 mm, n_D 1.4600 (20°).[55,121,122] The reaction of nitric acid with 1, 2, 4–trimethylcyclohexane yields a tertiary nitro product, b.p. 100–110°/15 mm, n_D 1.4583 (18°).[55]

A continuous process is described for liquid-phase nitrations of paraffins and cycloparaffins under pressure.[65] n–Heptane, n–dodecane, 2, 4, 4–trimethylpentane, and cyclohexane are nitrated with nitrogen dioxide to the nitro derivatives.

The nitration of (+)–3–methylheptane with 50% nitric acid at 100° produces racemic 3–methyl–3–nitroheptane.[32] The nitration of cis– or trans–decalin with 50% nitric acid yields trans–9–nitrodecalin in both cases.[32] The hydrocarbon itself is not isomerized. The nitration of cis– or trans–hydrindane results in cis–8–nitrohydrindane in both cases.[32] These results, the neglible effect of acids upon the nitration, and the order of reactivity of the hydrogen atom (tertiary > secondary > primary) all favor a radical substitution mechanism.[32]

The nitration of side chains of aromatic compounds has been studied extensively with toluene.[92,186,199–201,204–206] At 100° nitrogen dioxide or nitric acid (if nitric oxides are present) nitrates toluene to approximately the same mixture of products.[200]

	NO$_2$	HNO$_3$
C$_6$H$_5$CH$_2$NO$_2$	49.8%	52.0%
C$_6$H$_5$CH(NO$_2$)$_2$	3.6%	3.4%
C$_6$H$_5$CO$_2$H	26.6%	24.5%
Residue	13.8%	18.0%

Elevated temperatures favor the formation of the mononitro product. If nitric acid is used for the nitration, the addition of p–formaldehyde facilitates formation of nitrogen oxides.[200,205] The reactions are carried out in open vessels. To ensure the necessary concentration of nitrogen dioxide in accordance with the following equilibrium, concentrated nitric acid is added to the aqueous phase of the reaction mixture.

$$3NO_2 + H_2O \rightleftharpoons 2HNO_3 + NO$$

Addition of concentrated nitric acid to the aqueous phase instead of the hydrocarbon phase avoids nuclear nitration. Addition of oxygen permits better utilization of nitrogen by conversion of nitric oxide to nitrogen dioxide. Oxygen also increases the rate of nitration. The slightly increased oxidation of the side chain is caused by oxygen exclusively. Phenylnitromethane is extracted with diethylamine, which reacts with phenylnitromethane to form a crystalline compound (VIII), soluble in water.

$$[C_6H_5CH{=}NO_2\ ]^-[NH_2(C_2H_5)_2]^+$$

VIII

Diethylamine can be regenerated with 10% sodium hydroxide.[205] This procedure shortens the extraction time 10- to 20-fold if a large amount of toluene is used.

The mononitro compound of toluene is not converted to the dinitro compound by nitrogen dioxide. The following reaction sequence has been proposed instead.[211]

$$C_6H_5CH_3 + NO_2\cdot \rightarrow C_6H_5CH_2\cdot \xrightarrow{NO} C_6H_5CH_2NO$$

$$\rightarrow C_6H_5CH{=}NOH \xrightarrow{NO_2} C_6H_5CH(NO_2)_2$$

The conversion of the aldoxime to the dinitro product is known as the Ponzio reaction.[58] The side products of this reaction are benzaldoxime hydroperoxide and benzaldehyde, and therefore it is conceivable that the Ponzio reaction proceeds by a radical mechanism. Aromatic nitroso compounds might be converted to nitro compounds by a radical mechanism.[214]

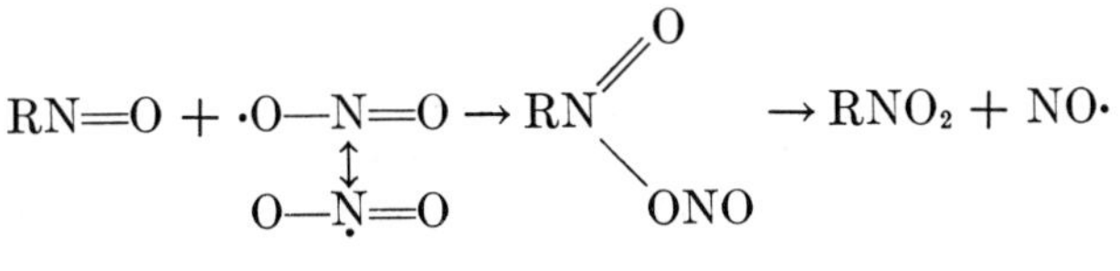

$$RN{=}O + \cdot O{-}N{=}O \rightarrow RN{\overset{\displaystyle /\!\!/O}{\underset{\displaystyle \setminus ONO}{}}} \rightarrow RNO_2 + NO\cdot$$
$$\underset{O{-}\overset{\cdot}{N}{=}O}{\updownarrow}$$

The nitration of 2–nitro-, 4–nitro-, 4–chloro-, 6–chloro-, or 4–bromotoluene at 110° with 70% nitric acid occurs in the side chain.[187] The nitration of o–nitro–m–xylene produces a mixture of ω–6–dinitro–m–xylene, m.p. 86°, and ω–4–dinitro–m–xylene, m.p. 64°.[187] The nitration of o–xylene with dilute nitric acid (sp. gr. 1.075) at 110° results in the mononitro product IX.[94]

$$CH_3$$

$$CH_2NO_2$$

IX

The nitration of o–xylene at 15–20° with nitrogen dioxide over a period of 25 days yields compound IX and o–tolyldinitromethane, m.p. 42°.[208] The reaction of m–xylene with nitrogen dioxide under the same conditions produces m–tolyldinitromethane, isolated as potassium salt, in 33% yield; m–tolylnitromethane, in 6% yield; and toluic acid, in 20% yield.[208] In the presence of oxygen the yields are 7, 54, and 7%, respectively.[208] The nitration of m–xylene with nitric acid (sp. gr. 1.4) at 100° forms analogous products.[208]

Mesitylene is nitrated at 100° by nitric acid to the nitro product X, m.p. 46°.[92]

$$C_6H_3(CH_3)_2CH_2NO_2$$

X

Further nitration with excess acid leads to nuclear and side-chain nitrations. A very low yield of m, m–xylyldinitromethane, m.p. 61°, is isolated from the nitration of mesitylene with nitrogen dioxide.[208]

Other side chains of aromatic compounds can be nitrated. n–Butyl benzene or isobutyl benzene is nitrated at 100° with nitric acid to form 1–nitro–1–phenylbutane, b.p. 151°/25 mm, n_D 1.5074 (20°), and 2–methyl–3–nitro–3–phenylpropane, b.p. 145°/25 mm, n_D 1.5075 (20°), respectively.[92]

The reactions of nitric acid and of nitrogen dioxide with mercuric paraffins, such as dibenzyl mercury, benzylmercuric chloride, and dibutyl mercury, have been investigated by Titov and Rusanov.[217] Nitric acid reacts only if it contains nitrogen dioxide. Nitrogen dioxide reacts rapidly even below room temperature. Either of two mechanisms could be operative. If the reaction proceeds with intermediate formation of the nitroso derivative, the final product should be phenyldinitromethane.

$$C_6H_5CH_2HgX \rightarrow C_6H_5CH_2NO \xrightarrow{\;NO_2\;} C_6H_5CH(NO_2)_2$$

If the HgX group acts only as a mobile hydrogen atom, no dinitro product should be formed; instead benzyl nitrite, benzyl nitrate, and phenylnitromethane should be formed.

$$C_6H_5CH_2HgX + \cdot NO_2 \rightarrow C_6H_5CH_2\cdot$$

$$C_6H_5CH_2\cdot + N_2O_4(NO_2) \Bigg\langle \begin{array}{l} \rightarrow C_6H_5CH_2ONO \\[2ex] \rightarrow C_6H_5CH_2ONO_2 \end{array}$$

The experiments confirmed the second mechanism.

The mercury compounds of hydrocarbons react with nitric acid and nitrogen dioxide much faster than the corresponding original hydrocarbons. Reactions which might be possible with compound XI cannot be achieved with the original hydrocarbon.

$$RHgR'$$

$$XI$$

R = halogen or R = R' = alkyl

Thus, the reaction with di–n–butyl mercury produces butyl nitrite, which cannot be prepared by nitration of butane.[217] The reaction of nitric acid (sp. gr. 1.1) with benzyl mercury chloride in chloroform produces a diphenylfuroxane, m.p. 115°, in 40% yield.[217]

Nitrations using dinitrogen pentoxide have received little attention. Titov and Shchitov proposed that dinitrogen pentoxide is in equilibrium with NO_2 and NO_3 radicals.[218]

$$N_2O_5 \rightleftharpoons \cdot NO_2 + NO_3 \cdot$$

The more reactive NO_3 radical abstracts the hydrogen atoms from the hydrocarbon. The hydrocarbon radical then undergoes further reaction with dinitrogen pentoxide and with nitrogen oxide to give nitro compounds and a nitrate plus some more oxidized products ($R'CO_2H$). Schematically the formation of these products is as follows.

$$RH + NO_3 \cdot \rightarrow R \cdot + HNO_3$$

$$R \cdot + N_2O_5 \rightarrow RONO_2 + NO_2$$

$$2R \cdot + 2NO_2 \rightarrow RNO_2 + RONO$$

$$R \cdot \xrightarrow{N_2O_4} \begin{cases} \rightarrow RONO + NO_2 \\ \rightarrow RONO_2 + NO \end{cases}$$

$$RONO + N_2O_5 \begin{cases} \rightarrow RONO_2 + N_2O_4 \\ \rightarrow R'CO_2H \end{cases}$$

The reaction of dinitrogen pentoxide with paraffins is retarded by nitrogen dioxide. This effect is in contrast to that observed with nitrogen dioxide in nitration processes using dilute nitric acid. It is explained by shifting of the equilibrium into the direction of the undissociated dinitrogen pentoxide.

Cyclohexane and dinitrogen pentoxide in carbon tetrachloride react at 0° to give nitrocyclohexane in 39% yield and cyclohexyl nitrate, b.p. 95°/40 mm, n_D 1.4578 (20°), in 41% yield.[218] In boiling carbon tetrachloride, adipic acid is obtained in addition.[218] The reaction with n–heptane under similar conditions produces mainly n–heptyl nitrate, b.p. 99°/40 mm, n_D 1.4220 (20°), and secondary nitroheptanes, n_D 1.4230 (20°).[218] The reaction with n–octane produces n–octyl nitrate, 110°/40 mm, n_D 1.4260 (20°), and secondary octane.[218]

While the mechanism of nitration with benzoyl nitrate, alkyl nitrites, and alkyl nitrates has not been investigated, the general pattern of these nitrations suggests a possible radical path. Durene in carbon tetrachloride and bromodurene in chloroform react rapidly with benzoyl nitrate to give methyl-group nitrated products, m.p. 52° and 89°, respectively.[247] In the latter case the nitro group is located at position 2 or 3.

Nitrations with alkyl nitrites and nitrates have been described in two patents.[189,190] The products appear to be similar to those obtained from nitrations using nitric acid and nitrogen dioxide. Thus, n–propyl nitrate nitrates at 203° and 400-psi cyclohexane, methylcyclohexane, n–nonane, or p–xylene to give nitrocyclohexane in 70% yield, 1–methyl–1–nitrocyclohexane in 26% yield, primary mononitro–n–nonane (plus secondary derivative) in 34% yield, and α–nitro–p–xylene in 42% yield, respectively.[190] n–Butyl nitrite reacts with 2, 3–dimethylbutane, n–nonane, n–decane, cyclohexane, methylcyclohexane, chlorocyclohexane, cumene, toluene, ethylbenzene, or p–xylene to give 2, 3–dimethyl–2–nitrobutane in 13% yield, primary (plus secondary) mononitrononane, primary (plus secondary) mononitrodecane, nitrocyclohexane in 35% yield, 1–methyl–1–nitrocyclohexane in 32% yield, 1–chloro–2–nitrocyclohexane in 27% yield, 2–nitro–2–phenylpropane in 38% yield, α–nitrophenylmethane in 27% yield, 1–nitro–1–phenylethane in 37% yield, and α–nitro–p–xylene in 29% yield, respectively.[189]

An interesting nitration of propyl chloride or butyl chloride uses ammonium nitrate and concentrated sulfuric acid in the presence of light.[1] The reaction with propyl chloride in the dark produces 2–chloro–2–nitropropane, b.p. 132°, n_D 1.4380 (20°), whereas under illumination 2–chloro–1–nitropropane, b.p. 140°, n_D 1.4450 (20°), is obtained.[1] The reaction with butyl chloride in the dark produces 2–chloro–2–nitrobutane, b.p. 151°, n_D 1.4323 (20°), while the photonitration yields 2–chloro–1–nitrobutane, b.p. 161°, n_D 1.455 (20°).[1]

Photonitration of diphenylamine with 1, 4, 3, 6–dianhydro–O–glucitol–2, 5–dinitrate yields mainly 2–nitrodiphenylamine, m.p. 73°, and 4–nitrodiphenylamine, m.p. 146°, plus smaller quantities of N–nitrosodiphenylamine, m.p. 67°, and 4–nitrosodiphenylamine, m.p. 134°.[81]

The reaction of 8–hydroxyquinoline and its derivatives with dilute nitric acid (7.5–25%) produces 5, 7–dinitro derivative in good yield.[223] An interesting feature of this reaction is that nitrogen dioxide is evolved from the re-action mixture prior to the formation of the dinitro compound. While the mechanism of this reaction is unknown, it is conceivable that the reaction proceeds by a free radical path.

Photochemical reaction of heptafluoroiodopropane with dinitrogen tetroxide produces perfluoro–1–nitropropane in low yield.[17,19] The reaction of triphenylmethyl radical with dinitrogen dioxide apparently results in two compounds, triphenylnitromethane, m.p. 147°, and triphenylmethyl nitrite, m.p. 95–100° (decomp.).[172]

Tetraphenylsuccinonitrile reacts rapidly with nitrogen dioxide at room temperature to give a product, m.p. 44°, for which structure XII was proposed.[248]

$$(C_6H_5)_2CCN$$
$$|$$
$$NO_2$$

XII

The reaction of aliphatic azo compounds with nitrogen dioxide is no doubt a free radical process. Decomposition of α, α'–azobisisobutyronitrile in boiling benzene in the presence of nitrogen dioxide results in α–nitrobisiso-butyronitrile, b.p. 67°/14 mm, m.p. 34°, in 31% yield.[198] In addition, 43% of tetramethylsuccinonitrile, m.p. 169°, plus 6.5% of tri(2–cyano–2–propylhydroxylamine), m.p. 79°, are obtained. Nitrogen dioxide reacts with dimethyl–α, α'–azobisisobutyrate in toluene at 100° to give methyl α–nitroisobutyrate, b.p. 77°/14 mm, in 33% yield.[198] The reaction of nitrogen dioxide with 3, 3'–azobis–3–cyanopentane produces 3–cyano–3–nitro-pentane, b.p. 89°/11 mm, in 21% yield, plus the dimer, m.p. 47°, in 14% yield.[198] The reaction of nitrogen dioxide with 1, 1'–azobis–1–cyanocyclo-hexane produces 1–cyano–1–nitrocyclohexane, m.p. 56°, in 25% yield, plus the symmetrical dimer, m.p. 223°, in 30% yield.[198]

Table 39.   Nitration of Saturated Hydrocarbons and Side Chains

C_n	Hydrocarbon	Nitrating agent (sp. gr.)	Product	% Yield	°C b.p./mm (m.p.)	n_D (°C)	Ref.
C_5	Isopentane	HNO_3 (1.42)	β,γ-Dinitro-β-methylbutane + β,γ,δ-Trinitro-β-methylbutane		105/44 (179)		164
C_6	$(CH_3)_3CCH_2CH_3$	HNO_3 (1.235)	$(CH_3)_3CCH(NO_2)CH_3$		168/748 (40)		117
	Methylcyclopentane	HNO_3 (1.075)	1-Nitro-1-methylcyclopentane + 2-Nitro-1-methylcyclopentane	32	92/40 99/40		118, 120, 146
	Cyclohexane	HNO_3 (1.075–1.2)	Nitrocyclohexane	44	110/40	1.4612 (19)	116, 144
	Cyclohexane	N_2O_4	Nitrocyclohexane + Cyclohexylnitrite	49 27	80/10 41/20	1.4612 (20) 1.4349 (20)	51, 186, 216
	n-Hexane	HNO_3 (1.42)	1-Nitrohexane	60	180		249, 250
	n-Hexane	HNO_3 (1.075)	2-Nitrohexane	50	176/758		90, 91, 186
	β,γ-Dimethylbutane	HNO_3 (1.1)	β-Nitro-β,γ-dimethylbutane + β,γ-Dinitro-β,γ-dimethylbutane		168/750 208		95, 96
C_7	n-Heptane	HNO_3 (1.42)	1-Nitroheptane + 2-Nitroheptane	60	193 195/760		249, 250 209
	Methylcyclohexane	HNO_3	1-Nitro-1-methylcyclohexane + 2-Nitro-1-methylcyclohexane		109/40 119/40	1.4580 (20) 1.4618 (19)	145
	$(CH_3)_3CCH_2CH_2CH_3$	HNO_3 (1.235)	$(CH_3)_3CCH(NO_2)CH_2CH_3$		89/40		119
	$(CH_3)_2CHCHCH_2CH(CH_3)_2$	HNO_3 (1.1)	$(CH_3)_2C(NO_2)CH_2CH(CH_3)_2$ + $(CH_3)_2C(NO_2)CH_2C(NO_2)$-$(CH_3)_2$		181/742 (81)	1.4235 (30)	95, 96
	Toluene	NO_2	$C_6H_5CH_2NO_2$		141/35		92, 199, 200, 205
	Toluene	HNO_3	$C_6H_5CH_2NO_2$	55	141/35		92, 199, 200, 205

Table 39. (cont.)   Nitration of Saturated Hydrocarbons and Side Chains

C_n	Hydrocarbon	Nitrating agent (sp. gr.)	Product	% Yield	°C b.p./mm (m.p.)	n_D (°C)	Ref.
	2-Nitrotoluene	70% HNO_3	ω-2-Dinitrotoluene	70	67		187
	4-Nitrotoluene	HNO_3	ω-4-Dinitrotoluene		91		187
	4-Chlorotoluene	HNO_3	4-Chloro-ω-2-nitrotoluene		112		187
	4-Bromotoluene	HNO_3	4-Bromo-ω-2-nitrotoluene		114		187
	6-Chlorotoluene	HNO_3	6-Chloro-ω-2-nitrotoluene		82		187
C_8	n-Octane	HNO_3 (1.42)	1-Nitrooctane	60	206		249, 250
	$(CH_3)_3CCH_2CH(CH_3)_2$	HNO_3 (1.075)	$(CH_3)_3CCH(NO_2)CH(CH_3)_2$ +		70/5	1.4388 (20)	148
			$(CH_3)_3CCH_2C(NO_2)(CH_3)_2$ +		100/34	1.4360 (20)	
			$(CH_3)_3CCH(NO_2)C(NO_2)(CH_3)_2$		124/21	1.4526 (20)	
	β,ε-Dimethylhexane (diisobutyl)	HNO_3 (1.075)	$(CH_3)_2C(NO_2)(CH_2)_2CH(CH_3)_2$ +	83	200/760	1.4305 (15)	92, 97
			$(CH_3)_2CHCH_2CH_2CH(CH_2-$ $NO_2)CH_3$ + $(CH_3)_2CHCH(NO_2)CH_2CH(CH_3)_2$- $(CH_3)_2C(NO_2)(CH_2)_2C(NO_2)-$ $(CH_3)_2$	} 17	100/20 (124)		
	Cumene	HNO_3 (1.075)	$C_6H_5C(NO_2)(CH_3)_2$		126/15		92
	o-Xylene	HNO_3 (1.075)	o-$CH_3C_6H_4CH_2NO_2$		145/23	1.5438 (18)	94
C_9	n-Nonane	HNO_3 (1.075)	Nitrononane	48	215 (decomp.)		249, 250
	β,ζ-Dimethylheptane (isobutylisoamyl)	HNO_3 (1.075)	$(CH_3)_2C(NO_2)(CH_2)_3CH(CH_3)_2$ +		113/25	1.4325 (18)	97
			$(CH_3)_2CNO_2(CH_2)_3C(NO_2)(CH_3)_2$		(74)		

Table 39. (cont.)   Nitration of Saturated Hydrocarbons and Side Chains

C_n	Hydrocarbon	Nitrating agent (sp. gr.)	Product	% Yield	°C b.p./mm (m.p.)	n_D (°C)	Ref.
C_{10}	β, η–Dimethyloctane (diisoamyl)	Conc. HNO$_3$	CH$_2$(NO$_2$)CH(CH$_3$)(CH$_2$)$_4$-CH(CH$_3$)$_2$+		126/17	1.4426 (21)	92, 93, 97, 209
			(CH$_3$)$_2$C(NO$_2$)(CH$_2$)$_4$-CH(CH$_3$)$_2$+		125/22.5	1.4357 (20)	
			(CH$_3$)$_2$CHCH(NO$_2$)(CH$_2$)$_3$-CH(CH$_3$)$_2$+ (CH$_3$)$_2$CHCH$_2$CH(NO$_2$)(CH$_2$)$_2$CH-(CH$_3$)$_2$		130/25		
			(CH$_3$)$_2$C(NO$_2$)(CH$_2$)$_4$C(NO$_2$)-(CH$_3$)$_2$		(102)		
C_{14}	Anthracene	NO$_2$	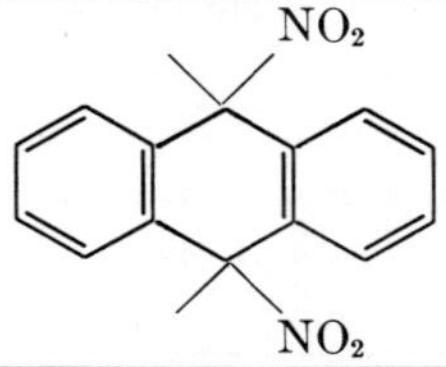		(194)		129
C_{15}	α, β–Diphenylpropane	HNO$_3$ (1.075)	C$_6$H$_5$CH$_2$CH(C$_6$H$_5$)CH$_2$NO$_2$		(153)		99

SUBSTITUTION NITRATION OF UNSATURATED COMPOUNDS

Nitration of olefins with nitrogen oxides, nitric acid, or related agents may lead not only to addition reactions but also to substitution reactions with preservation of the double bond. An excellent review by Dombrovskii gives the chronological developments in this area.[49]

The nitration mechanism of olefins with nitric acid has been investigated by Petrov and Bulygina.[162] They concluded that these nitrations proceed by a radical mechanism similar to that described by Titov[211,212] for the nitration of saturated compounds. As in the nitration of saturated compounds, the nitric acid is only a source of nitrogen dioxide radical. These investigators also observed that nitration of olefins may be accompanied by a shift of the double bond.

Thus, when n–octene–1 is nitrated with 20 or 80% nitric acid at 90–100°, an octene–2 derivative (I), b.p. 96°/4 mm, n_D 1.4692 (20°), is produced in 83% yield.[162]

$$CH_3(CH_2)_5CH{=}CH_2 \rightarrow CH_3(CH_2)_4CH{=}CHCH_2NO_2$$

I

Nitration of 2–ethylhexene–1 (possibly contaminated with some 2–ethylhexene–2) with nitric acid at 70–75° results in an 86% yield of a hexene–2 derivative (II), b.p. 79°/3 mm, n_D 1.4672 (20°).[162]

$$CH_3(CH_2)_3\underset{\underset{C_2H_5}{|}}{C}{=}CH_2 \rightarrow CH_3(CH_2)_2CH{=}\underset{\underset{C_2H_5}{|}}{C}CH_2NO_2$$

II

Isobutylene nitrated with nitric acid (sp. gr. 1.52) forms the nitro derivative III, b.p. 80°/40 mm, in 6–10% yield.[73]

$$(CH_3)_2C{=}CH_2 \rightarrow (CH_3)_2C{=}CHNO_2$$

III

Butadiene nitrated with nitric acid (sp. gr. 1.50) at −30° forms a mononitro product, b.p. 118°/760 mm, n_D 1.4211 (20°), which could be the 1–nitro derivative.[44]

The nitration of 1, 1–dichloropentene–1 (IV) or 1, 1, 5–trichloropentene–1 (V) with nitric acid (sp. gr. 1.495) at approximately 60° results in a mixture of saturated compounds.[254] On the basis of the products formed, these reactions fit the general picture of radical reactions. The nitration of IV produces a mixture of 1, 1, 1, 2–tetrachloropentane, 1, 1, 1–trichloro–2–nitropentane, and 1, 1–dichloro–1, 2–dinitropentane.

$$CH_3CH_2CH_2HC{=}CCl_2 \rightarrow CH_3CH_2CH_2CHClCCl_3$$
$$+ CH_3CH_2CH_2C(NO_2)CCl_3$$
$$+ CH_3CH_2CH_2C(NO_2)CCl_2NO_2$$

IV

The nitration of V results in a mixture of 1, 1, 1, 5–tetrachloro–2–nitropentane and 1, 1, 5–trichloro–1, 2–dinitropentane.

$$CH_2ClCH_2CH_2CH{=}CCl_2 \rightarrow CH_2ClCH_2CH_2CH(NO_2)CCl_3$$
$$+ CH_2ClCH_2CH_2CH(NO_2)CCl_2NO_2$$

V

The nitration of ethyl dimethyl acrylate results in the α–nitro derivative, b.p. $121°/24$ mm.[30,31] The nitration of methyl or ethyl p–nitrocinnamate with nitric acid (sp. gr. 1.5) in the presence of concentrated sulfuric acid produces α–nitro derivatives (VI), m.p. $127°$ and $109°$, respectively.[61]

$$p{-}NO_2C_6H_4CH{=}CHCO_2R \rightarrow p{-}NO_2C_6H_4CH{=}\underset{\underset{\displaystyle NO_2}{|}}{C}CO_2R$$

VI

R = CH₃, C₂H₅

α, 4–Dinitrocinnamic acid, which is prepared at $-20°$ to $-10°$ by nitration of 4–nitrocinnamic acid, is unstable and decomposes at $0°$ to give ω, 4–dinitrostyrene (VII), m.p. $199°$.[61]

$$p{-}NO_2C_6H_4CH{=}\underset{\underset{\displaystyle NO_2}{|}}{C}CO_2H \rightarrow p{-}NO_2C_6H_4CH{=}CHNO_2 + CO_2$$

VII

Nitration of 3–nitrocinnamic acid produces ω, 3–dinitrostyrene.[62] o–Nitrocinnamic acid, however, does not react.[62]

Cyclohexene does not react at 60–65° with nitric acid having a specific gravity of 1.075.[221] With more concentrated acid (sp. gr. 1.2), 1–nitrocyclohexene, b.p. $68°/1.5$ mm, n_D 1.5032 (20°); secondary nitrocyclohexene, b.p. $54°/2$ mm, n_D 1.4822 (20°), which is believed to be the allylic 3–nitrocyclohexene; cyclohexenepseudonitrosite, m.p. 145°; and some adipic acid are obtained.[221] The combined yield of nitro products is 16%.

The nitration of camphene with dilute nitric acid (sp. gr. 1.075) at 105–110° produces α–nitrocamphene (VIII), b.p. $119°/14$ mm, n_D 1.4950 (20°), in 7–7.7% yield and ω–nitrocamphene (IX), m.p. 64°, in 3.2–5.6% yield.[147]

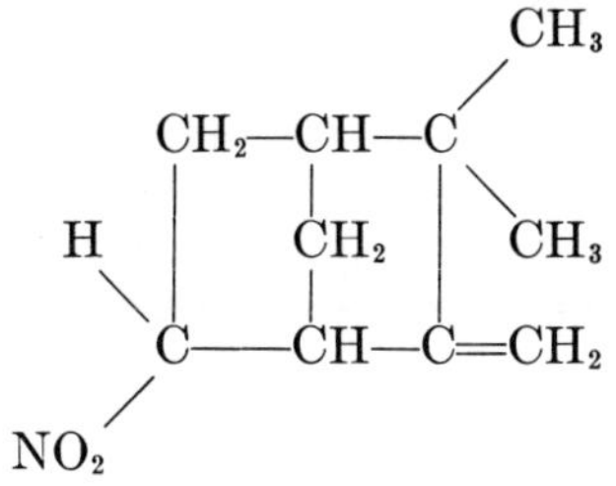

VIII 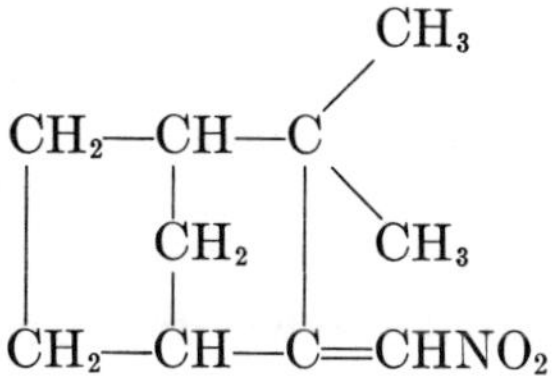   IX

α–Nitrocamphene can be converted into a crystalline stereoisomer, m.p. 116°.[147] The nitration is carried out equally well in an open vessel or in a sealed tube.[147] The reaction in a sealed tube is carried out for 30 hr; every 10 hr the tube is opened to release gases.

Nitration with tetranitromethane might be a radical process.[49] A number of compounds have been nitrated with tetranitromethane by Schmidt and co-workers.[179,180] Pyridine is used as the solvent; this apparently facilitates the production of nitrogen dioxide radicals from tetranitromethane. The nitration results in mononitro derivatives. For example, anethol or isosafrol is nitrated at 0° to give a high yield of β–nitroanethol (X), m.p. 48°, and β–nitroisosafrol (XI), m.p. 98°, respectively.[179]

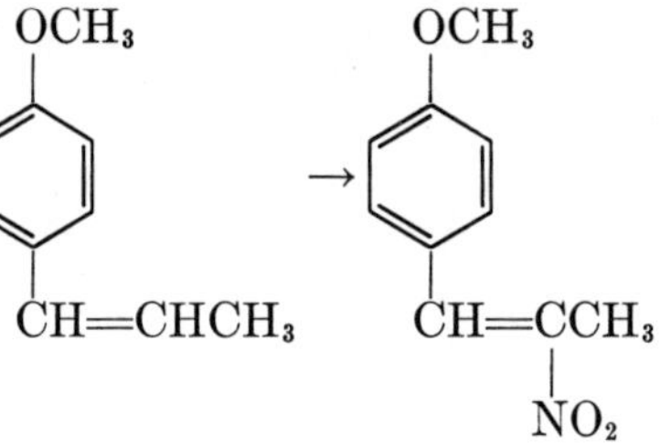

X

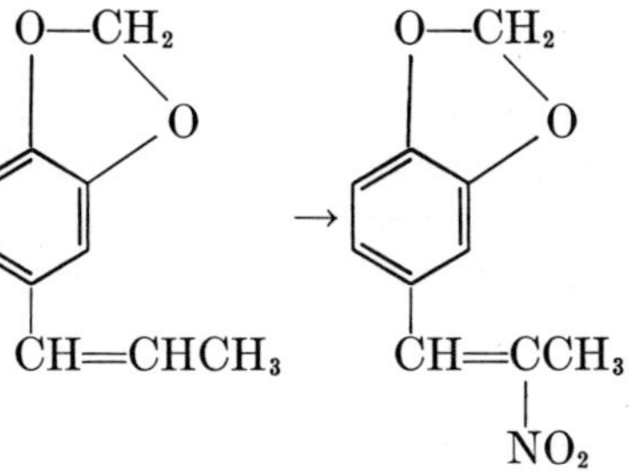

XI

Isoeugenol methyl ether, isomyristicine, isoapiol, asorone, and o–anethol are nitrated to give the corresponding β–nitro derivatives, m.p. 72°, 112°, 110°, 98°, and 52°, respectively, in high yield.[180] While this reaction appears to be a substitution reaction, it is conceivable that the addition of nitrogen dioxide to the double bond first produces a dinitro or nitronitrite derivative, which is then converted by the base to the unsaturated nitro derivative.

An interesting radical displacement reaction with dinitrogen tetroxide has been reported.[194] When dinitrogen tetroxide is added to β–bromostyrene at room temperature, the bromine atom is displaced by the nitro group to form β–nitrostyrene in 67% yield.

$$C_6H_5CH{=}CHBr + {\cdot}NO_2 \rightarrow C_6H_5CH{=}CHNO_2 + Br{\cdot}$$

1, 1–Dibromo–2–nitro–2–phenylethane, m.p. 73°, is a by-product of this interaction. When the order of addition is reversed, a lower yield (47%) of β–nitrostyrene is obtained.

REACTION OF NITRIC OXIDE WITH HYDROCARBONS IN THE PRESENCE OF CHLORINE

Nitric oxide reacts with hydrocarbons in the presence of chlorine and ultraviolet light to give a mixture of bisnitrosoalkane and chloronitrosoalkane. For example, reaction of nitric oxide with cyclohexane at 14° produces bisnitrosocyclohexane (I), m.p. 116°, and 1–chloro–1–nitrosocyclohexane (II).[130,140]

I   II

Light of a wavelength of 380–420 mμ is the most effective.[130] Depending on the ratio of nitric oxide to chlorine, the relative amounts of I and II may vary. When the ratio of nitric oxide to chlorine is 8:1, compound I is obtained in a 60% yield and compound II in 20% yield.

Compound II is difficult to purify. It can be oxidized by nitric acid to the gem–chloronitro derivative (III), b.p. 95°/15 mm, n_D 1.4783 (20°).[130,139,140] The gem–chloronitroso compounds can be reduced to the corresponding oximes by such reagents as sodium borohydride and lithium aluminum hydride or by catalytic hydrogenation.[141] They are also reduced photochemically, although in lower yield.[141] Since chloronitroso compounds absorb light of 650–680 mμ, the conversion can be achieved by daylight; the reaction produces hydrogen chloride.[141]

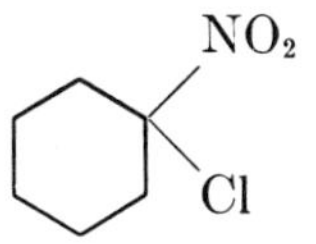

NO₂

III

On heating, nitroso compounds form the corresponding oximes.[140] Thus, compound I heated at 120° for 10 min and distilled at about 102°/15 mm results in solidification of the distillate, which is cyclohexanone oxime (IV), m.p. 92°.[140]

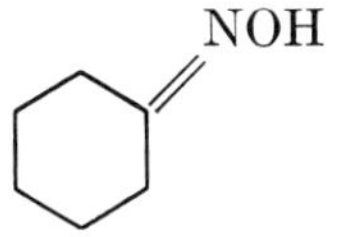

NOH

IV

Bisnitroso compounds can also be rearranged to the corresponding oxime derivatives at room temperatures by reaction with hydrogen chloride in ultraviolet light.[131] Under these conditions compound I forms IV in 93% yield after 1 hr,[131] and bisnitrosocyclooctane forms cyclooctanone oxime, m.p. 40°, in 91% yield.[136] If a stoichiometric amount of hydrogen chloride is used, the oxime is isolated as hydrogen chloride.[136] The oxime is converted by chlorine into the chloronitroso derivative; this reaction does not require light.[136]

Cyclohexanone- or cyclooctanone oxime hydrochloride is obtained when cyclohexane or cyclooctane is irradiated with fast electrons (2 mev) in the presence of nitric oxide.[143] First bisnitrosocyclohexane or -cyclooctane is formed, which is converted by irradiation and hydrogen chloride into the cyclohexanone- or cyclooctanone oxime hydrochloride, respectively. This reaction can be carried out in one step.[143] The hydrocarbon is irradiated (50 Mrads) for 91 min while a mixture of hydrogen chloride and nitric oxide is added at a rate of 10 liters/hr. A 46% yield of cyclohexanone oxime hydrochloride, m.p. 80°, and a 55% yield of cyclooctanone oxime hydrochloride, m.p. 40°, are obtained by this method.

To summarize, the reaction of hydrocarbons with nitric oxide in the presence of chlorine, hydrogen chloride, and ultraviolet light proceeds through several steps to give the corresponding oxime eventually. However, the reaction can be stopped at various stages for isolation of the intermediates.

The preparation of cyclohexanone oxime is of interest in connection with the preparation of Perlon, a German product closely related to U.S. nylon. Cyclohexanone oxime can be converted to ε–caprolactam by Beckmann rearrangement, which in turn can be converted to Perlon.[136]

In addition to cyclohexane and cyclooctane, other hydrocarbons undergo similar reactions with nitric oxide and chlorine. However, these reactions are less significant. For example, the reaction with *n*–heptane produces a mixture of three isomers of chloronitroso derivatives, which can be converted to the corresponding nitro compounds.[139,141] *n*–Heptanone–4–oxime and 2–methylcyclohexanone–1–oxime, b.p. 70°/0.9 mm, n_D 1.4935 (20°), m.p. 42°, are obtained photochemically in 21% and 14% yield, respectively, from reactions with the corresponding chloronitroso derivatives.[141] Toluene reacts with nitric oxide and chlorine to give traces of bis–(ω–nitrosotoluene), the main product (22%) being diphenylfuroxane (V), m.p. 114°.[139,140]

$$C_6H_5-C\overset{\displaystyle\|}{\underset{\displaystyle N}{}}-\overset{\displaystyle\|}{\underset{\displaystyle NO}{}}C-C_6H_5$$

$$\underset{\displaystyle O}{\diagdown\diagup}$$

V

Pure *trans*–decaline reacts with nitric oxide, chlorine, and hydrogen chloride under ultraviolet radiation to give *trans*–α–decalone oxime, m.p. 33°, and *cis*–β–decalone oxime, b.p. 154°/12 mm, in approximately equal quantities.[138] The reaction temperature is 14–16°, and oxygen and water are excluded. The highest purity of product is obtained with a 1:1 or 1:2 ratio of nitric oxide to chlorine. The hydrocarbon is first saturated with hydrogen chloride gas, and a mixture of nitric oxide and chlorine gas is then added. The reaction time is approximately 2½ hr. The free oxime is liberated from the hydrochloride by using dilute sodium hydroxide. The yield is 38%. The reaction with pure *cis*–decaline produces *cis*–β–decalone oxime in good yield plus a small amount of *cis*–α–decalone oxime.[138] A 1:4 to 1:7 ratio of nitric oxide to chlorine gives the best results.

MISCELLANEOUS REACTIONS OF NITRIC OXIDE AND NITROSO DERIVATIVES

The reactions of nitric oxide and of other nitrogen oxides are similar and have the general characteristics of free radical reactions. For example, the reaction of olefins with very pure nitric oxide has an induction period, and therefore some investigators could not achieve reaction of ethylenic compounds with absolutely pure nitric oxide. However, the reaction can be initiated with a trace of nitrogen dioxide.[36]

The reaction of nitric oxide with isobutylene produces an oil of complex composition in high yield.[36] Steam distillation of this oil results in α–nitroisobutylene, b.p. 64°/18 mm, n_D 1.4702 (20°), as the main product, in 49%

yield; β–nitroisobutylene, b.p. 48°/20 mm, n_D 1.4326 (20°), in 22% yield; a small amount of a crystalline pseudonitrosite (dimeric nitronitroso adduct); and bis–(1–nitro–2–nitroso–2–methylpropane), m.p. 81°.[36] The reaction of nitric oxide with cyclohexene results in cyclohexene pseudonitrosite, m.p. 153°, in low yield, and in a mixture of liquid products which are probably isomeric nitrocyclohexenes.[29] The nitro compound, b.p. 35°/0.01 mm, can be isolated in fairly pure form.[29] The reaction of nitric oxide with 1–methyl-cyclohexene yields nitromethylcyclohexane, b.p. 50°/0.01 mm.[29] The composition of the products of all these reactions suggests that at least part of the nitric oxide is converted to nitrogen dioxide. If oxygen is carefully excluded, conversion of nitric oxide to nitrogen dioxide may occur through dispro-portionation.[29,160]

The reactions of nitric oxide with haloolefins have been investigated by Park and co-workers.[158,160] Nitric oxide reacts with trifluorochloroethylene, hexafluoropropene, or tetrafluoroethylene in an autoclave at room tempera-ture. The reaction with trifluoroethylene results in a complex mixture of products, which can be separated by distillation to yield 1, 2–dichloro–1, 1, 2–trifluoro–2–nitrosoethane, b.p. 3.17°/630 mm, n_D 1.3455 (0°); 1, 2, 2–trichloro–1, 1, 2–trifluoroethane, b.p. 41°/630 mm, n_D 1.3557 (25°); 1–nitro–1, 1, 2–trifluoro–2–chloro–2–nitrosoethane, b.p. 62°/630 mm, n_D 1.349 (25°); 1, 1, 2–trifluoro–2–dichloro–1–nitroethane, b.p. 71°/630 mm, n_D 1.3669 (25°); and 1, 2–dinitro–1, 1, 2–trifluoro–2–chloroethane, b.p. 94°/630 mm, n_D 1.375 (25°). These are the products which would be expected from reaction of trifluorochloroethylene with NOCl, NO_2Cl, Cl_2, N_2O_3, and N_2O_4. The reaction of nitric oxide with hexafluoropropene produces mainly 2–nitroso–3–nitro–1, 1, 1, 2, 3, 3–hexafluoropropane, b.p. 42°/630 mm, n_D 1.306 (0°), and also 2, 3–dinitro–1, 1, 1, 2, 3, 3–hexafluoropropane, b.p. 68°/630 mm, n_D 1.3220 (25°). Equimolar quantities of nitric oxide and tetra-fluoroethylene react to form 1–nitroso–2–nitrotetrafluoroethane, b.p. 25°, in about 90% yield. All these reactions have been interpreted to proceed by a free radical mechanism.[160]

Nitric oxide reacts with tetrafluoroethylene, trifluorochloroethylene, or 1, 1–difluoro–2, 2–dichloroethylene in the presence of anhydrous ferric chloride.[158] Since nitroso compounds are not the major products formed in a static system in the absence of ferric chloride, experiments with ferric chloride are performed in a flow-type apparatus. The reactions are sensi-tive to temperature changes and to the ratio of reactants. The optimum experimental conditions for the highest yield of compounds of the type $ClCF_2CX_2NO$ (X = F or Cl) are a reaction temperature of 45–75° and a flow rate of 1 mole of olefin to about 2 moles of nitric oxide per 24 hr. Under these conditions the yields of products range from 71 to 76%. Thus, the re-action of nitric oxide with tetrafluoroethylene in the presence of ferric chloride produces 1–chlorotetrafluoro–2–nitrosoethane, b.p. −7°/630 mm.[158]

This reaction at 20° in the dark produces tetrafluoro–1–nitro–2–nitroso-ethane in 45% yield plus tetrafluoro–1, 2–dinitroethane in 10% yield; dinitrogen tetroxide accelerates the rate of the reaction.[28] The ferric chloride-catalyzed reactions of nitric oxide with trifluorochloroethylene or with 1, 1–difluoro–2, 2–dichloroethylene[158] form 1, 2–dichloro–1, 1, 2–trifluoro–2–nitrosoethane, b.p. 32°/630 mm, n_D 1.3455 (0°), and 1, 2, 2–trichloro–1, 1–difluoro–2–nitrosoethane, b.p. 72°/630 mm, n_D 1.3942 (25°), respectively. In addition to these products, all of the above reactions produce small amounts of the expected by-products from the addition of NOCl, NO_2Cl, Cl_2, N_2O_3, and N_2O_4 to these olefins.[158] Ferric chloride participates in these reactions by supplying the chlorine atom to the reacting system. Ferric chloride is reduced to the divalent state. These reactions are interpreted as free radical processes.[158]

Monomeric nitroso compounds are obtained in good yield from nitric oxide and the corresponding fluoroiodide or fluorobromoiodide.[16−19,79,80,85]

$$CF_3I \xrightarrow[\text{UV, Hg}]{\text{NO}} CF_3NO$$

The reactions are best performed in a sealed silica tube in the presence of mercury in ultraviolet light. The irradiation is carried out at room temperature for about 7 days.[79,80,85] If the same reactants are irradiated at 100° for 4 days instead of at room temperature for 7 days, a 25% yield of the nitro derivative is obtained.[85]

$$CF_3I \xrightarrow[\text{UV, 100°C}]{\text{NO}} CF_3NO_2$$

Nitric oxide and trifluoronitrosomethane are converted by oxygen at 100° to the nitro compound in 78% yield.[79,80] Other oxidizing agents, such as lead dioxide, can be used to convert the nitroso to the nitro compound.[79,80] Nitric oxide and trifluoronitrosomethane can also be converted by ultraviolet light, to compound I, b.p. 10°, in 96% yield.[86]

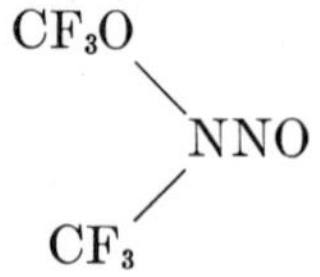

$$CF_3O \diagdown$$
$$NNO$$
$$CF_3 \diagup$$

I

In addition to the fluoroiodoalkanes, other polyhaloalkyl iodides can be converted with nitric oxide to nitroso compounds, which in turn can be transformed to the nitro derivatives.[79,80] The properties of the nitroso derivatives are listed in Table 40.

The photochemical reaction of trifluoroiodoethylene with nitric oxide in the presence of mercury at 80° and 40–60 atm of pressure results in a nitroso compound (II), b.p. −237°, which converts to a dimer, b.p. 45°.[71]

$$CF_2{=}CFI + NO \xrightarrow{\text{UV}} CF_2CFNO \rightarrow \text{Dimer}$$

II

Nitrosomethane can be made by photochemical decomposition of t-butyl nitrite.[43]

$$(CH_3)_3CONO \xrightarrow{\text{UV}} CH_3NO + (CH_3)_2CO$$

The irradiation is carried out at 25° for about 290 min. Nitrosomethane is isolated as a dimer, m.p. 122°. Prolonged irradiation slowly transforms the material into a trimer. On heating, the blue color of the monomeric form is observed.

Nitric oxide reacts with diethyl peroxide at 180° to give ethyl nitrite in about 66% yield.[106]

$$C_2H_5O\cdot + NO\cdot \rightleftharpoons C_2H_5ONO$$

This reaction is probably of no preparative value. The following decompositions are likewise of little preparative value: d–2–octyl nitrite at 100° to give d–2–octanol (80%), b.p. 68°/15 mm, n_D 1.4249 (20°), nitric oxide, and octan–2–one, b.p. 75°/20 mm, n_D 1.4159 (20°);[103] and n–octyl nitrite at 116° in butyric acid to give nitric oxide, water, n–octanoic acid (23%), n–octyl octanoate (25%), and n–octyl butyrate (51%).[25] The latter decomposition is also carried out in benzaldehyde and hexanal.[26]

The thermal and photochemical reactions of nitrites in the steroid series and their application to synthetic problems have been reviewed by Nussbaum and Robinson.[150] Subsequent papers[151,152] deal with synthetic applications of photolysis of nitrites. The photolysis of nitrites of some steroids is accompanied by carbon-carbon fission. For example, on irradiation with ultraviolet light, compound III is converted to compound IV, m.p. 238°.[152]

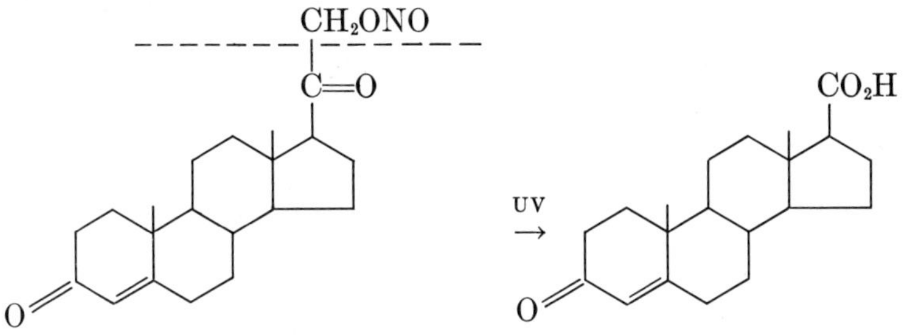

III   IV

A number of nitro compounds of the benzene and pyridine series containing the atomic arrangement V can be converted by ultraviolet light to nitroso compounds.

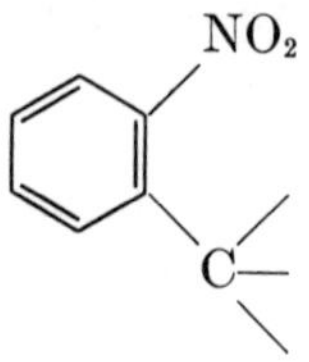

V

The first such transformation reported was the conversion of o–nitrobenzaldehyde to p–nitrosobenzoic acid.[41,181a]

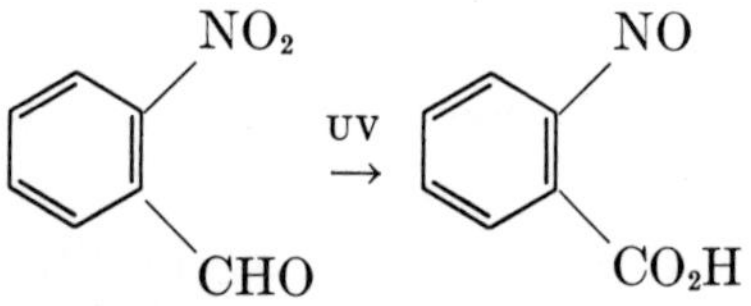

The irradiation is carried out at room temperature. Not all nitro compounds having group V are isomerized. o–Nitrocinnamic aldehyde, for example, is not.[181a] The conversion of benzylidene–o–nitroacetophenone to indigo and the preparation of various isatogenes by photochemical transformation of suitable o–nitroacetylenes or ethylenes are related to these reactions.[181b]

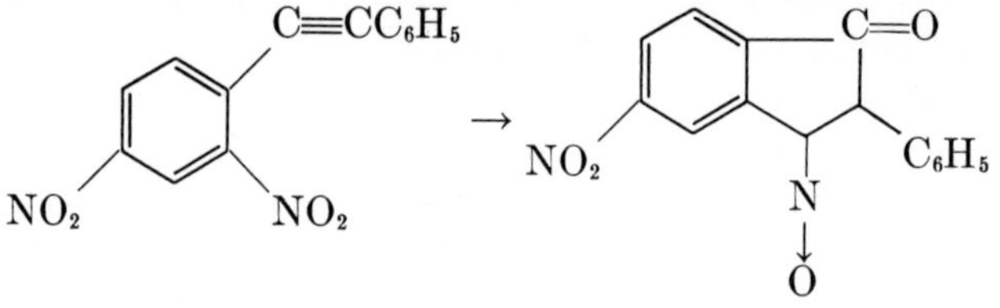

Nitric oxide reacts with α, α'–azobisisobutyronitrile in boiling benzene to give tris–(2–cyano–2–propyl)hydroxylamine (VI) in 50% yield.[66,67]

$$(CH_3)_2CN{=}NC(CH_3)_2 \rightarrow 2(CH_3)_2C\cdot + N_2$$
$$\quad\quad | \quad\quad | \quad\quad\quad\quad\quad |$$
$$\quad\quad CN \quad CN \quad\quad\quad\quad CN$$

$$2(CH_3)_2C\cdot + NO \rightarrow NCC(CH_3)_2N\ O\ C(CH_3)_2CN$$
$$\quad\quad | \quad\quad\quad\quad\quad\quad\quad\quad\quad\quad |$$
$$\quad\quad CN \quad\quad\quad\quad\quad\quad\quad\quad C(CH_3)_2CN$$

VI

N–nitrosodiphenylamine reacts with 2–cyano–2–propyl radicals to give compound VI in 56% yield.[66]

$$(C_6H_5)_2NNO \rightarrow (C_6H_5)_2N\cdot + \cdot NO$$

$$3(CH_3)_2\overset{\underset{\textstyle CN}{|}}{C}\cdot + \cdot NO \rightarrow VI$$

Compound VI is also obtained, in 25% yield, from the reaction of nitrosoisobutyronitrile and α, α'-azobisisobutyronitrile.[66]

$$(CH_3)_2\overset{\underset{\textstyle CN}{|}}{C}NO + 2(CH_3)_2\overset{\underset{\textstyle CN}{|}}{C}\cdot \rightarrow VI$$

Various other nitroso compounds react in an analogous manner, with the formation of tertiary hydroxylamine derivatives.[66] The reactions are carried out in boiling toluene over a period of $2\frac{1}{2}$ hr. The products are usually obtained in good yield.

Nitric oxide reacts with diphenyldiazomethane in cyclohexane[87]:

$$(C_6H_5)_2C{=}N_2 + NO \rightarrow (C_6H_5)_2C{=}NNO_2 + C_6H_5\overset{\underset{\textstyle O}{\|}}{C}C_6H_5 + N_2O$$

VII

The product, VII, m.p. 67°, is produced in 30–40% yield.

A radical mechanism is favored for the formation of 1, 2–oxazine derivatives from nitrosobenzene and *trans*–1, 2–pentadiene.[3] When the reactants are kept for 12 hr at 0° to room temperature, a 72% yield of products, b.p. 94°/2 mm, n_D 1.5614 (20°), is isolated; the main product is 2–phenyl–3–methyl–3, 6–dihydro–1, 2–oxazine (VIII).[3] If an ionic mechanism is operative, the predominant product should be IX.

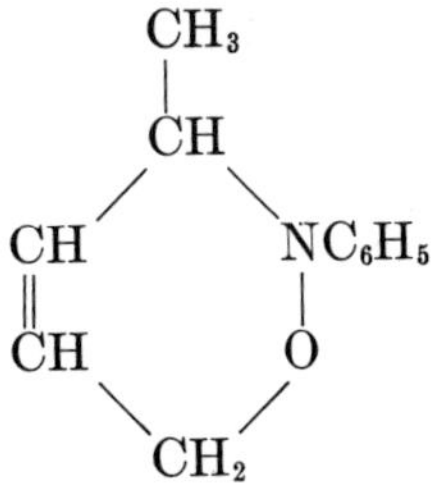

VIII 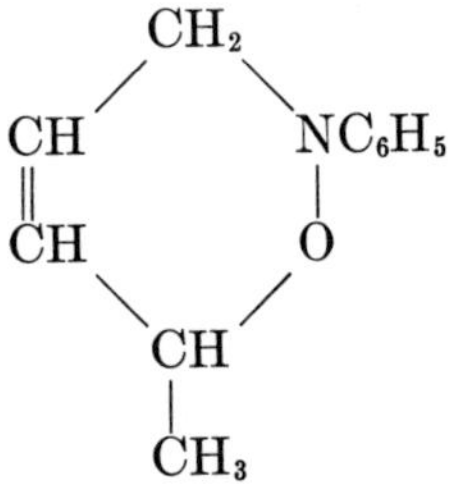   IX

Other additions of nitroso compounds to dienes are cited.[3]

An interesting formation of oximes has been reported in a patent.[168]

Nitric oxide reacts with methylethyl ketone in the presence of a base (pyridine or diethylamine) and a metal salt (cupric chloride, cupric bromide, manganous sulfide, or chromous chloride) to give diacetylmonoxime (X), in 32–40% yield.

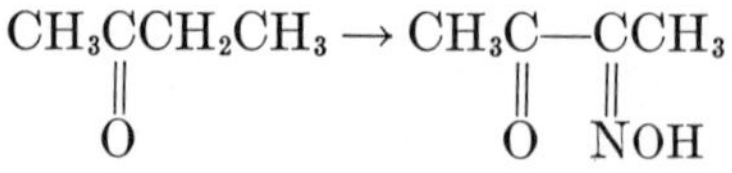

$$CH_3CCH_2CH_3 \rightarrow CH_3C{-}CCH_3$$

(with $\|$ O beneath the first structure; and $\|$ O, $\|$ NOH beneath the product)

X

Similarly, nitric oxide reacts with phenylacetonitrile to give α–oximino-phenylacetonitrile (XI), in high yield.

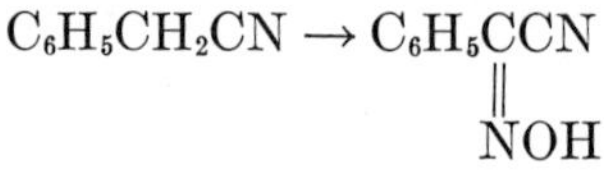

$$C_6H_5CH_2CN \rightarrow C_6H_5CCN$$

(with $\|$ NOH beneath)

XI

While the mechanism of this reaction is obscure, radical intermediates might be involved.

Oximes can also be produced by irradiation of nitrosyl sulfuric acid and a saturated hydrocarbon.[231] The hydrocarbons are cyclopentane, cyclohexane, and n–hexane. Sometimes the hydrocarbon is saturated with hydrogen chloride or bromide prior to addition of the nitrosyl sulfuric acid. The free oxime is obtained by neutralization of the oxime-sulfuric acid product with ammonia. The reaction with n–hexane produces a mixture of oximes.

Another interesting route to oxime formation is by reaction of a mixture of nitric oxide, cyclohexane peroxide, and ferrous sulfate in aqueous metha-nol at 0–5°.[40] In 12 hr an ϵ–nitrosohydroxylamine derivative (XII) of caproic acid, m.p. 61°, or the oxime (XIII) of adipohemialdehyde, m.p. 107°, is formed. This reaction definitely proceeds by a free radical path.

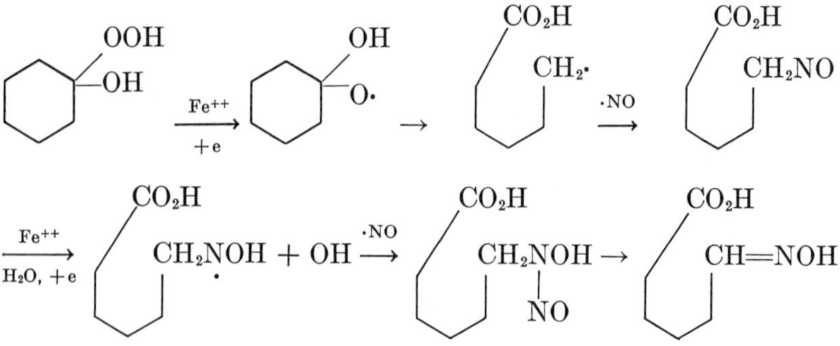

Bubbling of nitric oxide through an alkane or a cycloalkane at 160–300°

and 125–600 psi results in the formation of nitro products with good conversions.[188] Nitrocyclohexane is produced from cyclohexane, with 70% conversion. Primary and secondary mononitro derivatives are obtained from nonane. Xylene is converted to α–nitro p–xylenes. Methylcyclohexane and 1, 3–dimethylcyclohexane are converted to 1–methyl–1–nitrocyclohexane (plus secondary derivative) and 1, 3–dimethyl–1–nitrocyclohexane (plus secondary derivative), respectively.

Interesting nitrosation reactions have been discovered by Baudisch.[22] Anion XIV, which is diamagnetic, is converted by light to the paramagnetic XV, which in turn reacts with hydrogen peroxide to yield the paramagnetic XVI.

$$[Fe^{III}NO(CN)_6]^{--} \rightarrow [Fe^{II}NO(CN)_5]^{---} \rightarrow [FeH_2O(CN)_5]^{---}$$

XIV   XV   XVI

The reaction of XV with benzene in the presence of hydrogen peroxide forms o–nitrosophenol. o–Nitrosophenol can also be formed by reacting a nitrosyl (NOH) radical in the presence of an oxidizing agent.[46] The nitrosyl radical can be formed by reduction of nitrous acid or by oxidation of hydroxylamine. Many phenols react with the nitrosyl radical in the presence of copper salts to give o–nitrosophenols.[46] Copper ions and many other metal ions react with o–nitrosophenols to form stable complexes which resist further oxidation.[46]

Nitric oxide reacts with cyclohexane or with cyclooctane when the mixture is irradiated with fast electrons (2 mev), to give bisnitrosocyclohexane or cyclooctane, respectively.[143] These compounds can be transformed by irradiation in the presence of hydrogen chloride into cyclohexanone- and cyclooctanone oxime hydrochloride, respectively.[143] The reaction can be carried out in one step: A mixture of nitric oxide and hydrogen chloride is passed through the hydrocarbon at a rate of 10 liters/hr. The mixture is irradiated (50 Mrads) for 91 min. A 46% yield of cyclohexanone oxime hydrochloride, m.p. 80°, and a 55% yield of cyclooctanone oxime hydrochloride, m.p. 40°, are obtained.

The conversion of bisnitrosodecalines into the corresponding decalone oxime hydrochlorides proceeds rapidly (20–40 min) in the presence of hydrogen chloride and ultraviolet radiation.[137] In the absence of light several days are required for completion of this reaction. Thus, bis(trans–α–nitrosodecaline) (XVII), bis(trans–β–nitrosodecaline) (XVIII), and bis(cis–β–nitrosodecaline) (XIX) in ethereal solution are converted to trans–α–decalone oxime hydrochloride (XX), trans–β–decalone oxime hydrochloride (XXI), and cis–β–decalone oxime hydrochloride (XXII), in yields ranging from 80 to 90%.

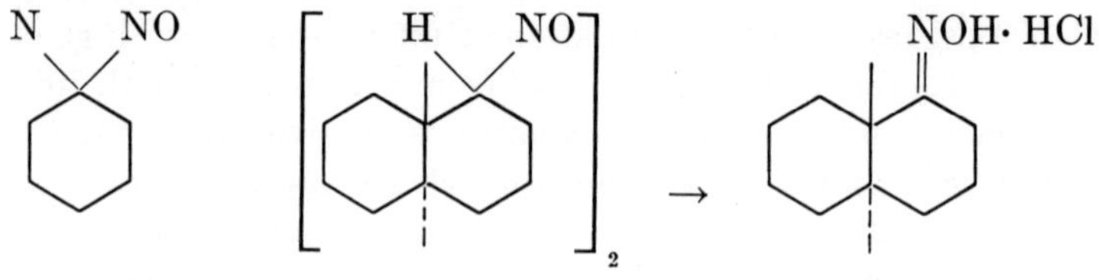

XVII   XX

XVIII   XXI

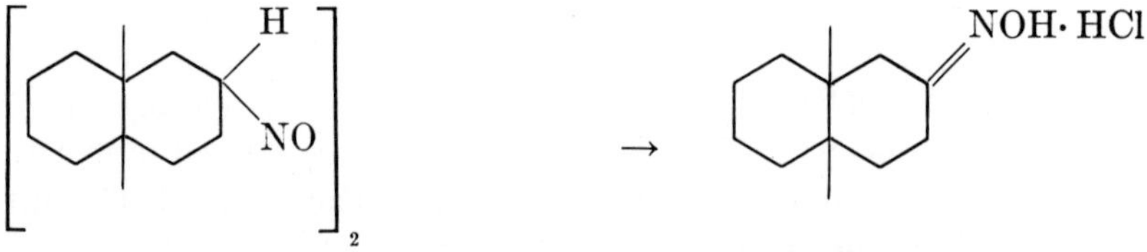

XIX   XXII

gem–Chloronitroso compounds can be reduced with lithium aluminum hydride or sodium borohydride to the corresponding ketoximes.[141] The reduction can also be achieved photochemically.[141] However, the yields are lower than those obtained with hydride reduction. Thus, 1–chloro–1–nitroso–2–methylcyclohexane is converted to 2–methylcyclohexanone oxime (XXIII), b.p. 70°/0.9 mm, m.p. 42°, n_D 1.4935 (20°), in 14% yield.

XXIII

Table 40.   Reaction of Nitric Oxide with Haloalkyl Iodides

C_n	Alkyl iodide	Product	% Yield	°C b.p./mm	Ref.
C_1	CF_3I	CF_3NO	75	−84	18, 79, 80, 85
C_2	C_2F_5I	C_2F_5NO	80	−42	19, 79, 80
C_3	C_3F_7I	C_3F_7NO	83	−12	16, 17, 19, 79, 80
C_4	C_4F_9I	C_4F_9NO	81	16/730	79, 80
C_5	$C_5F_{11}I$	$C_5F_{11}NO$	71	19/230	79, 80
C_7	$C_7F_{15}I$	$C_7F_{15}NO$	75	40/63	79, 80
C_1	$CBrF_2I$	$CBrF_2NO$	50	−12	79, 80
	$CClF_2I$	$CClF_2NO$	50	−35	79, 80
C_2	$CBrF_2CF_2I$	$CBrF_2CF_2NO$	52	18	79, 80
	$CClF_2CF_2I$	$CClF_2CF_2NO$	68	−2	79, 80
C_4	$(C_2F_5)(CF_3)CFI$	$(C_2F_5)(CF_3)CFNO$	86	24	79, 80

Table 41.   Reaction of Nitroso Compounds with 2-Cyano-2-Propyl Radical

Product, $RNOC(CH_3)_2CN$

C_n	Nitroso compound	$C(CH_3)_2CN$ $\mid$ $R = NCC(CH_3)_2$	% Yield	°C (m.p.)	Ref.
C_4	$(CH_3)_2C(CN)NO$		25	(77)	66
C_6	C_6H_5NO	C_6H_5	75	(95)	66
	$p-ClC_6H_4NO$	$p-ClC_6H_4$	60	(96)	66
	$o-ClC_6H_4NO$	$o-ClC_6H_4$	60	(95)	66
	$m-ClC_6H_4NO$	$m-ClC_6H_4$	47	(106)	66
C_7	$p-CH_3C_6H_4NO$	$p-CH_3C_6H_4$	35	(89)	66
	$o-CH_3C_6H_4NO$	$o-CH_3C_6H_4$	70	(85)	66
	$m-CH_3C_6H_4NO$	$m-CH_3C_6H_4$	60	(74)	66
C_9	$sym-(CH_3)_3C_6H_3NO$	$sym-(CH_3)_3C_6H_3$	20	(122)	66

REACTIONS OF NITROSYL CHLORIDE AND NITROSYL BROMIDE

Nitrosyl chloride reacts with a variety of olefins to give nitrosochlorides.

$$\underset{/}{\overset{\backslash}{C}}=\underset{\backslash}{\overset{/}{C}} + NOCl \rightarrow \underset{/}{\overset{\backslash}{C}}\underset{Cl}{\overset{|}{-}}\underset{NO}{\overset{|}{C}}\overset{/}{\underset{\backslash}{}}$$

Reactions with olefins of the structures $RR'C{=}CH_2$, $RCH{=}CH_2$, and $RCH{=}CHR$ usually do not produce crystalline products, whereas reactions with olefins of the structures $R''C{=}CHR'$ and $R''C{=}CR''$ do produce crystalline products. The crystalline nitrosochlorides are dimers. The re-reactions are carried out by passing nitrosyl chloride into the olefin or into a solution of the olefin in methylene chloride, chloroform, carbon tetra-chloride, or sulfur dioxide at −70 to 0°. Sometimes temperatures of 50 to 100° are used.[79] During the reaction the nitroso group is often oxidized with nitrosyl halide to the nitro group.[79]

$$CF_2{=}CF_2 + NOCl \rightarrow CF_2ClCF_2NO \overset{NOCl}{\longrightarrow} CF_2ClCF_2NO_2$$

The reactions of nitrosyl chloride have been used extensively in the study of terpenes. The halogen in nitrosochlorides is very reactive and undergoes a variety of reactions. The halogen can also be removed as hydrogen chloride to form a double bond. The nitroso group readily rearranges to an oxime group. Beckham, Fessler, and Kise[24] have reviewed the reactions of nitrosyl chloride with various compounds. Because the mechanism for these re-actions has not been established, a complete tabulation of the reactions was not attempted. In nearly all the investigations to date, no free radical cata-lysts were used. However, it is not clear whether light was completely ex-cluded during the reactions. The dissociation of nitrosyl halides will be facilitated under light, and under such conditions radical mechanisms might be operative. Indeed, Park, et al.[159] recently showed that an ionic mecha-nism is untenable for the reactions of nitrosyl chloride with fluoroolefins in the presence of ferric ions and light, and they proposed a radical mechanism. Russian workers[251-253] and Haszeldine[79] proposed a polar mechanism for the reaction of nitrosyl chloride with polyhaloolefins. Comparison of their results with those of Park, et al.[159] indicates that the order of addition is the same in all these reactions of nitrosyl halides.

Nitrosyl chloride reacts with trimethylethylene in ether to give the nitro-sochloride, m.p. 70°, in 48% yield.[48] The same reactants in the presence of hydrogen chloride produce the oxime of 2–methyl–2–chlorobutanone–3, m.p. 45°.[48] The use of excess nitrosyl chloride in the preparation of nitroso-chloride may produce 2–methyl–2, 3–dichloro–3–nitrosobutane, m.p.103°.[48] Nitrosyl chloride reacts with isopropylethylene to give 3–chloro–4–nitro–2–methylbutane and 3, 4–dichloro–2–methylbutane.[154] Nitrosyl chloride re-acts with α, β–unsaturated alcohols or esters to yield oximes.[163]

The photochemical reaction of nitrosyl chloride with n–heptane results in di–n–propyl ketone as the main product.[113-115] The photochemical reaction of nitrosyl chloride with toluene produces benzaldoxime hydrochlo-ride.[113-115] The reaction of nitrosyl chloride with n–hexane in ultraviolet light results in oximes of methyl–n–butyl and ethyl–n–propyl ketones.[135] β, β– and γ, γ–chloronitrosohexanes were assumed as intermediates. All these reactions are of little preparative interest.

However, the preparation of cyclohexanone oxime has received much at-tention.[4,14,83,105,123,149,196] (See the section on the reaction of nitric oxide with cyclohexane in the presence of chlorine.) Nitrosyl chloride reacts with cyclo-hexane in ultraviolet light to give a 71% yield of cyclohexanone oxime hy-drochloride. In the dark no reaction occurs. The presence of aqueous or anhydrous hydrogen chloride accelerates the formation of oxime.

The reaction is carried out at $-30°$ to $+15°$. A very dilute solution with respect to nitrosyl chloride is used; otherwise chlorination of the hydrocar-bon occurs. The free oxime, m.p. 88°, is obtained by treating the hydro-chloride with ammonia or sodium carbonate.

Nitrogen compounds such as nitric acid, dinitrogen trioxide, dinitrogen tetroxide, and butyl nitrite can also be used (in the presence of hydrogen chloride and ultraviolet light) to convert cyclohexane to cyclohexanone oxime.[123] Nitrosyl bromide reacts with cyclohexane to give cyclohexanone oxime.[156]

In contrast to the reaction of pure nitrosyl chloride with cyclohexane in ultraviolet light, the reaction of cyclohexane with a mixture of nitrosyl chloride and nitric oxide in a ratio of 2:6 results in the formation of bis(nitro-socyclohexane) (I), m.p. 116°.[142]

I

The same product is obtained by passing nitrosyl chloride into cyclohexane in ultraviolet light in the presence of excess nitrogen, to remove hydrogen chloride, which isomerizes the nitroso compound to the cyclohexanone oxime.[50] The temperature is maintained between 15 and 30°, and the yields range between 30 and 50%.[50]

The photochemical reaction of nitrosyl chloride with cyclooctane forms cyclooctanone oxime in high yield.[4,14] The photochemical reaction of nitrosyl chloride with ethylbenzene results in acetophenone oxime in 50% yield.[4] The reaction of nitrosyl chloride with n-heptyl bromide, after acid hydrolysis of the reaction product, produces 1-bromo-6-heptanone.[4]

A reaction of little preparative significance is the interaction of nitrosyl chloride with peracids. The reaction of nitrosyl chloride with peroxyphenylacetic acid in ether or petroleum ether at 0° produces bis–α–nitrosotoluene, m.p. 120°, benzyl nitrite, b.p. 31°/1 mm, n_D 1.4986 (24.8°), and α–nitrotoluene, b.p. 62°/0.6 mm, n_D 1.5320 (24.8°).[104] No mechanism has been proposed for this reaction.

$$C_6H_5CH_2CO_3H + NOCl$$

$$\rightarrow C_6H_5CH_2NO \begin{cases} \rightarrow \text{dimer} \\ \rightarrow C_6H_5CH_2NO_2 + C_6H_5CH_2ONO + CO_2 + HCl + \tfrac{1}{2}O_2 \end{cases}$$

Table 42. Reactions of Nitrosyl Chloride and Nitrosyl Bromide with Unsaturated Compounds

C_n	Unsaturated compound	Nitrosyl halide	Product	% Yield	°C b.p./mm (m.p.)	n_D (°C)	Ref.
C_2	$CH_2=CH_2$	NOCl	Bisethylenenitrosochloride		(71)		23
	$CH_2=CHCl$	NOCl	1,1-Dichloro-2-nitroethane	20	45/5	1.4765 (15)	251
	$CH_2=CHF$	NOCl	$CHClFCH_2NO_2$	54	56/18		252, 253
	$CH_2=CCl_2$	NOCl	1,1-Dichloro-2-nitroethylene	20	59/12	1.5172 (20)	251
	$CHF=CHCl$	NOCl	$CHClFCCl=NOH$	45	77/60	1.4472 (20)	252, 253
	$CCl_2=CHCl$	NOCl	1, 1, 2, 2-Tetrachloro-2-nitro-ethane	88	63/8		79, 251
	$CCl_2=CHF$	NOCl	$CHClFCCl_2NO_2$	55	68/33	1.399 (20)	252, 253
	$CF_2=CFH$	NOCl	1, 1, 2-Trifluoro-2, 2-dichloro-1-nitroethane+	60	71/630		159
			1, 1, 2-Trifluoro-1, 2, 2-tri-chloroethane	28	41/630		
	$CCl_2=CF_2$	NOCl	$CClF_2CCl_2NO_2$	57	72/151		79, 80
	$CCl_2=CF_2$	NOCl	$CClF_2CCl_2NO+$	9.3	15/200		159
			$CClF_2CCl_3$	36			
	$CClF=CF_2$	NOCl (FeCl$_3$)	$CF_2ClCClFNO$	82			159
	$CClF=CF_2$	NOCl	$CF_2ClCClFNO_2$	67	75 77	1.3727 (20)	79, 80 252, 253
	$CF_2=CF_2$	NOCl (FeCl$_3$)	CF_2ClCF_2NO	79			159
	$CF_2=CF_2$	NOCl	$CF_2ClCF_2NO_2$	63	37	1.3145 (22)	79, 80

Table 42. (cont.) Reactions of Nitrosyl Chloride and Nitrosyl Bromide with Unsaturated Compounds

C_n	Unsaturated compound	Nitrosyl halide	Product	% Yield	°C b.p./mm (m.p.)	n_D (°C)	Ref.
	$CF_2=CF_2$	NOBr	1-Bromotetrafluoro-2-nitro-ethane+ 1,2-Dibromotetrafluoroethane	37 10	55 45		79, 80
C_3	Propylene	NOCl	Bispropylenenitrosochloride		(91)		23
	Allyl chloride	NOCl	1,2-Dichloro-3-nitropropane	55	95/8	1.4762 (20)	251
C_4	Butene-1	NOCl	$C_2H_5CHClCH_2NO_2$+ $C_2H_5CHClCH_2Cl$		56/4 42/40	1.4510 (20) 1.4445 (20)	155
	Isobutylene		α-Chloroisobutyroaldehyde	60	(103)		153
C_5	Isopropylethylene	NOCl	$(CH_3)_2CHCHClCH_2NO_2$+ $(CH_3)_2CHCHClCH_2Cl$		76/7 43/20	1.4548 (20) 1.4475 (20)	154
C_6	2,3-Dimethyl-2-butene	NOCl	$(CH_3)_2C(NO)C(Cl)(CH_3)_2$		(122)		42
	Cyclohexene	NOCl	Cyclohexenenitrosochloride	64	(153)		2
C_8	1,2-Dimethylcyclohexene	NOCl	1,2-Dimethyl-1-chloro-2-nitrosocyclohexane		(78)		42
	$C_6H_5C≡CH$	NOCl	α-Chloro-β-nitrostyrene		128/13 (55)		161
C_{10}	8,9-Dihydrolimonene	NOCl	8,9-Dihydrolimonenenitroso-chloride	64	(95)		2

REACTION OF DINITROGEN TRIOXIDE WITH UNSATURATED COMPOUNDS

Dinitrogen trioxide forms an equilibrium mixture with nitric oxide and nitrogen dioxide.

$$NO + NO_2 \rightleftharpoons N_2O_3 + 9.6 \text{ kcal}$$

Dinitrogen trioxide is stable only at low temperatures. At $-10°$ it begins to decompose into nitric oxide and nitrogen dioxide, and at $25°$ at normal pressure only 10% of the dinitrogen trioxide is undissociated. Because the equilibrium shifts easily, a 1:1 mixture of nitric oxide and nitrogen dioxide at room temperature reacts similarly to dinitrogen trioxide. Since nitric oxide and nitrogen dioxide are radical in character, dinitrogen trioxide would be expected to react with olefins by a radical mechanism.

Dinitrogen trioxide reacts readily with unsaturated compounds, and multiple products result from most of these reactions. The early investigations on the reactions of "nitrous fumes" with olefins[169] contained many discrepancies, which are now attributed to the composition of the nitrous fumes employed. These fumes were produced from arsenic trioxide and nitric acid or from sodium nitrite and a mineral acid. Depending on the condition of preparation, the fumes contained dinitrogen trioxide and varying amounts of nitric oxide and nitrogen dioxide. When oxygen is not excluded, nitric oxide is rapidly oxidized to nitrogen dioxide. Thus, the interpretation of results is complicated. This fact was not fully recognized until comparatively recently, however.[108]

Because of these complications in earlier work and because of uncertainties associated with the mechanisms of these reactions, a detailed discussion of the reactions of dinitrogen trioxide with unsaturated compounds is not presented here. The reader is referred to the comprehensive and critical review by Riebsomer.[169] Several examples of additions of dinitrogen trioxide to olefins are listed in Table 43. The mechanism of formation of these products has not yet been investigated. Because of the fair yields and the crystallinity of the products, these reactions may be of particular interest for mechanistic studies and were therefore included here.

Dinitrogen trioxide reacts with many terpenes and with propenylbenzene derivatives to give crystalline dimeric products, which are commonly referred to as pseudonitrosites.

$$RCH{=}CHR' + N_2O_3 \rightarrow \underset{\underset{NO}{|}}{R}CH{-}\underset{\underset{NO_2}{|}}{C}HR'$$

Pseudonitrosites can also be obtained from the reaction of olefins with a mixture of nitric oxide and nitrogen dioxide. Styrene pseudonitrosite is prepared in 65% yield by the latter method.[20] Diallyldimethylsilane or allyl-pentamethyldisiloxane reacts with nitric oxide in the presence of nitrogen dioxide to give dimers of 1–nitro–2–nitroso–4–dimethyl–4–sila–6–heptene (I), m.p. 89°, and 1–nitro–2–nitroso–3–pentamethylsiloxanylpropane (II), m.p. 96°, respectively.[38]

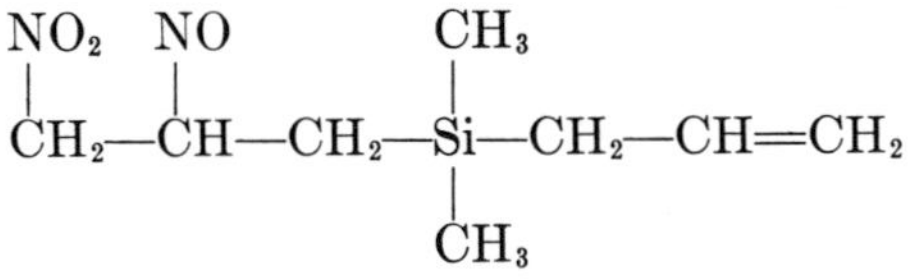

$$\begin{array}{ccc} NO_2 & NO & CH_3 \\ | & | & | \\ CH_2\!-\!CH\!-\!CH_2\!-\!Si\!-\!CH_2\!-\!CH\!=\!CH_2 \\ & & | \\ & & CH_3 \end{array}$$

I

$$\begin{array}{ccc} NO_2 & NO & CH_3 \\ | & | & | \\ CH_2\!-\!CH\!-\!CH_2\!-\!Si\!-\!O\!-\!Si(CH_3)_3 \\ & & | \\ & & CH_3 \end{array}$$

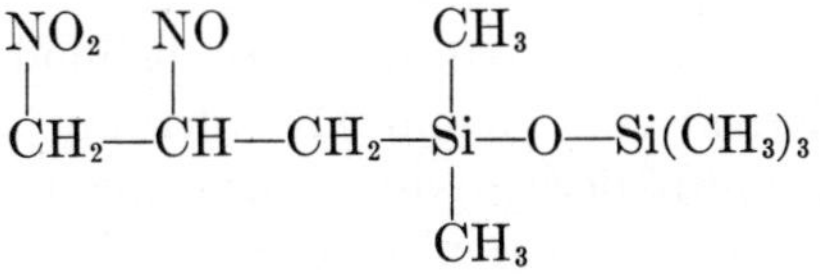

II

Under the same conditions vinyltrimethylsilane reacts to give 1–nitro–3, 3–dimethyl–3–sila–2–butanone oxime.[38]

Dinitrogen trioxide reacts with methyl allyl ether[124] or ethyl allyl ether[125] at −10° to give a solid pseudonitrosite and an oil, which could be the mono-meric nitronitroso compound. The exact positions of the nitro and nitroso groups were not established. Dinitrogen trioxide reacts at 0° with a petroleum ether solution of petroselic acid to give two solid pseudonitrosites, m.p. 84° and 91°, and an oil.[245] Methylnitro–11–nitroso–10–undecanoate, m.p. 82°, is obtained in 30% yield from the reaction of dinitrogen trioxide with methyl-undecylenate.[157]

The reaction of dinitrogen trioxide with diphenylacetylene in ether produces mainly two dinitrostilbene isomers: III, m.p. 106° , and IV, m.p. 186°.[175]

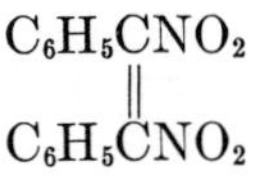

$$\begin{array}{cc} C_6H_5CNO_2 & C_6H_5CNO_2 \\ \| & \| \\ C_6H_5CNO_2 & NO_2CC_6H_5 \end{array}$$

III 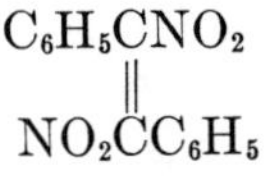   IV

On standing or on treatment with alkali hydroxide, the pseudonitrosites often convert to nitroolefins.

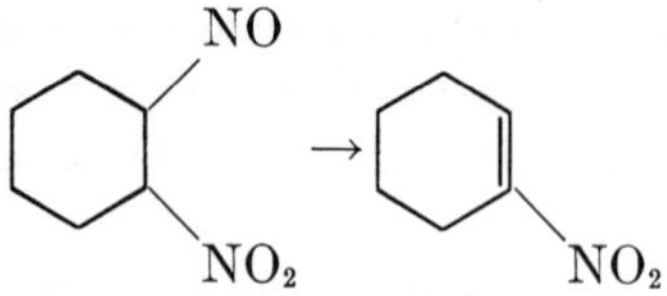

For example, the pseudonitrosites of the following olefins can be converted to the corresponding nitroolefins: cyclohexene,[234] Δ′–phenylcyclohexene,[68] anethole,[229] stilbene,[234] α– and β–phellandrene,[229] camphene,[84,112] isosafrole,[229] methyl isoeugenol,[228] and isoeugenol.[229]

The reaction of dinitrogen trioxide with trimethylethylene forms 2, 3–dinitro–2–methylbutane in 10–20% yield and the dimer of 3–nitroso–2–nitro–2–methylbutane in 9–17% yield.[132] Dinitrogen trioxide reacts with cinnamic acid or α–methylcinnamic acid with simultaneous decarboxylation to give ω–nitrostyrene, m.p. 58°, and β–nitro–β–methylstyrene, m.p. 64°, respectively.[56] Dinitrogen trioxide in boiling benzene reacts with the benzal derivatives of phthalic acid anhydride or phthalimide to give the corresponding dinitro derivatives (V), m.p. 110° (decomp.) and 85° (decomp.), respectively.[63] These dinitro derivatives can be converted by heat or a base to the corresponding unsaturated nitro compounds (VI), m.p. 195° (decomp.) and 199°, respectively.[63]

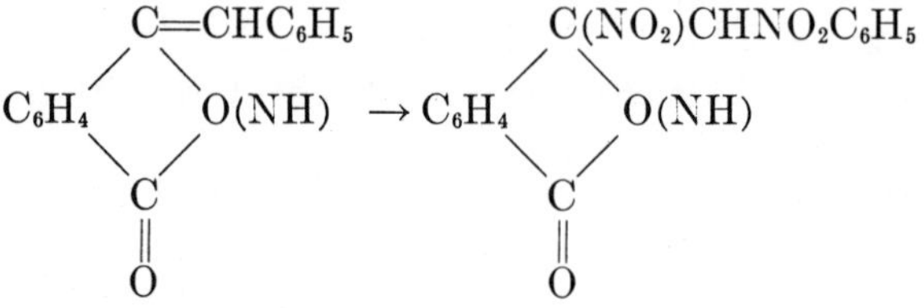

V

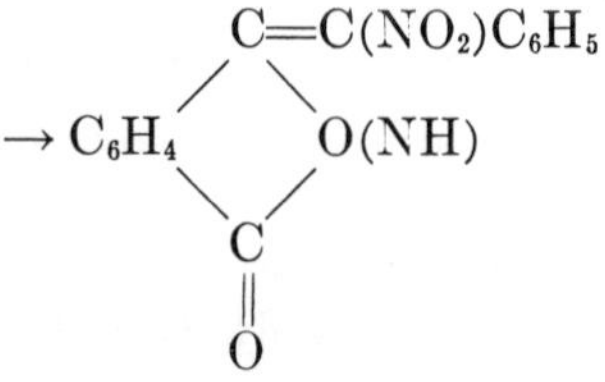

VI

The addition of dinitrogen trioxide to olefins seems to be independent of the electronic demands of the groups attached to the unsaturated systems. With unsymmetrical olefins containing terminal double bonds, the nitro group is formed at the terminal position and in preference to the isomeric nitrite group. Thus, dinitrogen trioxide in ether at 0°C and methyl methacrylate react to form 2–methyl–3–nitro–2–nitrosopropionate, m.p. 130° (decomp.), in 47% yield.[184] The same result is obtained by using a mixture of nitric oxide and nitrogen dioxide.[184] Dinitrogen trioxide adds to p–nitro-styrene to give 2–nitro–1–nitroso–1–p–nitrophenylethane in 62% yield, which, being unstable, rearranges to the α, β–dinitroacetophenone oxime, m.p. 134°, in 34% yield.[184]

The additions of dinitrogen trioxide to olefins parallel those of dinitrogen tetroxide and nitryl chloride,[184] and it is probable that all these reactions involve free radical processes. In view of this, a thorough investigation of these processes might be rewarding.

REACTION OF DINITROGEN TETROXIDE (NITROGEN DIOXIDE) WITH UNSATURATED COMPOUNDS

Dinitrogen tetroxide is a dimer of nitrogen dioxide. The two compounds form an equilibrium mixture:

$$2NO_2 \rightleftharpoons N_2O_4 + 14.7 \text{ kcal}$$

With increasing temperature the equilibrium shifts to the left. At 27°, 20% of dinitrogen tetroxide is converted to nitrogen dioxide, at 50°, 40% is converted, at 100°, 89%, and at 135°, 99%. Nitrogen dioxide is paramagnetic and has other radical properties. The odd electron in nitrogen dioxide is located on either the nitrogen or the oxygen atom. Therefore, not only the nitro group but also the nitrite (–ONO) group can enter into reactions with unsaturated compounds. The latter group can be oxidized to the nitrate (–ONO$_2$) group. Radicals can also react directly with dinitrogen tetroxide to form nitrites and nitrates[211]:

$$R\cdot + N_2O_4 \left\{ \begin{array}{l} \rightarrow RONO_2 + NO\cdot \\ \\ \rightarrow RONO + NO_2\cdot \end{array} \right.$$

Without suitable precautions the reactions of dinitrogen tetroxide or nitrogen dioxide with unsaturated systems yield a mixture of impure products. In the past, reasonably pure materials were isolated only from reactions with substituted olefins. Levy and co-workers[15,107–111,170,240–244] overcame the difficulties experienced by earlier workers by the use of pure dinitrogen tetroxide, conversion of nitronitrite to the stable nitroalcohol, the use of ethers and esters as solvents, control of the temperature (room temperature or lower), and prevention of interference from dinitrogen trioxide by carrying out the reaction in an atmosphere of oxygen gas. They found that the reaction of dinitrogen tetroxide with an olefin yields a mixture of a

Table 43. Reaction of Dinitrogen Trioxide with Unsaturated Compounds

C_n	Unsaturated compound	Product (pseudonitrosite)	% Yield	°C (m.p.)	Ref.
C_{10}	2-Methoxypropenylbenzene	$2\text{-}CH_3OC_6H_4CH(NO)CH(NO_2)CH_3$	53	(130)	69
	2-Methoxy-3-chloropropenylbenzene	$2\text{-}CH_3O\text{-}3\text{-}ClC_6H_3CH(NO)CH(NO_2)CH_3$	21	(120)	69
	2-Methoxy-5-chloropropenylbenzene	$2\text{-}CH_3O\text{-}5\text{-}ClC_6H_3CH(NO)CH(NO_2)CH_3$	64	(116)	69
	Anethole	$p\text{-}CH_3OC_6H_4CH(NO)CH(NO_2)CH_3$	40	(121)	229
C_{11}	2-Methoxy-5-methylpropenylbenzene	$2\text{-}CH_3O\text{-}5\text{-}CH_3C_6H_3CH(NO)CH(NO_2)CH_3$	58	(132)	69
	2-Methoxy-3-methylpropenylbenzene	$2\text{-}CH_3O\text{-}3\text{-}CH_3C_6H_3CH(NO)CH(NO_2)CH_3$	20	(124)	69
	Benzal acetone	$C_6H_5CH(NO)CH(NO_2)COCH_3$	25	(109)	232
	Methylphenylisocrotonate	$C_6H_5CH(NO)CH(NO_2)CH_2CO_2CH_3$	60	(118)	232
	2,3-Dimethoxypropenylbenzene	$2,3\text{-}(CH_3O)_2C_6H_3CH(NO)CH(NO_2)CH_3$	21	(126)	69
	Isosafrole	$(CH_2O)_2C_6H_3CH(NO)CH(NO_2)CH_3$	40	(128)	229
	Anisal acetone	$p\text{-}CH_3OC_6H_4CH(NO)CH(NO_2)COCH_3$	15	(111)	233
C_{14}	Stilbene	$C_6H_5CH(NO)CH(NO_2)C_6H_5$	63	(123)	176, 177, 234
C_{16}	Anisalacetophenone	$p\text{-}CH_3OC_6H_4CH(NO)CH(NO_2)COC_6H_5$	15	(112)	233
C_{23}	3,4-Dibenzyloxypropenylbenzene	$3,4\text{-}(C_6H_5CH_2O)_2C_6H_3CH(NO)CH(NO_2)CH_3$	81	(120)	37

dinitroparaffin, a nitroalcohol, and a nitroalkyl nitrate. The first products are the dinitroparaffin and the nitronitrite. The latter is unstable and must be converted by water or alcohol to a nitroalcohol to obtain good yields and to separate the products. The total yield of products is 65–85%.[108] The nitronitrate is formed by oxidation of the nitronitrite compound.[108]

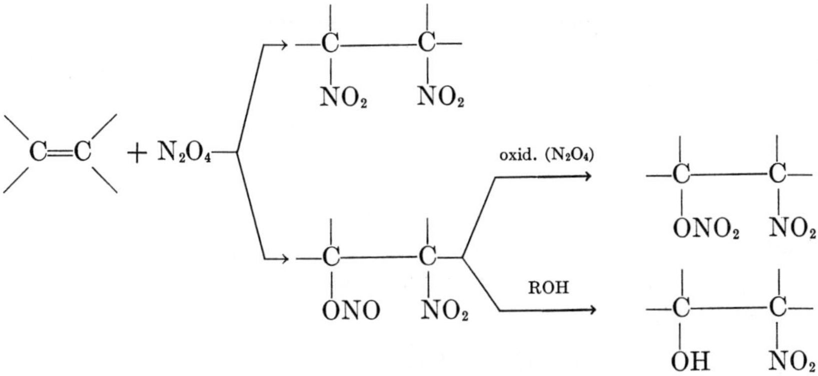

R = H or alkyl

The nitrite group always attaches itself to the carbon atom with the fewest hydrogen atoms.

During the reaction of dinitrogen tetroxide with olefins, dinitrogen tetroxide is reduced to dinitrogen trioxide. It is sometimes advantageous to introduce oxygen into the reaction mixture in order to oxidize the lower nitrogen oxide. In the absence of oxygen the amount of dinitro product is of the same order as the combined amount of nitroalcohol and nitronitrate. Addition of oxygen favors the formation of the nitronitrate. The products are purified by extraction and distillation. Because some of the products are explosive, care and a shatterproof screen should be used during the distillation operation.

Dinitrogen tetroxide reacts with ethylene in the absence of a solvent to give 1, 2–dinitroethane, 2–nitroethanol, and 2–nitroethyl nitrate.[110]

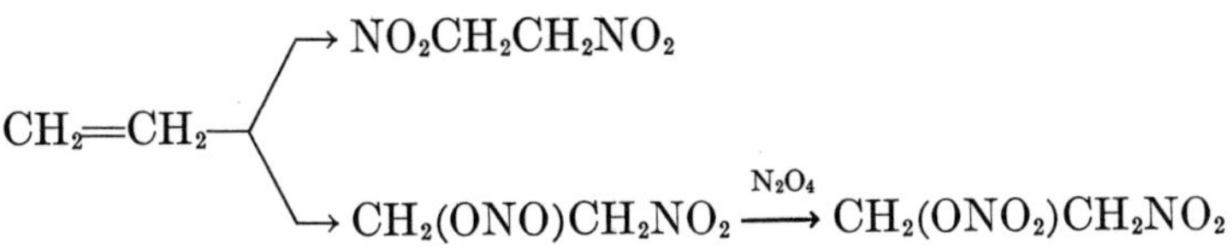

$$CH_2=CH_2 \begin{cases} \rightarrow NO_2CH_2CH_2NO_2 \\ \rightarrow CH_2(ONO)CH_2NO_2 \xrightarrow{N_2O_4} CH_2(ONO_2)CH_2NO_2 \end{cases}$$

Since dinitroethane is a powerful explosive (91% of the blasting power of gelatin), the reaction mixture must be handled with care. 2–Nitroethanol (61% of gelatin blasting power) is insensitive to friction, impact, and initiation. The reaction of dinitrogen tetroxide with ethylene is also described in a number of patents,[238-240,243,244] most of which do not report the physical constants or the yields of the products.

The reaction of nitrogen dioxide with ethylene can also be carried out under pressure. Ethylene reacts with nitrogen dioxide containing nitric oxide at 20–60° and 50 atm.[226] The unstable product is converted by steam to 2–nitroethanol. The same reactants in carbon tetrachloride at 40–50° and 100 psi form 1, 2–dinitroethane and 2–nitroethanol.[52] These reactants in a mixed solvent of carbon tetrachloride and dioxane at 0–10° produce bis-ethylenenitrosonitrate, m.p. 127°; in the absence of dioxane a lower yield of product is obtained.[47] Perhaps this effect is due to the presence of peroxides in dioxane.

Dinitrogen tetroxide reacts with propylene, but, contrary to the reaction with ethylene, a solvent such as ether is required.[109,242] Otherwise extensive oxidation occurs. The products are analogous to those formed with ethylene. The nitrite group attaches itself to the carbon atom with the fewest hydrogen atoms. The nitronitrite is partially oxidized to nitronitrate.

$$CH_3CH{=}CH_2 \Big\langle \begin{array}{l} \longrightarrow CH_3CH(NO_2)CH_2NO_2 \\[2mm] \longrightarrow CH_3CH(ONO)CH_2NO_2 \end{array} \Big\langle \begin{array}{l} \xrightarrow{\text{oxid.}} CH_3CH(ONO_2)CH_2NO_2 \\[2mm] \xrightarrow{H_2O} CH_3CH(OH)CH_2NO_2 \end{array}$$

The nitronitrite product is usually converted with water to β–nitroisopropanol. The presence of oxygen increases the yield of nitronitrate. The total yield of products is 70–75%. Separation of the products is achieved by distillation. β–Nitroisopropyl nitrate is a powerful explosive (75% of gelatin blasting power) and is insensitive to friction or impact. The products from reactions with oxygen are easier to separate than those from reactions without oxygen, since in the latter case a substantial amount of 4–nitro–3–methyl furazan oxide (I), which complicates the separation of products, is formed.

$$\begin{array}{ccc} CH_3C\!\!\!\!&\text{———}&\!\!\!\!CNO_2 \\ \| & & \| \\ N & & N \\ \diagdown & \diagup & \diagdown \\ & O & \quad O \end{array}$$

I

Dinitrogen tetroxide reacts with isobutylene in an ether or ester solvent at −10 to 0° to yield mainly two products: 1, 2–dinitroisobutane and the nitronitrite, which is converted with water to nitro–t–butanol.[111,242] The yield of nitro–t–butyl nitrate, b.p. 78°/1 mm, n_D 1.449 (20°), is low but can be increased up to 30% at the expense of the dinitro product by using oxygen.

$$C(CH_3)_2\!=\!CH_2 \Big\langle \begin{array}{l} \rightarrow C(CH_3)_2(NO_2)CH_2NO_2 \\[2ex] \rightarrow C(CH_3)_2(ONO)CH_2NO_2 \end{array}$$

$$\begin{array}{l} \overset{\text{oxid.}}{\longrightarrow} C(CH_3)_2(ONO_2)CH_2NO_2 \\[2ex] \overset{\text{H}_2\text{O}}{\longrightarrow} C(CH_3)_2(OH)CH_2NO_2 \end{array}$$

Michael and Carlson isolated bis–(α, β–nitrosonitric ester) (II) in 7–12% yield from the reaction of dinitrogen tetroxide with isobutylene.[133]

$$[CH_3)_2C(ONO_2)CH_2NO]_2$$

II

The reaction of dinitrogen tetroxide with butene–1 yields 1, 2–dinitro-butane and 1–nitrobutan–2–ol.[111,242] The reaction of dinitrogen tetroxide with butene–2 yields 2, 3–dinitrobutane in two forms, one a liquid and the other a solid, plus 2–nitrobutan–3–ol.[111,242] Dinitrogen tetroxide reacts with 2, 4, 4–trimethylpentene–1 or with 2, 4, 4–trimethylpentene–2 to give a high yield of products.[15,170] No solvents are required. The relative yields of products depend on the sequence of addition of the reactants. The products are isolated by distillation. The addition of oxygen is superfluous, since nitrooctyl nitrite is more stable than the corresponding nitrites of lower homologues. The reaction yields little nitrate. The reaction of dinitrogen tetroxide with the pentene–1 derivative results in 1, 2–dinitro–2, 4, 4–trimethylpentane and 1–nitro–2, 4, 4–trimethylpentan–2–ol.[15,170]

$$CH_2\!=\!C(CH_3)CH_2C(CH_3)_3 \Big\langle \begin{array}{l} \rightarrow NO_2CH_2C(CH_3)(NO_2)CH_2C(CH_3)_3 \\[2ex] \rightarrow NO_2CH_2C(CH_3)(ONO)CH_2C(CH_3)_3 \rightarrow \end{array}$$

$$\overset{\text{H}_2\text{O}}{\longrightarrow} NO_2CH_2C(CH_3)(OH)CH_2C(CH_3)_3$$

Similarly, the reaction of the pentene–2 derivative yields 2, 3–dinitro–2, 4, 4–trimethylpentane and 3–nitro–2, 4, 4–trimethylpentan–2–ol.[15]

The reaction of dinitrogen tetroxide with 2–ethylbut–1–ene in ether at 0° in the absence of oxygen gives a mixture of dinitro and nitronitroso compounds in high yield.[165] To separate the products, the nitroso compound is converted to nitroalcohol. The reaction of dinitrogen tetroxide with decene–1 yields under similar conditions the corresponding dinitroalcohol and nitroalcohol.[165] The mixture cannot be entirely resolved, however. The corresponding nitroalcohol and dinitroalkane from octadecene can be separated by fractional crystallization.[166]

The reactions of dinitrogen tetroxide with ethereal solutions of various olefins in the presence of oxygen gas result in a mixture of products which can be hydrolyzed to nitromethane and the corresponding aldehyde or ketone.[128] The reaction with isobutylene, for example, produces 1, 2–dinitro-isobutane, nitro–t–butyl nitrite, and nitro–t–butyl nitrate, and hydrolysis of this mixture produces nitromethane and acetone. Similar reactions take place with butene–1; butene–2; 2, 3–dimethyl–1–butene; 2, 3–dimethyl–2–butene; 2–methyl–1–butene; 2–methyl–2–butene; 2, 4, 4–trimethylpentene–1; 2, 4, 4–trimethylpentene–2; 2–ethylbutene–1; 2, 3, 3–trimethylbutene–1; and 2–isopropenylbenzene.

Dinitrogen tetroxide reacts with trimethylethylene at −60° to give a 42% yield of III, m.p. 97°, a 58% yield of IV, and a dinitro derivative.[230]

$$(CH_3)_2C\text{------}CCH_3 \qquad\qquad (CH_3)_2C\text{------}CHCH_3$$
$$\underset{ONO_2}{|}\quad \underset{NOH}{\|} \qquad\qquad\qquad \underset{ONO}{|}\quad \underset{NO_2}{|}$$

$$\text{III} \qquad\qquad\qquad\qquad \text{IV}$$

The reaction of dinitrogen tetroxide with tetramethylethylene produces 2, 3–dinitro–2, 3–dimethylbutane, m.p. 210°, in 19% yield, the nitric ester of 2–nitroso–2, 3–dimethylbutanol–3 (V), m.p. 88°, plus an addition compound of the two products, m.p. 100°.[134,178]

$$(CH_3)C(ONO_2)C(NO_2)(CH_3)_2$$

$$\text{V}$$

Nitrogen dioxide reacts with an ethereal solution of undecylenic acid at 0° to give a sensitive nitronitrosite, which on standing transforms into the 1–hydroxy–2–nitro derivative, m.p. 121°.[224] The reaction with petroselic acid (VI) under similar conditions results in two solid products and an oil.[246]

$$CH_3(CH_2)_{10}CH{=}CH(CH_2)_4CO_2H$$

$$\text{VI}$$

One of the solids is the 6, 7–dinitro derivative, m.p. 121°.

In the addition reaction of dinitrogen tetroxide to cyclohexene, solvents are not required but can be used if desired.[15,170] The purity of the cyclohexene is an important factor. If oxygen is present during the reaction, it is easier to separate the products. The products isolated are 1, 2–dinitrocyclohexane, 2–nitrocyclohexanol, and 2–nitrocyclohexyl nitrate. The cyclohexanol derivative is obtained from nitrocyclohexyl nitrite, which is formed first. The nitroalcohol is formed by hydrolysis of the nitronitrite.

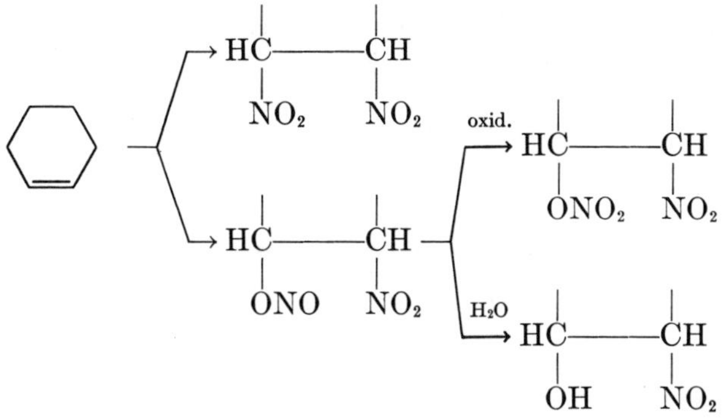

The individual yields of products depend on the sequence of addition of the reagents and on the presence or absence of oxygen. Two isomers of 2–nitro-cyclohexanol have been isolated: the *cis* isomer boils at 82°/1.3 mm; the *trans* isomer boils at 88°/1.7 mm and melts at 47°.[34]

When dinitrogen tetroxide reacts with cyclohexene at 15° in excess bromoform, a high yield of bromonitrocyclohexane (VII), b.p. 95°/2 mm, is obtained.[20]

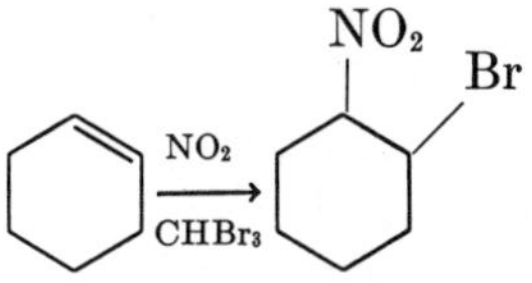

VII

This result illustrates the free radical nature of nitrogen dioxide reactions with olefins. The similar reaction of dinitrogen dioxide with cyclohexene in bromotrichloromethane produces a complex mixture of products consisting mainly of 31% of 2–bromonitrocyclohexane, m.p. 39°, 35% of 2–bromo–2–chlorocyclohexane, and 29% of 2–chlorocyclohexanol.[33] While this reaction is of little preparative value, it confirms the free radical nature of the nitrogen dioxide reactions.

The reaction of methyl acrylate with a mixture of dinitrogen tetroxide and oxygen at 0° results, after hydrolysis, in methyl–3–nitroacrylate, 2–hydroxy–3–nitropropionate, oxalic acid dihydrate (up to 80%), plus some polymers.[182] A radical mechanism is proposed.[182]

The reaction of dinitrogen tetroxide with diphenylethylene yields two products: α, α–diphenyl–β–nitroethyl alcohol and α, α–diphenyl–α, β–dinitroethane.[236] The latter can be converted with a base to α, α–diphenyl–β–nitroethylene, m.p. 87°. A mixture of dinitrogen tetroxide and oxygen reacts rapidly with styrene in carbon tetrachloride at −50°.[20] After removal of the solvent and addition of alcohol to the residue, a 47% yield of crystalline ω–nitroacetophenone, m.p. 105°, is obtained. A reaction path involving free radical intermediates was proposed.[20]

$$C_6H_5CH{=}CH_2 \xrightarrow[O_2]{N_2O_4} \underset{\substack{|\\OONO_2}}{C_6H_5CHCH_2NO_2} \to \underset{\substack{\|\\O}}{C_6H_5CCH_2NO_2}$$

Reactions of dinitrogen tetroxide with butadiene[166,174] or diphenylbutadiene[237] produce the butene–2 derivatives 1, 4–dinitrobutene–2 and α, δ–diphenyldinitrobutene, respectively.

$$RCH{=}CHCH{=}CHR \to RCH(NO_2)CH{=}CHCH(NO_2)R$$

R = H or C₆H₅

Only a few reactions of dinitrogen tetroxide with halogenated olefins have been reported. The reaction of dinitrogen tetroxide with tetrachloroethylene in the presence of oxygen at 100° for 3 hr produces 1, 2–dinitrotetrachloroethylene in high yield.[27] The reaction of dinitrogen tetroxide with tetrabromoethylene in the presence of oxygen at 60° produces dinitrotetrabromoethylene.[27] The reaction of dinitrogen tetroxide with diphenyldichloroethylene produces 1, 1–diphenyl–1, 2–dinitro–2, 2–dichloroethane.[27]

The reactions of nitrogen dioxide with perfluoroolefins proceed by a free radical path.[88,89] Dinitrogen tetroxide reacts with tetrafluoroethylene at 0° to give 1, 2–dinitro–1, 1, 2, 2–tetrafluoroethane in only 7.5% yield.[45] At elevated temperatures a better yield, 53–90%, is obtained.[78,79,88,89] In addition to the dinitro product, the nitronitrite is formed in low yield.

$$CF_2{=}CF_2 + NO_2 \left\{ \begin{array}{l} \to \underset{\substack{|\quad|\\NO_2\ NO_2}}{CF_2{-}CF_2} \\[2em] \to \underset{\substack{|\quad|\\NO_2\ ONO}}{CF_2{-}CF_2} \end{array} \right.$$

In a closed vessel explosions may occur at elevated temperatures if the products are not diluted with a solvent such as chloroform, carbon tetrachloride, difluorochloromethane, or dichlorotetrafluoroethane.[88,89] The use of a solvent has little effect upon the yield of products.

The reaction of nitrogen dioxide with perfluoropropylene requires a higher temperature than the tetrafluoroethylene reaction.[88,89] At 100° mainly the nitronitrite is formed, in 90% yield. If the temperature is raised to about 150°, the yield of dinitro product increases to 15–20%.

$$CF_3CF=CF_2 \Big\langle \begin{array}{l} \longrightarrow CF_3CF(NO_2)CF_2ONO \\ \\ \longrightarrow CF_3CF(NO_2)CF_2NO_2 \end{array}$$

The reaction of nitrogen dioxide with perfluoroisobutylene at 180° results in a 1:1 mixture of dinitro- and nitronitrite products.[88,89] The reaction of nitrogen dioxide with perfluorocyclobutene should be performed within the narrow temperature range of 130–140°.[88,89] Below 130° no reaction occurs, while above 160° the reaction takes place explosively. The reaction of nitrogen dioxide with trifluorochloroethylene produces a dinitro compound[78,79] and a mixture of other products.[88,89] Because the starting materials are volatile, all these reactions are carried out in a sealed vessel.

Dinitrogen tetroxide reacts with *trans*–stilbene in ether to give a complex mixture of products.[64,177,183,192,193] The reaction is assumed to be homolytic in nature.[64,183] When the reaction is carried out in an atmosphere of nitrogen gas at 0–5°, the products are: meso–α , α'–dinitro–1, 2–diphenylethane (VIII), m.p. 235°, *dl*–1, 2–dinitro–1, 2–diphenylethane (IX), m.p. 152°, *erythro*– (X) and *threo*–1–hydroxy–2–nitro–1, 2–diphenylethane (XI), and benzaldehyde.[64,183,192,193]

$$\begin{array}{cc} NO_2 & NO_2 \\ | & | \\ C_6H_5C\!\!-\!\!-\!\!-\!\!CC_6H_5 \\ | & | \\ H & H \end{array}$$

VIII

$$\begin{array}{cc} NO_2 & H \\ | & | \\ C_6H_5C\!\!-\!\!-\!\!-\!\!CC_6H_5 \\ | & | \\ H & NO_2 \end{array}$$

IX

$$\begin{array}{cc} NO_2 & OH \\ | & | \\ C_6H_5C\!\!-\!\!-\!\!-\!\!CC_6H_5 \\ | & | \\ H & H \end{array}$$

X

$$\begin{array}{cc} NO_2 & H \\ | & | \\ C_6H_5C\!\!-\!\!-\!\!-\!\!CC_6H_5 \\ | & | \\ H & OH \end{array}$$

XI

All the products can be separated by chromatography. *cis*–Stilbene under identical conditions is isomerized to *trans*–stilbene, whereas compounds VIII through XI are not isomerized.[64] When the reaction is carried out in an atmosphere of oxygen gas, no dinitrostilbene is formed and the products are: a mixture of *erythro*– (XII) and *threo*–α–nitrato–α'–nitrobibenzyl (XIII), α–nitro–α–phenylacetophenone (XIV), and *erythro*– (X) and *threo*–α–hydroxy–α'–nitrobibenzyl (XI).[192,193] All the products can be separated by chromatography.

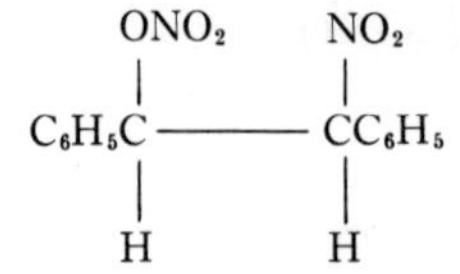

XII 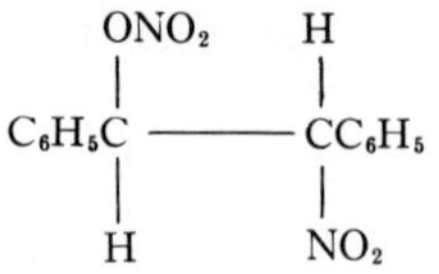   XIII 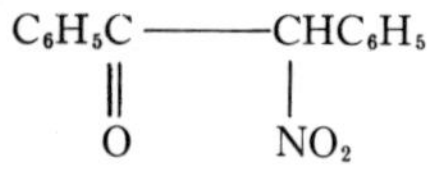   XIV

Oxygen has a pronounced effect upon the interaction of dinitrogen tetroxide with camphene.[192,193] When excess dinitrogen tetroxide is added to an ethereal solution of camphene at 0° in an atmosphere of nitrogen, a mixture of the following products is obtained: a 5% yield of dl–ω–nitrocamphene (XV), m.p. 64°, a 30% yield of 3–(nitromethyl)–3–nitrocamphenilane (XVIa), m.p. 142°, and a 35% yield of 3–(nitromethyl)–3–hydroxycamphenilane (XVIb), m.p. 38°.

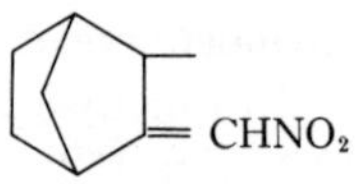

XV 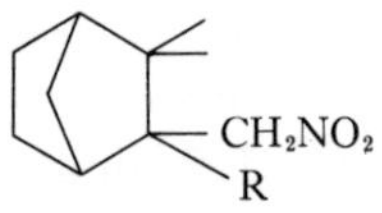   XVI   XVIa   R = NO_2
                               XVIb   R = OH

If the crude reaction mixture is treated with a base, a 37% yield of XV, m.p. 64°, is obtained. Treatment of XVIa and XVIb with a base results in XV in 30% and 35% yields, respectively. The products can be resolved by chromatography. The same starting materials in an oxygen atmosphere produce 3–isopropylidenecyclopentylnitromethyl ketone (XVII), m.p. 76°, in 24% yield, and 10–nitro–2–nitratocamphene (XVIII), m.p. 98°, in 5% yield.

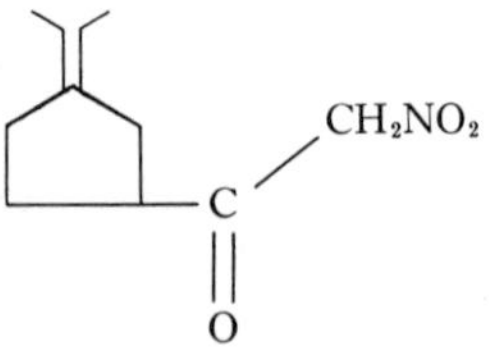

XVII 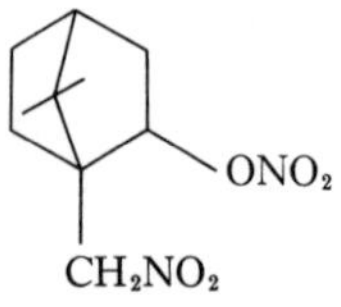   XVIII

Several reactions of dinitrogen tetroxide with acetylenes are reported.[39,60,174,235] The reaction with propyne does not yield any valuable products.[174] No reactions of dinitrogen tetroxide with monoalkyl acetylenes are reported. However, dialkyl acetylenes, for example, butyne–2, give well-defined products.[60,174] The reaction of dinitrogen tetroxide with butyne–2 in ether at

0–10° yields *cis*– and *trans*–2, 3–dinitro–2–butene.[60] The reaction with hexyne–3 produces *cis*– and *trans*–3, 4–dinitro–3–hexene in 4.5 and 31% yields, respectively, propionic acid in 60% yield, dipropionyl in 16% yield, and 4, 4–dinitro–3–hexanone in 8% yield.[60] A free radical mechanism is proposed for these reactions.[60] The reaction of dinitrogen tetroxide with hexadiyne–2, 4 yields a tetranitrohexadiene.[174] The reaction with phenyl acetylene in ether yields phenyldinitroethylene,[235] and the reaction with di-diphenyl diacetylene in the absence of oxygen produces a compound which is believed to be the 1, 4–dinitro–1, 4–diphenylbutatriene (XIX), in 34% yield.[174]

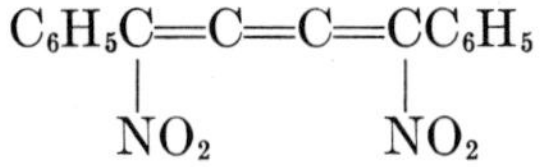

$$C_6H_5C{=}C{=}C{=}CC_6H_5$$

with NO_2 groups below each terminal carbon

XIX

Dinitrogen tetroxide reacts at 0° with tolan (1, 2–diphenyl acetylene) in ether to give three crystalline products in 40% yield: *cis*– and *trans*–1, 2–dinitrostilbene[39,235] and 5–nitro–2–phenylisatogen (XX), m.p. 234°.[39]

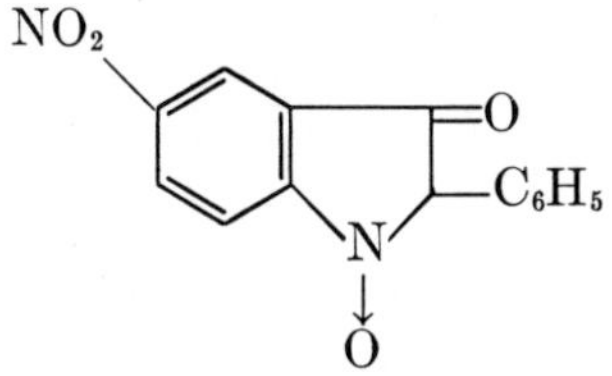

XX

The relative yields of the products depend on the experimental conditions. The *cis* and *trans* products are formed by a radical path.[39]

Table 44.   Reaction of Dinitrogen Tetroxide (Nitrogen Dioxide) with Unsaturated Compounds

C_n	Unsaturated compound	N_2O_4 + O_2 or N_2	Product	% Yield	°C b.p./mm (m.p.)	n_D (°C)	Ref.
C_2	$CH_2=CH_2$	O_2	1,2-Dinitroethane+ 2-Nitroethanol+ 2-Nitroethyl nitrate	35–40 12–20 12–20	88/1 (39) 63/0.5 74/1	1.443 (20) 1.455 (20)	52, 110, 238, 239, 240, 243, 244
	$CCl_2=CCl_2$	O_2	1,2-Dinitrotetrachloroethane		(143)		27
	$CBr_2=CBr_2$	O_2	1,2-Dinitrotetrabromoethane	100	(155)		27
	$CF_2=CF_2$	O_2	1,2-Dinitro-1,1,2,2-tetrafluoroethane+ $CF_2(NO_2)CF_2ONO$	53–90 7.5	58	1.3249 (20) 1.3265 (25) 1.348 (25) 1.3002 (0)	79, 88 45 78 88
	$CCl_2=CF_2$		1,1-Dichlorodifluoro-1, 2-dinitroethane	47	81/103	1.4116 (25)	78, 79
	$CClF=CF_2$		1-Chlorotrifluoro-1, 2-dinitro-ethane	51	100	1.3748 (25)	78, 88
C_3	Propylene	O_2	Dinitropropane+ β-Nitroisopropyl alcohol+ β-Nitroisopropyl nitrate	20–30 35–40 2–20	88/1 106/20 71/1	1.441 (20) 1.447 (20)	109, 241, 242
	$CF_3CF=CF_2$		$CF_3CF(NO_2)CF_2ONO$+ $CF_3CF(NO_2)CF_2NO_2$	90	57 76	1.3276 (20) 1.3141 (20)	88
C_4	2-Butyne	O_2	trans-2, 3-Dinitro-2-butene+ cis-2, 3-Dinitro-2-butene	34 7	71/8 96/1.5	1.4678 (20) 1.4776 (20)	60, 174
	Butene-1	O_2	$CH_3CH_2CH(NO_2)CH_2NO_2$+ $CH_3CH_2CH(OH)CH_2NO_2$	39 33	90/1 59/1		111, 242
	Butene-2	O_2	$CH_3CH(NO_2)CH(NO_2)CH_3$ (two forms)+ 2-Nitrobutan-3-ol	30 35	76/<1 (41) 60/1		111, 242

Table 44. (cont.)   Reaction of Dinitrogen Tetroxide (Nitrogen Dioxide) with Unsaturated Compounds

C_n	Unsaturated compound	N_2O_4 + O_2 or N_2	Product	% Yield	°C b.p./mm (m.p.)	n_D (°C)	Ref.
	Isobutylene	O_2	$C(CH_3)_2(NO_2)CH_2NO_2+$	35–42	(52)		111, 242
			$C(CH_3)_2(OH)CH_2NO_2$	25–30	66/1 (26)	1.443 (20)	
	Tetramethylethylene		2,3-Dinitro-2,3-dimethyl-butane	20	(209) (213)		134 178
	Methyl acrylate	O_2	Methyl 3-nitroacrylate+	13	45/0.8 (34)		185
			Methyl 2-hydroxy-3-nitro-propionate	27	95/0.8 (44)		
	Butadiene	N_2	1,4-Dinitrobutene-2	42	(59)		166, 174
	$(CF_3)_2C=CF_2$		$(CF_3)_2C(NO_2)CF_2NO_2+$		92	1.3212 (20)	88
			$(CF_3)_2C(NO_2)CF_2ONO$		48	1.2870 (20)	
	Perfluorocyclobutene		$CF_2CF(NO_2)CF(NO_2)CF_2+$		62/100	1.3640 (20)	88
			$CF_2CF(ONO)CF(ONO)CF_2$		20		
C_6	3-Hexyne		trans-3,4-Dinitro-3-hexene	31	54/1	1.4640 (20)	60
	$(C_2H_5)_2C=CH_2$	N_2	$(C_2H_5)_2C(NO_2)CH_2(NO_2)+$	23	91/1	1.461 (20)	165
			$(C_2H_5)_2C(OH)CH_2NO_2$	41	73/1	1.453 (20)	
	Hexadiyne-2, 4		Tetranitrohexadiene	23	(56)		166, 174
	Cyclohexene	O_2	1, 2-Dinitrocyclohexane+	30–42	112/<1 (46)		15, 34, 170
			2-Nitrocyclohexanol+	25–54	94/<1		
			2-Nitrocyclohexyl nitrate	2–18	98/<1		
C_7	1-Methylcyclohexene	O_2	1-Methyl-trans-1, 2-dinitro-cyclohexane+		(91)		34
			1-Methyl-trans-2-nitrocyclo-hexanol		(72)		

Table 44. (cont.) Reaction of Dinitrogen Tetroxide (Nitrogen Dioxide) with Unsaturated Compounds

C_n	Unsaturated compound	N_2O_4 + O_2 or N_2	Product	% Yield	°C b.p./mm (m.p.)	n_D (°C)	Ref.
C_8	2, 4, 4–Trimethyl-pentene–1	O_2	1, 2–Dinitro–2, 4, 4–trimethyl-pentane+	32–53	96/<1 (19.5)	1.464 (20)	15, 170
			1–Nitro–2, 4, 4–trimethyl-pentan–2–ol	31–43	60/<1	1.452 (20)	
	2, 4, 4–Trimethyl-pentene–2		2, 3–Dinitro–2, 4, 4–trimethyl-pentane+	48	68/0.5 (46)		15
			3–Nitro–2, 4, 4–trimethyl-pentan–2–ol	32	48/0.5		
	Phenyl acetylene		Phenyldinitroethylene	39	(81)		235
C_{10}	Camphene	N_2	3–(Nitromethyl)–3–nitro-camphenilane+	30	(142)		192, 193
			3–(Nitromethyl)–3–hydroxy-camphenilane	35	(38)		
	Camphene	O_2	3–Isopropylideneecyclopentyl-nitromethyl ketone	24	(76)		192, 193
	Diphenylethylene		α, α–Diphenyl–α, β–dinitro-ethane+		(68)		236
			α, α–Diphenyl–β–nitroethyl alcohol		(106)		
C_{14}	Tolan	O_2	cis–1, 2–Dinitrostilbene+ trans–1, 2–Dinitrostilbene	24	(108) (186)		39, 235
	trans–Stilbene	O_2	α–Nitro–α–phenylaceto-phenone+	24	(74)		192, 193
			erythro– and threo–α–Hydroxy-α'–nitrobibenzyl+	29	(98, 105)		
			threo– and erythro–α–Nitrato-α'–nitrobibenzyl	25			

Table 44. (cont.) Reaction of Dinitrogen Tetroxide (Nitrogen Dioxide) with Unsaturated Compounds

C_n	Unsaturated compound	N_2O_4 $+ O_2$ or N_2	Product	% Yield	°C b.p./mm (m.p.) n_D (°C)	Ref.
	trans–Stilbene	N_2	Meso–1, 2–dinitro–1, 2–diphenyl-ethane+	24	(220, decomp.) 235	183, 192 64
			dl–1, 2–Dinitro–1, 2–diphenyl-ethane+	34	(149)	
			erythro– and threo–1–Hydroxy–2–nitro–1, 2–diphenylethane	20	(99, 106)	
C_{16}	Diphenyl diacetylene	N_2	1, 4–Dinitro–1, 4–diphenyl-butatriene		(112)	174
	Diphenylbutadiene ($C_6H_5CH\!=\!CHCH\!=\!CHC_6H_5$)		α, δ–Diphenyldinitrobutene ($C_6H_5CH(NO_2)CH\!=\!CHCH(NO_2)C_6H_5$)	35	(158)	237
C_{18}	Octadec–1–ene	N_2	$CH_3(CH_2)_{15}CH(NO_2)CH_2NO_2+$ $CH_3(CH_2)_{15}CH(OH)CH_2NO_2$	92	(37) (55)	166

NITROHALOGENATION OF UNSATURATED COMPOUNDS WITH A MIXTURE OF NITROGEN DIOXIDE AND A HALOGEN

A mixture of dinitrogen tetroxide and a halogen reacts with olefins or acetylenes and results in addition of a nitro group and a halogen atom to the unsaturated compound.[13,195] When the unsaturated compound has a terminal double bond, the NO_2 group attaches itself to the CH_2 group:

$$CH_3CH{=}CH_2 \xrightarrow{\;N_2O_4\,+\,I_2\;} CH_3CHICH_2NO_2$$

When the unsaturated compound has an electron-withdrawing substituent such as a halogen or a cyano group, the NO_2 group adds to that carbon atom which does not carry the electron-withdrawing substituent:

$$ClCH{=}CH_2 \xrightarrow{\;N_2O_4\,+\,Cl_2\;} Cl_2CHCH_2NO_2$$

There seems to be little doubt that these reactions proceed by a radical path, since nitrohalogenations in the liquid or vapor phase result in the same products.[13] For example, the reaction of dinitrogen tetroxide and chlorine with vinyl bromide results in 1–bromo–1–chloro–2–nitroethane, and the reaction of dinitrogen tetroxide and bromine with vinyl bromide results in 1, 1–dibromo–2–nitroethane.[13]

The liquid-phase reactions are carried out at 0–25°.[13,195] Chloroform and carbon tetrachloride are the most common solvents; moisture, polarizing substances, and photoexcitation are usually excluded.[13] The duration of the reactions varies between 1 and 30 hr. The most common by-product is the addition product of halogen to the unsaturated compound.

Table 45. Reaction of Dinitrogen Tetroxide with Unsaturated Compounds in the Presence of a Halogen

C_n	Unsaturated compound	Halogen	Product	% Yield	°C b.p./mm (m.p.)	n_D (°C)	Ref.
C_3	$CH_3CH=CH_2$	I_2	1-Nitro-2-propyl iodide	70	40/0.2	1.5374 (20)	195
	$CH_2=CHCN$	Cl_2	$CHNO_2=CHCN$ (formed during distillation)	25	58/2	1.4877 (25)	13
	$CH_3CH=CHCl$	Cl_2	$CH_3CHNO_2CHCl_2$	24	54/3.5	1.4629 (25)	13
C_4	Butene-1	I_2	1-Nitro-2-butyl iodide	62	47/0.4	1.5295 (20)	195
	Methyl acrylate	I_2	Methyl 3-nitro-2-iodopropionate	75	84/0.3	1.5284 (20)	195
C_8	Phenyl acetylene	I_2	α-Iodo-β-nitrostyrene	86	(49)		195
C_{10}	Camphene	I_2	3-Nitromethyl-3-iodocamphenilane	50	(119)		195
C_{14}	Tolan	I_2	cis-α-Nitro-α'-iodostilbene+ $trans$-α-Nitro-α'-iodostilbene	15 66	(113) (176)		195
	$trans$-Stilbene	I_2	1, 2-Diphenyl-2-nitroethyl iodide	96	(147)		195
	cis-Stilbene	I_2	1, 2-Diphenyl-2-nitroethyl iodide	63	(145)		195
C_2	$CH_2=CHCl$	Cl_2	$CH_2NO_2CHCl_2$	36	55/8	1.4663 (20)	13
	$CH_2=CHCl$	Br_2	$CH_2NO_2CHBrCl$	28	41/0.5	1.4980 (20)	13
	$CH_2=CHCl$	I_2	$CHBrClCH_2Br+$ $CHClCH_2NO_2$	24 62	44/4 decomp.	1.5540 (20)	13
	$CH_2=CHBr$	Cl_2	$CHBrClCH_2NO_2+$ $CH_2ClCHBrCl$	41 32	48/1.2 35/3	1.5070 (20)	13
	$CH_2=CHBr$	Br_2	$CHBr_2CH_2NO_2+$ $CH_2Br_2CHBr_2$	35 58	60/1 47/2.5	1.5400 (20) 1.5802 (20)	13
	$CHCl=CHCl$	Cl_2	$CHCl_2CHClNO_2$	7.2	40/3	1.4827 (25)	13
	$CH_2=CCl_2$	Cl_2	CCl_3CHNO_2	40	59/6	1.4845 (25)	13
	$CH_2=CCl_2$	Br_2	$CBrCl_2CH_2NO_2$	25	89/11	1.5168 (25)	13

REACTION OF NITRYL CHLORIDE WITH UNSATURATED COMPOUNDS

Reactions of nitryl chloride with unsaturated compounds, mostly olefins, are carried out in the absence of a catalyst. Most of the reactions are carried out at 0–25°, and pentane, chloroform, or excess olefin is used as a solvent. In the reactions with terminal olefins the NO_2 group attaches itself to the CH_2 group.

$$RCH{=}CH_2 + NO_2Cl \rightarrow RCHClCH_2NO_2$$

While most workers have not discussed the mechanism of the reactions, there is evidence[173,185] that the reaction of nitryl chloride with unsaturated compounds proceeds by a radical mechanism.

Nitryl chloride adds to several acetylenes. It reacts with diethyl acetylene at −40° to give *trans*–3–chloro–4–nitrohexene–3, b.p. 61°/12 mm, n_D 1.4678 (20°), in low yield.[173] The reaction of nitryl chloride with dibutyl acetylene produces 5–chloro–6–nitrodecene–5 (probably the *trans* isomer) and 5–chloro–6–nitrodecene–4 (shift of the double bond).[173] The reaction of nitryl chloride with 1–phenylhexyne–1 yields a mixture of *cis*– and *trans*–butyl-phenylchloronitroethylene.[173]

Various olefins, starting with ethylene, react smoothly with nitryl chloride to give mainly nitrochloroalkanes.[167,191,225] The reaction of nitryl chloride with propene results in 1–nitro–2–chloropropane and a small amount of pseudonitrosite, m.p. 136°.[167] The reaction of nitryl chloride with isobutylene forms 1–nitro–2–chloroisobutane in 18% yield, nitro–*t*–butyl nitrite, b.p. 82°/1 mm, n_D 1.4599 (25°), in 25% yield, plus the pseudonitrosite, m.p. 87°.[167] Nitryl chloride reacts with cyclohexene in ether at 0–25° in the presence of oxygen[34] or in the absence of oxygen[167,191] to give 1–chloro–2–nitrocyclohexane as the main product in 30–40% yield. The reaction of nitryl chloride with styrene forms 1–chloro–2–nitro–2–phenylethylene, b.p. 78°/13 mm, in low yield.[191] The reaction of nitryl chloride with stilbene in ether results in α, α'–dichlorobibenzyl, m.p. 193°,[191] whereas the same reaction in benzene results in α–chloro–α'–nitrobibenzyl, m.p. 220° (decomp.), in 27% yield.[191] Nitryl chloride reacts with phenyl acetylene to give α–chloro–β–nitrostyrene, m.p. 54°, in 34% yield, plus a small amount of α, α–dichloroacetophenone, in 90% yield.[60,191]

The reaction of nitryl chloride with acrylic acid at 0° produces 2–chloro–3–nitropropionic acid, in high yield; the product can be dehydrohalogenated to 3–nitroacrylic acid.[185] Similarly, the reaction of nitryl chloride with acrylonitrile in the absence of a solvent produces 2–chloro–3–nitropropionitrile, in 76% yield; the product can be converted with sodium acetate to

3–nitroacrylonitrile.[185] In the presence of ether the reaction with acrylonitrile produces 2–chloro–3–nitropropionitrile in only 25% yield plus 3–nitro-acrylonitrile in 48% yield.[185] Nitryl chloride reacts with methyl acrylate to give methyl 2–chloro–3–nitropropionate in 69% yield, dimethyl 2–chloro–4–nitromethylpentanedioate in 5–10% yield, and methyl 2, 3–dichloro-propionate in 6% yield.[185]

Nitryl chloride reacts with several haloolefins. The reaction of nitryl chloride with vinyl bromide produces 1–chloro–1–bromo–2–nitroethane,[191] and the reaction of nitryl chloride with 1, 2–dichloroethylene produces 1, 1, 2–trichloro–2–nitroethane in high yield.[191] Nitryl chloride adds to trichloro-or tetrachloroethylene to form 1, 1, 1, 2–tetrachloro–2–nitroethane, b.p. 76°/18 mm, and 1, 1, 1, 2, 2–pentachloro–2–nitroethane, m.p. 192°, re-spectively.[191] The reaction of nitryl chloride with 1, 1–dichloropentene–1 around 0° forms 1, 1, 1, 2–tetrachloropentane; 1, 1, 1–trichloro–2–nitro-pentane; and 1, 1–dichloro–1, 2–dinitropentane.[254] The reaction of nitryl chloride with 1, 1, 5–trichloropentene–1 forms 1, 1, 1, 2, 5–pentachloro-pentane; 1, 1, 1, 5–tetrachloro–2–nitropentane; and 1, 1, 5–trichloro–1, 2–dinitropentane.[254] The formation of such diversified products suggests a free radical path for these reactions.

Nitryl chloride can be used advantageously for nitration of enol ace-tates.[12] The reactions are carried out at −40 to 0° in ether, chloroform, or methylene chloride. Nitryl chloride adds to vinyl acetate to give, as ex-pected, α–chloro–β–nitroethyl acetate, in 36% yield. However, with other acetates, such as I, II, III, and IV, the reaction is more complex, since nitration of the acetates is accompanied by conversion of the carbon atom carrying the ester group to an aldehyde or a keto group.

$$(CH_3)_2C{=}CHOCOCH_3 \qquad CH_3CH{=}C(CH_3)OCOCH_3$$

$$I \qquad\qquad II$$

$$CH_2{=}C(C_6H_5)OCOCH_3 \qquad CH_3CH{=}C(C_6H_5)OCOCH_3$$

$$III \qquad\qquad IV$$

Thus, the reaction of nitryl chloride with compound I produces 2–nitro–2–methylpropanal in 12% yield; with II, 3–nitro–2–butanone in 36% yield; with III, compound V in 36% yield; and with IV, compound VI in 28% yield.

$$C_6H_5COCH_2NO_2 \qquad C_6H_5COCHNO_2CH_3$$

$$V \qquad\qquad VI$$

Table 46.   Reaction of Nitryl Chloride with Unsaturated Compounds

C_n	Unsaturated compound	Product	% Yield	°C b.p./mm (m.p.)	n_D (°C)	Ref.
C_2	$CH_2=CH_2$	1-Nitro-2-chloroethane	50	68/13	1.4500 (20)	225
	$CH_2=CHBr$	1-Chloro-1-bromo-2-nitroethane	85	76/15		191
	$ClCH=CHCl$	1,1,2-Trichloro-2-nitroethane	67	63/13		191
	$CF_2=CF_2$	1-Chlorotetrafluoro-2-nitroethane	57	37		79, 80
C_3	$CH_3CH=CH_2$	1-Nitro-2-chloropropane	40	67/13	1.4480 (20)	225
			55	32/1	1.4388 (25)	167
	3-Chloropropene-1	1-Nitro-2,3-dichloropropane	61	103/13	1.4827 (20)	225
	Acrylonitrile	2-Chloro-3-nitropropionitrile	76	83/1	1.4743 (20)	185
	Acrylic acid	2-Chloro-3-nitropropionic acid	41	(79)		185
C_4	Butene-1	1-Nitro-2-chlorobutane	47	78/13	1.4480 (20)	225
	Butene-2	2-Chloro-3-nitrobutane	25	45/6	1.4421 (25)	167
	Isobutylene	1-Nitro-2-chloro-2-methylpropane	36	67/13	1.4470 (20)	82, 167, 225
	Methyl acrylate	Methyl 2-chloro-3-nitropropionate	69	88/4	1.4573 (20)	185
	$CH_2=CHOCOCH_3$	$CH_2NO_2CHClOCOCH_3$	36	66/2	1.4446 (26)	10
C_5	Pentene-1	1-Nitro-2-chloropentane	40	91/13	1.4480 (20)	225
	2-Methylbutene-1	1-Nitro-2-chloro-2-methylbutane	40	75/13	1.4550 (20)	225
	3-Methylbutene-1	1-Nitro-2-chloro-3-methylbutane	47	89/13	1.4510 (20)	225
C_6	Hexene-1	1-Nitro-2-chlorohexane	42	99/13	1.4513 (20)	225
	2-Methylpentene-1	1-Nitro-2-chloro-2-methylpentane	35	90/13	1.4550 (20)	225

Table 46. (cont.) Reaction of Nitryl Chloride with Unsaturated Compounds

C_n	Unsaturated compound	Product	% Yield	°C b.p./mm (m.p.)	n_D (°C)	Ref.
C_6	4-Methylpentene-1	1-Nitro-2-chloro-4-methylpentane	41	95/13	1.4490 (20)	225
	$(CH_3)_2C=CHOCOCH_3$	$(CH_3)_2CNO_2CHO$	12	49/3	1.4398 (26)	10
	$CH_3CH=C(CH_3)OCOCH_3$	$CH_3COCHNO_2CH_3$	36	56/2	1.4360 (26)	10
	Cyclohexene	1-Chloro-2-nitrocyclohexane + trans-Dichlorocyclohexane + Cyclohexene pseudonitrosite	30	121/9 75/15 (151)	1.4887 (25) 1.4886 (16.6)	34, 167, 191
C_7	Heptene-1	1-Nitro-2-chloroheptane	39	116/13	1.4540 (20)	225
C_8	$C_6H_5C≡CH$	α-Chloro-β-nitrostyrene	34	(54)		60, 191
C_9	Cinnamic acid	α-Chloro-β-nitro-β-phenylpropionic acid	43	(162)		191
C_{10}	$CH_2=CC_6H_5OCOCH_3$	$C_6H_5COCH_2NO_2$	36	105		10
	Dibutylacetylene	5-Chloro-6-nitrodecene-5 + 5-Chloro-6-nitrodecene-4	14.3 4.4	76/0.3 109/0.2	1.4688 (20) 1.4655 (20)	173
C_{11}	$CH_3CH=CC_6H_5OCOCH_3$	$C_6H_5COCHNO_2CH_3$	28	124		10
C_{14}	1-Phenylhexyne-1	trans-Butylphenylchloronitroethylene + cis-Butylphenylchloronitroethylene	21 3.5	84/0.1 88/0.05	1.5386 (20) 1.5365 (20)	173
	Stilbene (in C_6H_6)	α-Chloro-α'-nitrobibenzyl	27	(220 decomp.)		191

REFERENCES

[1] Aliev and Degtyarenko, *Izvest. Vysshikh Ucheb. Zavedenii Neft i. Gaz.*, **1958**, 109: *Chem. Abs.*, **53**, 10006d (1959).

[2] Allison, U.S. 2,485,180 (1949).

[3] Arbuzov and Pisha, *Dok. Akad. Nauk*, **116**, 71 (1957).

[4] Artemev, *et al.*, *Khim. Nauka i. Prom*, **3**, 629 (1958).

[5] Asinger, *Chem. Ber.*, **77**, 73 (1944).

[6] Bachman, Atwood, and Polack, *J. Org. Chem.*, **19**, 322 (1954).

[7] Bachman, Hass, and Addison, *J. Org. Chem.*, **17**, 914 (1952).

[8] Bachman, Hass, and Hewett, *J. Org. Chem.*, **17**, 928 (1952).

[9] Bachman, Hewett, and Millikan, *J. Org. Chem.*, **17**, 935 (1952).

[10] Bachman and Hokama, *J. Org. Chem.*, **25**, 178 (1960).

[11] Bachman and Kohn, *J. Org. Chem.*, **17**, 942 (1952).

[12] Bachman, *et al.*, *J. Org. Chem.*, **17**, 906 (1952).

[13] Bachman, *et al.*, *J. Org. Chem.*, **25**, 1312 (1960).

[14] Badische Aniline and Soda Fabrik. Akt. Ges., Brit. 788,436 (1958).

[15] Baldock, Levy, and Scaife, *J. Chem. Soc.*, **1949**, 2627.

[16] Banus, *Nature*, **171**, 173 (1952).

[17] Banus, *J. Chem. Soc.*, **1953**, 3755.

[18] Barr and Haszeldine, *J. Chem. Soc.*, **1955**, 1881.

[19] Barr and Haszeldine, *J. Chem. Soc.*, **1956**, 3416.

[20] Baryshnikova and Titov, *Dok. Akad. Nauk*, **91**, 1099 (1953).

[21] Baryshnikova and Titov, *Dok. Akad. Nauk*, **114**, 777 (1957).

[22] Baudisch, *Science*, **108**, 443 (1948).

[23] Beckham, U.S. 2,417,675 (1947).

[24] Beckham, Fessler, and Kise, *Chem. Revs.*, **48**, 319 (1951).

[25] Beckwith, *Australian J. Chem.*, **13**, 321 (1960).

[26] Beckwith and Evans, *J. Chem. Soc.*, **1962**, 130.

[27] Biltz, *Chem. Ber.*, **35**, 1528 (1902).

[28] Birchall, *et al.*, *Proc. Chem. Soc.*, **1959**, 367.

[29] Bloomfield and Jeffrey, *J. Chem. Soc.*, **1944**, 120.

[30] Bouveault and Wahl, *C.r.*, **131**, 687 (1900).

[31] Bouveault and Wahl, *Bull. soc. chim. France*, **25** (3), 800 (1901).

[32] Brain, Univ. Mich. Microfilm 59–2707, Diss. Abs., **20**, 515 (1959).

[33] Brand and Stevens, *Chem. Ind.*, **1956**, 469.

[34] Brand and Stevens, *J. Chem. Soc.*, **1958**, 629.

[35] Brooks, *et al.*, *The Chemistry of Petroleum Hydrocarbons*, vol. 3, p. 85, Reinhold, New York (1955).

[36] Brown, *J. Am. Chem. Soc.*, **79**, 2480 (1957).

[37] Bruckner and Fodor, *Chem. Ber.*, **76**, 466 (1943).

[38] Burkhard, U.S. 2,756,246 (1956).

[39] Campbell, Shavel, and Campbell, *J. Am. Chem. Soc.*, **75**, 2400 (1953).

[40] Chiusoli and Minisci, *Gazz. chim. ital.*, **88**, 261 (1958).

[41] Ciamician and Silber, *Chem. Ber.*, **34**, 2040 (1901).

[42] Closs and Brois, *J. Am. Chem. Soc.*, **82**, 6068 (1960).

[43] Coe and Doumani, *J. Am. Chem. Soc.*, **70**, 1516 (1948).

[44] Coe and Doumani, U.S. 2,478,243 (1950).

[45] Coffmann, *et al.*, *J. Org. Chem.*, **14**, 747 (1949).

[46] Cronheim, *J. Org. Chem.*, **12**, 1 (1947).

[47] Crowder, U.S. 2,402,315 (1946).

[48] Danilov and Ogloblin, *Zh. Obsh. Khim.*, **22**, 2113 (1952).

[49] Dombrovskii, *Usp. Khim.*, **22**, 777 (1953).

[50] Donaruma, *J. Org. Chem.*, **23**, 1338 (1958).

[51] Doumani, Coe, and Altane, U.S. 2,465,984 (1949).

[52] E. I. du Pont de Nemours and Co., Brit. 603,344 (1948).

[53] Ellis, *The Chemistry of Petroleum Derivatives*, p. 1039, Chem. Catalog Co., New York (1934).

[54] Ellis, *The Chemistry of Petroleum Derivatives*, pp. 619, 1087, Reinhold, New York (1937).

[55] Engler and Halmai, *Chem. Ber.*, **43**, 397 (1910).

[56] Erdman, *Chem. Ber.*, **24**, 2771 (1891).

[57] Escoruela, *Ion*, **6**, 128 (1946).

[58] Fieser and Doering, *J. Am. Chem. Soc.*, **68**, 2252 (1946).

[59] Francis and Young, *J. Chem. Soc.*, **73**, 928 (1898).

[60] Freeman and Emmons, *J. Am. Chem. Soc.*, **79**, 1712 (1957).

[61] Friedlander and Mähly, *Ann. Chem.*, **229**, 211 (1885).

[62] Friedlander and Lazarus, *Ann. Chem.*, **229**, 233 (1885).

[63] Gabriel, *Chem. Ber.*, **18**, 1251 (1885).

[64] Gardikes, Pagano, and Shechter, *Chem. Ind.*, **1958**, 632.

[65] Geiseler, *Ang. Chem.*, **67**, 270 (1955).

[66] Gingras and Waters, *J. Chem. Soc.*, **1954**, 1920.

[67] Gingras and Waters, *Chem. Ind.*, **1953**, 615.

[68] Govindachari, *Chem. Ind.*, **1954**, 757.

[69] Govindachari and Pai, *J. Org. Chem.*, **18**, 1253 (1953).

[70] Gowenlock and Lüttke, *Quart. Revs.*, **12**, 321 (1958).

[71] Griffin and Haszeldine, *Proc. Chem. Soc.*, **1959**, 369.

[72] Grundmann, *Ang. Chem.*, **56**, 159 (1943).

[73] Haitinger, *Ann. Chem.*, **193**, 366 (1878).

[74] Hass and Alexander, *Ind. Eng. Chem.*, **41**, 2266 (1949).

[75] Hass, Hodge, and Vanderbilt, *Ind. Eng. Chem.*, **28**, 339 (1936).

[76] Hass and Riley, *Chem. Revs.*, **32**, 373 (1943).

[77] Hass and Shechter, *Ind. Eng. Chem.*, **39**, 817 (1947).

[78] Hass and Whitaker, U.S. 2,447,504 (1948).

[79] Haszeldine, *J. Chem. Soc.*, **1953**, 2075.

[80] Haszeldine, Brit. 770,619 (1957).

[81] Hayward, Kitchen, and Livingstone, *Can. J. Chem.*, **1962**, 434.

[82] Himel, U.S. 2,511,915 (1950).

[83] Ito, *Bull. Chem. Soc. Japan*, **29**, 227 (1956).

[84] Jagelki, *Chem. Ber.*, **32**, 1498 (1899).

[85] Jander and Haszeldine, *J. Chem. Soc.*, **1954**, 912.

[86] Jander and Haszeldine, *J. Chem. Soc.*, **1954**, 696.

[87] Kirmse, *Naturw.*, **46**, 379 (1959).

[88] Knunyants and Fokin, *Dok. Akad. Nauk*, **111**, 1035 (1956).

[89] Knunyants and Fokin, *Izvest. Akad. Nauk*, **1957**, 1439.

[90] Konowalov, *C.r.*, **114**, 26 (1892): *Chem. Abs.*, **62** (2), 575 (1892).

[91] Konowalov, *J. Russ. Chem. Soc.*, **25**, 472 (1894): *Chem. Soc. Abs.*, **66** (1), 265 (1894).

[92] Konowalov, *Chem. Ber.*, **28**, 1852 (1895).

[93] Konowalov, *Chem. Ber.*, **29**, 2199 (1896).

[94] Konowalov, *J. Russ. Phys. Chem. Soc.*, **37**, 530 (1905): *Chem. Soc. Abs.*, **88** (1), 762 (1905).

[95] Konowalov, *J. Russ. Phys. Chem. Soc.*, **37,** 1119 (1905).

[96] Konowalov, *Chem. Z.*, **1906** (1), 737.

[97] Konowalov, *J. Russ. Phys. Chem. Soc.*, **38,** 109 (1906): *Chem. Soc. Abs.*, **92** (1), 1 (1907).

[98] Konowalov, *J. Russ. Phys. Chem. Soc.*, **38,** 449 (1906): *Chem. Soc. Abs.*, **92** (1), 203 (1907).

[99] Konowalov and Dobrowolsky, *J. Russ. Phys. Chem. Soc.*, **37,** 551 (1905): *Chem. Soc. Abs.*, **88** (1), 763 (1905).

[100] Konowalov and Jatzewitch, *J. Russ. Phys. Chem. Soc.*, **37,** 542 (1905): *Chem. Soc. Abs.*, **88** (1), 763 (1905).

[101] Konowalov and Jebenko, *J. Russ. Phys. Chem. Soc.*, **31,** 1027 (1899): *Chem. Soc. Abs.*, **78** (1), 324 (1900).

[102] Konowalov and Kotsina, *J. Russ. Phys. Chem. Soc.*, **31,** 1027 (1899); *Chem. Soc. Abs.*, **78** (1), 324 (1900).

[103] Kornblum and Oliveto, *J. Am. Chem. Soc.*, **71,** 226 (1949).

[104] Labes, *J. Org. Chem.*, **24,** 295 (1959).

[105] Lemetre, Caprara, and Giolitti, *Ital.*, 573, 954 (1958).

[106] Levy, *J. Am. Chem. Soc.*, **75,** 1801 (1953).

[107] Levy and Rose, *Quart. Revs.*, **1,** 358 (1947).

[108] Levy and Scaife, *J. Chem. Soc.*, **1946,** 1093.

[109] Levy and Scaife, *J. Chem. Soc.*, **1946,** 1100.

[110] Levy, Scaife, and Wilder-Smith, *J. Chem. Soc.*, **1946,** 1096.

[111] Levy, Scaife, and Wilder-Smith, *J. Chem. Soc.*, **1948,** 52.

[112] Lipp, *Ann. Chem.*, **399,** 241 (1913).

[113] Lynn, *J. Am. Chem. Soc.*, **41,** 368 (1919).

[114] Lynn and Arkley, *J. Am. Chem. Soc.*, **45,** 1045 (1923).

[115] Lynn and Hilton, *J. Am. Chem. Soc.*, **44,** 645 (1922).

[116] Markownikoff, *Ann. Chem.*, **302,** 1 (1898).

[117] Markownikoff, *Chem. Ber.*, **32,** 1441 (1899).

[118] Markownikoff, *Ann. Chem.*, **307,** 335 (1899).

[119] Markownikoff, *Chem. Ber.*, **33,** 1906 (1900).

[120] Markownikoff and Konowalov, *Chem. Ber.*, **28,** 1234 (1895).

[121] Markownikoff and Rudewitsch, *J. Russ. Chem. Soc.*, **25,** 385 (1893): *Chem. Soc. Abs.*, **76** (1), 581 (1899).

[122] Markownikoff and Rudewitsch, *J. Russ. Chem. Soc.*, **30,** 586 (1898): *Chem. Soc. Abs.*, **76** (1), 581 (1899).

[123] Martello, *et al.*, *Chim. ind. Milan*, **38,** 932 (1956).

[124] Maslow, *Zh. Obsh. Khim.*, **10,** 1915 (1940).

[125] Maslow, *Zh. Obsh. Khim.*, **15,** 165 (1945).

[126] McCleary and Degering, *Ind. Eng. Chem.*, **30,** 64 (1938).

[127] McKinney, in *The Chemistry of Petroleum Hydrocarbons*, edited by Brooks, *et al.*, vol. III, p. 643, Reinhold, New York (1955).

[128] McKinnis, U.S. 2,811,560 (1957).

[129] Meisenheimer, *Ann. Chem.*, **330,** 133 (1904).

[130] Metzger and Müller, *Chem. Ber.*, **90,** 1179 (1957).

[131] Metzger and Müller, *Chem. Ber.*, **90,** 1185 (1957).

[132] Michael and Carlson, *J. Org. Chem.*, **4,** 169 (1939).

[133] Michael and Carlson, *J. Org. Chem.*, **5,** 1 (1940).

[134] Michael and Carlson, *J. Org. Chem.*, **5,** 14 (1940).

[135] Michell and Carson, *J. Chem. Soc.*, **1936,** 1005.

[136] Müller, Fries, and Metzger, *Chem. Ber.*, **90,** 1188 (1957).

[137] Müller and Heuschkel, *Chem. Ber.*, **92,** 63 (1959).

[138] Müller and Heuschkel, *Chem. Ber.*, **92**, 71 (1959).
[139] Müller and Metzger, *Chem. Ber.*, **87**, 1282 (1954).
[140] Müller and Metzger, *Chem. Ber.*, **88**, 165 (1955).
[141] Müller, Metzger, and Fries, *Chem. Ber.*, **87**, 1449 (1954).
[142] Müller and Schmid, *Chem. Ber.*, **92**, 514 (1959).
[143] Müller and Schmid, *Chem. Ber.*, **94**, 1364 (1961).
[144] Nametkin, *Chem. Ber.*, **42**, 1372 (1909).
[145] Nametkin, *J. Russ. Phys. Chem. Soc.*, **42**, 691 (1910): *Chem. Soc. Abs.*, **98** (1), 830 (1910).
[146] Nametkin, *J. Russ. Phys. Chem. Soc.*, **43**, 1603 (1911): *Chem. Soc. Abs.*, **102** (1), 175 (1912).
[147] Nametkin and Fantalova, *Dok. Akad. Nauk*, **87**, 979 (1952).
[148] Nametkin and Zabrodina, *Dok. Akad. Nauk*, **75**, 395 (1950).
[149] Naylor and Anderson, *J. Org. Chem.*, **18**, 115 (1953).
[150] Nussbaum and Robinson, *Tetrahedron*, **17**, 35 (1962).
[151] Nussbaum, *et al.*, *Tetrahedron*, **18**, 373 (1962).
[152] Nussbaum, *et al.*, *J. Org. Chem.*, **27**, 20 (1962).
[153] Ogloblin, *Zh. Obsh. Khim.*, **22**, 2121 (1952).
[154] Ogloblin, *Zh. Obsh. Khim.*, **27**, 2541 (1957).
[155] Ogloblin, *Zh. Obsh. Khim.*, **28**, 3245 (1958).
[156] Olin Mathieson Chem. Corp., Brit. 709,760 (1954).
[157] Ourisson, *C.r.*, **230**, 1532 (1950).
[158] Park, Stefani, and Lacher, *J. Org. Chem.*, **26**, 3319 (1961).
[159] Park, Stefani, and Lacher, *J. Org. Chem.*, **26**, 4017 (1961).
[160] Park, *et al.*, *J. Org. Chem.*, **26**, 3316 (1961).
[161] Perrot and Berger, *C.r.*, **235**, 185 (1952).
[162] Petrov and Bulygina, *Dok. Akad. Nauk*, **77**, 1033 (1951).
[163] Pfleger and Landauer, *Ann. Chem.*, **610**, 115 (1957).
[164] Poni and Costachescu, *Am. Sci. Univ. Jassy*, **2**, 119 (1903): *Chem. Soc. Abs.*, **84** (1), 596 (1903).
[165] Porter and Wood, *J. Inst. Pet.*, **37**, 388 (1951).
[166] Porter and Wood, *J. Inst. Pet.*, **38**, 877 (1952).
[167] Price and Sears, *J. Am. Chem. Soc.*, **75**, 3275 (1953).
[168] Reilley, U.S. 2,749,358 (1956).
[169] Riebsomer, *Chem. Revs.*, **36**, 196 (1945).
[170] Scaife, Brit. 587,992 (1947).
[171] Schiekh, *Ang. Chem.*, **62**, 547 (1950).
[172] Schlenck, Mair, and Bornhardt, *Chem. Ber.*, **44**, 1169 (1911).
[173] Schlubach and Braun, *Ann. Chem.*, **627**, 28 (1959).
[174] Schlubach and Rott, *Ann. Chem.*, **594**, 59 (1955).
[175] Schmidt, *Chem. Ber.*, **34**, 619 (1901).
[176] Schmidt, *Chem. Ber.*, **34**, 623 (1901).
[177] Schmidt, *Chem. Ber.*, **34**, 3536 (1901).
[178] Schmidt, *Chem. Ber.*, **36**, 1775 (1903).
[179] Schmidt and Fischer, *Chem. Ber.*, **53**, 1529 (1920).
[180] Schmidt, *et al.*, *Chem. Ber.*, **55**, 1751 (1922).
[181] Schönberg, *Präparative Organische Photochemie*, Springer, Berlin (1958).
  a. p. 156.
  b. p. 161.
[182] Shechter and Conrad, *J. Am. Chem. Soc.*, **75**, 5610 (1953).
[183] Shechter, Gardikes, and Pagano, *J. Am. Chem. Soc.*, **81**, 5421 (1959).
[184] Shechter and Ley, *Chem. Ind.*, **1955**, 535.

[185] Shechter, *et al.*, *J. Am. Chem. Soc.*, **74**, 3052 (1952).

[186] Shorigin and Topchiev, *Chem. Ber.*, **67**, 1362 (1934).

[187] Societe Chimique des Usines du Rhone, German 239, 953: *Chem. Soc. Abs.*, **102** (1), 176 (1912).

[188] Spaeth, U.S. 2,883,432 (1959).

[189] Spaeth, U.S. 2,883,433 (1959).

[190] Spaeth, U.S. 2,883,434 (1959).

[191] Steinkopf and Kühnel, *Chem. Ber.*, **75**, 1323 (1942).

[192] Stevens, *J. Am. Chem. Soc.*, **81**, 3593 (1959).

[193] Stevens, *Chem. Ind.*, **1957**, 1546.

[194] Stevens, *J. Org. Chem.*, **25**, 1658 (1960).

[195] Stevens and Emmons, *J. Am. Chem. Soc.*, **80**, 338 (1958).

[196] Svit, Narodni podnik, Austrian 172,618 (1952).

[197] Tilney-Bassett and Waters, *Chem. Ind.*, **1956**, 957.

[198] Tilney-Bassett and Waters, *J. Chem. Soc.*, **1957**, 3129.

[199] Titov, *Zh. Obsh. Khim.*, **7**, 1695 (1937).

[200] Titov, *Zh. Obsh. Khim.*, **10**, 1878 (1940).

[201] Titov, *Zh. Obsh. Khim.*, **16**, 1896 (1946).

[202] Titov, *Zh. Obsh. Khim.*, **17**, 382 (1947).

[203] Titov, *Zh. Obsh. Khim.*, **18**, 191 (1948).

[204] Titov, *Zh. Obsh. Khim.*, **18**, 465 (1948).

[205] Titov, *Zh. Obsh. Khim.*, **18**, 473 (1948).

[206] Titov, *Zh. Obsh. Khim.*, **18**, 534 (1948).

[207] Titov, *Zh. Obsh. Khim.*, **18**, 1312 (1948).

[208] Titov, *Zh. Obsh. Khim.*, **19**, 258 (1949).

[209] Titov, *Zh. Obsh. Khim.*, **19**, 1461 (1949).

[210] Titov, *Zh. Obsh. Khim.*, **22**, 1329 (1952).

[211] Titov, *Usp. Khim.*, **21**, 881 (1952).

[212] Titov, *Usp. Khim.*, **27**, 845 (1958).

[213] Titov and Barishnikova, *Zh. Obsh. Khim.*, **22**, 1335 (1952).

[214] Titov and Laptev, *Zh. Obsh. Khim.*, **18**, 741 (1948).

[215] Titov and Matveeva, *Dok. Akad. Nauk*, **83**, 101 (1952).

[216] Titov and Matveeva, *Zh. Obsh. Khim.*, **23**, 238 (1953).

[217] Titov and Rusanov, *Dok. Akad. Nauk*, **82**, 65 (1952).

[218] Titov and Shchitov, *Dok. Akad. Nauk*, **81**, 1085 (1951).

[219] Topchiev, *Khim. Nauka i. Prom.* **2**, 515 (1957).

[220] Topchiev, *Nitration of Hydrocarbons and Other Organic Compounds*, 2nd ed., Moscow akad. Nauk S.S.S.R. (1956). Translation by Matthews, Pergamon Press (1959).

[221] Topchiev and Fantalova, *Dok. Akad. Nauk*, **88**, 83 (1953).

[222] Urbanski, *Chem. Tech. Berlin*, **6**, 442 (1954).

[223] Urbanski, *Roczniki Chem.*, **32**, 415 (1958).

[224] Vasileev, *Zh. Obsh. Khim.*, **26**, 712 (1956).

[225] Ville and Dupont, *Bull. soc. chim. France*, **1956**, 804.

[226] Volkov, U.S.S.R. 66,229 (1946): *Chem. Abs.*, **41**, 2074c (1947).

[227] Wallach and Beschke, *Ann. Chem.*, **332**, 7 (1904).

[228] Wallach and Beschke, *Ann. Chem.*, **332**, 335 (1904).

[229] Wallach and Müller, *Ann. Chem.*, **332**, 305 (1904).

[230] Weghofer, *Erdöl u. Kohle*, **4**, 1 (1951).

[231] Welz, U.S. 2,818,380 (1957).

[232] Wieland, *Ann. Chem.*, **329**, 225 (1903).

[233] Wieland and Bloch, *Ann. Chem.*, **340**, 63 (1905).

[234] Wieland and Blümich, *Ann. Chem.*, **424,** 75 (1921).
[235] Wieland and Blümich, *Ann. Chem.*, **424,** 100 (1921).
[236] Wieland, Rahn, and Reindel, *Chem. Ber.*, **54,** 1770 (1921).
[237] Wieland and Stenzel, *Chem. Ber.*, **40,** 4825 (1907).
[238] Wilder-Smith, U.S. 2,384,047 (1945).
[239] Wilder-Smith and Scaife, U.S. 2,384,048 (1945).
[240] Wilder-Smith and Scaife, Brit. 575,604 (1946).
[241] Wilder-Smith, Scaife, and Baldock, Brit. 580,260 (1946).
[242] Wilder-Smith, Scaife, and Baldock, U.S. 2,472,550 (1949).
[243] Wilder-Smith, Scaife, and Stanley, U.S. 2,424,510 (1947).
[244] Wilder-Smith, Stanley, and Scaife, Brit. 576,618 (1946).
[245] Williams and Vasileeva, *Zh. Obsh. Khim.*, **18,** 77 (1948).
[246] Williams and Vasileeva, *Zh. Obsh. Khim.*, **18,** 457 (1948).
[247] Willstätter and Kubli, *Chem. Ber.*, **42,** 4151 (1909).
[248] Wittig and Pockels, *Chem. Ber.*, **69,** 790 (1936).
[249] Worstall, *Am. Chem. J.*, **20,** 202 (1898).
[250] Worstall, *Am. Chem. J.*, **21,** 210 (1899).
[251] Yakubovich and Lemke, *Zh. Obsh. Khim.*, **19,** 649 (1949).
[252] Yakubovich, Spanskii, and Lemke, *Zh. Obsh. Khim.*, **24,** 2257 (1954).
[253] Yakubovich, Spanskii, and Lemke, *Dok. Akad. Nauk*, **96,** 773 (1954).
[254] Zakharkin, *Izvest. Akad. Nauk*, **1957,** 1064.

CHLORINATION OF SATURATED ALIPHATIC AND ALICYCLIC COMPOUNDS

Most substitution chlorinations are carried out with elemental chlorine. Chlorinating agents such as sulfuryl chloride are useful mainly in small-scale work only. The chlorination process using chlorine gas is catalyzed by heat or light. A distinction must be made between vapor-phase and liquid-phase chlorination processes, although a clear-cut separation of the two is not always possible. In the present work we are dealing with liquid-phase processes.

Substitution chlorinations are of tremendous practical importance. Chlorinated products are used as starting materials in a variety of syntheses. It is therefore not surprising that the literature dealing with various aspects of chlorination reactions is extensive. The subject has been reviewed many times, particularly the halogenation of aliphatic paraffins and haloparaffins.[33−37,132,133,177,178,239,263,291,308−312,314,317−320,355,400−405,439,442,488,521] However, most review articles cover the broad area of halogenation rather than specific halogenations carried out under free radical conditions. In the present work an attempt was made to survey free radical substitution halogenations in reports published mainly during the last decade. The results are included in Table 47. A cross section of various classes of compounds is included in the table to provide a guide for experimental work.

Photochemical chlorination of ethyl chloride has been studied by Städel,[509] Denzel,[110] and D'ans and Kautzach.[102] Hass and co-workers[177,178] published extensive reports on vapor-phase chlorination of lower paraffins and alkyl halides; their work was reviewed by McBee and Ungnade.[317] Some of the conclusions drawn by these workers on the basis of vapor-phase experiments are also valid for liquid-phase chlorinations; namely: (1) Carbon skeleton rearrangement rarely occurs if pyrolytic conditions are avoided. (2) Hydrogen atoms are substituted in the order tertiary > secondary > primary. (3) Moisture, surfaces, and light do not appreciably affect the ratio of substitution.

Since substitution chlorinations are always exothermic, the heat must be dissipated by cooling, dilution, etc. Thermal chlorination is inexpensive and is less sensitive to inhibition than photochemical chlorination. In thermal chlorination dissociation of the chlorine molecule is caused by heat. In photochemical chlorination chlorine atoms are produced through absorption of light quanta of about 365 mμ by the chlorine molecule. Photochemical chlorination is carried out at room temperature or even lower temperatures. Oxygen usually inhibits chlorination.

Chlorination by agents such as sulfuryl chloride can be initiated by heat, light, or peroxide. Peroxide-initiated chlorination is usually carried out in boiling carbon tetrachloride, chloroform, methylene chloride, or benzene and occasionally in chlorobenzene or dichlorobenzene.[255] The reaction proceeds rapidly in the absence of light and is completed when the evolution of sulfur dioxide has ceased. The substitution of hydrogen atoms during chlorination with sulfuryl chloride follows the same pattern as that in photochlorination and thermal chlorination, namely: tertiary > secondary > primary. The reaction is inhibited by oxygen, sulfur, or iodine.

The chlorine atoms produced in chlorination with elemental chlorine and chlorination with sulfuryl chloride may exhibit different selectivity. The sulfuryl chloride method is more selective. This difference in selectivity is attributed to hydrogen abstraction by the SO_2Cl radical.[65,66,457]

The dependence of selectivity on the solvent has been investigated. Russell[452,453,455] and Walling and Mayahi[540] showed that the attack of a chlorine atom on a branched-chain hydrocarbon such as 2, 3–dimethylbutane can be altered drastically by the choice of solvent. Photochlorination of 2, 3–dimethylbutane at 55° in carbon tetrachloride gives a tertiary/primary substitution ratio of 3.5, whereas in benzene and chlorobenzene the ratio is 10 to 15, in t–butylbenzene 24, and in 1–chloronaphthalene 37.[452] The selectivity increases with the amount of solvent, its basicity, and decrease in temperature. Russell explains this solvent effect by a complexed chlorine atom.[455]

In aliphatic hydrocarbon substitution reactions, various groups exhibit a pronounced directive effect.[13,66] In chlorination with either elemental chlorine or sulfuryl chloride, groups such as Cl, Cl_2, and Cl_3[13,65,66] and groups such as CH_2Cl, $CHCl_2$, Cl_3Si, Cl_3C, and CF_3[66] tend to influence the substitution in favor of 2 (β) and 3 (γ) isomers along the chain. The presence of CF_2 and CF_3 groups on adjacent positions immobilizes the α position.[214,]

[215,219,220,222,224,318] The direction of attack by the chlorine atom is away from the CF_2 and CF_3 groups. The CF_3 group is more effective than the CF_2 group.

Thus, photochlorination of compound I gives a mixture of II and III in a ratio of 3:2.[214]

$$CH_3CF_2CH_2CH_3 \xrightarrow{Cl_2} CH_3CF_2CH_2CH_2Cl + CH_3CF_2CHClCH_3$$

$$\text{I} \qquad\qquad\qquad \text{II} \qquad\qquad\qquad \text{III}$$

Compound IV is photochlorinated to a mixture of V and VI in a ratio of 5:4.[215]

$$CF_3CH_2CH_2CH_3 \xrightarrow{Cl_2} CF_3CH_2CH_2CH_2Cl + CF_3CH_2CHClCH_3$$

$$\text{IV} \qquad\qquad\qquad \text{V} \qquad\qquad\qquad \text{VI}$$

Polychlorination tends to take place at the carbon atom which is already affected. Thus chlorination of compound VII occurs as follows.[224]

$$CH_3CH_2CF_3 \xrightarrow{Cl_2} CH_2ClCH_2CF_2 + CHCl_2CH_2CF_3 + CCl_3CH_2CF_3$$

$$\text{VII}$$

If the tertiary hydrogen atoms are flanked by CF_3 groups, they are not substituted.[222]

$$(CF_3)_2CHCH_3 \xrightarrow{Cl_2} (CF_3)_2CHCCl_3$$

Photochlorination of 1, 1–difluoro–2, 2–dichloroethane yields a mixture of products[209] rather than 1, 1–difluoro–2, 2, 2–trichloroethane exclusively.[217] Photochlorination of compounds of the general formula VIII at 100–150° in a silica vessel proceeds slowly over a period of 3–4 weeks; the yields are almost quantitative.[186]

$$C_nF_mH \rightarrow C_nF_mCl$$

$$\text{VIII}$$

$$n = 2 \text{ to } 7$$

$$m = 5 \text{ to } 15$$

Photochlorination of ethane sulfochloride results in a mixture of β–monochloro and β, β–dichloro derivatives.[466] No further chlorination to the trichloro derivative is possible, since further chlorination is accompanied by elimination of sulfur dioxide from the molecule. However, ethane sulfofluoride can be chlorinated to the β, β, β–trichloro product.[466] The sulfohalide group has a directive effect on the β–position.

Benzoyl peroxide-catalyzed chlorination of n–heptane with sulfuryl chloride gives 1–chloroheptane in 15% yield.[255] Photochemical chlorination of n–heptane gives 1–chloro-, 2–chloro-, and 1, 7–dichloroheptane.[354] If the ratio of n–heptane to chlorine is 1:2, about 80% of the product is the dichloro compound.[354] The photochlorinations of n–decane[15] and of n–octadecane[154] each produce a mixture of products.

The photochlorination of cyclopropane proceeds smoothly.[511] Unless special precautions are taken, the first isolatable products are dichlorides, mainly the 1, 1 product. The monochloride and the 1, 2–dichloro product are also isolated. Further photochlorination or peroxide-catalyzed sulfuryl chloride chlorination of the 1, 1 product gives the 1, 1, 2–trichloro derivative, which in turn can be converted to the 1, 1, 2, 2 derivative. The tetrachloro compound can be chlorinated with sulfuryl chloride at 63° to pentachlorocyclopropane. Photochlorination of methylcyclopropane at $-20°$ results in cyclopropyl carbinyl chloride.[67]

Photochlorination of cyclopentane produces mainly monochloro and dichloro derivatives.[356]

The chlorination of cyclohexane has been studied extensively. Photochlorination,[245,246,302,356] chlorination in the presence of dimethyl-α, α'-azoisobutyrate,[144] chlorination with sulfuryl chloride,[255] chlorination with trichloromethanesulfonyl chloride,[241] and chlorination with p–toluene sulfodichloroamide (dichloroamine T)[517] have been investigated. Photochlorination of cyclohexane to the tetrachloro stage gives a 1, 2, 4, 5 isomer, m.p. 173°.[246] When this isomer is chlorinated with sulfuryl chloride under ultraviolet light, two pentachloro isomers, m.p. 56° and 107°, are obtained. Upon photochemical chlorination of these isomers, hexachloro products, m.p. 109° and 71°, respectively, are obtained. However, photochlorination of 1, 2, 4, 5–tetrachlorocyclohexane (m.p. 174°) to hexachlorocyclohexane gives a product melting at 173°.[244] Chlorination of 1, 1, 4, 4–tetrachlorocyclohexane with sulfuryl chloride in carbon tetrachloride in light results in 1, 1, 2, 4, 4, 5–hexachlorocyclohexane, m.p. 146°.[245] Chlorination of cycloheptane with N–chlorosuccinimide in the presence of benzoyl peroxide produces cycloheptyl chloride in 30% yield.[77] Chlorination of cyclooctane with sulfuryl chloride in the presence of light or benzoyl peroxide gives cyclooctyl chloride in 55–83% yield.[331]

Photochlorination of norbornane in methylene chloride gives a product, b.p. 52°/20 mm, n_D 1.4851 (20°), in 35% yield.[268] The product consists of 70% exo and 20–25% endo compounds. Halogenations using such halogen donors as sulfuryl chloride, carbon tetrachloride, or phosphorus pentachloride in the presence of light, benzoyl peroxide, or azobisisobutyronitrile give a product which consists of 90–95% exo compound.

Saturated hydrocarbons can also be chlorinated by using polyhaloalkanes in the presence of organic peroxides.[547,548] Di–t–butyl peroxide or benzoyl peroxide are usually employed, and the reaction temperature ranges from 85° to 140°. The reactions are performed in an autoclave in an atmosphere of nitrogen gas. Chloroform, carbon tetrachloride, or hexachloroethane can be used as halogen donors. Thus, isobutane, n–pentane, n–heptane, methylcyclohexane, and chlorobicyclo–(2, 2, 1)–heptane are converted to the corresponding monochloro derivatives.[547,548] In the presence of di–t–butyl peroxide, bromoform is converted with carbon tetrachloride to chlorotribromomethane.[549] Under similar conditions n–butyl chloride is converted in 14% yield to a dichloro derivative consisting mainly of 1, 3 isomer.[548] A quantitative study of the reaction of chloromethane with cyclohexane has been reported.[454]

t–Butyl hypochlorite has recently been studied as a chlorinating agent.[485, 538,539] Hypochlorites can act by ionic or radical mechanisms. The chemistry of hypochlorites has been reviewed by Anbar and Ginsburg.[8] Under free radical conditions t–butyl hypochlorite is moderately selective. Its advantage over atomic chlorine or sulfuryl chloride is that it does not produce acidic products. The reactions are initiated by azonitriles or light, and they are inhibited by oxygen or phenol. The relative reactivities of the hydrogen atoms toward t–butyl hypochlorite are the same as in all free radical processes, namely: tertiary > secondary > primary.[538] Photochlorination of isopropyl bromide and of t–butyl bromide with t–butyl hypochlorite yields mostly 2–bromo–2–chloropropane and 1–bromo–2–chloro–2–methylpropane, respectively.[485] A 100% rearrangement occurs in the removal of hydrogens from the methyl group of isopropyl bromide and t–butyl bromide. The thermal or photochemical decomposition of n–butyl hypochlorite, yielding tetramethylene chlorohydrin and butyl butyrate, is a case of intramolecular hydrogen abstraction.[247]

$$n\text{–}C_4H_9OCl \rightarrow n\text{–}C_4H_9O\cdot + Cl\cdot$$

$$
\begin{array}{ccc}
O\cdot\ H\text{—}CH_2 & & OH\quad \overset{\cdot}{C}H_2 \\
|\qquad | & \rightarrow & |\qquad | \\
CH_2\quad CH_2 & & CH_2\quad CH_2 \\
\diagdown\ \diagup & & \diagdown\ \diagup \\
CH_2 & & CH_2
\end{array}
$$

$$HO(CH_2)_4\cdot + n\text{–}C_4H_9OCl \rightarrow HO(CH_2)_4Cl + n\text{–}C_4H_9O\cdot \quad \text{etc.}$$

Butyl butyrate might be formed from butyroaldehyde. The chemistry of hypochlorite reactions under free radical conditions warrants further investigation. 1–Methylcyclopentyl hypochlorite rearranges at low temperature to give an open-chain ω–haloketone, 6–chlorohexan–2–one, b.p. 86°/16 mm.[84]

Table 47. Chlorination of Saturated Aliphatic and Alicyclic Compounds

C_n	Saturated compound	Chlorinating agent	Initiator	Product	Ratio	% Yield	°C b.p./mm (m.p.)	n_D (°C)	Ref.
C_2	Ethylene chloride	SO_2Cl_2	Bz_2O_2	1, 2–Trichloroethane		70	113	1.4708 (20)	255
	C_2Cl_5H	Cl_2	F_2	Hexachloroethane					333
	C_2F_5H	Cl_2	UV	C_2F_5Cl			–36		186
	Ethane sulfochloride	Cl_2	UV	β–Chloroethane sulfochloride+		70	96/17		466
				β,β–Dichloroethane sulfochloride		15	104/17		
	Ethane sulfofluoride	Cl_2	UV	β–Chloroethane sulfofluoride		80	66/14		466
	β–Chloroethane sulfofluoride	Cl_2	UV	β,β–Dichloroethane sulfo-fluoride+		30	68/14		466
				β,β,β–Trichloroethane sulfo-fluoride		50	77/14		
C_3	Cyclopropane	Cl_2	UV	1,1–Dichlorocyclopropane+			75	1.4377 (25)	511
				Monochlorocyclopropane+			44/770		
				1,2–Dichlorocyclopropane			87	1.4502 (25)	
	n–Propyl bromide	SO_2Cl_2	Bz_2O_2	1–Bromo–2–chloropropane+		50	116	1.4746 (20)	255
				1–Bromo–3–chloropropane		30	69/62	1.4950 (20)	
	1–Chloropropane	Cl_2	UV	1,1–Dichloropropane+		15		1.4292 (20)	270
				1,2–Dichloropropane+		59		1.4390 (20)	
				1,3–Dichloropropane		26		1.4510 (20)	
	2–Chloropropane	Cl_2	UV	1,2–Dichloropropane+		43		1.4390 (20)	270
				2,2–Dichloropropane		57		1.4127 (20)	
	n–Propyl chloride	SO_2Cl_2	Bz_2O_2	1,2–Dichloropropane+		60	97		255
				1,3–Dichloropropane		40	123		
	$CH_3CF_2CH_3$	Cl_2	UV	$CH_3CF_2CH_2Cl$		55	101/760	1.3506 (20)	219
				$CH_3CF_2CCl_3$		62	(53)		318

Table 47. (cont.)   Chlorination of Saturated Aliphatic and Alicyclic Compounds

C_n	Saturated compound	Chlorinating agent	Initiator	Product	Ratio	% Yield	°C b.p./mm (m.p.)	n_D (°C)	Ref.
	$CH_3CF_2CH_3$	Cl_2	UV	$CCl_3CF_2CCl_3$			194	1.4806 (20)	219
	$CH_3CH_2CF_3$	$Cl_2 + H_2O$	UV	$CH_2ClCH_2CF_3+$	1.0	45		1.3350 (20)	224
				$CHCl_2CH_2CF_3+$	2.0	72		1.3631 (20)	
				$CCl_3CH_2CF_3$	1.3	95		1.3900 (20)	
	$CH_3CH_2CF_3$	$Cl_2 + H_2O$	UV	$CCl_3CCl_2CF_3$			153 (109)		224
	1, 1, 1-Trifluoropropane	Cl_2	UV	3–Chloro–1, 1, 1–trifluoro-propane+		18	45	1.334 (25)	181
				3, 3–Dichloro–1, 1, 1–trifluoro-propane+		57	72	1.359 (25)	
				3, 3, 3–Trichloro–1, 1, 1–tri-fluoropropane		10	95	1.388 (25)	
	1, 1–Dichlorocyclo-propane	Cl_2	UV	1, 1, 2–Trichlorocyclopropane			124/763	1.4782 (25)	511
	1, 1–Dichlorocyclo-propane	SO_2Cl_2	Bz_2O_2	1, 1, 2–Trichlorocyclopropane					511
	1, 1, 2–Trichlorocyclo-propane	Cl_2	UV	1, 1, 2, 2–Tetrachlorocyclo-propane			146/762	1.4976 (25)	511
	$CH_3CClFCH_2Cl$	Cl_2	UV	$CH_3CClFCCl_3$					212
	$CH_3CF_2CH_2Cl$	Cl_2	UV	$CH_3CF_2CHCl_2$			79	1.3833 (20)	219
	$CCl_3CH_2CH_2Cl$	Cl_2	UV	$CCl_3CH_2CHCl_2$			72/16		109
	$CCl_3CH_2CHCl_2$	Cl_2	UV	$CCl_3CH_2CCl_3$			206/760	1.5179 (20)	109
	1, 1, 2, 2–Tetrachloro-cyclopropane	SO_2Cl_2	Bz_2O_2	1, 1, 2, 2, 3–Pentachlorocyclo-propane			191/755	1.5098 (25)	511
	$CH_3CHClCF_3$	$Cl_2 + H_2O$	UV	$CH_3Cl_2CF_3+$	2	80	49 (13)	1.3478 (20)	224
				$CH_2ClCHClCF_3$	1		77	1.3671 (20)	

Table 47. (cont.)   Chlorination of Saturated Aliphatic and Alicyclic Compounds

C_n	Saturated compound	Chlorinating agent	Initiator	Product	Ratio	% Yield	°C b.p./mm (m.p.)	n_D (°C)	Ref.
	3-Bromo-1,1,1-fluoropropane	Cl_2	UV	3-Bromo-3-chloro-1,1,1-trifluoropropane+		51	91	1.395 (25)	181
				3-Bromo-3,3-dichloro-1,1,1-trifluoropropane		14	116		181
	3-Chloro-1,1,1-trifluoropropane	Cl_2	UV	3,3,3-Trichloro-1,1,1-trifluoropropane		73	95	1.388 (25)	181
	$CH_3CF_2CHCl_2$	Cl_2	UV	$CH_3CF_2CCl_3$			102 (48)		219
	$CH_3CF_2CCl_3$	Cl_2	UV	$CH_2ClCF_2CCl_3$		46	151/760	1.4459 (20)	219,318
	C_3F_7H	Cl_2	UV	C_3F_7Cl			-1		186
	$CH_2ClCF_2CF_2Cl$	Cl_2	UV	$CHCl_2CF_2CF_2Cl+$ $CCl_3CF_2CF_2Cl$			92/760 112/760	1.3750 (20) 1.3961 (20)	318
	3-Chloro-1,1,1,2,2-pentafluoropropane	Cl_2	UV	3,3-Dichloro-1,1,1,2,2-penta-fluoropropane		61	53/771	1.326 (20)	199
	$CH_2ClCF_2CCl_3$	Cl_2	UV	$CHCl_2CF_2CCl_3$			174	1.4641 (20)	219
	$CHCl_2CClFCF_3$	Cl_2	UV	$CCl_3CClFCF_3$			112	1.3980 (20)	220
	$CHCl_2CClFCClF_2$	Cl_2	UV	$CCl_3CClFCClF_2$			153	1.4392 (20)	220
	$CHF_2CClFCClF_2$	Cl_2	UV	$CClF(CClF_2)_2$			74/760	1.3501 (20)	138
C_4	1,1-Dichlorobutane	SO_2Cl_2	Bz_2O_2	1,1,3-Trichlorobutane+		48	154/750	1.4593 (25)	66
				1,1,4-Trichlorobutane+		37	184/754	1.4753 (25)	
				1,1,2-Trichlorobutane+		13	157/746	1.4667 (25)	
				1,1,1-Trichlorobutane		2	133/750	1.4483 (25)	
	1,1,1-Trichlorobutane	SO_2Cl_2	Bz_2O_2	1,1,1,4-Tetrachlorobutane+		50	87/20	1.4858 (25)	66
				1,1,1,3-Tetrachlorobutane+		42	70/20	1.4772 (25)	
				1,1,1,2-Tetrachlorobutane		8	69/20	1.4812 (25)	
	t-Butyl chloride	SO_2Cl_2	Bz_2O_2	1,2-Dichloro-2-methylpropane		46	107	1.4323 (25)	321

Table 47. (cont.) Chlorination of Saturated Aliphatic and Alicyclic Compounds

C_n	Saturated compound	Chlorinating agent	Initiator	Product	Ratio	% Yield	°C b.p./mm (m.p.)	n_D (°C)	Ref.
	$CH_3CF_2CH_2CH_3$	$Cl_2 + H_2O$	UV	$CH_3CF_2CHClCH_3 +$ $CH_3CF_2CH_2CH_2Cl$	2 3		72 93	1.3631 (20) 1.3709 (20)	214
	$CF_3CH_2CH_2CH_3$	$Cl_2 + H_2O$	UV	$CF_3CH_2CHClCH_3 +$ $CF_3CH_2CH_2CH_2Cl$	4 5		66 87	1.3433 (20) 1.3505 (20)	215
	$CF_3CH_2CH_2CH_3$	Cl_2	UV	$CF_3CH_2CCl_2CCl_3$		100	87/30	1.4528 (25)	216
	$CH_3CF_2CHClCH_3$	$Cl_2 + H_2O$	UV	$CH_3CF_2CCl_2CH_3 +$ $CH_3CF_2CHClCH_2Cl$	2 1		90 (44) 123	1.3752 (50) 1.404 (20)	214
	$CH_3CF_2CH_2CH_2Cl$	$Cl_2 + H_2O$	UV	$CH_3CF_2CH_2CHCl_2$			119	1.4017 (20)	214
	$CH_2ClCF_2CH_2CH_3$	$Cl_2 + H_2O$	UV	$CH_2ClCF_2CH_2CH_2Cl +$ $CH_2ClCF_2CHClCH_3$	4 1		142 116	1.4153 (20) 1.4025 (20)	214
	$CH_2ClCF_2CH_2CH_3$	Cl_2	UV	$CCl_3CF_2CCl_2CCl_3$			270		224
	1-Chlorobutane	SO_2Cl_2	Bz_2O_2	1, 3–Dichlorobutane + 1, 4–Dichlorobutane + 1, 2–Dichlorobutane + 1, 1–Dichlorobutane		47 24 22 7	133/744 154/749 123/743 115/752	1.4414 (25) 1.4522 (25) 1.4425 (25) 1.4305 (25)	66, 255
	$CF_3CH_2CHClCH_3$	$Cl_2 + H_2O$	UV	$CF_3CH_2CCl_2CH_3 +$ $CF_3CH_2CHClCH_2Cl$	8 6		99 115	1.355 (20)	215
	$CF_3CH_2CF_2CH_3$	Cl_2	UV	$CF_3CCl_2CF_2CCl_3$		100	171	1.4227 (20)	216
	$CF_3CH_2CH_2CH_2Cl$	$Cl_2 + H_2O$	UV	$CF_3CH_2CH_2CHCl_2 +$ $CF_3CH_2CHClCH_2Cl$	2 1		110 115		215
	$CH_3CF_2CF_2CH_3$	Cl_2	UV	$CH_3CF_2CF_2CCl_3$			123	1.3908 (20)	216
	$CH_3CF_2CH_2CHCl_2$	$Cl_2 + H_2O$	UV	$CH_3CF_2CH_2CCl_3 +$ $CH_3CF_2CHClCHCl_2$	7 1		139 146	1.4245 (20) 1.431 (20)	214
	$CCl_3CF_2CH_3$	Cl_2	UV	$CCl_3CF_2CF_2CCl_3$			209	1.4502 (20)	216

Table 47. (cont.) Chlorination of Saturated Aliphatic and Alicyclic Compounds

C_n	Saturated compound	Chlorinating agent	Initiator	Product	Ratio	% Yield	°C b.p./mm (m.p.)	n_D (°C)	Ref.
	$(CF_3)_2CHCH_3$	Cl_2	UV	$(CF_3)_2CHCCl_3$+ $[(CF_3)_2CHCCl_2]_2$		90 5	107 (112)	1.3690 (20)	222
	C_4F_9H	Cl_2	UV	C_4F_9Cl			29		186
	1, 1, 1, 3, 3, 3-Hexa-fluoro-2-methylpropane	Cl_2	UV	2–Chloromethyl–1, 1, 1, 3, 3, 3–hexafluoropropane		60	58		185
	1, 1, 2, 2, 3, 4–Hexa-fluorocyclobutane	Cl_2	UV	1, 2–Dichlorohexafluorocyclo-butane		87	59		193
	Methylcyclopropane	Cl_2	UV	Cyclopropyl carbinyl chloride			86/736	1.4349 (20)	67
	1, 1, 1, 2, 2, 4, 4, 4–Octa-fluorobutane	Cl_2	UV	2, 2–Dichlorooctafluorobutane		90	64		198
	$(CH_3)_2C(OH)CCl_3$	SO_2Cl_2	UV	$(CH_3)(ClCH_2)C(OH)CCl_3$			99/14	1.514 (20)	274
	1–Nitrobutane	Cl_2	UV	$Cl(CH_2)_4NO_2$+ $CH_3CHClCH_2CH_2NO_2$		67	106/12 88/12	1.4585 (20) 1.4504 (20)	134
C_5	Cyclopentane	Cl_2	UV	Chlorocyclopentane+ Dichlorocyclopentane			114/752 80/50	1.4500 (20) 1.4682 (20)	356
	$C_5F_{11}H$	Cl_2	UV	$C_5F_{11}Cl$			60		186
	$(CH_3)(C_2H_5)C(OH)CCl_3$	SO_2Cl_2	Bz_2O_2	$CH_3CHCl(CH_3)C(OH)CCl_3$			63/0.7		274
C_6	n–Hexane	Cl_3CSO_2Cl	Bz_2O_2 or UV	2–Chlorohexane			56/65		241
	Cyclohexane	Cl_2	UV	Chlorocyclohexane+ Dichlorocyclohexane			141/752 106/50	1.4623 1.481 (20)	302, 356
	Cyclohexane	Cl_2	Dimethyl-α, α′–azoiso-butyrate	Cyclohexyl chloride		57	142	1.4642 (16)	144
	Cyclohexane	SO_2Cl_2	Bz_2O_2	Cyclohexyl chloride		89	67/62	1.462 (20)	255
	Cyclohexane	Cl_3CSO_2Cl	Bz_2O_2 or UV	Cyclohexyl chloride			140	1.4610 (25)	241

Table 47. (cont.)   Chlorination of Saturated Aliphatic and Alicyclic Compounds

C_n	Saturated compound	Chlorinating agent	Initiator	Product	Ratio	% Yield	°C b.p./mm (m.p.)	n_D (°C)	Ref.
	Cyclohexane	p–Toluene–sulfodi–chloro–amide	Bz₂O₂	Chlorocyclohexane		50	142		517
	Cyclohexane	Cl₂	UV	1, 2, 4, 5–Tetrachlorocyclohexane			(173)		179
	1, 2, 4, 5–Tetrachloro-cyclohexane	Cl₂	UV	Hexachlorocyclohexane + Heptachlorocyclohexane			(173) (117)		244
	Tetrachlorocyclohexane (m.p. 174)	Cl₂	UV	Nonachlorocyclohexane + Octachlorocyclohexane			(95) (259)		179
	1, 1, 4, 4–Tetrachloro-cyclohexane	SO₂Cl₂	UV	1, 1, 2, 4, 4, 5–Hexachlorocyclo-hexane			(146)		245
	Hexachlorocyclohexane (m.p. 145)	Cl₂	UV	Octachlorocyclohexane			(259)		179
	1, 2, 4, 5–Tetrachloro-cyclohexane (m.p. 174)	SO₂Cl₂	UV	Pentachlorocyclohexane (two isomers)			(56) (107)		246
	Pentachlorocyclohexane (m.p. 56)	Cl₂	UV	Hexachlorocyclohexane			(109)		246
	Pentachlorocyclohexane (m.p. 107)	Cl₂	UV	Hexachlorocyclohexane			(71)		246
	$C_6F_{13}H$	Cl₂	UV	$C_6F_{13}Cl$			85		186
C_7	Cycloheptane	NCS	Bz₂O₂	Cycloheptyl chloride		30	172		77
	n–Heptane	Cl₂	UV	1–Chloroheptane + 2–Chloroheptane + 1, 7–Dichloroheptane			160/754 147/754 119/28	1.4284 (20) 1.4222 (20) 1.4707 (20)	354
	n–Heptane	SO₂Cl₂	Bz₂O₂	1–Chloroheptane		15	158	1.428 (20)	255

Table 47. (cont.) Chlorination of Saturated Aliphatic and Alicyclic Compounds

C_n	Saturated compound	Chlorinating agent	Initiator	Product	Ratio	% Yield	°C b.p./mm (m.p.)	n_D (°C)	Ref.
C_7	$C_7F_{15}H$	Cl_2	UV	$C_7F_{15}Cl$			109		186
	1–H–Decafluoro–2–tri-fluoromethylcyclohexane	Cl_2	UV	1–Chlorodecafluoro–2–trifluoro-methylcyclohexane		78	103		193
C_8	Cyclooctane	SO_2Cl_2	Bz_2O_2	Cyclooctyl chloride		83	30/0.25	1.4857 (18)	331
	Cyclooctane	SO_2Cl_2	UV	Cyclooctyl chloride		55			331
C_9	n-$C_6H_{13}C(CH_3)(OH)CCl_3$	SO_2Cl_2	Bz_2O_2	n-$C_5H_{11}CHClC(CH_3)(OH)CCl_3$			127/1.2	1.501 (20)	274
C_{10}	Adamantane	SO_2Cl_2	Bz_2O_2	Hexachloroadamantane			(184)		544
	Adamantane	Cl_2	UV	Dodecachloroadamantane			(290)		544
C_{14}	1,1–Di(p–chlorophenyl)-ethane	Cl_2	Bz_2O_2	1,2,2,2–Tetrachloro–1,1–di(p–chlorophenyl)ethane		86	(91)		19
	1,1–Di(p–chlorophenyl)-ethane	SO_2Cl_2	Bz_2O_2	1,2–Dichloro–1,1–di(p–chloro-phenyl)ethane		18	(88)		19
	β,β,β–Trichloro–α,α–bis-(4–bromophenyl)-ethane	Cl_2	UV	α,β,β,β–Tetrachloro–α–bis-(4–chlorophenyl)ethane			(92)		435
	β,β,β–Trichloro–α,α–bis-(4–fluorophenyl)-ethane	Cl_2	UV	β,β,β–Tetrachloro–α,α–bis-(4–fluorophenyl)ethane		80	159/4 (55)		435
C_{16}	1,1–Di(p–tolyl)ethane	Cl_2	Bz_2O_2	1,2,2–Trichloro–1,1–di(p–tolyl)-ethane		60	175/0.7 (85)	1.6159 (21)	19
	1,1–Di(p–tolyl)ethane	SO_2Cl_2	Bz_2O_2	1,2–Dichloro–di(p–tolyl)ethane		38	125/0.01 (91)		19

BROMINATION OF SATURATED ALIPHATIC AND ALICYCLIC COMPOUNDS

While the reaction of chlorine with carbon-hydrogen bonds is an exothermic process and the chlorine atoms are nonselective in their abstraction and substitution of the hydrogen atoms, a characteristic feature of the bromination reaction is that the bromine atom is comparatively selective.[65,537] Most bromination reactions are endothermic processes, except for the reactions involving very weak carbon-hydrogen bonds. Kharasch and co-workers[260] have shown that liquid-phase photobromination of aliphatic and alicyclic compounds is a free radical chain process. Light, oxygen, or peroxide accelerates the rate of photobromination reactions. Thus, the bromination of cyclohexane in the dark in the absence of oxygen or peroxide proceeds slowly, whereas in the presence of light and oxygen the yield of cyclohexyl bromide is 100%.[260] Some of the more interesting bromination reactions are summarized in Table 48.

Most brominations under free radical conditions are carried out with elemental bromine at temperatures from 0° to 25°. In some cases an incandescent lamp is sufficient to initiate the reaction, but in most cases ultraviolet light is essential. The photobromination of fluorinated compounds proceeds slowly over a period of several days despite the use of strong ultraviolet light and silica vessels.[181,186,193,200]

Photochemical bromination of norbornane produces norbornyl bromide, b.p. 69°/17 mm, n_D 1.5147 (20°), in 25% yield.[268] The product consists of about 75% of exo isomer. Bromination of norbornane with bromotrichloromethane results in an 84% yield of product, consisting of about 98% of exo isomer.[268]

Bromination of cyclopropane produces 1,3–dibromopropane in high yield; oxygen together with light accelerate the reaction.[259] Cyclohexane has been brominated with N–bromosuccinimide to give cyclohexyl bromide.[96] Fast electrons and γ rays accelerate the reaction. The results are essentially the same as those obtained by ultraviolet light or thermal initiation. Cyclohexane has also been brominated with a mixture of bromine and chlorine catalyzed by light.[503] Bromination of aliphatic and alicyclic compounds with N–bromosuccinimide has received little attention.[234]

Sometimes a hydrogen atom can be substituted for bromine by using a bromoalkane. Thus, in the presence of benzoyl peroxide at 95°, chloroform was converted with carbon tetrabromide to bromotrichloromethane.[549] Similarly, bromotrichloromethane brominates dichloromethane to bromodichloromethane.[549]

Table 48. **Bromination of Saturated Aliphatic and Alicyclic Compounds**

C_n	Saturated compound	Brominating agent	Initiator	Product	% Yield	°C b.p./mm (m.p.)	n_D (°C)	Ref.
C_2	C_2F_5H	Br_2	UV	C_2F_5Br		−20		186
C_3	$CF_3CF_2CFH_2$	$Br_2 + H_2O$	UV	CF_3CF_2CBrFH	76	35		200
	C_3F_7H	Br_2	UV	C_3F_7Br		12		186
C_4	Isobutane	Br_2	$UV + O_2$	t-Butyl bromide+ 1, 2–Dibromo–2–methylpropane	60 40			260
	C_4F_9H	Br_2	UV	C_4F_9Br		43		186
	1–Bromo–1, 2, 2, 3, 3, 4–hexa-fluorocyclobutane	Br_2	UV	1, 2–Dibromohexafluorocyclo-butane	71	95		193
C_5	$C_5F_{11}H$	Br_2	UV	$C_5F_{11}Br$		75		186
	$(CH_3)_2CBrC_2H_5$	NBS	Bz_2O_2	2, 3–Dibromo–2–methylbutane	20	171	1.5102 (20)	77
C_6	Cyclohexane	Br_2	UV	Cyclohexyl bromide	100			260
	Cyclohexane	$Br_2 + Cl_2$	UV	Cyclohexyl bromide+ Cyclohexyl dibromide	45 38			503
	Cyclohexane	NBS	Bz_2O_2	Cyclohexyl bromide	30	52/13	1.4915 (25)	77
	2–Methylpentane	Br_2	UV	2–Bromo–2–methylpentane	90	92/40		456
	2, 3–Dimethylbutane	Br_2	UV	2, 3–Dibromo–2, 3–dimethylbutane	80	(167 decomp.)		168, 456
	2–Chloro–2, 3–dimethylbutane	Br_2	UV	2, 3–Dibromo–2, 3–dimethylbutane	80	(173)		258

Table 48. (cont.)   Bromination of Saturated Aliphatic and Alicyclic Compounds

C_n	Saturated compound	Brominating agent	Initiator	Product	% Yield	°C b.p./mm (m.p.)	n_D (°C)	Ref.
C_6	$C_6F_{13}H$	Br_2	UV	$C_6F_{13}Br$		100		186
C_7	2, 2, 3–Trimethylbutane	Br_2	UV	2–Bromo–2, 3, 3–trimethylbutane	96	(150)		456
C_{10}	N–Ethyl phthalimide	NBS	Bz_2O_2	N–(1, 2–Dibromoethyl)-phthalimide	27	(122)		567
	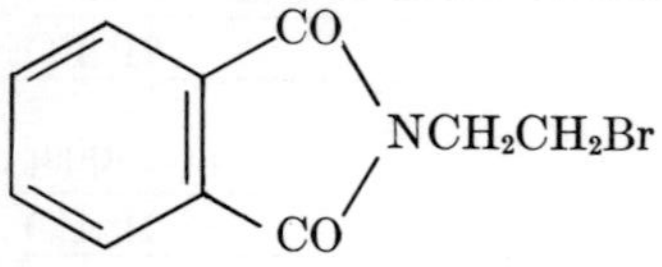	NBS	Bz_2O_2	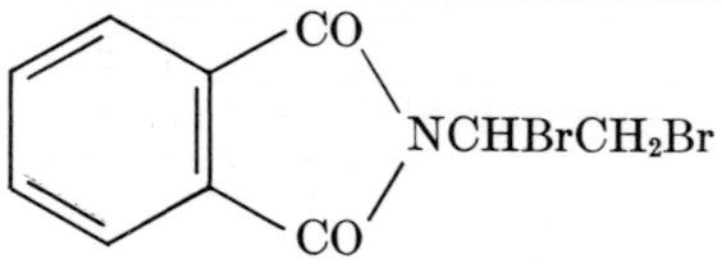	89	(122)		567

HALOGENATION OF UNSATURATED COMPOUNDS

Halogenation of many unsaturated compounds proceeds by a free radical mechanism. Photochemical bromination and chlorination proceed through a chain process. Chlorination of unsaturated compounds with sulfuryl chloride in the presence of peroxide is also a free radical chain process.

Although various free radical halogenation reactions have frequently been reported in the literature, only a few systematic studies have been conducted. Also, a comprehensive compilation of data dealing specifically with free radical halogenations is not available. In the present work it was not possible to present all the data on free radical halogen addition reactions. The results of the last decade are covered, and many older references are included in addition. A cross section of the more interesting and important reactions is given in Tables 49 and 50. The following discussions are limited to unusual results, significant systematic studies, and miscellaneous information which is not included in the tables.

Chlorination

At 40–60° vinyl chloride is chlorinated photochemically to 1, 1, 2–trichloroethane.[471] In the dark no reaction takes place, and the process is strongly inhibited by oxygen. In ultraviolet light of 4360 A cis– and trans–dichloroethylene are converted with chlorine to tetrachloroethane.[348] The reaction is inhibited by oxygen. The chlorination of trichloroethylene[349] and of tetrachloroethylene[473] at 80–120° in ultraviolet light produces penta- and hexachloroethane, respectively. These reactions are retarded by oxygen. In the presence of a large amount of oxygen, tetrachloroethylene is converted to trichloroacetic acid and phosgene.[473]

Many papers have described the chlorination of various unsaturated compounds containing fluorine.[62,138,182,184,185,193,196,200,216,223,225,226,303] Fluorine-containing unsaturated compounds are usually interacted with chlorine at or near room temperature in sunlight, or more conveniently, ultraviolet light. Sometimes the chlorination is carried out at a slightly elevated temperature. For instance, hexafluorodichlorocyclopentene is chlorinated at 70° to give the corresponding tetrachloro product in quantitative yield.[226] In most cases the addition of chlorine proceeds rapidly, in a matter of minutes. However, the reaction of 1, 1, 3, 3, 3–pentafluoropropene requires 24 hr of daylight and 4 hr of ultraviolet light to produce 1, 2–dichloro–1, 1, 3, 3, 3–pentafluoropropane.[199] Similarly, perfluorocyclohexene is chlorinated in

24 hr to 1, 2–dichlorodecafluorocyclohexane.[193] Nonafluoro–2–trifluoro-methylcyclohexene at 80° is chlorinated in 4 days to 1, 2–dichloronon-afluoro–1–trifluoromethylcyclohexane.[193] Sometimes chlorination starts in the dark and is completed in ultraviolet light. Thus, 1, 1–difluoroethylene is converted to 1, 2–dichloro–1, 1–difluoroethane in 98% yield.[200]

Chlorination at elevated temperatures may be reversible or chlorinolysis may occur. Octachloro–1, 3–pentadiene and 1, 1, 2, 3, 3, 4, 5, 5, 5–nona-chloro–1–pentene each undergo chlorinolysis on photochemical chlorination above 52°.[58] The pentadiene degrades to carbon tetrachloride and hexa-chloroethane, and the major degradation product of the pentene is 5–heptachloropropane. At 36–52° the pentadiene is stable toward degradation but the pentene is not.

In photochlorination of tetraphenylbutatriene[562] the terminal double bonds are not affected.

$$(C_6H_5)_2C{=}C{=}C{=}C(C_6H_5)_2 + Cl_2 \rightarrow [-CCl{=}C(C_6H_5)_2]_2$$

Stepwise photochemical chlorination of 4–phenylbutadiene–1–carboxylic acid has been demonstrated.[139]

$$C_6H_5CH{=}CHCH{=}CHCO_2H \rightarrow C_6H_5CH{=}CHCHClCHClCO_2H$$
$$\rightarrow C_6H_5(CHCl)_4CO_2H$$

1, 1–Dichloro–2–methyl–3–acetoxypropene is chlorinated in a nonpolar solvent in the absence of a catalyst to give 1, 1, 1, 2–tetrachloro–3–acetoxy–2–methylpropane.[357]

Photochlorination of 3–(p–chlorophenyl)–1, 1–dichloro–2–methylpropene in the presence of iodine leads to 3–(p–chlorophenyl)–1, 1, 3, 3–tetrachloro–2–methylpropene, b.p. 120°/0.2 mm, n_D 1.5712 (20°), with preservation of the double bond.[275] Such allylic chlorination with chlorine gas is infrequent.

The photochemical chlorination of α– and γ–2, 4, 5, 6–tetrachlorocyclo-hexenes has been thoroughly investigated,[388] because γ–hexachlorocyclo-hexane is of commercial importance. Wavelength and intensity of light have no effect upon the yield of the γ isomer prepared from α–tetrachlorocyclo-hexene, but an increase in temperature increases the yield. A chlorine concentration of 1–10% has no effect, but a concentration of less than 1% decreases the yield.

When a mixture of maleic anhydride, benzene, and chlorine gas is ir-radiated with ultraviolet light at 70°, α–phenyl–α′–chlorosuccinic anhy-dride (I), m.p. 103°, is obtained in 18% yield.[124,126]

$$
\begin{array}{c}
\text{H} \qquad\quad \text{O} \\
\text{C}_6\text{H}_5\!\!-\!\!\!\!\underset{\displaystyle H-\underset{\displaystyle Cl}{\overset{\displaystyle }{|}}-\text{C}}{\overset{\displaystyle }{|}}\!\!-\!\!\text{C}
\end{array}
$$

I

A yield of about 45% is obtained with a mixture of chlorine and benzoyl peroxide or a mixture of sulfuryl chloride and benzoyl peroxide.[124,126] Impure pentachlorocyclohexyl maleic anhydride is also produced in the last reaction.

Sulfuryl chloride reacts with ethylenic compounds to form the corresponding dichlorides.[255,256] The reaction is usually catalyzed by organic peroxides such as benzoyl peroxide. The temperature of the reaction is 70–100°. In the absence of initiators most olefins do not react at all or react very slowly. However, many olefins contain traces of peroxides and therefore do not require an additional initiator. For example, allyl chloride or cyclohexene in boiling carbon tetrachloride reacts rapidly with sulfuryl chloride in the absence of added initiator to give 1, 2, 3–trichloropropane and dichlorocyclohexane, respectively.[256] The chlorination of cyclohexene in the presence of a quinol antioxidant produces dichlorocyclohexane and 2–chlorocyclohexyl sulfite, b.p. 74°/0.002 mm, in lower yield.[48] The chlorination of cyclohexene in the presence of iodine yields dichlorocyclohexane plus 3–chlorocyclohexene in lesser quantity.[48]

A number of commercial compounds are chlorinated by using a large excess of sulfuryl chloride over the substrate. No initiator is used; the starting materials probably contain some peroxides. Thus, cinnaldehyde and cinnamic acid are converted to α, β–dichloro–β–phenyl propioaldehyde and propionic acid, respectively.[119] No yields were reported. In the absence of added peroxide 3–hexene is converted with sulfuryl chloride at 50–55° to 3, 4–dichlorohexane, b.p. 69°/30 mm, n_D 1.4490 (20°).[506] The reaction of tetraphenylethylene with sulfuryl chloride in the absence of peroxide proceeds slowly.[256] Addition of ascaridole, benzoyl peroxide, or benzaldehyde brings about a rapid reaction, to give tetraphenyldichloroethane. Dihydromyrcene reacts with either one or two moles of sulfuryl chloride in the presence of benzoyl peroxide to give either the dichloro or the tetrachloro derivative.[48]

Table 49.   Chlorination of Unsaturated Compounds

C_n	Unsaturated compound	Chlorinating agent	Initiator	Product	% Yield	°C b.p./mm (m.p.)	n_D (°C)	Ref.
C_2	$CF_2=CH_2$	Cl_2	UV	$CF_2ClCClCH_2$	98	47	1.3619 (20)	200
	$CH_2=CHCl$	Cl_2	UV	1, 1, 2-Trichloroethane				471
	cis-Dichloroethylene	Cl_2	UV	CH_2Cl_4				349
	trans-Dichloroethylene	Cl_2	UV	CH_2Cl_4				348
	$HCCl=CHCl$	SO_2Cl_2	Ascaridole	$HCCl_2CCl_2H$	85	144	1.4942 (20)	256
	$HCCl=CHCl$	Cl_2		$HCCl_2CCl_2H$				348
	Trichloroethylene	Cl_2	UV	Pentachloroethane				349
	$CHF=CHF$	Cl_2	UV	$CClFHCClFH$	99	58	1.376 (20)	200
	$CCl_2=CCl_2$	Cl_2	UV	C_2Cl_6				473
	$CCl_2=CCl_2$	Cl_2	F_2	C_2Cl_6	85	(184)		333
C_3	Allyl chloride	Cl_2	UV	$CH_2ClCHClCH_2Cl$	81			50
	Allyl chloride	SO_2Cl_2	Ascaridole	1, 2, 3-Trichloropropane	80			256
	Propylene chloride	SO_2Cl_2	Bz_2O_2	1, 2, 2-Trichloropropane+ 1, 2, 3-Trichloropropane+ 1, 1, 2-Trichloropropane	48 37 15	123 156 132		255
	3, 3, 3-Trifluoropropene	Cl_2	UV	2, 3-Dichloro-1, 1, 1-trifluoro-propane	80	76	1.365 (25)	181
	1-Chloro-3, 3, 3-trifluoropropene	Cl_2	UV	2, 3, 3-Trichloro-1, 1, 1-trifluoro-propane	85	107	1.398 (25)	181
	2-Chloro-3, 3, 3-trifluoropropene	Cl_2	UV	2, 2, 3-Trichloro-1, 1, 1-trifluoro-propane	90	104	1.392 (25)	181
	$CF_2=CFCHF_2$	Cl_2	UV	$CClF_2CClFCHF_2$	92	53/735		138
	1, 1, 3, 3, 3-Pentafluoropropene	Cl_2	UV	1, 2-Dichloro-1, 1, 3, 3, 3-penta-fluoropropane	90	51	1.323 (20)	199
	Hexafluoropropene	Cl_2	UV	1, 2-Dichlorohexafluoropropane	90	35		196
	$CF_2=CClCF_3$	Cl_2	UV	$CF_2ClCClClCF_3$	100	72	1.3519 (20)	225

Table 49. (cont.)   Chlorination of Unsaturated Compounds

C_n	Unsaturated compound	Chlorinating agent	Initiator	Product	% Yield	°C b.p./mm (m.p.)	n_D (°C)	Ref.
	$CHCl=CFCF_3$	Cl_2	UV	$CCl_3CClFCF_3$	100	112 (12)	1.4002 (20)	223, 225
	$CF_2=CFCBrF_2$	Cl_2	UV	$CClF_2CClFCClF_2 +$ $CBrF_2CClFCClF_2$	22 52	73/743 93/749		138
	$CF_2=CClCClF_2$	Cl_2	UV	$CClF_2CCl_2CClF_2$		112/747		330
	$CCl_2=CFCF_3$	Cl_2	UV	$CCl_3CClFCF_3$	100	112 (12)	1.4002 (20)	213, 223 225
	$CClF=CFCF_2$	Cl_2	UV	$CCl_2FCClFCF_3$		71/737		330
C_4	$CF_2=CH_2CH_2CH_3$	Cl_2	UV	$CF_2ClCHClCH_2CH_3$		97	1.3878 (20)	215
	1,1,3,3,3-Pentafluoro-2-methyl-propene	Cl_2	UV	1,2-Dichloro-1,1,3,3,3-penta-fluoro-2-methylpropane	100	75	1.345 (23)	185
	$trans$-$CF_3CH=CHCF_3$	Cl_2	UV	$CF_3CHClCHClCF_3$	79	78		182
	Fluoroperbutyne	Cl_2	UV	$CF_3CCl=CClCF_3$	100	68	1.344 (25)	182
	Hexachlorobutene-2	Cl_2	UV	Octachlorobutane	76	(79)		480
	$CF_3CF=CFCF_3$	Cl_2	UV	$CF_3CClFCClFCF_3$	88	62		193
	Perfluorocyclobutene	Cl_2	UV	1,2-Dichlorohexafluorocyclobutane	71			193
	$CF_3CCl=CClCF_3$	Cl_2	UV	$CF_3CCl_2CCl_2CF_3$	100	131		216
	$CF_2ClCF=CFCF_2Cl$	Cl_2	UV	$CFCl_2CF_2CFClCF_2Cl$		134		184
	$CFCl_2CF_2CF=CF_2$	Cl_2	UV	$CFCl_2CF_2CFClCF_2Cl$	100	133		187
	$CF_2ClCCl=CClCClF_2$	Cl_2	UV	$CF_2ClCCl_2CCl_2CClF_2$		102/28	1.4581 (25)	303
	2-Chloro-1,1,1,4,4,4-hexa-fluorobut-2-ene	Cl_2	UV	$CF_3CCl_2CClHCF_3$	92	104	1.3636 (25)	182, 216
	Pentachlorobutadiene	Cl_2	UV	Heptachlorobutene		72/0.1	1.5529 (20)	442
	$CF_2=CHCH=CF_2$	Cl_2	UV	$CF_2ClCHClCHClCF_2Cl$	33	52/22	1.4094 (25)	10
	$CF_2=CFCF=CF_2$	Cl	UV	$CF_2ClCFClCFClCF_2Cl$		134		184

Table 49. (cont.)   Chlorination of Unsaturated Compounds

C_n	Unsaturated compound	Chlorinating agent	Initiator	Product	% Yield	°C b.p./mm (m.p.)	n_D (°C)	Ref.
C_5	Pentafluoro-1-trifluoromethyl-cyclobutene	Cl_2	UV	1,2-Dichloropentafluoro-1-tri-fluoromethylcyclobutane	91	80		193
C_6	$CCl=CClCF_2CF_2CF_2$	Cl_2	UV	$CCl_2CCl_2CF_2CF_2CF_2$	100	(152)		226
	$(CH_3)_3CCH=CH_2$	SO_2Cl_2	Bz_2O_2	1,2-Dichloro-3,3-dimethylbutane	61	52/11	1.4551 (20)	125
	1,2,3,4,5,6-Hexachlorohexene-1	Cl_2	UV	1,1,2,2,3,4,5,6-Octachloro-hexane		(124)		6
	$CHCl_2CCl_2CHClCHClCCl=CHCl$	Cl_2	UV	$(CHClCCl_2CCl_3)_2$		(108)		443
	$(CCl_2=CHCH_2)_2SO_2$	Cl_2	UV	$C_6H_6Cl_6SO_2$	45	(187)		359
	$CF_2=CFCF_2CF_2CF=CF_2$	Cl_2	UV	$CClF_2CClFCF_2CF_2CClFCClF_2$		89/50		138
	Cyclohexene	SO_2Cl_2	Ascaridole	Dichlorocyclohexane	90	79/22	1.4903 (20)	48, 256
	Decafluorocyclohexene	Cl_2	UV	1,2-Dichlorodecafluorocyclohexane	62	108 (37)	1.338 (20)	62, 193
C_7	Nonafluoro-2-trifluoromethylcyclo-hexene	Cl_2	UV	1,2-Dichlorononafluoro-1-tri-fluoromethylcyclohexane	65	130		193
C_{10}	Dihydromyrcene (1 mole)	SO_2Cl_2 (1 mole)	Bz_2O_2	Dihydromyrcene dichloride	54	55/0.2		48
	Dihydromyrcene (1 mole)	SO_2Cl_2 (2 moles)	Bz_2O_2	Dihydromyrcene tetrachloride	67	(50)		48
C_{11}	$C_6H_5CH=CHCH=CHCO_2H$	Cl_2	UV	$C_6H_5CH=CHCHClCHClCO_2H$	80	(126)		139
	$C_6H_5CH=CHCHClCHClCO_2H$	Cl_2	UV	$C_6H_5CHClCHClCHClCHClCO_2H$	95	(180)		139
C_{14}	Stilbene	SO_2Cl_2	Ascaridole	α,α'-Stilbene dichloride + β,β'-Stilbene dichloride	45 33	(192) (91)		256
C_{26}	Tetraphenylethylene	SO_2Cl_2	Ascaridole	$(C_6H_5)_2CClCCl(C_6H_5)_2$		(184)		256
C_{28}	$(C_6H_5)_2C=C=C=C(C_6H_5)_2$	Cl_2	Bz_2O_2 or UV	$[CCl=C(C_6H_5)_2]_2$	89	(167)		562

Bromination

Like photochemical chlorination, photochemical bromination of olefins can be accelerated or retarded by oxygen. Thus, photobromination of tetrachloroethylene is accelerated by a small amount of oxygen and is retarded by a large amount of oxygen, probably because some photosensitized oxidation processes compete with the bromination.[555] Bromination reactions are more easily reversible than chlorinations, especially at somewhat elevated temperatures. Thus, dibromotetrachloroethane decomposes readily at 150° by a chain process.[87] The reaction is sensitized by bromine.

Bromination of acetylene has been studied thoroughly[56,350] and results in a mixture of cis- and trans-dibromoethylenes.[353] t-Butylacetylene is brominated to cis-1, 2-dibromo-t-butylethylene in high yield.[353] Bromination of propargyl alcohol produces mainly trans-2, 3-dibromo-2-propen-1-ol.[352] Bromination of tolan results in trans-dibromostilbene.[38] Cyclohexene is brominated to trans-dibromocyclohexane.[39,40] Bromination of 2-butyne-1, 4-diol, its diacetate, or tetramethylbutynediol produces cis-dibromo derivatives in high yield,[38] while bromination of cis-2-butene-1, 4-diol results in a dl-2, 3-dibromo derivative.[39] trans-2-Butene-1, 4-diol, its diacetate, and trans-tetramethylbutenediol are brominated to the corresponding meso-2, 3-dibromo compounds.[39]

Many papers have reported photochemical bromination of unsaturated compounds, mostly olefins.[61,138,182,184,189,193,200,201,218,329,341,358,380,443,450] For many brominations daylight or bright sunshine can be utilized. In most cases, however, an artificial light source, mostly ultraviolet light, is employed. Most of the reactions proceed smoothly and give the expected products in high yields. In photochemical or benzoyl peroxide-catalyzed bromination of 1, 1, 1-trichloropropene (II), an 85% yield of a mixture, b.p. 61°/1 mm, n_D 1.5637 (20°), of compounds III and IV is obtained.[358]

$$CCl_3CH=CH_2 + Br_2 \rightarrow CCl_3CHBrCH_2Br + CCl_2BrCHClCH_2Br$$

$$\text{II} \qquad\qquad\qquad \text{III} \qquad\qquad\qquad \text{IV}$$

Compound IV is apparently formed through isomerization of the initial radical A into B.

$$CCl_3\dot{C}HCH_2Br \rightarrow \dot{C}Cl_2CHClCH_2Br$$

$$\text{A} \qquad\qquad\qquad \text{B}$$

The bromination of compound II under ionic conditions leads to the normal addition product.

In the photochemical bromination of cis– and trans–3, 4–di–H–hexachloro-hexatriene–1, 3, 5 (V)[443] and of tetraphenylbutatriene (VI),[562] the terminal double bonds are not affected.

$$(=CHCCl=CCl_2)_2 + Br_2 \rightarrow (-CHBrCCl=CCl_2)_2$$

V

$$(C_6H_5)_2C=C=C=C(C_6H_5)_2 + Br_2 \rightarrow [-CBr=C(C_6H_5)_2]_2$$

VI

Photochemical bromination of 1, 4–diphenyl–1–nitrobutadiene produces 1, 4–diphenyl–1–nitrobutadienedi bromide.[553]

A radical process has been postulated for the bromination of cinnamic acid.[31,32] The acid reacts readily with bromine in the dark in the absence of oxygen. In the presence of oxygen the reaction is very slow. When irradiated, the reaction proceeds rapidly.

exo–cis–3, 6–endoxo–Δ4–Tetrahydrophthalic anhydride (VII) reacts with bromine under free radical conditions to give both cis– (VIII), m.p. 331°, and trans– (IX), m.p. 163°, dibromo products.[44]

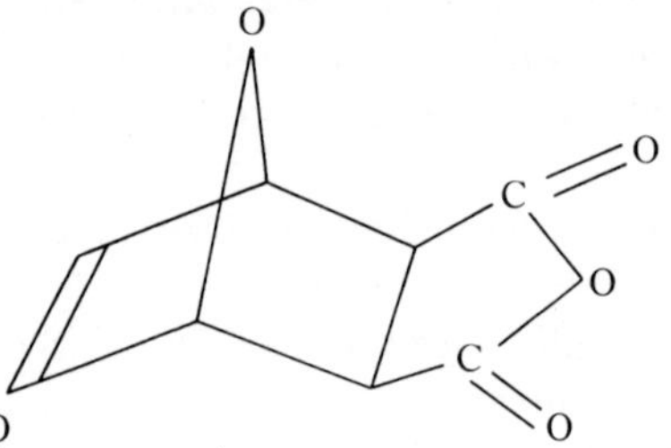

VII

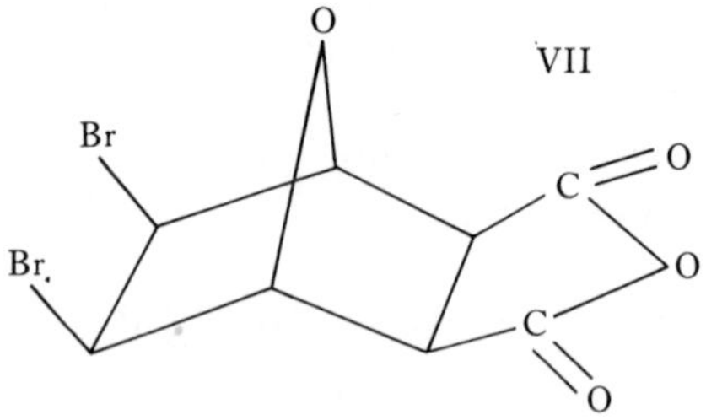

VIII

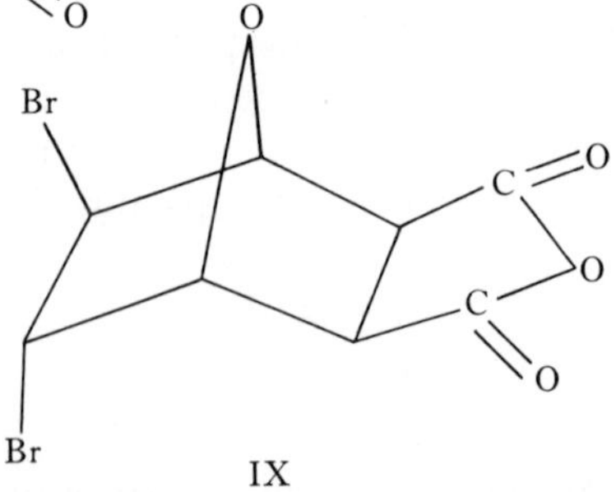

IX

Under ionic conditions only the trans product is obtained. Therefore the cis product is formed by a free radical mechanism. exo–cis–3, 6–endo–Methylene–Δ4–tetrahydrophthalic anhydride undergoes a free radical reaction with bromine to yield a mixture of a cis compound, m.p. 256°, and a trans compound, m.p. 188°.[43] Again, under ionic conditions only the trans product is obtained.

Table 50. Bromination of Unsaturated Compounds

C_n	Unsaturated compound	Brominating agent	Initiator	Product	% Yield	°C b.p./mm (m.p.)	n_D (°C)	Ref.
C_2	CH≡CH	Br_2	UV	Dibromoethylene		61/163	1.5408 (21)	56, 350, 353
	CH_2=CHCl	Br_2	UV	$CH_2BrCBrClH$				471
	trans–Dichloroethylene	Br_2	UV	$C_2Cl_2Br_2H_2$				351
	CF_2=CFH	Br_2	UV	$CF_2BrCHBrF$	82	70/630	1.4191 (24)	184, 380
C_3	CH_3C≡CH	Br_2	UV	Dibromopropene	50	45/36	1.5318 (20)	353
	CF_3CH=CH_2	Br_2	UV	$CF_3CHBrCH_2Br$	90	116	1.4286 (25)	189, 218
	HC≡CCH_2OH	Br_2	UV	2, 3–Dibromo-2–propen-1–ol	74	55/1 (28)	1.5796 (20)	352
	CF_3CH=CH_2	Br_2	UV	$CF_3CHBrCH_2Br$	90	116	1.4286 (25)	218
	1–Bromo-3, 3, 3–trifluoro-propene	Br_2	UV	2, 3, 3–Tribromo-1, 1, 1–trifluoro-propane	95	70/30	1.483 (25)	181
	2–Bromo-3, 3, 3–trifluoropropene	Br_2	UV	2, 2, 3–Tribromo-1, 1, 1–trifluoro-propane	98	61/20	1.480 (25)	181
	CHCl=$CClCHF_2$	Br_2	UV	$CBrClHCBrClCHF_2$		87/24	1.5078 (20)	201
	CF_2=$CFCHF_2$	Br_2	UV	$CBrF_2CBrFCHF_2$		95/741		138
	Hexafluoropropene	Br_2	UV	$CF_3CBrCFBrF_2$		70/734	1.3588 (20)	329
	CF_3CClH=CF_2.	Br_2	UV	$CF_3CBrClHCBrF_2$	82	104		341
	CF_2=$CClCBrF_2$	Br_2	UV	$CBrF_2CBrClCBrF_2$		87/50	1.4719 (20)	138
	CF_2=$CClCClF_2$	Br_2	UV	$CBrF_2CBrClCClF_2$		86/100	1.4471 (20)	330
	CF_2=$CFCBrF_2$	Br_2	UV	$CBrF_2CBrFCBrF_2$	100	132/733	1.4284 (20)	138
C_4	trans–CF_3CH=$CHCF_3$	Br_2	UV	$CF_3CBrHCBrHCF_3$	82	60/120		182
	Fluoroperbutyne	Br_2	UV	CF_3CBr=$CBrCF_3$	98	105	1.396 (25)	182
	CF_3CF=$CFCF_3$	Br_2	UV	$CF_3CBrFCBrFCF_3$	75	96	1.355 (20)	193
	$(CF_3)_2C$=CF_2	Br_2	UV	$(CH_3)_2CBrCF_2Br$	35	96/740 (41)		61

Table 50. (cont.) Bromination of Unsaturated Compounds

C_n	Unsaturated compound	Brominating agent	Initiator	Product	% Yield	°C b.p./mm (m.p.)	n_D (°C)	Ref.
	$CF_2=CFCF=CF_2$	Br_2	UV	$CF_2BrCFBrCFBrCF_2Br$	100	130/70	1.464 (25)	184
	Perfluorocyclobutene	Br_2	UV	1,2-Dibromohexafluorocyclobutane	65	95		193
	4,4-Dichlorohexafluoro-but-1-ene	Br_2	UV	1,2-Dibromo-4,4-dichlorohexafluorobutane	91	65/5	1.427 (20)	187
	$CF_2ClCF=CFCF_2Cl$	Br_2	UV	$CF_2ClCFBrCFBrCF_2Cl$	95	172/960	1.425 (25)	184
	$CFCl=CFCFClCFCl_2$	Br_2	UV	$CFClBrCFBrCFClCFCl_2$		149/52	1.4929 (25)	450
	2-Bromo-1,1,1,4,4,4-hexa-fluorobut-2-ene	Br_2	UV	$CF_3CBr_2CBrHCF_3$		79/45		182
	$(CH_3)_2C(OH)C\equiv CH$	Br_2	UV	$(CH_3)_2C(OH)CBr=CHBr$	91	118/30		113
	2-Butyne-1,4-diol	Br_2	UV	cis-2,3-Dibromo-2-butene-1,4-diol	66	(116)		38
	cis-2-Butene-1,4-diol	Br_2	UV	dl-2,3-Dibromo-1,4-butanediol	72	(85)		39
	trans-2-Butene-1,4-diol	Br_2	UV	Meso-2,3-dibromo-1,4-butanediol	77	(133)		39
C_6	$(CH_3)_3CC\equiv CH$	Br_2	UV	cis-1,2-Dibromo-t-butylethylene	90	74/16	1.5124 (20)	353
	Dimethylethynylcarbinol	Br_2	UV	Dibromovinyldimethylcarbinols + 2,3-Dibromo-2,3-dimethylbutane	86	76–80/6 55/6 (173)	1.5422 (20)	352
	$(C_2H_5)(CH_3)C(OH)C\equiv CH$	Br_2	UV	1,2-Dibromo-3-methylpentene-3-ol	92	108/19		113
	cis-$(=CHCCl=CCl_2)_2$	Br_2	UV	$(CHBrCl=CCl_2)_2$		(128)		443
	trans-$(=CHCCl=CCl_2)_2$	Br_2	UV	$(CHBrCl=CCl_2)_2$		(123)		443
	Cyclohexene	Br_2	UV	trans-Dibromocyclohexane	92	101/13		39
	α-3,4,5,6-Tetrachlorocyclo-hexene	Br_2	UV	α-1,2-Dibromo-3,4,5,6-tetra-chlorocyclohexane + γ-1,2-Dibromo-3,4,5,6-tetra-chlorocyclohexane		(166) (123)		433
	Perfluorocyclohexene	Br_2	UV	1,2-Dibromodecafluorocyclohexane	83	139 (31)		193

Table 50. (cont.)   Bromination of Unsaturated Compounds

C_n	Unsaturated compound	Brominating agent	Initiator	Product	% Yield	°C b.p./mm (m.p.)	n_D (°C)	Ref.
C_7	Nonafluoro-2-trifluoromethyl-cyclohexene	Br_2	UV	1,2-Dibromononafluoro-1-trifluoro-methylcyclohexane	57	160		193
	$HC{\equiv}CC(CH_3)_2OCOCH_3$	Br_2	UV	$CH_3CO_2C(CH_3)_2CBr{=}CHBr$	77	71/2	1.5184 (21.5)	352
C_8	$C_6Cl_5CH{=}CHBr$	Br_2	UV	$C_6Cl_5CHBrCHBr_2$	95	(115)		236
	2-Butyne-1,4-diol diacetate	Br_2	UV	cis-2,3-Dibromo-2-butene-1,4-diol diacetate	78	(62)		38
	Tetramethylbutynediol	Br_2	UV	cis-2,3-Dibromo-2,5-dimethyl-3-hexene-2,5-diol	78	(149)		38
	trans-Tetramethylbutenediol	Br_2	UV	Meso-2,3-dibromo-2,5-dimethyl-2,5-hexanediol		(82)		39
	trans-2-Butene-1,4-diol diacetate	Br_2	UV	Meso-2,3-dibromo-1,4-butane-diol diacetate		(85)		39
C_{10}	Ethynylcyclohexanol	Br_2	UV	1-(1,2-Dibromovinyl)cyclohexanol		(74)		113
	1-Ethynylcyclohexyl acetate	Br_2	UV	cis-1-(Dibromovinyl)cyclohexyl acetate	82	116/2.5	1.5321 (19)	352
C_{14}	Tolan	Br_2	UV	trans-Dibromostilbene	69	(204)		38
C_{15}	$C_6H_5CH{=}CHSO_2C_6H_4\text{-}p\text{-}CH_3$	Br_2	UV	$C_6H_5CHBrCHBrSO_2C_7H_7$		(132)		265
C_{16}	$C_6H_5C(NO_2){=}CHCH{=}CHC_6H_5$	Br_2	UV	$C_6H_5C(NO_2){=}CHCBrHCBrHC_6H_5$		(106)		553
C_{20}	$(p\text{-}CH_3C_6H_4SO_2CH_2CH_2C{\equiv})_2$	Br_2	UV	$(p\text{-}CH_3C_6H_4SO_2CH_2CH_2CBr{=})_2$		(173)		86
C_{28}	$(C_6H_5)_2C{=}C{=}C{=}C(C_6H_5)_2$	Br_2	UV	$[CBr{=}C(C_6H_5)_2]_2$	80	(148)		562

HALOGENATION INVOLVING HALOGEN EXCHANGE

At the beginning of the century Eibner[127] observed that chlorine reacts with bromobenzene under the influence of light to give chlorobenzene.

$$C_6H_5Br + Cl_2 \rightarrow C_6H_5Cl + Br_2$$

At the time the observation received little attention. In 1934 Asinger[14] reported on the exchange of a bromine atom for a chlorine atom in various brominated toluenes. In the last decade a number of investigators have studied exchange reactions with various bromine- and iodine-containing compounds. Goerner and Nametz[160] used sulfuryl chloride as the chlorine atom source and benzoyl peroxide as the initiator. Voegtli, et al.[534] applied the method to brominated benzene derivatives and to substances related to DDT. They used sulfuryl chloride as the chlorine atom source and light as the initiator. The halogen interchange reaction has been applied extensively to brominated and iodinated fluoroalkanes.[26,47,181,182,184,187,193,195,196,198,199,202,335]

$$CH_2ICH_2CF_3 + Br_2 \rightarrow CH_2BrCH_2CF_3$$

$$CH_2ICH_2CF_3 + Cl_2 \rightarrow CH_2ClCH_2CF_3$$

Further examples are given in Table 51.

Generally, the exchange reactions of bromine for iodine are carried out with elemental bromine in the presence of light. In the exchange reactions of chlorine for bromine or for iodine various chlorine atom sources are used. Most common are chlorine or sulfuryl chloride in the presence of benzoyl peroxide or light. Carbon tetrachloride[26] and iodochloride[335] are also used. In some reactions no catalyst is used, and the reactions are achieved by heat.[202]

If a molecule contains both bromine and iodine, the reaction with chlorine may involve only iodine-chlorine interchange. For example[197]:

$$CBrF_2CH_2I + Cl_2 \rightarrow CBrF_2CH_2Cl$$

If the halogen interchange is performed with substances containing an olefinic bond, the unsaturation may be preserved[138]

$$CF_2{=}CFCF_2I + Cl_2 \rightarrow CF_2{=}CFCClF_2$$

or the exchange reaction and the addition of halogen to the olefinic bond may occur simultaneously.[534]

$$(p{-}BrC_6H_4)_2C{=}CCl_2 + Cl_2 \rightarrow (p{-}ClC_6H_4)_2CClCCl_3$$

In some cases the exchange reaction and the substitution halogenation proceed simultaneously to give a complex mixture of products. Thus, 1, 1, 1–trifluoro–3–iodopropane reacts with chlorine in ultraviolet light to give 3–chloro–1, 1, 1–trifluoropropane, 3–chloro–1, 1, 1–trifluoro–3–iodopropane, and 3, 3–dichloro– and 3, 3, 3–trichloro–1, 1, 1–trifluoropropane.[181]

A related reaction is the photochemical replacement of an SO_2Cl group for bromine or chlorine. Photobromination of 2–phenylethylene–1–sulfochloride (I) in the presence of a small amount of oxygen results in three products.[444]

$$C_6H_5CH{=}CHSO_2Cl \rightarrow C_6H_5CHBrCHBrSO_2Cl + C_6H_5CHBrCHBrCl$$

I	II	III

$$+ \; C_6H_5CHBrCHBr_2$$

IV

When oxygen is excluded, product II is not formed. No reaction occurs in the dark. Photochlorination of I produces V, b.p. 84°/1.4 mm, in 86% yield.

$$C_6H_5CHClCHCl_2$$

V

Photochemical chlorination of p–bromobenzenesulfonyl chloride yields p–dichlorobenzene.[334]

Miller and Walling have studied the mechanism of the halogen interchange reaction in detail,[334] and Milligan has reported on the effect of substituents on the rate of halogen interchange.[335]

Table 51. Chlorination Involving Halogen Exchange

C_n	Starting material	Chlorinating agent	Initiator	Product	% Yield	°C b.p./mm (m.p.)	n_D (°C)	Ref.
C₁	CF₃I	Cl₂	UV	CF₃Cl		−80		26
	CF₃I	CCl₄	UV	CF₃Cl	60			26
C₂	CBrF₂CH₂I	Cl₂	UV	1-Bromo-2-chloro-1,1-difluoro-ethane	83	71/770	1.404 (20)	197
	1,2-Dichloro-1,2,2-trifluoro-iodoethane	Cl₂	UV	1,1,2-Trichlorotrifluoro-ethane	77	47		184
	1-Bromo-2-chloro-1,1,2-tri-fluoroiodoethane	Cl₂	UV	1-Bromo-2,2-dichloro-trifluoroethane	83	70		184
C₃	1,1,1-Trifluoro-3-iodopropane	Cl₂	UV	3-Chloro-1,1,1-trifluoropropane	80	46/773	1.339 (20)	181, 195
	1,1,1-Trifluoro-3-iodopropane	Cl₂	UV	3-Chloro-1,1,1-trifluoro-3-iodo-propane+	43	119	1.450 (20)	181
				3-Chloro-1,1,1-trifluoropropane+	16	45	1.334 (25)	
				3,3-Dichloro-1,1,1-trifluoro-propane+	12	72	1.360 (25)	
				3,3,3-Trichloro-1,1,1-trifluoro-propane	11	95	1.390 (25)	
	3-Chloro-1,1,1-trifluoro-3-iodopropane	Cl₂		3,3-Dichloro-1,1,1-trifluoro-propane	80	73/766	1.3631 (20)	181, 195
	3,3-Dichloro-1,1,1-trifluoro-3-iodopropane	Cl₂	UV	3,3,3-Trichloro-1,1,1-trifluoro-propane		95	1.389 (25)	181
	3-Chloro-1,1,1,2,2-penta-fluoro-3-iodopropane	Cl₂	UV	3,3-Dichloro-1,1,1,2,2-penta-fluoropropane	87	53/771	1.326 (20)	199
	1-Chlorohexafluoro-1-iodo-propane	Cl₂	UV	1,1-Dichlorohexafluoropropane	75	35		196
	CF₂=CFCF₂I	Cl₂	UV	CF₂=CFCClF₂		6.3/739		138

Table 51. (cont.) Chlorination Involving Halogen Exchange

C_n	Starting material	Chlorinating agent	Initiator	Product	% Yield	°C b.p./mm (m.p.)	n_D (°C)	Ref.
C$_4$	1,1,1-Trifluoro-3-iodobutane	Cl$_2$	UV	3-Chloro-1,1,1-trifluorobutane	93	65	1.3438 (20)	195
	1,1,1,4,4-Hexafluoro-2-iodobutane	Cl$_2$	UV	2-Chloro-1,1,1,4,4-hexafluoro-butane	76	51	1.298 (25)	182
	1-Chlorohexafluoro-2-iodo-cyclobutane	Cl$_2$	UV	1,2-Dichlorohexafluorocyclobutane	95	60		193
	1,2,4-Trichlorohexafluoro-4-iodobutane	Cl$_2$	UV	1,1,3,4-Tetrachlorohexafluoro-butane	96	133		187
	1,1,1,3,3-Pentafluoro-3-iodo-2-trifluoromethylpropane	Cl$_2$ + H$_2$O	UV	1,2-Dichloro-1,1,3,3,3-penta-fluoro-2-trifluoromethylpropane	88	63		198
C$_5$	1,3-Dichlorononafluoro-1-iodo-pentane	Cl$_2$	UV	1,3-Trichlorononafluoropentane	70	119	1.345 (20)	196
C$_6$	C$_3$F$_7$[CF$_2$CF(CF$_3$)]I	Cl$_2$	Heat	C$_3$F$_7$[CF$_2$CF(CF$_3$)]Cl	100	84/760	1.2826 (26)	202
	Bromobenzene	Cl$_2$	UV	Chlorobenzene	68	130/740		127, 334, 534
	Bromobenzene	SO$_2$Cl$_2$	Bz$_2$O$_2$	Chlorobenzene				334
	p-BrC$_6$H$_4$Br	Cl$_2$	UV	p-ClC$_6$H$_4$Cl	90	170 (52)		534
	p-ClC$_6$H$_4$Br	Cl$_2$	UV	p-ClC$_6$H$_4$Cl	90	170 (25)		534
	o-ClC$_6$H$_4$Br	Cl$_2$	UV	o-ClC$_6$H$_4$Cl	82	175/740	1.4928 (24)	534
	m-ClC$_6$H$_4$Br	Cl$_2$	UV	m-ClC$_6$H$_4$Cl	85	166/742		534
	p-FC$_6$H$_4$Br	Cl$_2$	UV	p-FC$_6$H$_4$Cl	79	128/740		534

Table 51. (cont.) Chlorination Involving Halogen Exchange

C_n	Starting material	Chlorinating agent	Initiator	Product	% Yield	°C b.p./mm (m.p.)	n_D (°C)	Ref.
C_7	Decafluoro-1-iodo-2-trifluoro-methylcyclohexane	Cl_2	UV	1-Chlorodecafluoro-2-trifluoro-methylcyclohexane	85	103		193
	p-Bromotoluene	SO_2Cl_2	Bz_2O_2	p-Chlorotoluene+	22	49/12	1.5209 (20)	160
				p-Bromobenzyl chloride+	38	112/12 (38)		
				p-Bromobenzyl bromide	11	115/12 (61)		
	o-Bromotoluene	SO_2Cl_2	Bz_2O_2	o-Chlorotoluene+	25	56/20	1.5263 (20)	160
				o-Bromobenzyl chloride	32	112/17	1.5880 (20)	
C_9	$C_3F_7[CF_2CF(CH_3)]_2I$	Cl_2	Heat	$C_3F_7[CF_2CF(CF_3)]_2Cl$	89	134/760	1.299 (22)	202
	$p\text{-}BrC_6H_4CH_3$	Cl_2	UV	$p\text{-}ClC_6H_4CCl_3$	95			534
C_{12}	$C_3F_7[CF_2CF(CF_3)]_3I$	Cl_2	Heat	$C_3F_7[CF_2CF(CF_3)]_3Cl$	98	75/8	1.3091 (22)	202
C_{14}	$(p\text{-}BrC_6H_4)_2CHCCl_3$	Cl_2	UV	$(p\text{-}ClC_6H_4)_2CClCCl_3$	86	(92)		534
	$(p\text{-}BrC_6H_4)_2C{-}Cl_2$	Cl_2	UV	$(p\text{-}ClC_6H_4)_2CClCCl_3$	90			534
C_{15}	$C_3F_7[CF_2CF(CF_3)]_4I$	Cl_2	Heat	$C_3F_7[CF_2CF(CF_3)]_4Cl$	85	112/10	1.3169 (20)	202

Table 52.   Bromination Involving Halogen Exchange

C_n	Starting material	Brominating agent	Initiator	Product	% Yield	°C b.p./mm	n_D (°C)	Ref.
C_2	1, 2-Dichloro-1, 2, 2-tri-fluoroiodoethane	Br_2	UV	1-Bromo-1, 2-dichloro-trifluoroethane	80	72		184
	1-Bromo-2-chloro-1, 1, 2-trifluoroethane	Br_2	UV	1, 2-Dibromo-1-chloro trifluoroethane	76	92		184
C_3	$CF_3CH_2CH_2I$	Br_2	UV	$CF_3CH_2CBr_2H$	68	110		181
	1, 1, 1, 3, 3-Pentafluoro-3-iodo-propane	Br_2	UV	1-Bromo-1, 1, 3, 3, 3-pentafluoro-propane	55	44	1.320 (18)	198
	3-Bromo-1, 1, 1-trifluoro-3-iodo-propane	Br_2	UV	3, 3-Dibromo-1, 1, 1-trifluoro-propane	68	111		181
C_4	1, 1, 1, 4, 4-Hexafluoro-2-iodo-butane	Br_2	UV	2-Bromo-1, 1, 4, 4, 4-hexafluoro-butane	81	70		182
C_7	Decafluoro-1-iodo-2-trifluoro-methylcyclohexane	Br_2	UV	1-Bromodecafluoro-2-trifluoro-methylcyclohexane	78	115		193

SIDE-CHAIN AND RELATED SUBSTITUTION HALOGENATION

Substitution halogenation reactions occur with methyl and *t*–butyl groups of aromatic and heterocyclic compounds, with activated methylene groups such as those present in ethyl and *n*–propyl side chains of aromatics and heterocyclic compounds, and with tertiary hydrogen atoms of compounds such as cumene and triphenylmethane. The hydrogen atoms of these diverse classes of compounds have similar reactivity, and the substitution reactions of these compounds seem to proceed by one common mechanism. The scope of substitution halogenation reactions is evident from the size of Table 53. Side-chain halogenation of compounds containing silicon is included on page 341.

Hydrogens of methyl, methylene, or methene groups can be substituted with a halogen by a variety of agents. Elemental chlorine in conjunction with light, peroxide, or azonitrile is frequently used.[172,276,277,516] The selectivity of the chlorine atom increases when sulfuryl chloride is used in the presence of peroxide, azonitrile, or light.[255,532] Under free radical conditions, chlorination of aromatic or hetero compounds carrying side chains does not always ensure side-chain substitution chlorination, and nuclear substitution or addition chlorination may proceed simultaneously or exclusively.[254,520] For example, photochlorination of 2, 7–dimethyldibenzo–1–dioxin produces 2, 7–dimethyl–3, 8–dichlorodibenzo–*p*–dioxin, m.p. 231°.[520]

Photochlorination of toluene has received considerable attention. Side-chain chlorination with N–chlorosuccinimide (NCS) in the presence of peroxide or light has also been studied extensively.[2,207,208] Even though no catalyst is used in some of the reactions with NCS, there is little doubt that these reactions proceed by a free radical mechanism. The chlorination of toluene, xylene, or ethyl benzene with NCS is inhibited by oxygen and hydroquinone[2,207,208]—a sign of a radical process.

Other chlorinating agents are employed less frequently than chlorine, sulfuryl chloride, and NCS. Carbon tetrachloride can be a chlorine atom donor under free radical conditions. Thus, toluene has been chlorinated with carbon tetrachloride to give benzyl chloride in low yield.[367] Chlorination with trichloromethanesulfonyl chloride in ultraviolet light or in the presence of benzoyl peroxide has also been achieved.[241] Good selectivity by this agent was demonstrated.

For the bromination reactions of side chains of aromatic, heterocyclic, and related compounds, a wider range of agents is available. Bromination with elemental bromine in the presence of light, oxygen, or peroxide was early recognized as a free radical process. The bromination of toluene,[261] ethyl benzene,[261] and phenanthrene[18,410,411] was studied in the 1930s.

Photobromination in polar solvents may lead to concurrent nuclear and side-chain bromination. Thus, photobromination of durene in acetic acid shows the influence of free radical and polar effects; side-chain as well as nuclear bromination takes place.[429]

N–Bromosuccinimide (NBS) is frequently used in free radical bromination in the presence of peroxide or ultraviolet light.[76,234] Side chains of aromatic hydrocarbons are readily brominated with NBS. Benzylic hydrogens, in particular, are readily substituted by bromine atoms. Methyl groups are easily attacked by NBS.[115,234] For example, toluene reacts with NBS in the presence of benzoyl peroxide to give a high yield of benzyl bromide.[374,414,470] Similarly, more complex molecules can be brominated in the side chain to give bromo derivatives. For example, p–methylstilbene can be brominated to p–bromomethylstilbene.[267] The reaction of NBS in the presence of ultraviolet light with deuterium-containing toluene, chlorotoluene, methoxytoluene, and ethyl benzene has been investigated,[552] and NBS bromination of toluene by irradiation with fast electrons has been studied on a decagram scale.[95]

As in the case of NCS, no catalysts are used in some of the reactions with NBS. Under such conditions radical and ionic reaction products can be produced. When bromination occurs in the nucleus of an aromatic or a heterocyclic compound, polar mechanisms are probably operating. In side-chain substitutions, there is little doubt that the reactions proceed by a free radical mechanism. There are a number of examples in which both processes occur. For example, 2– or 3–methylthiophene react with NBS in the absence of peroxide to give both nuclear and side-chain bromo derivatives.[114] In the presence of electronegative groups many compounds are brominated in the side chain without the use of a catalyst. For example, the reactions with p–nitrotoluenes give p–nitrobenzyl bromides in good yield.[75]

Methylnaphthalenes, di- and triphenylmethane, and fluorene and its derivatives also undergo side-chain bromination in the absence of a catalyst. For example, the reactions with 1– and 2–methylnaphthalene give the corresponding bromomethylnaphthalenes in good yield.[75,78,283] It is possible that in all these reactions the yields can be increased and the reaction times reduced by using a peroxide catalyst.[115]

Tetraline,[27] 1–ethylnaphthalene,[78] bibenzyl,[27] 1, 2, 3, 4–tetrahydrophenanthrene,[27] and acenaphthene[27,162] can be readily brominated with NBS. The brominated products can be readily dehydrobrominated to give naphthalene,[27] vinyl naphthalene,[78] stilbene,[27] phenanthrene,[27] and acenaphthylene,[27] respectively.

The stereochemical course of benzylic bromination has been studied by Dauben and McCoy.[106] NBS reacts with (−)–α–deuterioethyl benzene in boiling carbon tetrachloride in the presence of benzoyl peroxide to give phenylmethylcarbinyl bromide, which is 99.7% racemized. Dauben and McCoy also summarize previous work dealing with the racemization of optically active radical intermediates, and many earlier references on NBS bromination are given.

Reaction with NBS in the presence of a free radical initiator does not always ensure side-chain bromination. For instance, bromination of 2–benzylthio–4(5)–methylglyoxaline in carbon tetrachloride at 0° to 5° in the presence of benzoyl peroxide produces 2–benzylthio–5(4)–bromo–4(5)–methylglyoxaline in 96% yield, and no side-chain bromination occurs.[205] Another example is 3–methyl coumarin, which can react with NBS in boiling carbon tetrachloride in the presence of benzoyl peroxide to give 2–bromo–3–bromomethyl coumarin, which is brominated both in the side chain and in the nucleus.[135,136] The bromination of p–tolylboric acid with NBS under free radical conditions does not affect the hydroxyl groups and side-chain brominations occur in high yield.[522] Depending on the amount of NBS used, mono or dibromo compounds are obtained.

Recently a number of variously substituted N–monobromo– and N, N–dibromohydantoins were prepared and applied to side-chain and related bromination studies.[55,92,371,374,458] The most promising among the agents appears to be 1, 3–dibromo–5, 5–dimethylhydantoin (DBDMH).[422] This agent is as convenient to use as NBS, and the yields of bromo products are as high as those obtained with NBS. An advantage of DBDMH over NBS is that it is more stable, carries more bromine per weight, and is less soluble in nonpolar solvents.[422] Reactions with this agent have been reviewed briefly.[363,422]

Photobromination of side chains of aromatic compounds with bromotrichloromethane is carried out at 60–75° with a sun lamp of 275 watts.[240] Most reactions are completed within 6 hr. However, tolunitrile is brominated for 23 hr. The following compounds are brominated in moderate to good yield to the corresponding α–bromo derivatives: toluene, ethyl benzene, cumene, p–chlorotoluene, p–bromotoluene, methyl p–toluate, p–methylanisole, p–xylene, α–bromo–p–xylene, and p–tolunitrile.

Carbon tetrabromide is also used for side-chain bromination.[238] The reaction is achieved by heat. Substitution bromination of benzene, bromobenzene, and naphthalene has been reported. Since carbon tetrabromide easily dissociates under the influence of visible light and in the presence of other free radical initiators, it is possible that this reagent may prove of greater selectivity under these conditions. Side chains of aromatic compounds can also be brominated with a mixture of bromine and chlorine in ultraviolet light; toluene is converted to benzyl bromide in 71% yield.[503]

Table 53. Side-Chain and Related Substitution Halogenation

C_n	Starting material	Halogenating agent	Initiator	Product	% Yield	°C b.p./mm (m.p.)	n_D (°C)	Ref.
C_5	2-Methylthiophene	NBS	Bz_2O_2	2-Bromomethylthiophene	84	55/1.5	1.6050 (25)	114
	3-Methylthiophene	NBS	Bz_2O_2	3-Bromomethylthiophene	90	50/1.5	1.6035 (25)	82, 114
	5-Methyluracil	NCS	Bz_2O_2	5-Chloromethyluracil	50	(223)		546
	5-Methyl-2,4,6-trichloropyrimidine	NBS	Bz_2O_2 UV	5-Bromomethyl-2,4,6-trichloropyrimidine	78 85	(134)		176
C_6	2,5-Dimethylfurane	NBS		5-Methyl-2-(bromomethyl)-furane		70/2		79
	2,5-Dimethylthiophene	NBS		5-Methyl-2-(bromomethyl)-thiophene		90/13		79, 283
	2,6-Dimethylthiouracil	NCS		6-Chloromethyl-2-methyl-thiouracil	30	(230)		546
	2,5-Dimethyl-4,6-dichloropyrimidine	NBS	Bz_2O_2	2-Methyl-5-bromomethyl-4,6-dichloropyrimidine	74	(109)		176
	2,5-Dimethyl-4,6-dichloropyrimidine	Br_2	UV	2-Methyl-5-bromomethyl-4-bromo-6-chloropyrimidine	35	(136)		176
C_7	$C_6H_5CH_3$	Cl_2	AIBN	Benzyl chloride				144
	$C_6H_5CH_3$	SO_2Cl_2	Bz_2O_2	Benzyl chloride Benzal chloride	75 90	97/62 104/30	1.5390 (20) 1.5503 (20)	255, 427 255
	$C_6H_5CH_3$	NCS	UV or Bz_2O_2	Benzyl chloride	93			207, 208
	$C_6H_5CH_3$	Cl_3CSO_2Cl	Bz_2O_2 or UV	Benzyl chloride	70			241
	$C_6H_5CH_3$	NBS	AIBN	Benzyl bromide	93	78/15		532
	$C_6H_5CH_3$	NBS	Methyl-α,α'-azoiso-butyrate	Benzyl bromide	66			145
	$C_6H_5CH_3$	Br_2	Peroxide or O_2	Benzyl bromide	98			261

Table 53. (cont.) Side-Chain and Related Substitution Halogenation

C_n	Starting material	Halogenating agent	Initiator	Product	% Yield	°C b.p./mm (m.p.)	n_D (°C)	Ref.
	$C_6H_5CH_3$	$Br_2 + Cl_2$	UV	Benzyl bromide	71			503
	$C_6H_5CH_3$	CBr_4	Heat	Benzyl bromide	77			238
	$C_6H_5CH_3$	CCl_3Br	UV	Benzyl bromide	34	83/22		240
	Benzyl bromide	CBr_4	Heat	Benzal bromide	55			238
	Benzal bromide	CBr_4	Heat	Benzotribromide	27	(56)		238
	$p-BrC_6H_4CH_3$	Br_2	UV	$p-BrC_6H_4CH_2Br$	52	125/12 (62)		160
	$p-BrC_6H_4CH_3$	NBS	Bz_2O_2	$p-BrC_6H_4CH_2Br$	64	120/6 (61)		342
	$o-BrC_6H_4CH_3$	Br_2	UV	$o-BrC_6H_4CH_2Br$	79	129/16		160
	$o-BrC_6H_4CH_3$	NBS	Bz_2O_2	$o-BrC_6H_4CH_2Br$	69	169/11		342
	$m-BrC_6H_4CH_3$	Br_2	UV	$m-BrC_6H_4CH_2Br$	74	126/12 (40)		160
	$m-BrC_6H_4CH_3$	NBS	Bz_2O_2	$m-BrC_6H_4CH_2Br$	55	113/10		342
	$p-ClC_6H_4CH_3$	CCl_3Br	UV	$p-$Bromobenzyl bromide	42	(61)		240
	$p-ClC_6H_4CH_3$	CCl_3Br	UV	$p-$Chlorobenzyl bromide	58	(50)		240
	$p-ClC_6H_4CH_3$	SO_2Cl_2	Bz_2O_2	$p-$Chlorobenzyl chloride	70	115/30 (29)		255
	$p-ClC_6H_4CH_3$	NBS	Bz_2O_2	$p-ClC_6H_4CH_2Br$	76	110/8 (48)		342, 527, 552
	$o-ClC_6H_4CH_3$	NBS	Bz_2O_2	$o-ClC_6H_4CH_2Br$	81	110/10		342
	$m-ClC_6H_4CH_3$	NBS	Bz_2O_2	$m-ClC_6H_4CH_2Br$	73	96/6		342
	$p-ClC_6H_4CH_3$	1-Bromo-3, 5, 5-trimethyl-hydantoin	Bz_2O_2	$p-ClC_6H_4CH_2Br$	40	(50)		92
	2, 6-Dichlorotoluene	SO_2Cl_2	Bz_2O_2	2, 6-Dichlorobenzyl chloride	60	85/3 (49)		307
	3, 4-Dichlorotoluene	SO_2Cl_2	Bz_2O_2	3, 4-Dichlorobenzyl chloride	60	84/1.5	1.5763 (22)	307
	2, 4, 5-$Cl_3C_6H_2CH_3$	Cl_2	UV	2, 4, 5-$Cl_3C_6H_2CCl_3$		(80)		281

Table 53. (cont.) Side-Chain and Related Substitution Halogenation

C_n	Starting material	Halogenating agent	Initiator	Product	% Yield	°C b.p./mm (m.p.)	n_D (°C)	Ref.
	2, 3, 4, 5, 6-Penta-chlorotoluene	Cl_2	UV	2, 3, 4, 5, 6-Pentachloro-1-di-chloromethylbenzene		(117)		172, 281
	$p\text{-}NO_2C_6H_4CH_3$	Br_2	UV	$p\text{-}NO_2C_6H_4CHBr_2$		(77)		129
	$p\text{-}NO_2C_6H_4CH_3$	NBS		$p\text{-}NO_2C_6H_4CH_2Br$		(98)		75
	$p\text{-}NO_2C_6H_4CH_3$	NBS	Bz_2O_2	$p\text{-}NO_2C_6H_4CH_2Br$	78	(99)		342, 527
	$o\text{-}NO_2C_6H_4CH_3$	NBS	Bz_2O_2	$o\text{-}NO_2C_6H_4CH_2Br$	30	(44)		527
	$m\text{-}NO_2C_6H_4CH_3$	NBS	Bz_2O_2	$m\text{-}NO_2C_6H_4CH_2Br$	64	170/8		342
	$m\text{-}NO_2C_6H_4CH_3$	1, 3-Dibromo-5, 5-dimethyl-hydantoin	Bz_2O_2	$m\text{-}NO_2C_6H_4CH_2Br$	55	(54)		55
	$m\text{-}NO_2C_6H_4CH_3$	1, 3-Dibromo-5-methyl-5-isopropyl-hydantoin		$m\text{-}NO_2C_6H_4CH_2Br$	48	(53)		92
	$o\text{-}NO_2C_6H_4CH_3$	1, 3-Dibromo-5-methyl-5-isopropyl-hydantoin		$o\text{-}NO_2C_6H_4CH_2Br$	39	(47)		92
	p-Toluene sulfonyl chloride	NBS	AIBN	ω-Bromo-p-toluene sulfonyl chloride		(62)		399
	p-Toluene sulfonyl chloride	1, 3-Dibromo-5, 5-dimethyl-hydantoin	AIBN	ω-Bromo-p-toluene sulfonyl chloride				399
	p-Toluene sulfonyl fluoride	NBS	AIBN	ω-Bromo-p-toluene sulfonyl fluoride	42	(75)		399

Table 53. (cont.)   Side-Chain and Related Substitution Halogenation

C_n	Starting material	Halogenating agent	Initiator	Product	% Yield	°C b.p./mm (m.p.)	n_D (°C)	Ref.
	p-Toluene sulfonyl fluoride	1,3-Dibromo-5,5-dimethylhydantoin	AIBN	ω-Bromo-p-toluene sulfonyl fluoride				399
	p-Tolylboric acid	NBS (1 mole)	Bz₂O₂	ω-Bromo-p-tolylboric acid	90	(165)		522
	o-Tolylboric acid	NBS (1 mole)	Bz₂O₂	ω-Bromo-o-tolylboric acid	79	(148)		522
	m-Tolylboric acid	NBS (1 mole)	Bz₂O₂	ω-Bromo-m-tolylboric acid		(214)		522
	p-Tolylboric acid	NBS (2 moles)	Bz₂O₂	ω,ω-Dibromo-p-tolylboric acid		(160-170 decomp.)		522
	o-Tolylboric acid	NBS (2 moles)	Bz₂O₂	ω,ω-o-Dibromo-o-tolylboric acid	56	(163)		522
	m-Tolylboric acid	NBS (2 moles)	Bz₂O₂	ω,ω-m-Dibromo-m-tolylboric acid	69	(160 decomp.)		522
	4-Methyl-5-carbethoxy-2-imidazolone	NBS		4-Bromomethyl-5-carbethoxy-2-imidazolone	98	(220 decomp.)		120
	2,6-Dimethylpyrone	NBS		2-Methyl-6-(bromomethyl)-1,4-pyrone		135/0.5 (112)		79, 283
C₈	Ethyl benzene	SO₂Cl₂	Bz₂O₂	α-Chloroethyl benzene	85	91/30		255
	Ethyl benzene	NCS	UV	C₆H₅CHClCH₃	60	87/21		208
	Ethyl benzene	Cl₃CSO₂Cl	Bz₂O₂ or UV	α-Chloroethyl benzene		77/17	1.5230 (25)	241
	Ethyl benzene	Cl₂	UV	Phenylpentachloroethane		(35)		172, 320
	Ethyl benzene	NBS	Bz₂O₂	α-Bromoethyl benzene	87	87/14	1.5588 (25)	106, 414
	Ethyl benzene	CCl₃Br	UV	α-Bromoethyl benzene	72	77 (12)		240
	Ethyl benzene	CBr₄ (1 mole)	Heat	1-Phenyl-1-bromoethane	67			238
	Ethyl benzene	CBr₄ (2 moles)	Heat	1-Phenyl-1,2-dibromoethane	70			238

Table 53. (cont.)   Side-Chain and Related Substitution Halogenation

C_n	Starting material	Halogenating agent	Initiator	Product	% Yield	°C b.p./mm (m.p.)	n_D (°C)	Ref.
	Ethylpentachloro-benzene	Cl_2	UV	1-Pentachlorophenyl-2-chloro-ethane		(89)		446, 447
	$C_6Cl_5CH_2CH_3$	Cl_2	UV	$C_6Cl_5C_2H_2Cl_3$		(87)		281
	$C_6Cl_5CH_2CH_3$	Br_2	UV	$C_6Cl_5CHBrCH_3$	52	(124)		236
	$C_6Cl_5CHBrCH_3$	Br_2	UV	$C_6Cl_5CHBrCH_2Br$	76	(94)		236
	1,4-Bischloromethyl benzene	Cl_2	UV	1,4-Bistrichloromethyl benzene		(110)		172
	1,2,3,4-Tetrachloro-5,6-dimethyl benzene	Cl_2	UV	1,2,3,4-Tetrachloro-5,6-bisdichloromethyl benzene		(149)		172
	1,2,3,5-Tetrachloro-4,6-dimethyl benzene	Cl_2	UV	1,2,3,5-Tetrachloro-4,6-dichloromethyl benzene		(95)		172
	1,2,4,5-Tetrachloro-3,6-dimethyl benzene	Cl_2	UV	1,2,4,5-Tetrachloro-3,6-dichloromethyl benzene		(127)		172
	2,3,4,5,6-Penta-chloro-1-(trichloro-ethyl) benzene	Cl_2	UV	2,3,4,5,6-Pentachloro-1-(α,β,β,β-tetrachloroethyl) benzene		(126)		172
	p-Xylene	NBS	Bz_2O_2	p-$CH_3C_6H_4CH_2Br$	48	106/12		342, 414
	o-Xylene	NBS	Bz_2O_2	o-$CH_3C_6H_4CH_2Br$	86	97/9		342, 414
	m-Xylene	NBS	Bz_2O_2	m-$CH_3C_6H_4CH_2Br$	62	98/9		342, 414
	p-Xylene	NBS	Bz_2O_2	p-Xylylene bromide		(143)		414, 545
	o-Xylene	NBS	Bz_2O_2	o-Xylylene bromide		(98)		545
	m-Xylene	NBS	Bz_2O_2	m-Xylylene bromide		(71)		545
	p-Xylene	CCl_3Br	UV	α-Bromo-p-xylene	48	63/7 (35)		240
	m-Xylene	CBr_4 (1 mole)	Heat	m-Xylyl monobromide	67			238
	m-Xylene	CBr_4 (2 moles)	Heat	m-Xylyl dibromide	48			238

Table 53. (cont.) Side-Chain and Related Substitution Halogenation

C_n Starting material	Halogenating agent	Initiator	Product	% Yield	°C b.p./mm (m.p.)	n_D (°C)	Ref.
p–Xylene	NCS	UV	ω–Chloro-p-xylene	70	92/18		208
p–Xylene	NCS	UV	ω, ω′–Dichloro-p-xylene	60	114/19 (97)		208
p–Xylene	Cl₂	UV	1, 4–Bischloromethyl benzene		(100)		172
p–Xylene	Cl₂	UV	α, α, α′, α′–Pentachloro-p-xylene		161/10 (43)		550
p–Xylene	Cl₂	UV	p–CCl₃C₆H₄CCl₃	87	(109)		289, 319
4–(Chloromethyl)-toluene	Cl₂	UV	1, 4–Bis(trichloromethyl) benzene		(110)		319
o–Xylene	NCS	UV	ω–Chloro-o-xylene	72	93/17		208
o–Xylene	NCS	UV	ω, ω′–Dichloro-o-xylene	71	134/23		208
o–Xylene	Cl₂	UV	o–Dichloromethylbenzotrichloride		(54)		172
o–Xylene	Cl₂	UV	1–(Dichloromethyl)-2-(trichloromethyl) benzene		(48)		319
p–Xylene	SO₂Cl₂	Bz₂O₂	(p–ClCH₂)₂C₆H₄	41	(97)		427
m–Xylene	Cl₂	UV	m–CCl₃C₆H₄CCl₃	80	114/1		306
m–Xylene	SO₂Cl₂	Bz₂O₂	m–Xylyl chloride	80	101/30	1.5345 (20)	255
m–Xylene	SO₂Cl₂	Bz₂O₂	(m–ClCH₂)₂C₆H₄ + m–CH₃C₆H₄CH₂Cl	48 34	199		427
m–Xylene	NCS	UV	ω–Chloro-m-xylene	73	105/33		208
m–Xylene	NCS	UV	ω, ω′–Dichloro-m-xylene	68	151/35		208
α–Bromo-p-xylene	CCl₃Br	UV	α, α′–Dibromo-p-xylene	30	(144)		240
p–CNC₆H₄CH₃	NBS	Bz₂O₂	p–CNC₆H₄CH₂Br	80	(115)		527
o–CNC₆H₄CH₃	NBS	Bz₂O₂	o–CNC₆H₄CH₂Br	43	(74)		527

Table 53. (cont.)   Side-Chain and Related Substitution Halogenation

C_n	Starting material	Halogenating agent	Initiator	Product	% Yield	°C b.p./mm (m.p.)	n_D (°C)	Ref.
	p-HO$_2$CC$_6$H$_4$CH$_3$	NBS	Bz$_2$O$_2$	p-HO$_2$CC$_6$H$_4$CH$_2$Br	95	(220)		527
	o-HO$_2$CC$_6$H$_4$CH$_3$	NBS	Bz$_2$O$_2$	o-HO$_2$CC$_6$H$_4$CH$_2$Br	73	(132, decomp.)		527
	o-Toluic acid	Br$_2$	UV	α-Bromo-o-toluic acid +	84	(147)		130
				α,α-Dibromo-o-toluic acid	77	(170)		
	p-Methylanisole	NBS	Bz$_2$O$_2$	p-BrCH$_2$C$_6$H$_4$OCH$_3$	65	110/2	1.5823 (20)	141
	p-Methylanisole	CCl$_3$Br	UV	p-Bromomethylanisole	24	108/8		240
	p-CNC$_6$H$_4$CH$_3$	CCl$_3$Br	UV	p-Bromomethyltolunitrile	30	(115)		240
	o-Methoxytoluene	NBS	Bz$_2$O$_2$	o-CH$_3$OC$_6$H$_4$CH$_2$Br	50	134/11		342
	Methoxyl-p-toluene sulfonate	NBS	AIBN	ω-Bromomethyl-p-toluene sulfonate		(65)		399
	1,3-Diacetyl-4-methyl-2-imidazolone	NBS		1,3-Diacetyl-4-bromomethyl-2-imidazolone	70	(80)		120
	n-Propyl benzene	CBr$_4$	Heat	1-Phenyl-1-bromopropane	47			238
	n-Propyl benzene	SO$_2$Cl$_2$	Bz$_2$O$_2$	1-Phenyl-1-chloropropane	50			66
C$_9$	CH$_3$C$_6$H$_4$CO$_2$CH$_3$	Cl$_2$	UV	ClCH$_2$C$_6$H$_4$CO$_2$CH$_3$	81	93/1 (40)		389
	Methyl-o-toluate	Br$_2$	UV	Methyl-α-bromo-o-toluate	66	(32)		130
	Methyl-p-toluate	Cl$_3$CBr	UV	Methyl-α-bromo-p-toluate	18	(55)		240
	m-Tolyl acetate	Br$_2$	UV	m-CH$_3$CO$_2$C$_6$H$_4$CHBr$_2$	75	165/11		129
	Mesitylene	Cl$_2$	UV	1,3,5-Tristrichloromethyl benzene+		(90)		172
				1-Chloro-2,4,6-tristrichloromethyl benzene		(175)		
	Cumene	CCl$_3$Br	UV	Cumyl bromide	34			240
	Cumene	Br$_2$	UV	Cumyl bromide	73			456

Table 53. (cont.) Side-Chain and Related Substitution Halogenation

C_n	Starting material	Halogenating agent	Initiator	Product	% Yield	°C b.p./mm (m.p.)	n_D (°C)	Ref.
	Cumene	Br₂	UV	1,2-Dibromo-2-phenylpropane	74	121/16		456
	1,3,5-Trichloro-2,4,6-trimethyl benzene	Cl₂	UV	1,3,5-Trichloro-2,4,6-tris-dichloromethyl benzene		(178)		172
	1-Chloromethyl-4-ethyl benzene	Cl₂	UV	1-(Pentachloroethyl)-4-(trichloromethyl) benzene		(115)		310
	1,3-Diacetyl-4-methyl-5-methyl-2-imidazolone	NBS		1,3-Diacetyl-4-bromomethyl-5-methyl-2-imidazolone	81	(84)		120
				1,3-Diacetyl-4,5-bis(bromomethyl)-2-imidazolone	49	(109)		120
C_{10}	t-Butyl benzene	SO₂Cl₂	Bz₂O₂	β-Chloro-t-butyl benzene	70	119/30	1.5253 (20)	255, 532
	t-Butyl benzene	SO₂Cl₂	AIBN	Neophyl chloride	94	87/3		532
	p-Cymene	NBS	Bz₂O₂	8-Bromo-p-cymene	24	87/1	1.5642 (25)	28
	p-Cymene	Cl₂	UV	1-(Heptachloroisopropyl)-4-(trichloromethyl) benzene		(128)		311
	Durene	NBS		1,2,4,5-Tetrakisbromomethyl benzene		(160)		429
	Durene	Br₂ + CH₃CO₂H	UV	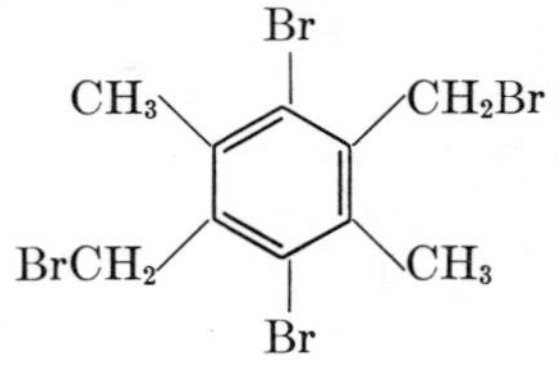				429

Table 53. (cont.) Side-Chain and Related Substitution Halogenation

C_n	Starting material	Halogenating agent	Initiator	Product	% Yield	°C b.p./mm (m.p.)	n_D (°C)	Ref.
	Durene	CBr$_4$	Heat	Duryl monobromide	34	111/4		238
	2-Acetoxy-6-methyl-benzoic acid	Br$_2$ (1 mole)	UV	2-Acetoxy-6-bromomethyl-benzoic acid		(101)		131
	Acetyl-o-cresotinic acid	Br$_2$	UV	Acetyl-ω-bromo-o-cresotinic acid +	70	(161)		130
				Acetyl-ω,ω-dibromo-o-cresotinic acid	68	(145)		
	3-Methyl coumarin	NBS	Bz$_2$O$_2$	2-Bromo-3-bromomethyl coumarin	63	(62)		135, 136
	2-Bromo-3-methyl coumarin	NBS	Bz$_2$O$_2$	2-Bromo-3-bromomethyl coumarin				135, 136
	3-Methyl coumarin	NBS		3-Bromomethyl coumarin		(120)		344
	6-Methyl coumarin	NBS		6-(Bromomethyl) coumarin		(148)		283
	Lepidine	NBS	Bz$_2$O$_2$	ω-Bromolepidine		(66)		175
	Quinaldine	NBS	Bz$_2$O$_2$	ω-Dibromoquinaldine	76	(120)		173
	Quinaldine	NBS	Bz$_2$O$_2$ + UV	ω-Bromoquinaldine +	55	(56)		173
				ω-Dibromoquinaldine	12	(115–120)		
	Quinaldine 1-oxide	NBS		ω-Dibromoquinaldine 1-oxide +	22	(108)		174
				ω-Bromoquinaldine 1-oxide	14	(138)		
C_{11}	p-t-Butyltoluene	NBS	AIBN	p-t-Butylbenzyl bromide	95	93/1.5		532
	Methyl 2-acetoxy-6-methyl benzoate	Br$_2$ (1 mole)	UV	Methyl 2-acetoxy-6-bromomethyl benzoate	84	(99)		131
	Methyl 2-acetoxy-6-methyl benzoate	Br$_2$ (2 moles)	UV	Methyl 2-acetoxy-6-dibromomethyl benzoate		(69)		131
	α-Methylnaphthalene	NCS	UV	α-Chloromethylnaphthalene	59	137/5		208

Table 53. (cont.)   Side-Chain and Related Substitution Halogenation

C_n	Starting material	Halogenating agent	Initiator	Product	% Yield	°C b.p./mm (m.p.)	n_D (°C)	Ref.
	α-Methylnaphthalene	NBS		α-Bromomethylnaphthalene		175/10 (56)		283
	1-Methyl-4-bromo-naphthaline	Br₂	UV	1-Bromomethyl-4-bromo-naphthaline	46	(103)		51
	1-Methyl-4-bromo-naphthaline	NBS	Bz₂O₂	1-Bromomethyl-4-bromo-naphthaline				51
	β-Methylnaphthalene	NCS	UV	β-Chloromethylnaphthalene	56	143/5		208
	2-Methylnaphthalene	NBS		2-Naphthylmethyl bromide	95	172/20 (38) (54)		75 88
	2-Methylnaphthalene	Br₂	UV	2-Naphthylmethyl bromide	75			88
	4,6-Dimethyl coumarin	NBS		4-Methyl-6-(bromomethyl) coumarin		(178)		283, 284
	4,7-Dimethyl coumarin	NBS		4-Methyl-7-(bromomethyl) coumarin		(196)		283, 284
	4-Methyl-7-methoxy coumarin	NBS	Bz₂O₂	4-Bromomethyl-7-methoxy coumarin		(214)		468
	Antipyrine	NBS (2 moles)		1-Phenyl-2-methyl-3-bromo-methyl-4-bromo-5-pyrazolone		(134)		285
C_{12}	Acenaphthene	NBS	Bz₂O₂	trans-1,3-Dibromoacenaphthene		(118)		162
	4-Methylantipyrine	NBS		1-Phenyl-2-methyl-3, 4-di-bromomethyl-5-pyrazolone		(175)		285
	2,3-Dimethylnaph-thaline	NBS		2-Methyl-3-(bromomethyl)-naphthaline		178/10 (104)		283
	2,6-Dimethylnaph-thaline	NBS		2-Methyl-6-(bromomethyl)-naphthaline		195/14 (92 decomp.)		283

Table 53. (cont.) Side-Chain and Related Substitution Halogenation

C_n	Starting material	Halogenating agent	Initiator	Product	% Yield	°C b.p./mm (m.p.)	n_D (°C)	Ref.
	2,7-Dimethylnaph-thaline	NBS		2-Methyl-7-(bromomethyl)-naphthaline		200/15 (100 decomp.)		283
	1,2-Dimethylnaph-thaline	NBS (2 moles)	Bz_2O_2	1,2-Bisbromomethylnaph-thalene	74	(153)		429, 430
	1,3-Dimethylnaph-thaline	NBS (2 moles)	Bz_2O_2	1,3-Bisbromomethylnaph-thalene		(118)		430
	1,4-Dimethylnaph-thaline	NBS (2 moles)	Bz_2O_2	1,4-Bisbromomethylnaph-thalene		(188)		430
	1,5-Dimethylnaph-thaline	NBS (2 moles)	Bz_2O_2	1,5-Bisbromomethylnaph-thalene		(212)		430
	1,6-Dimethylnaph-thaline	NBS (2 moles)	Bz_2O_2	1,6-Bisbromomethylnaph-thalene		(125)		430
	1,7-Dimethylnaph-thaline	NBS (2 moles)	Bz_2O_2	1,7-Bisbromomethylnaph-thalene		(132)		430
	1,8-Dimethylnaph-thaline	NBS (2 moles)	Bz_2O_2	1,8-Bisbromomethylnaph-thalene		(130)		430
	2,3-Dimethylnaph-thaline	NBS (2 moles)	Bz_2O_2	2,3-Dibromomethylnaph-thalene		(145)		208, 429, 430
	2,6-Dimethylnaph-thaline	NBS (2 moles)	Bz_2O_2	2,6-Dibromomethylnaph-thalene		(182)		430
	2,7-Dimethylnaph-thaline	NBS (2 moles)	Bz_2O_2	2,7-Dibromomethylnaph-thaline		(147)		430
C_{13}	1,2,3-Trimethyl-naphthaline	NBS (3 moles)	Bz_2O_2	1,2,3-Trisbromomethyl-naphthaline		(152)		430
	1,2,4-Trimethyl-naphthaline	NBS (3 moles)	Bz_2O_2	1,2,4-Trisbromomethyl-naphthaline		(182)		430

Table 53. (cont.) Side-Chain and Related Substitution Halogenation

C_n	Starting material	Halogenating agent	Initiator	Product	% Yield	°C b.p./mm (m.p.)	n_D (°C)	Ref.
	1, 2, 5-Trimethyl-naphthaline	NBS (3 moles)	B_2zO_2	1, 2, 5-Trisbromomethyl-naphthaline		(187)		430
	1, 2, 6-Trimethyl-naphthaline	NBS (3 moles)	B_2zO_2	1, 2, 6-Trisbromomethyl-naphthaline		(167)		430
	1, 2, 7-Trimethyl-naphthaline	NBS (3 moles)	Bz_2O_2	1, 2, 7-Trisbromomethyl-naphthaline		(203)		430
	1, 3, 5-Trimethyl-naphthaline	NBS (3 moles)	Bz_2O_2	1, 3, 5-Trisbromomethyl-naphthaline		(190)		430
	1, 3, 6-Trimethyl-naphthaline	NBS (3 moles)	Bz_2O_2	1, 3, 6-Trisbromomethyl-naphthaline		(154)		430
	1, 3, 7-Trimethyl-naphthaline	NBS (3 moles)	Bz_2O_2	1, 3, 7-Trisbromomethyl-naphthaline		(170)		430
	1, 3, 8-Trimethyl-naphthaline	NBS (3 moles)	Bz_2O_2	1, 3, 8-Trisbromomethyl-naphthaline		(143)		430
	1, 4, 5-Trimethyl-naphthaline	NBS (3 moles)	Bz_2O_2	1, 4, 5-Trisbromomethyl-naphthaline		(175)		430
	1, 4, 6-Trimethyl-naphthaline	NBS (3 moles)	Bz_2O_2	1, 4, 6-Trisbromomethyl-naphthaline		(202)		430
	2, 3, 5-Trimethyl-naphthaline	NBS (3 moles)	Bz_2O_2	2, 3, 5-Trisbromomethyl-naphthaline		(160)		430
	2, 3, 6-Trimethyl-naphthaline	NBS (3 moles)	Bz_2O_2	2, 3, 6-Trisbromomethyl-naphthaline		(137)		430
	7-Acetoxy-4-methyl coumarin	NBS	Bz_2O_2	7-Acetoxy-4-(bromomethyl)-coumarin		(183)		468
	Fluorene	Br_2	UV	9-Bromofluorene	70	(103)		461, 472, 559

Table 53. (cont.)   Side–Chain and Related Substitution Halogenation

C_n	Starting material	Halogenating agent	Initiator	Product	% Yield	°C b.p./mm (m.p.)	n_D (°C)	Ref.
	Fluorene	NBS		9-Bromofluorene	47	(103)		80, 150
	2-Nitrofluorene	NBS	Bz_2O_2 or UV	9-Bromo-2-nitrofluorene	62	(143)		372
	2-Nitrofluorene	1,3-Dibromo-5,5-dimethyl-hydantoin	Bz_2O_2 or UV	9-Bromo-2-nitrofluorene				372
	Diphenylmethane	NBS		Benzhydryl bromide		182/20 (42)		75
	$(p\text{-ClC}_6H_4)_2CH_2$	Cl_2	UV	$(p\text{-ClC}_6H_4)CHCl$	58	190/5 (64)		97
	$(p\text{-ClC}_6H_4)_2CH_2$	1,3-Dibromo-5,5-dimethyl-hydantoin	Bz_2O_2	$(p\text{-ClC}_6H_4)_2CHBr$	66	(70)		55, 92
	$(p\text{-ClC}_6H_4)_2CH_2$	NBS	Bz_2O_2	$(p\text{-ClC}_6H_4)_2CHBr$		142		55, 92
	$(p\text{-NO}_2C_6H_4)_2CH_2$	NBS	Bz_2O_2 or UV	$(p\text{-NO}_2C_6H_4)_2CHBr$	44	(98)		372
	$(p\text{-NO}_2C_6H_4)_2CH_2$	1,3-Dibromo-5,5-dimethyl-hydantoin	Bz_2O_2 or UV	$(p\text{-NO}_2C_6H_4)_2CHBr$				372
	3-Ethyl-4-methyl-7-methoxycoumarin	NBS		3-α-Bromoethyl-4-methyl-7-methoxycoumarin	60	(125)		344
C_{14}	4,4'-Dichloro-2,2'-bitolyl	NBS	Bz_2O_2	2,2'-Bis(bromomethyl)-4,4'-dichlorobiphenyl		(115)		545
	4,4'-Dichloro-3,3'-bitolyl	NBS	Bz_2O_2	3,3'-Bis(bromomethyl)-4,4'-dichlorobiphenyl		(148)		545
	Bibenzyl	NBS	Bz_2O_2	Meso-α,α'-dibromobibenzyl	92	(238)		162
	erythro-2-Deutero-1,2-diphenylethyl bromide	NBS	Bz_2O_2	Meso-α,α'-dibromobibenzyl	71	(236)		162

Table 53. (cont.) Side-Chain and Related Substitution Halogenation

C_n	Starting material	Halogenating agent	Initiator	Product	% Yield	°C b.p./mm (m.p.)	n_D (°C)	Ref.
	$(p\text{-}ClC_6H_4)_2CHCH_3$	SO_2Cl_2		$(p\text{-}ClC_6H_4)_2CClCH_2Cl$		165/0.5 (88)		20
	Anthracene	1-Bromo-5,5-dimethyl-hydantoin	Bz_2O_2	9-Bromoanthracene	85	(98)		55, 92
	Anthracene	1,3-Dibromo-5,5-dimethyl-hydantoin		9-Bromoanthracene + 9,10-Dibromoanthracene	80 / 59	(100) / (218)		55, 92, 458
	Phenanthrene	1,3-Dibromo-5,5-dimethyl-hydantoin		9-Bromophenanthrene	50	(63)		422, 458
	Phenanthrene	N(1 or 3)-monobromo-5-methyl-5-ethyl-hydantoin		9-Bromophenanthrene		(64)		92
	3-n-Propyl-4-methyl-7-methoxycoumarin	NBS		3-(n-Bromopropyl)-4-methyl-7-methoxycoumarin		(128)		345
	9-Methylphenanthridine	NCS	Bz_2O_2	9-Chloromethylphenanthridine		(130)		143
	1,4-Diacetoxy-2-methylnaphthaline	1-Bromo-3,5,5-trimethyl-hydantoin		1,4-Diacetoxy-2-bromomethylnaphthaline		(138)		92
C_{15}	1,3-Diacetyl-4-methyl-5-(δ-carbomethoxyvaleryl)-2-imidazolone	NBS		1,3-Diacetyl-4-bromomethyl-5-(δ-carbomethoxyvaleryl)-2-imidazolone	92	(60)		120

Table 53. (cont.)   Side-Chain and Related Substitution Halogenation

C_n	Starting material	Halogenating agent	Initiator	Product	% Yield	°C b.p./mm (m.p.)	n_D (°C)	Ref.
	1,3-Diacetyl-4-methyl-5-benzoyl-2-imidazolone	NBS		1,3-Diacetyl-4-bromomethyl-5-benzoyl-2-imidazolone	89	(131)		120
C_{16}	4-Methyl-2,5-diphenyloxazole	NBS		4-Bromomethyl-2,5-diphenyloxazole	40	(162)		161
	Pyrene	NBS		3-Bromopyrene		239/1.8 (95)		80
	Pyrene	N(1 or 3)-monobromo-5-methyl-5-ethylhydantoin		3-Bromopyrene	78	(95)		92
C_{17}	1,3-Dipropionyl-4-methyl-5-(δ-carbomethoxyvaleryl)-2-imidazolone	NBS		1,3-Dipropionyl-4-bromomethyl-5-(δ-carbomethoxyvaleryl)-2-imidazolone	53	(60)		120
C_{18}	Hexaethyl benzene	Cl₂	UV	Hexa-(α-chloroethyl) benzene	23	(230, decomp.)		232
	Hexaethyl benzene	Br₂	UV	Hexa-(α-bromoethyl) benzene	89	(180, decomp.)		232
	1,2-Benzanthracene	NBS		10-Bromo-1,2-benzanthracene				80
	Chrysene	NBS		2-Bromochrysene		(152)		80
C_{19}	Triphenylmethane	Cl₂	Dimethyl-α,α'-azoisobutyrate	Triphenylmethyl chloride	77	(105)		144
	Triphenylmethane	SO₂Cl₂	Bz₂O₂	Triphenylmethyl chloride	72	(111)		255
	Triphenylmethane	NBS		Triphenylbromomethane		234/20 (150)		75
	9-Phenylfluorene	NBS		9-Bromo-9-phenylfluorene		(97)		75
C_{22}	3,3'-Dimethyl-2,2'-binaphthyl	NBS	Bz₂O₂	3,3'-Dibromomethyl-2,2'-binaphthyl	87	(172)		40

ADDITION HALOGENATION

Addition halogenations have been studied extensively since the insecticidal properties of benzene hexachloride were discovered by French and English scientists.[323,477] The English workers[323] demonstrated that the active principle is the γ isomer. Benzene hexachloride has attained considerable industrial importance, and millions of pounds are produced annually for control of various insects.

The addition chlorination of benzene proceeds by a free radical mechanism. The reaction is usually carried out between $-15°$ and $40°$ in the presence of light,[254,278,388,431,476,477] peroxide,[29,279,254,476] azonitrile,[121] azonitrile in conjunction with light,[121] light in conjunction with peroxide,[279,360] light and iodine,[81,266,375,433] or γ rays.[171] The patent literature on this subject is extensive, and no attempt was made to review it here. For details on the chemistry, stereochemical configuration of isomers, relation of structure to activity, and related compounds, Metcalf's monograph is recommended.[323] A laboratory procedure for the preparation of benzene hexachloride is described by Schönberg.[472]

Photochlorination of benzene in the presence of iodine stops at the 3, 4, 5, 6-tetrachlorocyclohexene stage.[81,375] Photobromination of this compound results in 1, 2–dibromo–3, 4, 5, 6–tetrachlorocyclohexane, m.p. 161°. Photochlorination of 3, 4, 5, 6–tetrachlorocyclohexene produces benzene hexachloride, $\alpha{:}\gamma = 8{:}1.$[81] Bromine adds to benzene very slowly in the dark.[412,416] In the light, hexabromocyclohexane is formed.[322] The reaction is also initiated by heat.[416] Simultaneous addition of a mixture of chlorine and bromine to benzene results in a mixture of α, β, and γ isomers of dibromo–3, 4, 5, 6–tetrachlorocyclohexane, m.p. 166°, 285°, and 123°, respectively.[434,436]

Other aromatic compounds also add chlorine under free radical conditions. Toluene is photochlorinated or chlorinated in the presence of benzoyl peroxide at $-20°$; a 64% yield of toluene hexachloride results.[65,254,533] Monochlorobenzene can be chlorinated to a mixture of heptachlorocyclohexanes.[254,323] Similarly, o– or p–dichlorobenzene can be converted to o–octachlorocyclohexane, m.p. 148°, and p–octachlorocyclohexane, m.p. 262°, respectively.[179,323] p–Octachlorocyclohexane is obtained from photochlorination of hexachlorocyclohexane, m.p. 145°.[179] Chlorination of p–dichlorobenzene produces nonachlorocyclohexane, m.p. 95°, which can also be obtained by photochlorination of cyclohexane or tetrachlorocyclohexane, m.p. 174°.[179] Photochlorination of fluorobenzene produces a mixture of fluorohexachlorocyclohexane, m.p. 65°, and 1–fluoro–1, 2, 3, 4, 4, 5, 6–heptachlorocyclohexane, m.p. 209°.[156,435] Further photochlorination may result in a mixture of enneachloromonofluorochlorocyclohexene isomers, m.p. 96° and 104°, and undecachloromonofluorocyclohexane, m.p. 315°.[435] Photochlorination of chlorobenzene in the presence of iodine yields mainly 1, 3, 4, 5, 6–pentachlorocyclohexene–1,[266] while photochlorination of o–dichlorobenzene yields mainly 1, 2, 3, 4, 5, 6–hexachlorocyclohexene–1.[266] The separation of the stereoisomer is complicated. Photochemical chlorination and bromination of naphthalene results in naphthalene tetrachloride[286] and naphthalene tetrabromide,[305,460] respectively.

Heterocyclic compounds can undergo photochemical addition chlorination. For example, phenazine reacts with chlorine to give a mixture of isomers of tetradecachlorotetradecahydrophenazine, m.p. 262°.[297]

Table 54. Addition Halogenation

C_n	Starting material	Halogenating agent	Initiator	Product	% Yield	°C b.p./mm (m.p.)	Ref.
C$_6$	Benzene	Cl$_2$	UV	α-C$_6$H$_6$Cl$_6$+ β-C$_6$H$_6$Cl$_6$+ γ-C$_6$H$_6$Cl$_6$	95	(159) (309) (113)	434, 436, 472
	Benzene	Cl$_2$ + Br$_2$	UV	α-C$_6$H$_6$Cl$_4$Br$_2$+ β-C$_6$H$_6$Cl$_4$Br$_2$+ γ-C$_6$H$_6$Cl$_4$Br$_2$		(166) (285) (123)	434, 436
	Benzene	Cl$_2$	UV + I$_2$	γ-3, 4, 5, 6-Tetrachlorocyclohexene-1		(30)	433
	Benzene	Br$_2$	UV	α-Hexabromocyclohexane+ β-Hexabromocyclohexane		(221) (254)	322, 416, 436
	C$_6$H$_5$Cl	Cl$_2$	UV + I$_2$	α-1, 3, 4, 5, 6-Pentachlorocyclo-hexene-1+ β-1, 3, 4, 5, 6-Pentachlorocyclo-hexene-1+ γ-1, 3, 4, 5, 6-Pentachlorocyclo-hexene-1+ δ-1, 3, 4, 5, 6-Pentachlorocyclo-hexene-1	24	(147) (125) (101) (140)	266
	C$_6$H$_5$F	Cl$_2$	UV	Fluorohexachlorocyclohexane+ 1-Fluoro-1, 2, 3, 4, 4, 5, 6-hepta-chlorocyclohexane		(65) (209)	156
	o-Cl$_2$C$_6$H$_4$	Cl$_2$	UV + I$_2$	1, 2, 3, 4, 5, 6-Hexachlorocyclo-hexene-1 (four isomers)	36		266
	p-Cl$_2$C$_6$H$_4$	Cl$_2$	UV	Nonachlorocyclohexane		(95)	179
	C$_6$H$_6$Cl$_4$	Br$_2$	UV	1, 2-Dibromo-3, 4, 5, 6-tetra-chlorocyclohexane	87	(161)	81, 434, 436

Table 54. (cont.)   Addition Halogenation

C_n	Starting material	Halogenating agent	Initiator	Product	% Yield	°C b.p./mm (m.p.)	Ref.
C_7	$C_6H_5CH_3$	Cl_2	Bz_2O_2 or UV	$C_6H_5Cl_2CH_3$ + $C_6H_5Cl_3CH_2Cl$	64 10	142/0.9 182/0.7	533
C_8	Phenyl trichloroacetate	Cl_2	UV	1, 2, 3, 4, 5, 6–Hexachlorocyclo-hexyl trichloroacetate	90	162/0.4	445
C_{10}	Naphthaline	Br_2	UV	1, 2, 3, 4–Tetrabromo–1, 2, 3, 4–tetrahydronaphthaline	12	(111)	305, 460
	Naphthalene	Cl_2	UV	Naphthaline tetrachloride		(182)	286
C_{13}	Diphenyl carbonate	Cl_2	UV	1, 2, 3, 4, 5, 6–Hexachlorocyclo-hexyl carbonate		(84–90)	445

ALLYLIC BROMINATION

The introduction of a bromine atom into the allylic position is of great significance in organic syntheses. Bromination of the allylic position by using elemental bromine is seldom achieved, since in most allylic compounds the addition reaction competes with the substitution reaction. However, bromination reactions of the allylic position with bromine are known. For example, cholesterol derivatives have been brominated in position 7 without the addition of bromine to position 5, 6.[42,462,463,465] Thus, a carbon tetrachloride or carbon disulfide solution of cholesteryl benzoate or cholesteryl tosylate reacts with bromine in ultraviolet light to give about 70% of 7-β-bromocholesteryl benzoate, m.p. 143°, and -tosylate, m.p. 110°, respectively.[462,463,465]

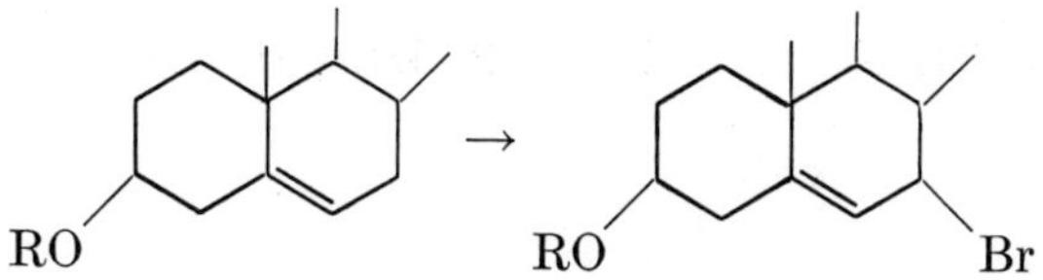

R = C_6H_5CO, $CH_3C_6H_4OSO_2$

For syntheses, the most important method for the introduction of a bromine atom into the allylic position is that using N–bromosuccinimide (NBS).

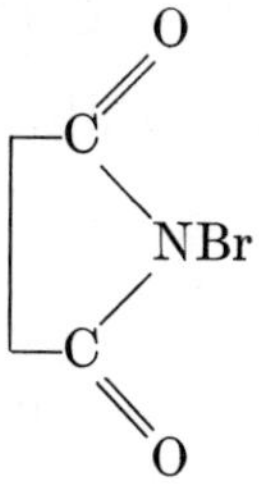

NBS

Wohl and Jaschinowski[560,561] were the first to suggest the use of N–halo-amides for the bromination of olefins. They were followed by Ziegler and his co-workers,[569] who evaluated many haloamides and were the first to suggest the use of NBS as the most suitable reagent for allylic bromination. Since that time NBS has been applied in many branches of organic chemistry, and a huge literature exists on the subject. The earlier results were reviewed by Djerassi[115] in 1948 and by Waugh[543] in 1951. In 1959 Horner and Winkelmann[234] summarized recent advances. Dauben and McCoy[105] recently published a paper dealing with a general survey of reaction variables in allylic bromination; in particular, the reaction with cyclohexene was thoroughly investigated. The reader can consult these articles for details. This chapter is restricted to a description of the general principles of allylic bromination.

Straight-chain and branched olefins with either terminal or nonterminal double bonds can be brominated by NBS only once in the allylic position. For instance, allyl bromide is not further brominated. In mono and bicyclic olefins the second bromine atom enters into the other allylic position in the same ring. A double bond may activate up to four allylic positions for one NBS bromination.[234]

Allylic bromination with NBS can be expressed by the following idealized reaction scheme.

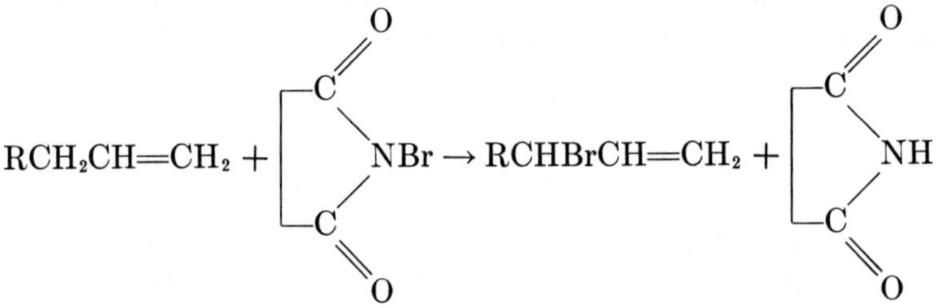

$$RCH_2CH{=}CH_2 + \underset{\text{(succinimide N-Br)}}{\text{NBr}} \rightarrow RCHBrCH{=}CH_2 + \underset{\text{(succinimide NH)}}{\text{NH}}$$

Many classes of compounds are brominated in accordance with this scheme, as shown in examples 1 through 4.

$$(CH_3)_2C{=}CHCH_2C_2H_5 \rightarrow (CH_3)_2C{=}CHBrC_2H_5 \qquad (1)$$

$$Cl_2C{=}CHCH_3 \rightarrow Cl_2C{=}CCH_2Br \qquad (2)$$

$$(C_6H_5)_2C{=}CHCH_3 \rightarrow (C_6H_5)_2C{=}CHCH_2Br \qquad (3)$$

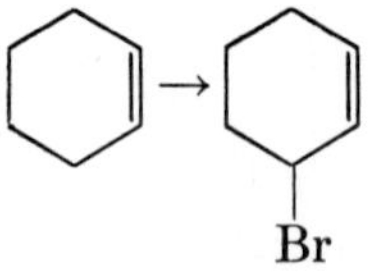

$$\text{cyclohexene} \rightarrow \text{3-bromocyclohexene} \qquad (4)$$

Many steroids containing allylic hydrogen also follow this scheme.

However, allylic brominations often do not proceed by such a clear-cut reaction scheme. The abstraction of the hydrogen atom which is α to the double bond by the succinimide radical (NS) results in an allylic radical which is resonance-stabilized (A and B). As a consequence, two products are frequently found:

$$RCH_2CH{=}CH_2 + NS\cdot \rightarrow R\overset{\cdot}{C}HCH{=}CH_2 \leftrightarrow RCH{=}CHCH_2\cdot$$
$$\qquad\qquad\qquad\qquad\qquad\qquad A \qquad\qquad\qquad B$$

$$A \leftrightarrow B \overset{Br\cdot}{\longrightarrow} ABr + BBr$$

For example, bromination of diallyl yields the following compounds.[30,250-252]

$$(CH_2{=}CHCH_2)_2 \xrightarrow{\text{NBS}} BrCH_2CH{=}CHCH_2CH{=}CH_2$$
$$+ CH_2{=}CHCHBrCH_2CH{=}CH_2$$

Another complication may arise through further bromination of the rearranged products α to the double bond.

$$BrCH_2CH{=}CHCH_2R \rightarrow BrCH_2CH{=}CHCHBrR$$

Also, hydrogen bromide may be eliminated from thermally unstable rearranged allylic bromides.[234,537]

The unique brominating properties of NBS have been attributed to the following factors[234]: (a) the near nonpolarity of the N—Br bond, which facilitates the separation of the bromine atom, (b) the close agreement of bond distances of NBrCO with those of C=C, (c) the similarity of bond

angles of $CO{-}N\diagup^{Br}$ and $C{=}C\diagup^{CH_3}$, and (d) the planarity of the NBS structure, which enables reactions to take place at the surface of NBS crystals.

Allylic bromination with NBS proceeds by a radical process,[74,475] apparently at the surface of the NBS crystals, since the best diluents for allylic bromination are those in which NBS is insoluble.[234] Dry carbon tetrachloride is the solvent of choice, followed by benzene. At the initiation of NBS bromination, the NBS, being heavier than the solvent, is at the bottom of the reaction vessel. At the end of the reaction the succinimide, being lighter than the solvent, floats on the surface of the reaction mixture. Solvents such as methylene chloride, chloroform, trichloroethylene, and chlorobenzene, in which NBS is partially soluble, can be used but are less suitable.

Solvents such as tetrachloroethane, pyridine, acetonitrile, and nitromethane dissolve NBS and are unsuitable for allylic bromination. In such solvents addition of bromine to the double bond occurs instead of allylic bromination. Further support for the theory that allylic bromination occurs at the surface of NBS crystals is provided by the fact that acceleration of the rate of bromination occurs when the surface of NBS is enlarged by depositing the crystals on neutral silica.[234]

The reaction of NBS is catalyzed by many radical initiators, such as a small amount of oxygen, peroxide, azonitriles, or redox systems. The reaction is also accelerated by light and by substances such as bromine, amines, or thiophenol. The reaction is inhibited or retarded by a large amount of oxygen, hydroquinones, dinitrobenzene, picric acid, nitroso compounds, or iodine.[105,234,537]

Benzoyl peroxide is frequently used as an initiator, in particular with systems which are not thermally sensitive. These reactions are usually carried out in boiling carbon tetrachloride. They may start suddenly and are then difficult to control. The ratio of NBS to benzoyl peroxide is usually 100:1, the ratio of carbon tetrachloride to NBS is usually 4:1, and the ratio of carbon tetrachloride to substrate is 10:1 to 20:1. Azobisisobutyronitrile can be used at lower temperatures to initiate NBS bromination. The ratio of NBS to azobisisobutyronitrile varies between 100:1 and 1000:1.

Photochemical NBS bromination can be carried out at room temperature. A redox system can be used to initiate the reaction at room temperature; for example, t–butyl hydroperoxide and cobalt and copper salts of carboxylic acids can be used.[234]

Whether NBS bromination can be initiated thermally is not certain, since the presence of small amounts of peroxides in the reaction mixture cannot be ruled out.[234,537]

Allylic bromination may be suppressed if NBS is soluble in the solvent or in the substrate. In this case, bromination of the double bond takes place. The addition of bromine to the double bond is facilitated by the presence of water, alcohol, acid, or other impurities which may liberate bromine from NBS. Thus, hydrogen bromide eliminated from thermally unstable rearranged allylic products will react with NBS to give bromine, which will add across the double bond. Further difficulties in bromination of the allylic position may be experienced if (a) the allylic position is shielded by bulky groups, (b) the allylic position is polarized by nitro, cyano, SO_2, and ethylene groups, (c) or the angle between the double bond and the allylic position deviates substantially from 120°. Further, side reactions of an oxidative nature may occur. Many hydroxy and amino compounds are oxidized by NBS. Addition of NBS to olefins to form 1:1 adducts may also take place.

In the last decade various attempts have been made to find other agents for allylic bromination. N–bromo derivatives of mono-, di-, and tri-chloroacetamide and of di- and trifluoroacetamide have been prepared.[379] The halogen substitution on the α–carbon of N–bromoacetamide is accompanied by a decrease in allylic bromination of cyclohexene in the following order:

$$CH_3 > CCl_2H > CCl_3 > CClH_2 > CF_3$$

Thus, bromination with compound I, II, III, or IV produces 3–bromocyclohexene in 62, 50, 19, and 13% yield, respectively.[381]

CH₃CONHBr	CCl₂HCONHBr	CCl₃CONHBr	CClH₂CONHBr
I	II	III	IV

Bromination with the higher perfluorinated N–bromoamides (V, VI, and

VII) produces the allylic bromo derivative of cyclohexene in poor yield.[381]

C$_2$F$_5$CONHBr n–C$_3$F$_7$CONHBr n–C$_4$F$_9$CONHBr

V   VI   VII

N–bromo and N, N–dibromo derivatives of alkyl-substituted hydantoins have been prepared[371] and evaluated[55] as brominating agents. 1, 3–Dibromo–5, 5–dimethylhydantoin (DBDMH) appears to be the most promising new agent. Bromination with this agent has several advantages over bromination with NBS[422]:

(a) It is more stable and can be stored more easily.

(b) It carries more bromine per unit weight, making it more economical.

(c) Like NBS, it is insoluble in carbon tetrachloride and benzene. It is less soluble than NBS in water, which makes its regeneration from dimethylhydantoin solution much easier than that of NBS from succinimide solution.

(d) The yield is high. For example, cyclohexene is brominated with DBDMH to give 3–bromocyclohexene in 85% yield.

N–bromo–t–butylamine has been used for allylic bromination.[57] Cyclohexene in isohexane in the presence of azobisisobutyronitrile was brominated to give the 3–bromo derivative in 59% yield.

HALOGENATION OF ORGANIC GERMANIUM AND SILICON COMPOUNDS

Although the chemistry of organosilicon compounds has been thoroughly reviewed,[122,155,441] there are no articles dealing with halogenation of germanium and silicon organic compounds from the standpoint of free radical chemistry. An attempt was made to collect all pertinent data on the bromination and chlorination of organic germanium and silicon compounds in the liquid phase. In some photochemical chlorinations a strict separation of liquid- and gas-phase reactions is difficult, and therefore several gas-phase reactions are included in the present work. Table 55, on chlorination, includes the reactions of aliphatic germanium and silicon compounds; alicyclic organic compounds; unsaturated silicon compounds; and side-chain, benzylic, and related chlorination. Similarly, Table 56, on bromination, includes reactions of saturated and unsaturated aliphatic organosilicon compounds, compounds with benzylic hydrogens, organosilicon compounds containing side chains in the aromatic portion of the molecule, and related compounds.

Chlorination

The chlorination of organogermanium compounds has received little attention. Organic germanium compounds can be chlorinated with chlorine in ultraviolet light[336] or with sulfuryl chloride in the presence of benzoyl peroxide.[393] Thus, a mixture of chloromethyl-,[336] dichloromethyl-,[336] and trichloromethyltrichlorogermane[409] is obtained when methyltrichlorogermane is chlorinated with chlorine until a temperature of 150° is reached, while a mixture of α– and β–chloroethyltrichlorogermane is obtained when ethyltrichlorogermane is reacted with sulfuryl chloride for 2 hr.[393]

Unsaturated silicon compounds containing vinyl[3,4,315] or propenyl groups[316] readily add chlorine to the double bond. The reactions are carried out in sunlight or more conveniently in ultraviolet light. Besides addition to the double bond, simultaneous substitution chlorination may also occur. Thus, depending on the ratio of chlorine to silane and/or the duration of the experiment, chlorination of trichlorovinyltrimethylsilane produces either product I or II.[315]

$$CCl_3CCl_2Si(CCl_3)_3 \qquad\qquad CCl_3CCl_2Si(CCl_3)_2CHCl_2$$

$$\text{I} \qquad\qquad\qquad\qquad \text{II}$$

Sometimes the photochemical chlorination of an unsaturated compound results only in substitution without addition to the double bond. Thus, compound III is photochlorinated to give γ–chloroisocrotyltrichlorosilane (IV).[395]

$$Cl_3SiCH{=}C(CH_3)_2 \xrightarrow[\text{UV}]{Cl_2} Cl_3SiCH{=}C(CH_3)(CH_2Cl)$$

$$\text{III} \qquad\qquad\qquad\qquad \text{IV}$$

The chlorination of saturated organosilicon compounds is carried out with elemental chlorine thermally, photochemically, or in the presence of azonitriles, or with sulfuryl chloride in the presence of free radical catalysts such as benzoyl peroxide, azobisisobutyronitrile, or light. Occasionally other chlorine atom carriers, such as carbon tetrachloride, chlorobenzene, or phosphorus pentachloride are used. Thus, carbon tetrachloride reacts with tetraethylsilane in ultraviolet light to give triethyl–α–chloroethylsilane in 15% yield.[419] Benzoyl peroxide does not catalyze this reaction, whereas in the presence of acetyl peroxide a mixture of α– and β–chloroethyl derivatives is obtained.[419] The reaction of chlorobenzene with triphenylsilane in the presence of di–t–butyl peroxide at 103–122° produces triphenylchlorosilane in 20–62% yield.[101] Tetraethylsilane is chlorinated with phosphorus pentachloride in ultraviolet light to give β–chloroethyltriethylsilane, b.p. 81°/11 mm, n_D 1.4564 (20°), in 19% yield.[494]

Photochlorination with elemental chlorine can sometimes be achieved under bright sunshine, daylight, or incandescent light, but more often it is convenient and more reliable to use an ultraviolet light source. The temperatures in photo and thermal chlorination can vary from 0° to 200°, depending on the substrate used and the degree of chlorination desired. Thermal chlorination often results in more complex reaction mixtures than photochemical chlorination. Also, the yields of products of thermal processes are often lower than those obtained in photochemical reactions. For example, chlorination of trichloro–(1, 1, 2, 2–tetrafluoroethyl)silane in ultraviolet light gives trichloro–(2–chloro–1, 1, 2, 2–tetrafluoroethyl)silane in 75% yield, whereas at 150° in the absence of light only a 59% yield of product is obtained.[191]

Methylchlorosilanes are photochemically chlorinated in such a way that the chloromethyl group, once formed, is further chlorinated in preference to an unsubstituted methyl group.[271,502] For example, dichloromethyldimethylchlorosilane is converted to trichloromethyldimethylchlorosilane,[502] and trimethylchlorosilane is chlorinated to a mixture of dimethylchloromethylchlorosilane and dimethyldichloromethylchlorosilane.[271] Similarly, chlorine reacts with dimethyldichlorosilane to give methylchloromethyldichlorosilane plus methyldichloromethyldichlorosilane.[271] The chlorination of methyltrichlorosilane, dimethyldichlorosilane, and trimethylchlorosilane with elemental chlorine in the presence of azobisisobutyronitrile follows more or less the same pattern as that observed in photochemical chlorination of these compounds.[347]

The chlorination of saturated aliphatic silicon compounds with sulfuryl chloride is usually carried out at 70–100°. Sometimes higher temperatures are used. Thus, trimethylchlorosilane is chlorinated in boiling chlorobenzene in the presence of benzoyl peroxide to give chloromethyldimethylchlorosilane.[321] Methyltrichlorosilane is either not chlorinated with sulfuryl chloride in the presence of benzoyl peroxide[492] or only a low yield of chloromethyltrichlorosilane is obtained.[518] But with sulfuryl chloride in ultraviolet light, methyltrichlorosilane is chlorinated to give a mixture of mono-, di-, and trichloromethyltrichlorosilane.[535] Chlorination with sulfuryl chloride in the presence of azobisisobutyronitrile produces chloromethyltrichlorosilane in low yield.[235]

Chlorination of ethyltrichlorosilane with sulfuryl chloride in the presence of benzoyl peroxide yields a mixture of α– and β–monochloro derivatives in a ratio of 1:2.5.[492] Further chlorination of the α isomer results in a mixture of α, α and α, β products in a ratio of 1:1, whereas the β isomer is chlorinated to give β, β–dichloroethyltrichlorosilane in 72% yield.[337,495]

In comparison, the photochlorination of α–chloroethyltrichlorosilane with chlorine at 151° results in α, α and α, β isomers in a 1:0.6 ratio and chlorination of β–chloroethyltrichlorosilane at 174° in ultraviolet light results in β, β and α, β isomers.[337,394]

Diethyldichlorosilane is chlorinated with sulfuryl chloride in the presence of benzoyl peroxide to give a mixture of α– and β–chloroethylethyldichlorosilane.[495] Triethylchloro- or triethylfluorosilane under similar conditions is converted to a mixture of α– and β–chloro isomers.[494]

The chlorination of the following series of compounds, either photochemically with chlorine or with sulfuryl chloride in the presence of benzoyl peroxide, shows that a decrease in the number of halogens (X) and an increase in the number of ethyl groups results in an increase in the α–chloro products and a corresponding decrease in the β–chloro products.[340,398,492,495,502]

$$(C_2H_5)_4Si$$

$$(C_2H_5)_3SiX$$

$$(C_2H_5)_2SiX_2$$

$$(C_2H_5)SiX_3$$

X = Cl or F

Chlorination of n–propyltrichlorosilane gives a mixture of α–, β–, and γ–monochlorinated products in a ratio of 1:3.5 : 3.1.[66,493] Because of the proximity of the $SiCl_3$ group, the α position in n–propyltrichlorosilane is more difficult to chlorinate than the β or γ position.[66,493]

The photochemical chlorination of 1, 1–dimethylsilacyclopentane (V) with elemental chlorine or with sulfuryl chloride produces 1–chloromethyl–1–methylsilacyclopentane (VII) predominantly and corresponding α– and β–chloro derivatives in addition.[142] The corresponding chlorination of 1, 1–dimethylsilacyclohexane (VI) produces the corresponding products.[142] The use of free radical catalysts accelerates the reactions, but the chloromethyl isomer is still the major product. However, the distribution of α– and β–chloro isomers is different. Thus, chlorination of V without a catalyst results in a higher yield of α product (VIII), whereas in the presence of a catalyst the β product (IX) predominates. Similar results are observed with compound VI.

$$\text{VIII} \qquad\qquad \text{IX}$$

Substitution of benzylic or methyl hydrogens of tolyl groups in organosilicon compounds can be achieved by reaction with elemental chlorine or sulfuryl chloride in the presence of free radical catalysts. For example, benzyltrichlorosilane is chlorinated with sulfuryl chloride in the presence of benzoyl peroxide to give α–chlorobenzyltrichlorosilane in 90% yield.[492] A similar result is obtained with chlorine in the presence of azobisisobutyronitrile. Further chlorination leads to the substitution of both benzylic hydrogen atoms for chlorine atoms.[346]

$$C_6H_5CH_2SiCl_3 \xrightarrow[\text{AIBN}]{Cl_2} C_6H_5CHClSiCl_3 \xrightarrow[\text{AIBN}]{Cl_2} C_6H_5CCl_2SiCl_3$$

Bromination

Bromine adds readily to olefinic silicon compounds in the presence of light to give the corresponding dibromo products. For example, methylvinyldichlorosilane or ethylvinyldichlorosilane reacts with bromine in ultraviolet light to give α, β–dibromoethylmethyl- and α, β–dibromoethylethyldichlorosilane, respectively, in 90–94% yield.[339] In both cases no substitution occurs.

Bromination of saturated organosilicon compounds can be achieved photochemically with elemental bromine or with a mixture of bromine and chlorine. By the first method, tetramethylsilane, trimethylchlorosilane, or dimethyldichlorosilane is converted to the corresponding monobromomethyl derivative.[504,505] By the second method, tetramethylsilane is converted to bromomethyltrimethylsilane,[204] trimethylchlorosilane to bromomethyldimethylchlorosilane,[503] dimethyldichlorosilane to a mixture of mono- and dibromomethylmethyldichlorosilane,[503] hexamethyldisiloxane to bromomethylpentamethyldisiloxane,[503] and phenyltrichlorosilane to bromophenyltrichlorosilane.[503] When a bromine-chlorine mixture is used, hydrogen chloride but no hydrogen bromide is evolved.

Side-chain, benzylic, and related brominations can be achieved photochemically with elemental bromine[9] or, more conveniently, with NBS in the presence of peroxide or ultraviolet light. Depending on the ratio of substrate to the brominating agent, monobromo or polybromo derivatives are obtained[158]:

$$(C_6H_5)_3SiC_6H_4CH_3 \xrightarrow[UV]{NBS} (C_6H_5)_3SiC_6H_4CH_2Br \xrightarrow[UV]{NBS} (C_6H_5)_3SiC_6H_4CHBr_2$$

In some cases NBS bromination proceeds readily in the absence of a catalyst. For example, benzyltriphenylsilane is converted to α–bromobenzyltriphenylsilane in 50% yield.[204]

The bromination of side chains of arylsilanes may be accompanied by a scission of the carbon-silicon bond. Thus, silane (X) is brominated with NBS in the presence of benzoyl peroxide or ultraviolet light to product XI in 63% yield.[564]

$$(p\text{–}CH_3C_6H_4)_4Si \xrightarrow{NBS} (p\text{–}BrCH_2C_6H_4)_3SiBr$$

$$\text{X} \qquad\qquad\qquad \text{XI}$$

Table 55. Chlorination of Organic Germanium and Silicon Compounds

C_n	Silicon or germanium compound	Chlorinating agent	Initiator	Product	% Yield	°C b.p./mm (m.p.)	n_D (°C)	Ref.
C_1	CH_3GeCl_3	Cl_2	UV	Chloromethyltrichlorogermane + Dichloromethyltrichlorogermane + Cl_3GeCCl_3	18 / 43	152 / 168 / 130/200 (106)	1.5000 (20) / 1.5100 (20)	336, 409
C_2	$(CH_3)_2GeCl_2$	Cl_2	UV	$CH_3Ge(CH_2Cl)Cl_2$	51	155/750	1.4930 (20)	409
	$C_2H_5GeCl_3$	SO_2Cl_2	Bz_2O_2	$CH_2ClCH_2GeCl_3$ + $CH_3CHClGeCl_3$	38 / 4	188/746 / 167/746	1.5094 (20) / 1.4948 (20)	393
C_1	CH_3SiCl_3	SO_2Cl_2	UV	$ClCH_2SiCl_3$ + $Cl_2CHSiCl_3$ + Cl_3CSiCl_3		118 / 143 / 156 (116)	1.4530 (20) / 1.4715 (20)	535
	CH_3SiCl_3	SO_2Cl_2	AIBN	$ClCH_2SiCl_3$		120		235
	CH_3SiCl_3	Cl_2	UV	$ClCH_2SiCl_3$ + $Cl_2CHSiCl_3$ + CCl_3SiCl_3	46 / 17 / 95	117 / 142 / 156/760 (121)	1.4727 (20)	249 / 451, 518
	Bis(trichlorosilyl)methane	SO_2Cl_2	Bz_2O_2	Bis(trichlorosilyl)dichloromethane	41	226		397
C_2	$(CH_3)_2SiCl_2$	Cl_2	UV	$(CH_3)(CH_2Cl)SiCl_2$ + $(CH_3)(CHCl_2)SiCl_2$ + $(CH_3)(CCl_3)SiCl_2$	37 / 38 / 6.5	121 / 107/225 / 109/150 (99)		271
	$(CH_3)_2SiCl_2$	SO_2Cl_2	AIBN	$(CH_3)(CH_2Cl)SiCl_2$		121		235
	$(CH_3)_2SiCl_2$	SO_2Cl_2	Bz_2O_2	$(CH_3)(CH_2Cl)SiCl_2$ + $(CH_3)(Cl_2CH)SiCl_2$		121 / 149	1.3936 (20) / 1.4679 (20)	528
	Ethyltrichlorosilane	Cl_2	UV	$CH_3CHClSiCl_3$ + $ClCH_2CH_2SiCl_3$	17 / 48	137 / 152	1.4559 (20) / 1.4640 (20)	326

Table 55. (cont.)   Chlorination of Organic Germanium and Silicon Compounds

C_n	Silicon or germanium compound	Chlorinating agent	Initiator	Product	% Yield	°C b.p./mm (m.p.)	n_D (°C)	Ref.
	Ethyltrichlorosilane	SO_2Cl_2	Bz_2O_2	$CH_3CHClSiCl_3$ + $CH_2ClCH_2SiCl_3$	90	138 152		492
	Vinyltrichlorosilane	Cl_2	UV	α,β-Dichloroethyltrichlorosilane	64	64/13	1.4876 (20)	4
	α-Chloroethyltrichlorosilane	Cl_2	UV	α,α-Dichloroethyltrichlorosilane + α,β-Dichloroethyltrichlorosilane	89	152 181		337
	β-Chloroethyltrichlorosilane	Cl_2	UV	β,β-Dichloroethyltrichlorosilane + α,β-Dichloroethyltrichlorosilane	93			337
	α-Chloroethyltrichlorosilane	SO_2Cl_2	Bz_2O_2	α,α-Dichloroethyltrichlorosilane + α,β-Dichloroethyltrichlorosilane	31 32	152/734 (113) 99/58		495
	β-Chloroethyltrichlorosilane	SO_2Cl_2	Bz_2O_2	β,β-Dichloroethyltrichlorosilane	72	172/739		495
	α-Chlorovinyltrichlorosilane	Cl_2	UV	α,α,β-Trichloroethyltrichlorosilane	73	91/17 (56)		4
	Dichlorovinyltrichlorosilane	Cl_2	UV	1,1,2,2-Tetrachloroethyltrichloro-silane		105/17	1.5149 (27)	3
	Trichlorovinyltrichlorosilane	Cl_2	UV	Pentachloroethyltrichlorosilane	94	99/6		315
	1,2-Bis(trichlorosilyl)ethane	Cl_2	UV	1,2-Bis(trichlorosilyl)chloroethane	95	225/737	1.4915 (20)	337
	1,2-Bis(trichlorosilyl)ethane	SO_2Cl_2	Bz_2O_2	1,2-Bis(trichlorosilyl)chloroethane	40			394, 397
	Trichloro(1,1,2,2-tetrafluoro-ethylsilane)	Cl_2	UV	Trichloro(2-chloro-1,1,2,2-tetra-fluoroethylsilane)	75	102		191
C_3	$(CH_3)_2Si(CCl_3)Cl$	Cl_2	UV	$(CH_3)(CH_2Cl)Si(CCl_3)Cl$	62	(62)		451
	$(CH_3)(CH_2Cl)Si(CCl_3)Cl$	Cl_2	UV	$(CH_2Cl)_2Si(CCl_3)Cl$	29	(sublimes at room temp.)		451
	$(CH_2Cl)_2Si(CCl_3)Cl$	Cl_2	UV	$(CH_2Cl)(CHCl_2)(CCl_3)SiCl$	38	(73)		451
	$(CH_2Cl)(CHCl_2)(CCl_3)SiCl$	Cl_2	UV	$(CHCl_2)_2(CCl_3)SiCl$	42	(67)		451
	$(CHCl_2)_2(CCl_3)SiCl$	Cl_2	UV	$(CHCl_2)(CCl_3)_2SiCl$	75	(85)		451

Table 55. (cont.) Chlorination of Organic Germanium and Silicon Compounds

C_n	Silicon or germanium compound	Chlorinating agent	Initiator	Product	% Yield	°C b.p./mm (m.p.)	n_D (°C)	Ref.
	$(CH_3)(CH_2Cl)(CHCl_2)SiCl$	Cl_2	UV	$(CH_2Cl)_2(CHCl_2)SiCl$	33	215/760	1.5320 (20)	451
	$(CH_2Cl)(CHCl)_2SiCl$	Cl_2	UV	$(CHCl_2)_2(CCl_3)SiCl$	50	(67)		451
	Trifluorodichloropropenyltri-chlorosilane	Cl_2	UV	Trifluorotetrachloropropyltrichloro-silane	95	119/8.5		316
	Trimethylchlorosilane	Cl_2	UV	Dimethylchloromethylchlorosilane+ Dimethyldichloromethylchlorosilane+ $CH_3(CH_2Cl)_2SiCl$	62 23 8	115/762 149/760 173	1.4369 (20) 1.461 (20)	271, 451
	Trimethylchlorosilane	SO_2Cl_2	Bz_2O_2	$(CH_3)_2(CH_2Cl)SiCl$	52	115	1.4360 (20)	321, 424
	$(CH_3)_3SiCl$	SO_2Cl_2	AIBN	$(CH_3)_2Si(CH_2Cl)Cl$		114/750		235
	$(CH_3)(C_2H_5)SiCl_2$	SO_2Cl_2	Bz_2O_2	$CH_3CHClSi(CH_3)Cl_2$+ $ClCH_2CH_2Si(CH_3)Cl_2$		136/744 157/744	1.4499 (20) 1.4399 (20)	338
	n-Propyltrichlorosilane	SO_2Cl_2	Bz_2O_2	α–Chloro–n–propyltrichlorosilane+ β–Chloro–n–propyltrichlorosilane+ γ–Chloro–n–propyltrichlorosilane	90	157/739 162/729 179/732		66, 493
	Isopropyltrichlorosilane	SO_2Cl_2	Bz_2O_2	α–Chloroisopropyltrichlorosilane+ β–Chloroisopropyltrichlorosilane		151 (109) 164		491
	Dichloromethyldimethylchloro-silane	Cl_2	UV	Trichloromethyldimethylchlorosilane		161/739 (122)		451, 502
C_4	$(CH_3)_4Si$	Cl_2	UV	$(CH_3)_3SiCH_2Cl$	33	97/734	1.4180 (20)	438, 551
	Diethyldichlorosilane	SO_2Cl_2	Bz_2O_2	α–Chloroethylethyldichlorosilane+ β–Chloroethylethyldichlorosilane	15 25	76/43 92/42		495
	$(C_2H_5)_2SiCl_2$	Cl_2	UV	$(CH_3CHCl)(C_2H_5)SiCl_2$+ $(CH_2ClCH_2)(C_2H_5)SiCl_2$+ Dichlorodiethyldichlorosilane		163 182 212	1.4573 (20) 1.4650 (20) 1.4865 (20)	325

Table 55. (cont.)   Chlorination of Organic Germanium and Silicon Compounds

C_n	Silicon or germanium compound	Chlorinating agent	Initiator	Product	% Yield	°C b.p./mm (m.p.)	n_D (°C)	Ref.
	$(CH_3)_3SiCH_2Cl$	Cl_2	UV	$(CH_3)_3SiCHCl_2+$	35	132	1.4425 (25.7)	438
				$(CH_3)_2Si(CH_2Cl)_2$	46	159	1.4575 (25.7)	
	$(CH_3)_3SiCH_2Cl$	SO_2Cl_2	Bz_2O_2	$(CH_3)_3SiCHCl_2+$ $(CH_3)_2Si(CH_2Cl)_2$		132 159	1.4452 (20) 1.4595 (20)	235
	CH₂CH₂–SiCl₂ (ring)	Cl_2	Heat	ClCHCH₂–SiCl₂–CH₂CH₂	73	184/745	1.4949 (20)	338
	CH₂CH₂–SiCl₂ (ring)	SO_2Cl_2	Bz_2O_2	ClCHCH₂–SiCl₂–CH₂CH₂			1.4879 (20)	396
	$Cl_3SiCH=C(CH_3)_2$	Cl_2	UV	$Cl_3SiCH=C(CH_3)CH_2Cl$	27	180/750	1.4802 (20)	395
C_5	Trichlorovinyltrimethylsilane	Cl_2	UV	$CCl_3CCl_2Si(CCl_3)_3+$ $CCl_3CCl_2Si(CCl_3)_2CHCl_2$		(134) (128)		315
C_6	Triethylfluorosilane	SO_2Cl_2	Bz_2O_2	$CH_3CHClSiF(C_2H_5)_2+$ $ClCH_2CH_2SiF(C_2H_5)_2$	60	93/113 101/77		494
	Triethylchlorosilane	SO_2Cl_2	Bz_2O_2	$CH_3CHClSiCl(C_2H_5)_2+$ $ClCH_2CH_2SiCl(C_2H_5)_2$	60	114/100 132/100		494
	Hexamethyldisilane	SO_2Cl_2	Bz_2O_2	Chloromethylpentamethyldisilane	42	60/14	1.4578 (20)	273
	Phenyltrichlorosilane	SO_2Cl_2	UV	m– and p–Chlorophenyltrichlorosilane	14	220–245		535
C_7	Benzyltrichlorosilane	SO_2Cl_2	Bz_2O_2	$C_6H_5CHClSiCl_3$	90	243/735		492
	Benzyltrichlorosilane	Cl_2	AIBN	$C_6H_5CCl_2SiCl_3+$ $C_6H_5CHClSiCl_3$	90 87	148/15 141/15	1.5557 (20) 1.5466 (20)	346
	$p\text{-}CH_3C_6H_4SiCl_3$	Cl_2	AIBN	p–(Chloromethyl)phenyltrichlorosilane	85	143/5	1.5480 (20)	346

Table 55. (cont.) Chlorination of Organic Germanium and Silicon Compounds

C_n	Silicon or germanium compound	Chlorinating agent	Initiator	Product	% Yield	°C b.p./mm (m.p.)	n_D (°C)	Ref.
	p-$CH_3C_6H_4SiCl_3$	Cl_2	AIBN	p-(Dichloromethyl)phenyltrichlorosilane	83	154/15	1.5541 (20)	346
	p-$CH_3C_6H_4SiCl_3$	Cl_2	AIBN	p-(Trichloromethyl)phenyltrichlorosilane	90	162/14 (66)		346
C_8	$(C_2H_5)_4Si$	SO_2Cl_2	Bz_2O_2	$(C_2H_5)_3SiCHClCH_3$	50	195/750	1.4535 (20)	392, 408
	$(C_2H_5)_4Si$	CCl_4	UV	$(C_2H_5)_3SiCHClCH_3$	15	69/9	1.4490 (17)	419
	Octamethylcyclotetrasiloxane	Cl_2	UV	Heptamethylchloromethylcyclotetrasiloxane		127/50	1.4158 (20)	272
C_{10}	$(CH_3)_3SiCH_2C_6H_5$	SO_2Cl_2	Bz_2O_2	α-Chlorobenzyltrimethylsilane	52	100/6	1.5132 (25)	204
C_{14}	$(CH_3)_2Si(C_6H_4Cl$-$p)_2$	Cl_2	UV	$(CH_3)Si(CHCl_2)(C_6H_4Cl$-$p)_2$			1.6062 (20)	159
	$(CH_3)_2Si(C_6H_4Cl$-$p)_2$	SO_2Cl_2	Bz_2O_2	$(CH_3)Si(CHCl_2)(C_6H_4Cl$-$p)_2$			1.6068 (20)	159
C_{16}	Diphenylmethyltrimethylsilane	SO_2Cl_2	Bz_2O_2	Diphenyl-α-chloromethyltrimethylsilane	74	150/3	1.5816 (20)	204
C_{18}	$(C_6H_5)_3SiH$	C_6H_5Cl	Di-t-butyl peroxide	$(C_6H_5)_3SiCl$	20–62	160/0.5 (89)		101
C_{19}	$CH_3Si(C_6H_5)_3$	Cl_2	UV	$Cl_3CSi(C_6H_5)_3$	38	(194)		159
	$CH_3Si(C_6H_4Cl$-$p)_3$	Cl_2	UV	$Cl_3CSi(C_6H_4Cl$-$p)_3$		(161)		159

Table 56. Bromination of Organic Silicon Compounds

C_n	Silicon compound	Brominating agent	Initiator	Product	% Yield	°C b.p./mm (m.p.)	n_D (°C)	Ref.
C_2	Dimethyldichlorosilane	$Br_2 + Cl_2$	UV	Bromomethylmethyldichlorosilane +	34	140/740	1.4750 (25)	503–505
				Dibromomethylmethyldichlorosilane	25	88/25	1.5185 (25)	
	Vinyltrichlorosilane	Br_2	UV	α,β-Dibromoethyltrichlorosilane	91	91/11	1.5370 (20)	4
C_3	Trimethylchlorosilane	$Br_2 + Cl_2$	UV	Bromomethyldimethylchlorosilane	51	130/740	1.4630 (25)	503–505
	Methylvinyldichlorosilane	Br_2	UV	α,β-Dibromoethylmethyldichloro-silane	94	101/4	1.5335 (20)	339
C_4	$C_2H_5SiCl_2CH=CH_2$	Br_2	UV	$C_2H_5Cl_2SiCHBrCH_2Br$	90	142/7	1.5320 (20)	339
	$(CH_3)_4Si$	Br_2	Cl_2	$(CH_3)_3SiCH_2Br +$	36	116	1.4421 (25)	204, 505
				$(CH_3)_3SiCH_2Cl$	9	96		
	$(CH_3)_4Si$	Br_2	UV	$(CH_3)_3(CH_2Br)Si$		115/748	1.442 (25)	504, 505
	$(C_2H_5)_2SiCl_2$	Br_2	UV	$(C_2H_5)(CH_3CHBr)SiCl_2 +$		110/95	1.4772 (25)	504
				$(C_2H_5)(CH_2BrCH_2)SiCl_2$		128/95	1.4908 (25)	
C_6	Hexamethyldisiloxane	$Br_2 + Cl_2$	UV	Bromomethylpentamethyldisiloxane	25	83/49	1.4279 (25)	280, 503
	$C_6H_5SiCl_3$	$Br_2 + Cl_2$	UV	Bromophenyltrichlorosilane	40	127/23		503
C_7	$C_6H_5CH_2SiH_3$	Br_2	UV	$C_6H_5CHBrSiBr_3$	89	131/1	1.6227 (20)	9
	$C_6H_5CH_2SiH_3$	Br_2	UV or heat	$C_6H_5CBr_2SiBr_3$	52	155/1	1.6514 (20)	9
C_{10}	$(CH_3)_3SiCH_2C_6H_5$	NBS		α-Bromobenzyltrimethylsilane +	60	98/4	1.5389 (20)	204
				$(CH_3)_3SiCBr_2C_6H_5$	21	127/4	1.5778 (20)	
	p-Tolyltrimethylsilane	NBS (1 mole)	Bz_2O_2	p-Trimethylsilylbenzyl bromide	66	128/12	1.5400 (20)	478
	p-Tolyltrimethylsilane	NBS (2 moles)	Bz_2O_2	p-Trimethylsilylbenzal bromide	70	123/1.9 (48)		478
	o-Tolyltrimethylsilane	NBS (1 mole)	Bz_2O_2	o-Trimethylsilylbenzyl bromide	65	130/15	1.5483 (20)	478

Table 56. (cont.) Bromination of Organic Silicon Compounds

C_n	Silicon compound	Brominating agent	Initiator	Product	% Yield	°C b.p./mm (m.p.)	n_D (°C)	Ref.
	o–Tolyltrimethylsilane	NBS (2 moles)		o–Trimethylsilylbenzal bromide	46	111/2.4	1.5730 (20)	478
	m–Tolyltrimethylsilane	NBS (1 mole)	Bz_2O_2	m–Trimethylsilylbenzyl bromide	59	128/13	1.5379 (20)	478
	m–Tolyltrimethylsilane	NBS (2 moles)	Bz_2O_2	m–Trimethylsilylbenzyl bromide	52	105/2.4	1.5665 (20)	478
C_{13}	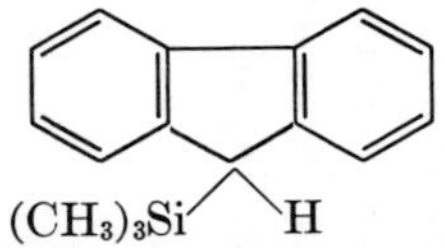 9-fluorenyl with $(CH_3)_3Si$ and H	NBS	UV	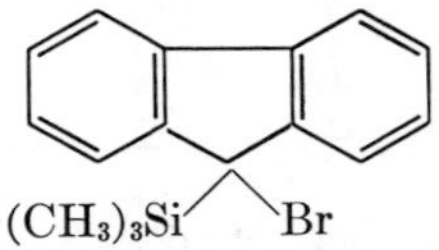 9-fluorenyl with $(CH_3)_3Si$ and Br		134		123
C_{16}	Diphenylmethyltrimethyl-silane	NBS	Bz_2O_2	Diphenyl–α–bromomethyltrimethyl-silane	89	167/4	1.5986 (20)	64, 204
C_{25}	p-$(C_6H_5)_3SiC_6H_4CH_3$	NBS (1 mole)	UV	p-$(C_6H_5)_3SiC_6H_4CH_2Br$	73	(175)		158
	p-$(C_6H_5)_3SiC_6H_4CH_3$	NBS (2 moles)	UV	p-$(C_6H_5)_3SiC_6H_4CHBr_2$	73	(184)		158
	Benzyltriphenylsilane	NBS		α–Bromobenzyltriphenylsilane	52	(144)		204
C_{28}	$(p$-$CH_3C_6H_4)_4Si$	NBS	Bz_2O_2 + UV	$(p$-$BrCH_2C_6H_4)_3SiBr$	63	(229 decomp.)		564

FLUORINATION OF ORGANIC COMPOUNDS

Organic fluorine compounds can be prepared by reaction with elemental fluorine, by reaction with fluorides such as those of silver, mercury, cobalt, antimony, lead, boron, and sodium, by reaction with anhydrous hydrogen fluoride, and by electrolysis. The fluorination of organic compounds with elemental fluorine no doubt proceeds by free radical processes. Thus, the reaction of fluorine with a saturated compound may proceed by the following sequence[45,310,311,312,406,537]:

$$F_2 \rightleftharpoons 2F\cdot$$

$$RH + F\cdot \rightarrow R\cdot + HF$$

$$R\cdot + F_2 \rightarrow RF + F\cdot \text{ etc.}$$

Similarly, the addition of fluorine to an olefin may proceed by the following scheme[312,332,333,406,537]:

$$F_2 \rightleftharpoons 2F\cdot$$

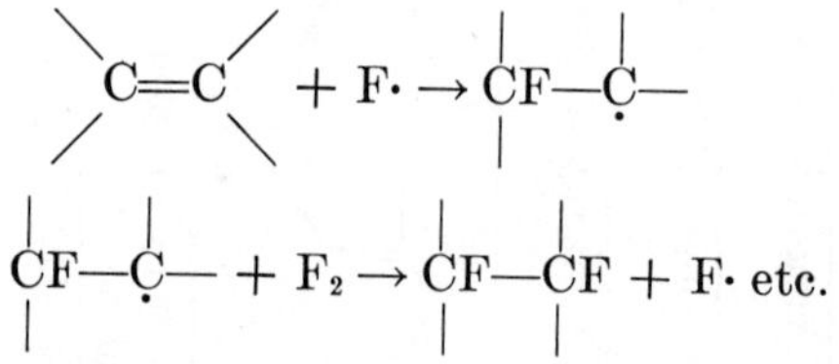

$$\diagdown C = C \diagup + F\cdot \rightarrow \overset{|}{C}F - \overset{|}{\underset{\cdot}{C}} -$$

$$\overset{|}{\underset{|}{C}}F - \overset{|}{\underset{\cdot}{C}} - + F_2 \rightarrow \overset{|}{\underset{|}{C}}F - \overset{|}{\underset{|}{C}}F + F\cdot \text{ etc.}$$

Fluorination of nitrogen-containing compounds has also been explained by a free radical mechanism; N radicals are postulated as intermediate species.[16,17,157,440] Fluorination of organic molecules with metal fluorides is more difficult to interpret. However, a free radical mechanism has been proposed for fluorination of nitrogen-containing compounds with metal fluorides;[565,566] the reaction of perfluoro–2–azopropene with fluorine is explained as follows[565]:

$$CF_3N{=}CF_2 + F\cdot \rightarrow (CF_3)_2N\cdot$$

$$(CF_3)_2N\cdot \rightarrow ((CF_3)_2N)_2$$

$$(CF_3)_2N\cdot + F\cdot \rightarrow (CF_3)_2NF$$

$$(CF_3)_2N\cdot + CF_3N{=}CF_2 \rightarrow (CF_3)_2NCF{=}NCF_3 + F\cdot$$

Since the formation of a carbon-fluorine bond is highly exothermic, the substitution of a hydrogen or a halogen for a fluorine atom is frequently accompanied by fragmentation of the molecule if no precautions are taken to ensure efficient mixing and cooling of the reactants. The fluorination of saturated and unsaturated polyhalogenated compounds is less destructive than fluorination of unsubstituted hydrocarbons. Well-defined fluoro derivatives are often obtained.[483,484] For example, difluorodichloro-ethylenes,[328,332] tetrachloroethylenes,[327,333] pentafluoro–2–chloropropene,[328] dichlorohexafluoro–2–butene,[332] hexafluorocyclobutene,[332] and tetrachloro- and pentachlorethane[327,333] can be fluorinated directly with little or no frag-mentation. Direct fluorination proceeds readily at room temperature or even at lower temperature and usually does not require a free radical catalyst. However, ultraviolet light, γ rays, or peroxide can facilitate the reaction.[490]

Over the last two decades much effort has been directed toward the de-sign and perfection of various fluorination reactors.[45,327,529] Since liquid-phase processes[312] have the advantages of economy and simplicity of design and operation over vapor-phase processes, it is desirable to have a good method for liquid-phase fluorinations.[519] Difficulties have been experienced in finding a suitable solvent, because fluorine attacks even such inert solvents as carbon tetrachloride and dichlorodifluoromethane. In addition, fluorine has little solubility in these solvents and the reaction tends to proceed at the liquid-gas interphase. Sometimes hydrogen fluoride can be used as a solvent, but it is very acidic and generally difficult to handle.[483,484] Pyridine is a suitable solvent below $-40°$, and 2–fluoropyridine is suitable at $-10°$ to room temperature.[483,484]

The development of the chemistry of fluorine-containing compounds has experienced tremendous growth since the beginning of World War II, and at present fluorine chemistry is very important industrially. For example, various Freons are used as refrigerating compounds and Teflon is a fre-quently used material because of its exceptional stability toward chemicals and heat. Because of this scientific and industrial interest in organic fluorine compounds, the various aspects of fluorine chemistry have been reviewed extensively.[33-37,45,295,308,312,314,400-406,439,483,484,507,508]

HALOGENATION OF KETONES

Halogenation of ketones under free radical conditions has been reported frequently, but there have been no systematic investigations of the subject. Ketones can be chlorinated photochemically with elemental chlorine or sulfuryl chloride in the presence of benzoyl peroxide or light. Bromination has been achieved photochemically with elemental bromine, N–bromosuc-cinimide (NBS),[234] or 1, 3–dibromo–5, 5–dimethylhydantoin[373] in the pres-ence of benzoyl peroxide or light and also in the absence of a catalyst. The noncatalyzed reactions generally follow the course of the catalyzed reactions, which are radical processes.

In bromination or chlorination of aliphatic ketones under free radical conditions the hydrogen atoms α to the keto group are substituted first. The rate of substitution probably follows the usual sequence: tertiary > secondary > primary. Thus, if a methyl group is on one side of the carbonyl group and a methylene group is on the other side, substitution of the hydrogen atom of the methylene group occurs more readily than substitution of the hydrogen atom of the methyl group. For example, butanone–2 is chlorinated photochemically or with sulfuryl chloride in the presence of benzoyl peroxide.[70,426] A 90% yield of a mixture of chloroketones consisting of 72% 3–chlorobutanone–2 and 28% 1–chlorobutanone–2 is obtained. A similar distribution of products is obtained in the gas-phase chlorination.[70]

Direct chlorination of acetone to the monochloro derivative does not require a catalyst.[148,239] Further chlorination to give the di-, tri-, or tetrachloro derivative is carried out under the influence of light. Chlorination beyond the tetrachloro step is difficult even in the presence of iodine, antimony pentachloride, or light.[153] If acetic acid is used as a catalyst, the pentachloro and hexachloro stages are reached easily.[153]

Under drastic conditions, 130–150° in ultraviolet light, chlorination of aliphatic ketones which contain more than two carbon atoms in addition to the carbonyl group can lead to the elimination of chlorinated hydrocarbons and the formation of a stable octachloromethylethyl ketone or a decachlorodiethyl ketone.[153] The following examples illustrate this point.

$$CH_3COCH_2CH_2CH_3 \rightarrow CCl_3COCCl_2CCl_3 + CCl_3COCCl_2CCl_2CCl_3$$

$$+ \; CCl_3COCH \begin{cases} CCl_3 \\ CCl_3 \end{cases}$$

$$CH_3COCH \begin{cases} CH_3 \\ CH_3 \end{cases} \xrightarrow[\text{UV}]{Cl_2} CCl_3COCH \begin{cases} CCl_3 \\ CCl_3 \end{cases} + CCl_3COCCl_2CCl_3$$

$$\begin{cases} CH_3 \\ CH_3 \end{cases} CHCOCH \begin{cases} CH_3 \\ CH_3 \end{cases} \xrightarrow[\text{UV}]{Cl_2} CCl_3CCl_2COCCl_2CCl_3$$

$$\underset{\underset{\displaystyle CH_2CH_3}{\diagdown}}{\overset{\overset{\displaystyle CH_3}{\diagup}}{CH_3COCH}} \xrightarrow[\text{UV}]{Cl_2} CCl_3COCCl_2CCl_3 + \underset{\underset{\displaystyle CCl_2CCl_3}{\diagdown}}{\overset{\overset{\displaystyle CCl_3}{\diagup}}{CCl_3COCCl}}$$

$$+ \; CCl_3COCCl_2CCl_2CCl_3$$

$$\underset{\underset{\displaystyle CH_3}{\diagdown}}{\overset{\overset{\displaystyle CH_3}{\diagup}}{CH_3COCH_2CH}} \xrightarrow[\text{UV}]{Cl_2} \underset{\underset{\displaystyle CCl_3}{\diagdown}}{\overset{\overset{\displaystyle CCl_3}{\diagup}}{CCl_3COCCl_2CCl}} \quad + \; CCl_3COCCl_2CCl_2CCl_3$$

$$+ \; CCl_3COCCl_2CCl_3$$

Acetone and methylethyl ketone condense partially to linear γ–diketones when chlorinated in acetic acid in ultraviolet light at 100°.[153] Thus, this reaction with chloroacetone produces decachlorohexadione–2, 5.

$$CH_3COCH_2Cl \xrightarrow[CH_3CO_2H]{Cl_2,\ UV} CCl_3COCCl_2CCl_2COCCl_3$$

Similarly, chlorination of α–chloroethylmethyl ketone produces tetra-decachlorooctadione–3, 6 as one of the products.

$$CH_3COCHClCH_3 \xrightarrow[CH_3CO_2H]{Cl_2,\ UV} CCl_3COCCl_2CCl_3$$

$$+ \; CCl_3CCl_2COCCl_2CCl_2COCCl_2CCl_3$$

The photolysis of perhalogenoacetones has been studied by Haszeldine and Nyman.[192] Acetones containing a predominance of fluorine atoms are photolyzed with carbon-carbon fission as the primary step, whereas those containing a predominance of chlorine atoms are photolyzed with carbon-chlorine fission. Thus, when 1, 3–dichlorotetrafluoroacetone is irradiated with ultraviolet light in a silica vessel, the major product is 1, 2–dichlorotetrafluoroethane, in 71% yield, and the other products are dichlorodifluoromethane and 1, 3–dichlorohexafluoropropane. The same starting material irradiated in the presence of chlorine, bromine, or iodine results in dichlorodifluoromethane, in 96% yield, bromochlorodifluoromethane, in 93% yield, and chlorodifluoroiodomethane, in 57% yield, respectively. Irradiation of 1, 1, 3–trichlorotrifluoroacetone with ultraviolet light results in 1, 1, 2–trichlorotrifluoroethane, in 21% yield, and 1, 1, 2, 2–tetrachlorodifluoroethane, in 10% yield. Photolysis of hexachloroacetone results in hexachloroethane, in 30% yield, plus trichloroacetyl chloride, in 10% yield.

The bromination or chlorination of cyclic ketones under free radical conditions seems to follow the pattern established for the aliphatic ketones; namely, a hydrogen α to the carbonyl group is substituted first. The second halogen atom enters the other α position.

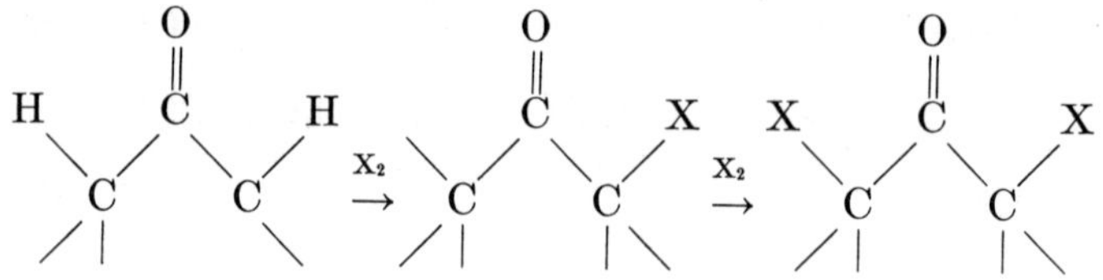

$$X = Br, Cl$$

Thus, photochlorination of cyclopentanone or cyclohexanone in the presence of iodine produces α-monochloroketones.[230] Bromination of cyclohexanone with 1, 3-dibromo-5, 5-dimethyl hydantoin produces 2-bromocyclohexanone in 66% yield.[373]

2-Methylcyclohexanone is brominated with NBS to give brominated methylcyclohexanone in 20% yield.[437] This product is probably a mixture of two products (I and II).

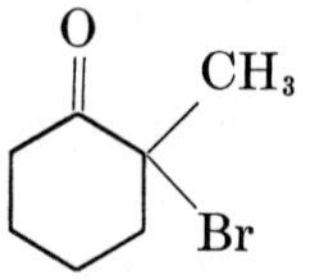

I 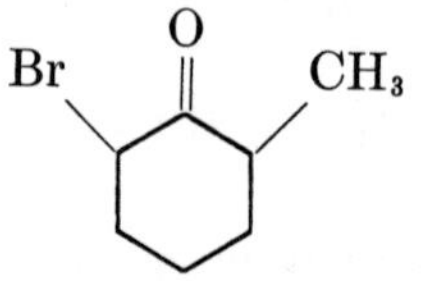   II

Cyclopentene-3, 5-dione (III) is brominated with NBS in ultraviolet light to give a mixture of 4, 4-dibromocyclopentene-3, 5-dione (IV) and 1, 4, 4-tribromocyclopentene-3, 5-dione (V).[111]

III   IV   V

Bromination of 2, 4-diphenyl-1, 3-dioxocyclopentene-4 (VI) with NBS in the absence of a catalyst results in the monobromo derivative (VII) in 70% yield.[449]

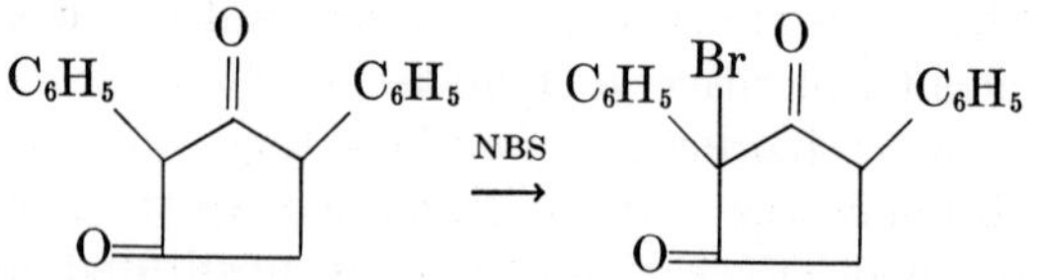

VI   VII

Photochlorination of a methanolic solution of cycloheptanone in the presence of iodine produces the monochloro derivative in 80% yield.[229] In the absence of iodine, 2, 7–dichlorocycloheptanone is obtained in 90% yield. Photobromination of cyclooctanone gives, depending on the amount of bromine used, 2–bromo-, 2, 8–dibromo-, or 2, 2, 8–tribromocyclooctanone.[231] Similarly, chlorination of cyclooctanone with sulfuryl chloride in ultraviolet light results in 2, 8–dichlorocyclooctanone, which can be photobrominated to 2, 8–dichloro–2–bromocyclooctanone.[231]

Bromination with NBS of perhydrostilbestrol (VIII)[531] seems to proceed according to the general scheme. However, substitution of the tertiary hydrogen atoms cannot be ruled out. The first bromine atom is introduced readily; the second and third bromine atoms are introduced more slowly. The second bromine atom preferentially enters the unbrominated nucleus. The reaction is nearly quantitative.

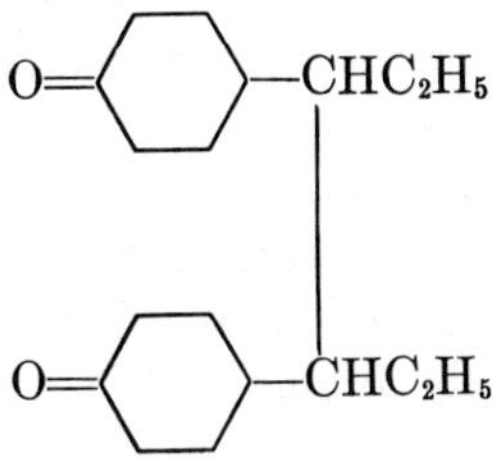

VIII

Bromo products are not isolated. Dehydrobromination yields three main products (IX, X, XI) plus some highly colored by-products.

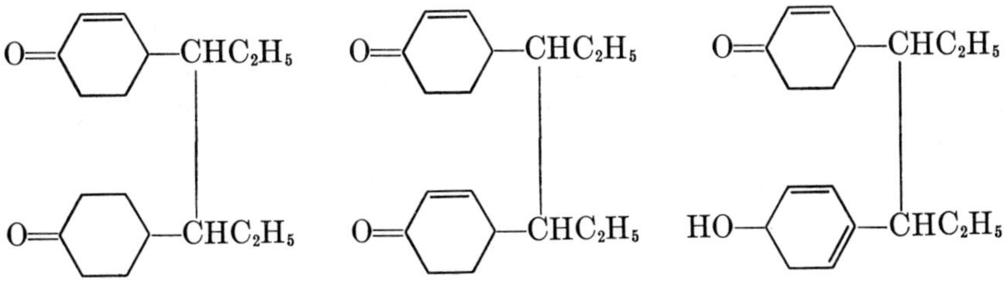

IX   X   XI

If a molecule contains both keto and ether functions, generally the halogens preferentially enter the position α to the keto group and no substitution α to the ether function occurs. Thus, tetrahydro–2–pyrone (XII) is brominated with NBS in light to give the dibromo derivative (XIII) in 50% yield.[497]

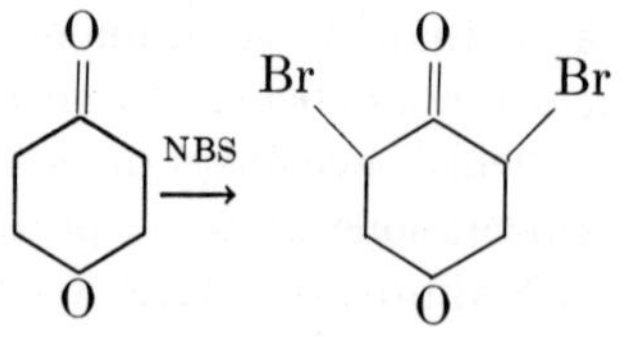

XII   XIII

NBS bromination of p–methoxyacetophenone[141] and photochemical bromination of 3, 4–dimethoxyacetophenone[526] result in the corresponding α–bromoketones.

$$p\text{–}CH_3OC_6H_4COCH_3 \xrightarrow{\text{NBS}} p\text{–}CH_3OC_6H_4COCH_2Br$$

$$3, 4\text{–}CH_3OC_6H_3COCH_3 \xrightarrow{\text{NBS}} 3, 4\text{–}CH_3OC_6H_3COCH_2Br$$

Photobromination of propioveratrone–α–propioguaiacone ether,[269] hesperedin triacetate,[568] hesperidin octaacetate,[568] and isosakuvanetin diacetate[568]—all compounds containing ether and keto groups—results in the respective bromo derivatives with the bromine atom located α to the keto group.

Molecules of the general structure XIV, containing a benzylic ether linkage, do not undergo cleavage on bromination with NBS in the presence of benzoyl peroxide, and the bromine atom enters the position α to the carbonyl group.[448]

$$3, 4\text{–}(C_6H_5CH_2O)C_6H_3\underset{\underset{O}{\|}}{C}CHRR'$$

XIV

R = alkyl

R' = H, CH$_3$

Similarly, no rupture of the carbon-sulfur bond occurs on bromination with NBS of compounds of the structure XV, containing thioether and keto functions. Substitution of hydrogen atoms for bromine atoms occurs α to the carbonyl (thioether) function.[164]

$$R\underset{\underset{O}{\|}}{C}CH_2SR'$$

XV

R = BrC$_6$H$_4$

R' = C$_6$H$_5$, p–FC$_6$H$_4$, p–ClC$_6$H$_4$, p–CH$_3$C$_6$H$_4$, p–NO$_2$C$_6$H$_4$, p–CH$_3$OC$_6$H$_4$, n–C$_{12}$H$_{25}$

In bromination of keto esters the bromine atom enters the position α to the keto group. If the keto group is flanked by a secondary and a tertiary carbon-hydrogen bond, the tertiary hydrogen atom is substituted in preference to the secondary. Thus, methyl δ, δ–dimethyllevulinate is brominated with NBS or bromine to give the δ–bromo derivative.[469] Photobromination of 2–butyryl–1–naphthol does not affect the hydroxy group.[7] If one mole of bromine is used, the 4–bromo derivative is obtained. With two moles of bromine, the α, 4–dibromo derivative is isolated. Bromination of 2, 4–dihydroxy–3,6–dimethoxyacetophenone and 2–acetoxy–3,4,6–trimethoxyacetophenone has been investigated.[118,151]

An extensive literature exists on photobromination and bromination with NBS of natural products, steroids, and related compounds containing a keto group. The general pattern of bromination of simple molecules appears to be applicable to these complex molecules.[116] In many cases the bromo products are not isolated but are further dehydrobrominated to give unsaturated ketones. NBS bromination of the flavanone series,[52,53,292] of enol acetates of 20–keto steroids,[117] and of cyclic 1, 3–diketone monoenolates[11,12] has been thoroughly investigated.

The action of NBS on a number of α, β–unsaturated ketones of the general structure XVI has also been investigated.[498]

$$RR'C\!\!=\!\!CR''CR'''$$
$$\overset{\|}{O}$$

XVI

R = C_6H_5

R' = H, C_6H_5

R'' = H, Br, C_6H_5

R''' = CH_3, C_6H_5, $CH_2C_6H_5$

The reaction of benzal acetone (R' = H, R'' = H, R''' = CH_3) with NBS in the presence of benzoyl peroxide in carbon tetrachloride does not produce bromomethylstyryl ketone; instead benzal acetone dibromide is obtained.[498] Although the experimental conditions favor a free radical reaction, the product is probably formed by a nonradical mechanism. Similarly, benzalacetophenone (R' = H, R'' = H, R''' = C_6H_5) is brominated to give benzalacetophenone dibromide.[498] In the presence of inhibitors and the absence of benzoyl peroxide, a similar result is obtained.[25]

However, β–phenylbenzalacetophenone (R' = C_6H_5, R'' = H, R''' = C_6H_5) reacts with NBS even in the absence of benzoyl peroxide to give α–bromophenylbenzalacetophenone.[498] This reaction most likely proceeds by a free radical mechanism. An entirely different result is obtained with α–phenylbenzalacetophenone (R' = H, R'' = C_6H_5, R''' = C_6H_5).[498] No bromination occurs at all. Instead, the compound is converted to its geometrical isomer, isobenzaldesoxybenzoin. Interestingly, this isomerization requires the presence of both NBS and benzoyl peroxide. α, β–Diphenylbenzalacetophenone (R', R'', R''' = C_6H_5) or α–bromobenzalacetophenone (R' = H, R'' = Br, R''' = C_6H_5) does not react with NBS in the presence of benzoyl peroxide.[498] As expected, benzylstyryl ketone (R' and R'' = H, R''' = $CH_2C_6H_5$) reacts smoothly with NBS in the presence of benzoyl peroxide to give 1, 4–diphenyl–1–bromo–3–butene–2–one (R' and R'' = H, R''' = $CHBrC_6H_5$) in high yield.[499]

Table 57. Halogenation of Ketones

C_n	Ketone	Halogenating agent	Initiator	Product	% Yield	°C b.p./mm (m.p.)	n_D (°C)	Ref.
C_3	CH_3COCH_3	Dibromo-dimethyl-hydantoin	B_2O_2 or UV	CH_3COCH_2Br	51	41/13		373
C_4	$CH_3COCH_2CH_3$	Br_2	UV	$CH_3COCHBrCH_3 +$ $CH_2BrCOCH_2CH_3$		133 145		426
	$CH_2COCH_2CH_2$	Dibromo-dimethyl-hydantoin		$CH_3COCHBrCH_3$	58	89/140		373
	$CH_3COCH_2CH_3$	SO_2Cl_2	B_2O_2	1-Chlorobutanone+ 2-Chlorobutanone	{90	55/30 115/775		70
	$CH_3COCHClCH_3$	Cl_2	UV	$CCl_3COC_2Cl_5$	90	91/0.03 (22)		153
	$(C_2H_5)_2CO$	Cl_2	UV	$(C_2Cl_5)_2CO$	100	127/0.02 (100)		153
C_5	Methyl-n-propyl ketone	Br_2	UV	Methyl-1-bromo-n-propyl ketone+ Bromomethyl n-propyl ketone		78/50 92/50	1.4563 (22) 1.4620 (23)	88
	Methyl-n-propyl ketone	Cl_2	UV	$CCl_3COC_3Cl_7 +$ $CCl_3COC_2Cl_5$	40 30	122/0.03 (28) 90/0.03 (22)		153
	Methylisopropyl ketone	Br_2	UV	Methyl-1-bromoisopropyl ketone		83/150	1.4590 (16)	88
	$CH_3COCH(CH_3)_2$	Dibromo-dimethyl-hydantoin		$CH_2COCBr(CH_3)_2$	58	49/22		373
	Cyclopentanone	Cl_2	I_2 + UV	2-Chlorocyclopentanone	56	79/12		230

Table 57. (cont.)   Halogenation of Ketones

C_n	Ketone	Halogenating agent	Initiator	Product	% Yield	°C b.p./mm (m.p.) n_D(°C)	Ref.
	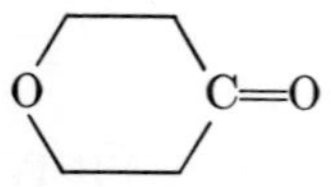	NBS	UV	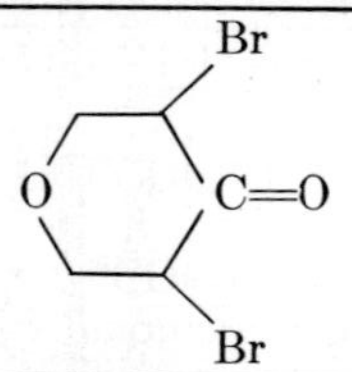	50	(156)	497
	Cyclopentene-3,5-dione	NBS	UV	4,4-Dibromocyclopentene-3,5-dione+	18	(81)	111
		(2 moles)		1,4,4-tribromocyclopentene-3,5-dione	58	(60)	
C_6	$CH_3COC(CH_3)_3$	Cl_2	UV	$CCl_3COC(CCl_3)_3$	70	143/0.05	153
	Cyclohexanone	Dibromodimethyl hydantoin		2-Bromocyclohexanone	66	96/15	373
	Cyclohexanone	Cl_2	I_2+UV	2-Chlorocyclohexanone	70	78/11	230
C_7	Cycloheptanone	Cl_2	I_2+UV	Monochlorocycloheptanone	80	94/12	229
	Cycloheptanone	Cl_2	UV	2,7-Dichlorocycloheptanone	90	120–130/12	229
C_8	$C_6H_5COCH_3$	Br_2	UV	$C_6H_5COCH_2Br$	80	134/15 (50)	526
	$C_6H_5COCH_3$	Dibromodimethyl hydantoin	Bz_2O_2 or UV	$C_6H_5COCH_2Br$	59	(47)	373
	Cyclooctanone	SO_2Cl_2	UV	2,8-Dichlorocyclooctanone		85/0.2 (47)	231
	Cyclooctanone	Br_2 (1 mole)	UV	2-Bromocyclooctanone	80	116/12	231

Table 57. (cont.) Halogenation of Ketones

C_n	Ketone	Halogenating agent	Initiator	Product	% Yield	°C b.p./mm (m.p.)	n_D (°C)	Ref.
	Cyclooctanone	Br_2 (2 moles)	UV	2,8–Dibromocyclooctanone	64	(82)		231
	Cyclooctanone	Br_2 (3 moles)	UV	2,2,8–Tribromocyclooctanone	79	(112)		231
	2,8–Dichlorocyclooctanone	Br_2	UV	2,8–Dichloro–2–bromocyclo-octanone	69	(93)		231
C_9	$C_6H_5COC_2H_5$	Br_2	UV	$C_6H_5COCHBrCH_3$		113/16		526
	$p–CH_3OC_6H_4COCH_3$	NBS	Bz_2O_2	$p–CH_3OC_6H_4COCH_2Br$		(70)		141
C_{10}	$3,4–(CH_3O)_2C_6H_3COCH_3$	Br_2	UV	$3,4–(CH_3O)_2C_6H_3COCH_2Br$		(81)		526
C_{14}	$C_6H_5COCH_2C_6H_5$	Dibromo-dimethyl-hydantoin	Bz_2O_2 or UV	$C_6H_5COCHBrC_6H_5$	83	(54)		373
	2–Butyryl–1–naphthol	Br_2	UV	4–Bromo–2–butyryl–1–naphthol		(56)		7
	4–Bromo–2–butyryl–1–naphthol	Br_2	UV	4–Bromo–2–α–bromobutyryl–1–naphthol		(123)		7
	$p–BrC_6H_4COCH_2SC_6H_5$	NBS		$p–BrC_6H_4COCHBrSC_6H_5$	76	(62)		164
	$p–BrC_6H_4COCH_2SC_6H_4–p–F$	NBS		$p–BrC_6H_4COCHBrSC_6H_4–p–F$	94	(99)		164
	$p–BrC_6H_4COCH_2SC_6H_4–p–Cl$	NBS		$p–BrC_6H_4COCHBrSC_6H_4–p–Cl$	83	(93)		164
	$p–BrC_6H_4COCH_2SC_6H_4–p–NO_2$	NBS		$p–BrC_6H_4COCHBrSC_6H_4–p–NO_2$	91	(119)		164
C_{15}	$p–BrC_6H_4COCH_2SC_6H_4–p–CH_3$	NBS		$p–BrC_6H_4COCHBrSC_6H_4–p–CH_3$	85	(93)		164
	$p–BrC_6H_4COCH_2SC_6H_4–p–OCH_3$	NBS		$p–BrC_6H_4COCHBrSC_6H_4–p–OCH_3$	83	(79)		164
C_{16}	$C_6H_5CH=CHC(O)CH_2C_6H_5$	NBS	Bz_2O_2	$C_6H_5CH=CHC(O)CHBrC_6H_5$	89	(81)		499
C_{17}	2,4–Diphenyl–1,3–dioxocyclopentene–4	NBS		2,4–Diphenyl–1,3–dioxo–2–bromo-cyclopentene–4	70	(85)		449

Table 57. (cont.)   Halogenation of Ketones

C_n	Ketone	Halogenating agent	Initiator	Product	% Yield	°C b.p./mm (m.p.)	n_D (°C)	Ref.
C_{20}	$p\text{-}BrC_6H_4COCH_2S\text{-}n\text{-}C_{12}H_{25}$	NBS		$p\text{-}BrC_6H_4COCHBrS\text{-}n\text{-}C_{12}H_{25}$	75	(43)		164
C_{21}	$3,4\text{-}(CH_3O)_2C_6H_3\text{-}$ 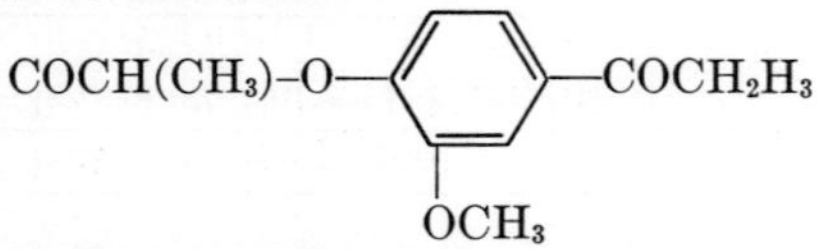 $COCH(CH_3)\text{-}O\text{-}C_6H_3(OCH_3)\text{-}COCH_2H_3$	Br_2	UV	$3,4\text{-}(CH_3O)_2C_6H_3COCH\text{-}$ 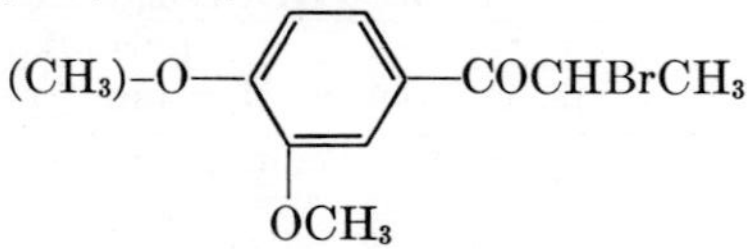 $(CH_3)\text{-}O\text{-}C_6H_3(OCH_3)\text{-}COCHBrCH_3$	70	(137)		269
C_{24}	$3,4\text{-}(C_6H_5CH_2O)_2C_6H_3COCH(CH_3)_2$	NBS	Bz_2O_2	$3,4\text{-}(C_6H_5CH_2O)_2C_6H_3COCHBr(CH_3)_2$		(76)		448
C_{24}	$3,4\text{-}(C_6H_5CH_2O)_2C_6H_3COCH_2C_2H_5$	NBS	Bz_2O_2	$3,4\text{-}(C_6H_5CH_2O)_2C_6H_3COCHBr\text{-}C_2H_5$		(101)		448
C_{25}	$3,4\text{-}(C_6H_5CH_2O)_2C_6H_3COCH_2CH(CH_3)_3$	NBS	Bz_2O_2	$3,4\text{-}(C_6H_5CH_2O)_2C_6H_3COCHBrCH\text{-}(CH_3)_2$		(113)		448
C_{26}	$3,4\text{-}(C_6H_5CH_2O)_2C_6H_3COCH_2C_4H_9$	NBS	Bz_2O_2	$3,4\text{-}(C_6H_5CH_2O)_2C_6H_3COCHBrC_4H_9$		(98)		448
C_{28}	$3,4\text{-}(C_6H_5CH_2O)_2C_6H_3COCH_2\text{-}n\text{-}C_6H_{13}$	NBS	Bz_2O_2	$3,4\text{-}(C_6H_5CH_2O)_2C_6H_3COCHBr\text{-}n\text{-}C_6H_{13}$		(90)		448
C_{30}	$3,4\text{-}(C_6H_5CH_2O)_2C_6H_3COCH_2\text{-}n\text{-}C_8H_{17}$	NBS	Bz_2O_2	$3,4\text{-}(C_6H_5CH_2O)_2C_6H_3COCHBr\text{-}n\text{-}C_8H_{17}$		(90)		448

HALOGENATION OF ETHERS

Although the halogenation of ethers has been studied for over a century, only recently has the subject been investigated systematically. The chemistry of haloalkylethers has been reviewed,[22,24,428,515] but no publication dealing specifically with chlorination and bromination of ethers under free radical conditions is available.

Direct chlorination of ethers is usually effected by light, and the reaction occurs by a free radical process. In a few cases sulfuryl chloride in the presence of benzoyl peroxide is employed.[23,54]

The chlorination of dimethyl ether has been studied by numerous investigators[85,112,137,146,290,361,423,428,459] and has been summarized by Rieche and Gross.[428] Photochemical chlorination of dimethyl ether produces a monochloro product first, which is then chlorinated to give α, $\alpha'-$ and α, α–dichloro products, the symmetrical product being formed preferentially. Further stepwise chlorination results in tri-, tetra-, penta-, and hexachloro products.

Photochlorination of diethyl ether has been investigated.[103,149,242,288,299] Oddo and Henry[227,364] summarized these earlier works. More recently, Hall and Ubertini[170] investigated the chlorination of diethyl ether. The chlorination of ethyl ether proceeds in such a way that the first chlorine atom enters the position α to the oxygen function. If no hydrogen chloride is eliminated from the mono product, the second chlorine atom enters position α' in preference to β. However, if hydrogen chloride is eliminated, chlorine adds to the double bond, to give the α, β product.[24]

$$RCH_2CH_2OCH_2CH_2R' \xrightarrow{Cl_2} RCH_2CHClOCH_2CH_2R' \qquad (1)$$

$$RCH_2CHClOCH_2CH_2R' \Big\langle \begin{array}{l} \xrightarrow{-HCl} RCH=CHOCH_2CH_2R' \qquad (2) \\[2em] \xrightarrow{Cl_2} RCH_2CHClOCHClCH_2R' + HCl \quad (3) \end{array}$$

$$RCH=CHOCH_2CH_2R' \xrightarrow{Cl_2} RCHClCHClOCH_2CH_2R' \qquad (4)$$

Chlorination at low temperature favors path 3, whereas chlorination at elevated temperature favors paths 2 and 4.

In contrast to dimethyl and diethyl ether, the chlorination of methylethyl ether has been little investigated. Photochlorination[54,290] of methylethyl ether or chlorination with sulfuryl chloride[54] produces chloromethylethyl ether, which is converted to chloromethyl–α–chloroethyl ether.

$$CH_3OC_2H_5 \xrightarrow{Cl\cdot} ClCH_2OC_2H_5 \rightarrow ClCH_2OCHClCH_3$$

Chlorinated ethers are sensitive. They undergo reactions which are frequently accompanied by a rupture of the carbon-oxygen bond. For example, photochlorination of β, β'–dichloroethyl ether in the presence of water at $-5°$ to $90°$ results in chloral hydrate in 55% yield.[90]

$$(ClCH_2CH_2)_2O \xrightarrow[\text{UV}]{H_2O,\ Cl_2} Cl_3CH(OH)_2 + HCl$$

In the absence of moisture, β, β'–dichloroethyl ether can be further chlorinated without rupture of the carbon-oxygen bond to give α, β, β'–trichlorodiethyl ether in 74% yield.[21, 370] Chlorination of β, β'–dichlorodiethyl ether with sulfuryl chloride under free radical conditions yields octachlorodiethyl ether, b.p. $105°/12$ mm.[407] Chlorination of diisopropyl ether in ultraviolet light produces a complex mixture of products.[169] The only isolatable product is 1, 3–dichloropropanone, b.p. $172°$, m.p. $42°$, n_D 1.4773 (25°).

Henne and Hinkamp[214,215] postulated that attack by a chlorine atom on a fluorinated aliphatic hydrocarbon is directed away from hydrogen atoms which are linked to a carbon atom which is α to a CF_2 or CF_3 group. Photochemical chlorination of fluorinated ethers also seems to follow this pattern.[378,383,384,417] For example, 2–chloro–1, 1, 2–trifluoroethyl methyl or ethyl ether is initially chlorinated at the nonfluorinated side of the oxygen.[378,382,417]

$$CH_3OCF_2CHClF \rightarrow ClCH_2OCF_2CHClF$$

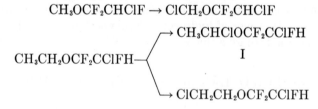

Further chlorination of ethers I and II gives, successively, III and IV, which are eventually fully chlorinated to product V.

$$ClCH_2CHClOCF_2CClFH$$

III

$$CCl_2HCHClOCF_2CClFH$$

IV

$$CCl_3CCl_2OCF_2CCl_2F$$

V

A similar directive effect is observed in the photochemical chlorination of 1, 1, 2, 2–tetrafluoroethylethyl ether.[383]

$$CH_3CH_2OCF_2CF_2H \left\{ \begin{array}{l} \rightarrow CH_3CHClOCF_2CF_2H \\ \quad\quad\quad VI \\ \\ \rightarrow CH_2ClCH_2OCF_2CF_2H \\ \quad\quad\quad VII \end{array} \right.$$

The ratio of VI to VII is 7:1. Further chlorination of VI gives products VIII and IX in a ratio of 1:1.

$$CH_3CHClOCF_2CF_2H \left\{ \begin{array}{l} \rightarrow CH_3CCl_2OCF_2CF_2H \\ \quad\quad\quad VIII \\ \\ \rightarrow CH_2ClCHClOCF_2CF_2H \\ \quad\quad\quad IX \end{array} \right.$$

Chlorination of VII gives one product.

$$CH_2ClCH_2OCF_2CF_2H \rightarrow CH_2ClCHClOCF_2CF_2H$$
$$\quad\quad VII \quad\quad\quad\quad\quad\quad\quad IX$$

Compound VIII is chlorinated to give product X,

$$CH_3CCl_2OCF_2CF_2H \rightarrow CH_2ClCCl_2OCF_2CF_2H$$
$$\quad\quad VIII \quad\quad\quad\quad\quad\quad X$$

and compound IX is chlorinated to give a mixture of X and XI in a ratio of 2:1.

$$CH_2ClCHClOCF_2CF_2H \rightarrow CH_2ClCCl_2OCF_2CF_2H$$
$$\quad IX \quad\quad\quad\quad\quad\quad X$$
$$+ CHCl_2CHClOCF_2CF_2H$$
$$\quad\quad\quad\quad\quad\quad\quad XI$$

An even more complex reaction is the photochlorination of 1, 1, 2–tri-fluoro–2–chloroethyl–*n*–propyl ether, which initially produces a mixture of three products (XII, XIII, XIV) in a weight ratio of 1.6:1.0:1.5.[384]

$$CH_3CH_2CH_2OCF_2CClFH \left\{ \begin{array}{ll} \rightarrow CH_3CH_2CHClOCF_2CClFH & XII \\ \\ \rightarrow CH_3CHClCH_2OCF_2CClFH & XIII \\ \\ \rightarrow CH_2ClCH_2CH_2OCF_2CClFH & XIV \end{array} \right.$$

Further photochlorination of XII leads to products XV and XVI in a ratio of 1.5:1.

XII⟨

→ CH₂ClCH₂CHClOCF₂CClFH

$$CH_2ClCH_2CHClOCF_2CClFH$$

XV

→ CH₃CHClCHClOCF₂CClFH

$$CH_3CHClCHClOCF_2CClFH$$

XVI

Photochlorination of XIII results in a 1:4 mixture of XVI and XVII; and photochlorination of XIV gives a mixture of XV, XVIII, and XIX, which are separable by gas chromatography.

$$CH_3CCl_2CH_2OCF_2CClFH$$

XVII

$$CHCl_2CH_2CH_2OCF_2CClFH$$

XVIII

$$CH_2ClCHClCH_2OCF_2CClFH$$

XIX

In all these chlorinations the attack by the chlorine atom is on the alkyl group rather than on the β–hydrogen in the fluorochloro moiety, and no α, α–dichloro product is obtained.

Photochlorination of saturated cyclic ethers seems to follow the general pattern observed with saturated aliphatic ethers. Thus, the formation of products in photochlorination of tetrahydrofuran depends on the temperature of chlorination and the amount of chlorine used.[166,167,425] If chlorination is carried out at $-30°$ to $-40°$ with 1 mole of chlorine, 2–chlorotetrahydrofuran is isolated in 38% yield. If 2 moles of chlorine is used, 2, 5–dichlorotetrahydrofuran in 45% yield plus some 2–chloro and 2, 3–dichloro products are obtained. Chlorination at room temperature results in 2, 3–dichlorotetrahydrofuran only.

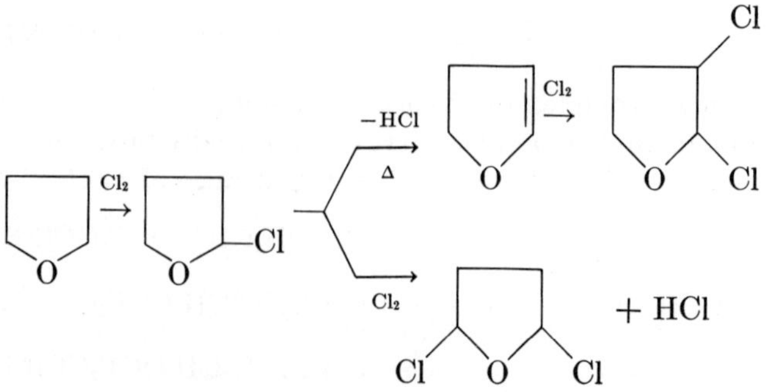

Tetrahydrofuran is chlorinated further with sulfuryl chloride under free radiation conditions to give a mixture of penta- and hexachlorotetrahydrofuran.[407]

Photochlorination of 3, 3, 4, 4–tetrafluorotetrahydrofuran produces the tetrachlorotetrafluoro derivative in high yield.[221]

$$\underset{\underset{O}{\diagdown\diagup}}{\overset{F_2C\text{——}CF_2}{\underset{H_2C\qquad CH_2}{|\qquad\quad|}}}\quad\underset{UV}{\overset{Cl_2}{\rightarrow}}\quad\underset{\underset{O}{\diagdown\diagup}}{\overset{F_2C\text{——}CF_2}{\underset{Cl_2C\qquad CCl_2}{|\qquad\quad|}}}$$

trans– or cis–2, 3–Dichloro–p–dioxane is photochlorinated at $-5°$ to give the corresponding 2, 3, 5–trichloro–p–dioxane derivative, m.p. 41° and 70°, respectively.[514] Photochemical chlorination of hexafluoropyran produces a fully halogenated derivative in 89% yield.[221]

$$\underset{\underset{O}{\diagdown\diagup}}{\overset{CF_2}{\underset{\underset{H_2C\qquad CH_2}{|\qquad\quad|}}{F_2C\qquad CF_2}}}\quad\underset{UV}{\overset{Cl_2}{\rightarrow}}\quad\underset{\underset{O}{\diagdown\diagup}}{\overset{CF_2}{\underset{\underset{Cl_2C\qquad CCl_2}{|\qquad\quad|}}{F_2C\qquad CF_2}}}$$

2, 3–Dichlorodioxane is chlorinated with sulfuryl chloride under free radical conditions to give a mixture of tetra-, penta-, and hexachlorodioxane.[407]

Bromination of dihydropyran, 3–bromodihydropyran, or 3–chlorodihydropyran with NBS in the presence of benzoyl peroxide yields a mixture of products.[385–387,418,479] The bromination is accompanied by a shift of the double bond.

Halogenation of pyrogallol–1, 3–dimethyl ether or its trimethyl ether with NBS, with NCS in the presence of a peroxide, or with t–butyl hypochlorite has been studied.[147] Chlorination was achieved, but only nuclear bromination occurred. No mechanism was proposed.

Bromination of dibenzyl ether, benzylalkyl ether, or benzylaryl ether with elemental bromine or with NBS in the presence of benzoyl peroxide or light is usually accompanied by cleavage of the carbon-oxygen bond and formation of the corresponding aldehyde or ketone.[234,301,368] However, photochlorination of methylbenzyl ether produces a mixture of α–chlorobenzylmethyl ether and chloromethylbenzyl ether.[54] Chloromethylbenzyl ether can be further chlorinated to give chloromethyl–α–chlorobenzyl ether in 51% yield. In contrast , p–nitrobenzylmethyl ether reacts with NBS in light to give dl–N–d–methoxy–p–nitrobenzyl succinimide (XX).[301]

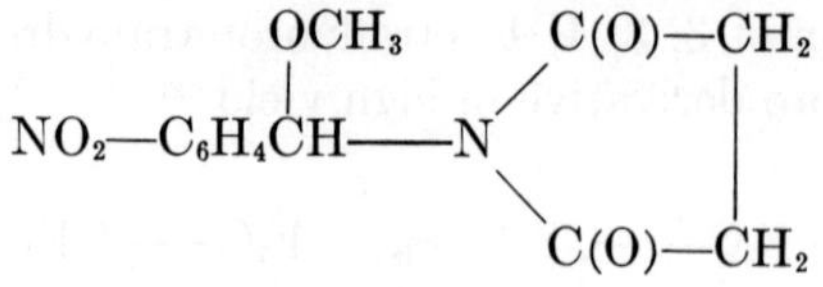

$$NO_2{-}C_6H_4\overset{\displaystyle OCH_3}{\underset{\displaystyle |}{CH}}{-\!\!-}N\overset{\displaystyle C(O){-}CH_2}{\underset{\displaystyle C(O){-}CH_2}{\Big\langle} \Big|}$$

XX

Table 58. Chlorination of Ethers

C_n	Ether	Chlorinating agent	Initiator	Product	% Yield	°C b.p./mm (m.p.)	n_D (°C)	Ref.
C_2	CH_3OCH_3	Cl_2	UV	$ClCH_2OCH_3$		59/759		85, 146
	CH_3OCH_3	Cl_2	UV	$ClCH_2OCH_2Cl +$ CH_3OCHCl_2	75	102 83		112, 361, 423, 428, 459
	CH_3OCH_3	Cl_2	UV	Hexachloroether		100		423, 428
	CH_2ClOCH_3	Cl_2	UV	$ClCH_2OCH_2Cl +$ CH_3OCHCl_2	62 19	102 84	1.4353 (20)	137, 165, 290, 428
	CH_2ClOCH_3	SO_2Cl_2	B_2O_2	$ClCH_2OCH_2Cl +$ CH_3OCHCl_2	51 35	95/755	1.4421 (20)	54
	$ClCH_2OCH_2Cl$	Cl_2	UV	Cl_2CHOCH_2Cl	51	129/750	1.4622 (20)	54, 112, 137
	Cl_2CHOCH_3	Cl_2	UV	Cl_2CHOCH_2Cl				137
	Cl_2CHOCH_2Cl	Cl_2	UV	$(Cl_2CH)_2O$		143	1.4728 (20)	112, 137
	$ClCH_2OCH_2Cl$	Cl_2	UV	CCl_3OCHCl_2		69/30	1.4825	415, 428
C_3	$ClCH_2OC_2H_5$	Cl_2	UV	$CH_2ClOCHClCH_3$		113		290
	$ClCH_2OC_2H_5$	SO_2Cl_2	B_2O_2	$CH_2ClOCHClCH_3$	53	107/752		54
	Vinylmethyl ether	Cl_2	UV	Tetrachloroethylmethyl ether		110		432
	$CH_3OCF_2CFH_2$	Cl_2	UV	$ClCH_2OCF_2CFH_2$		85/625	1.3514 (20)	378
	$CH_3OCF_2CF_2H$	Cl_2	UV	$ClCH_2OCF_2CF_2H$		72/628	1.3311 (20)	378
	$CH_3OCF_2CH_2Cl$	Cl_2	UV	$ClCH_2OCF_2CH_2Cl$		116/626	1.3974 (20)	378
	$CH_3OCF_2CHCl_2$	Cl_2	UV	$ClCH_2OCF_2CHCl_2$		137/627	1.4205 (20)	378
	CH_3OCF_2CClFH	Cl_2	UV	$ClCH_2OCF_2CFHCl$ CCl_3OCF_2CClFH		105/624 131/629	1.3768 (20) 1.4090 (20)	378 382
	CCl_3OCF_2CClFH	Cl_2	UV	$CCl_3OCF_2CCl_2F$		142/626	1.4187 (20)	382
	2-Chloro-1, 1, 2-trifluoro-ethylmethyl ether	Cl_2	UV	2-Chloro-1, 1, 2-trifluoroethyl-chloromethyl ether	56	112/745	1.3745 (25)	417

Table 58. (cont.) Chlorination of Ethers

C_n	Ether	Chlorinating agent	Initiator	Product	% Yield	°C b.p./mm (m.p.)	n_D (°C)	Ref.
C_4	Diethyl ether	Cl_2	UV	2–Chloroethylethyl ether	42	98/750		170
	α–Chloroethylethyl ether	Cl_2	UV	α, α′–Dichlorodiethyl ether	57	113	1.4183 (24)	170
	$(ClCH_2CH_2)_2O$	Cl_2	UV	α, β, β′–Trichlorodiethyl ether	74	85/13	1.4792 (25)	370
	$CH_3CH_2OCF_2CF_2H$	Cl_2	UV	$CH_3CHClOCF_2CF_2H$ + $CH_2ClCH_2OCF_2CF_2H$		82/615 60/100	1.364 (20) 1.424 (20)	383
	$CH_3CHClOCF_2CF_2H$	Cl_2	UV	$CH_2ClCHClOCF_2CF_2H$ + $CH_3CCl_2OCF_2CF_2H$		71/100 52/100	1.5228 (20) 1.4760 (20)	383
	$CH_3CCl_2OCF_2CF_2H$	Cl_2	UV	$CH_2ClCCl_2OCF_2CF_2H$	81	140/630		383
	$CH_2ClCH_2OCF_2CF_2H$	Cl_2	UV	$CH_2ClCHClOCF_2CF_2H$	93	71/100	1.5228 (20)	383
	$CH_2ClCHClOCF_2CF_2H$	Cl_2	UV	$CH_2ClCCl_2OCF_2CF_2H$ + $CHCl_2CHClOCF_2CF_2H$		160/630	1.4250 (20)	383
	$CH_3CH_2OCF_2CFClH$	Cl_2	UV	$CH_3CHClOCF_2CClIH$ + $CH_2ClCH_2OCF_2CFClH$		63/100 84/100	1.3755 (20) 1.3935 (20)	378, 382
	2–Chloro–1, 1, 2–trifluoro–ethylethyl ether	Cl_2	UV	1–Chloroethyl–2–chloro–1, 1, 2–trifluoroethylethyl ether + 2–Chloroethyl–2–chloro–1, 1, 2–trifluoroethylethyl ether	67	120/750 142/749	1.3742 (25) 1.3920 (25)	417
	$CH_3CHClOCF_2CClFH$	Cl_2	UV	$CH_2ClCHClOCF_2CClFH$		97/100	1.4080 (20)	382
	$CH_2ClCHClOCF_2CClFH$	Cl_2	UV	$CHCl_2CHClOCF_2CClFH$		85/23	1.4291 (20)	382, 417
	$CHCl_2CHClOCF_2CClFH$	Cl_2	UV	$CCl_3CCl_2OCF_2CFCl_2$		94/10	1.4575 (20)	382
	$CH_2ClCH_2OCF_2CClFH$	Cl_2	UV	$CH_2ClCHClOCF_2CFClH$		97/100	1.4080 (20)	382
	Tetrahydrofuran	Cl_2	UV	2–Chlorotetrahydrofuran	38	29/9	1.4607 (20)	166, 167
	Tetrahydrofuran	Cl_2	UV	2,5–Dichlorotetrahydrofuran	45	62/12	1.4858 (20)	166, 167

Table 58. (cont.)   Chlorination of Ethers

C_n	Ether	Chlorinating agent	Initiator	Product	% Yield	°C b.p./mm (m.p.)	n_D (°C)	Ref.
	Tetrahydrofuran	Cl_2	UV	2,3-Dichlorotetrahydrofuran		62/20		167, 425
	$\overline{CF_2CH_2OCH_2CF_2}$	Cl_2	UV	$CF_2CCl_2OCCl_2CF_2$	78	131/742	1.4120 (20)	221
	trans-2, 3-Dichloro-p-dioxane	Cl_2	UV	2, 3, 5-Trichlorodioxane	9	61/0.5 (41)	1.5173 (20)	514
	cis-2, 3-Dichloro-p-dioxane	Cl_2	UV	2, 3, 5-Trichlorodioxane	7	(70)		514
C_5	$CH_3CH_2CH_2OCF_2CClFH$	Cl_2	UV	$CH_3CH_2CHClOCF_2CClFH +$ $CH_3CHClCH_2OCF_2CClFH +$ $CH_2ClCH_2CH_2OCF_2CClFH$		38/8 69/34 65/14	1.3880 (25) 1.3875 (25) 1.3935 (25)	384
	$CH_3CH_2CHClOCF_2CClFH$	Cl_2	UV	$CH_2ClCH_2CHClOCF_2CClFH +$ $CH_3CHClCHClOCF_2CClFH$		74/10 63/10	1.4170 (25) 1.4082 (25)	384
C_5	$\overline{CF_2CF_2CH_2OCH_2CF_2}$	Cl_2	UV	$CF_2CF_2CCl_2OCCl_2CF_2$	89	159/737	1.4008 (20)	221
C_6	1, 2-Dichloro-1, 2-diethoxyethane	SO_2Cl_2	Bz_2O_2	1, 2-Dichloro-1, 2-bis-(α-chloroethoxy)ethane	32	108/12	1.4698 (25)	23
C_9	Chloromethylbenzyl ether	Cl_2	UV	Chloromethyl-α-chlorobenzyl ether	51	107/11		54

HALOGENATION OF HYDROXY COMPOUNDS

Although the chlorination of ethanol, phenols, and cresols has been studied extensively in industrial laboratories, the halogenation of hydroxy compounds under free radical conditions has received little attention. No review is available, probably because of the lack of systematic studies.

The chlorination of ethanol to chloral has been thoroughly studied by all major manufacturers of DDT since World War II. The photochlorination of ethanol proceeds by a complicated mechanism. Oxidation, substitution chlorination, and acetal formation occur concurrently, and many intermediate products can be isolated in the process. To utilize the ethanol effectively, water is often added to the reaction mixture to release the alcohol which is bound as acetal. The amount of water, the rate of chlorination, and other factors associated with production have been investigated extensively and are outside the scope of the present work. The final chlorination products are mainly chloral hydrate and alcoholate. This mixture is directly converted with chlorobenzene and oleum to DDT.

Concurrent oxidation and chlorination reactions often occur in photochemical and peroxide-catalyzed chlorination of other alcohols and phenols. For example, in ultraviolet light or in the presence of benzoyl peroxide, cyclohexanol is converted by chlorine into 2, 2, 6, 6–tetrachlorocyclohexanone.[467] 3, 5–Di–t–butyl–4–hydroxytoluene is photochlorinated to 1–methyl–1–chloro–3, 5–di–t–butylcyclohexadien–4–one, m.p. 103°.[390] However, the photochlorination of 1–chloro–2–naphthol yields 1, 4–dichloro–2–naphthol, m.p. 120°.[243]

Photochlorination of alcohols frequently results in formation of chlorinated ethers.[515] Thus, methanol is converted with chlorine to a dichloromethyl ether, b.p. 105° , n_D 1.435 (21°).[63] A mixture of ethanol and acetaldehyde is chlorinated at 20° to give a dichloroethyl ether, which in turn is chlorinated at 80° to give a trichlorodiethyl ether.[21] Photochlorination of propyl alcohol produces α–chloropropylpropyl ether, α, β–dichloropropylpropyl ether, b.p. 80°/15 mm, n_D 1.447 (16°), and 1, 2, 2–trichloropropylpropyl ether, b.p. 74°/10 mm, n_D 1.4575 (20°).[63,343,365,366] Photochlorination of isobutyl alcohol results in α, β–dichloroisobutylisobutyl ether, b.p. 83°/15 mm, n_D 1.437 (19°).[63]

Carbinols, in particular those containing a benzylic hydroxy group, are easily converted by NBS[512] and NCS[206] into the corresponding aldehyde or ketone. Since free radical catalysts are not used in most of these reactions, it is not clear whether the reactions are radical processes. A number of references on this matter are tabulated in Horner and Winkelmann's review.[234] The photochlorination of α, α, ω–trihydroperfluoroalkanol at 10–40°

results in ω–hydroperfluoroalkyl aldehyde.[59] Side products of this reaction are ω–chloro–ω'–hydroperfluoroalkane and α, α–dihydrofluoroalkyl ester, their yields depending on reaction conditions. Photochlorination of poly-fluorobutanol–1 or -pentanol–2 gives the corresponding aldehyde and ketone, respectively.[313] However, chlorination of polyfluorinated hexanol–3 or 2–methylpentanol–2 produces the chlorinated derivative without re-action of the hydroxy groups.[313]

If an unsaturated carbinol is photobrominated, the hydroxy group is usually preserved and the bromine adds to the unsaturated bond.[38,39,113,352] Thus, photobromination of proparyl alcohol produces 2, 3–dibromo–2–propen–1–ol.[352] Similarly, in the bromination of 2–methyl butyne–2–ol, 3–methyl pentyne–3–ol, or ethynylcyclohexanol, bromine is added at the triple bond.[113] The data are included in Table 50 on bromination of un-saturated compounds.

The photochlorination or chlorination of ethylene chlorohydrin (I) in the presence of acetylcyclohexane sulfonyl peroxide results in a complex mix-ture of products (II, III, IV, V).[501]

$$\underset{\overset{|}{OH}}{CH_2CH_2Cl} \overset{Cl_2}{\rightarrow} CH_2ClCHO + HCl$$

I

$$CH_2ClCHO + 2CH_2(OH)CH_2Cl \rightarrow CH_2ClCH(OCH_2CH_2Cl)_2$$

II

$$CH_2ClCHO \overset{Cl_2}{\rightarrow} CHCl_2CHO + HCl$$

III

$$CHCl_2CHO \overset{Cl_2}{\rightarrow} CHCl_2C\overset{\overset{\displaystyle Cl}{\diagup}}{\underset{\diagdown}{}}_O + HCl$$

IV

$$I + III \rightarrow CHCl_2C\overset{\displaystyle O}{\diagup}\!\!-\!\!O\!-\!CH_2CH_2Cl + HCl$$

V

Ethylene glycol reacts with chlorine in ultraviolet light to give, among other products, β–chloroethyldichloroacetate in 27% yield plus compound VI in 11% yield.[500]

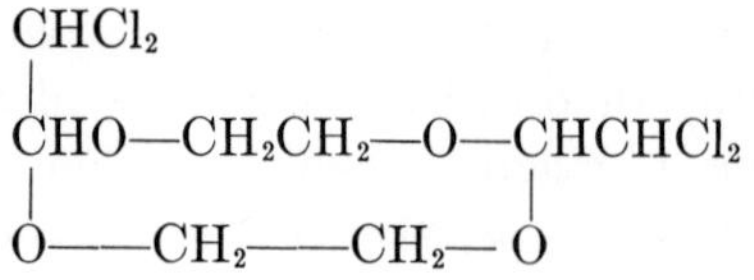

$$CHCl_2$$
$$CHO{-}CH_2CH_2{-}O{-}CHCHCl_2$$
$$O{-}{-}CH_2{-}{-}CH_2{-}O$$

VI

Photochlorination of 1, 2–propylene glycol at 50–110° or chlorination catalyzed by peroxide or azobisisobutyronitrile yields a mixture of dichloropyruvic acid; 1, 1, 3–dichloroacetone, b.p. 60°/2 mm, n_D 1.4900 (20°); and compound VII , b.p. 116°/10 mm, n_D 1.4848 (20°).[421]

$$ClCH_2CHCH_3O_2CCOCHCl_2$$

VII

A 50% aqueous solution of 1, 2–propylene glycol is photochlorinated to give dichloropyruvic acid in 40% yield.[421]

Diols containing ethylenic or acetylenic linkages are not oxidized during photobromination.[38,39] Thus, 2–butyne–1, 4–diol,[38] tetramethylbutynediol,[38] cis– or trans–2–butene–1, 4–diol,[39] or trans–tetramethylbutenediol[39] add 1 mole of bromine to the unsaturated bond to give the corresponding dibromoalkanol. The physical constants are included in Table 50 on bromination of unsaturated compounds.

Sometimes photochemical substitution chlorination can be achieved without affecting the hydroxyl groups. Thus, 1, 1, 1–trichloro–2–methylpropanol is chlorinated with sulfuryl chloride at 78–80° to give 1, 1, 1, 3–tetrachloro–2–methylpropanol.[274] Chlorination of 1, 1, 1–trichloro–2–methylbutanol or 1, 1, 1–trichloro–2–methyl–2–octanol results in a 1, 1, 1, 3–tetrachloro derivative.[274] The physical data for the products are shown in Table 47 on chlorination of aliphatic and alicyclic compounds.

Table 59. Photochlorination of Fluoroalcanols

C_n	Alcanol	Product	% Yield	°C b.p./mm (m.p.)	n_D (°C)	Ref.
C_3	$HCF_2CF_2CH_2OH$	HCF_2CF_2CHO	65	37	1.285 (25)	59
C_4	2, 2, 3, 3, 4, 4, 4–Heptafluoro–1–butanol	2, 2, 3, 3, 4, 4, 4–Heptafluoro–1–butanal	80	29/745		313
C_5	$H(CF_2CF_2)_2CH_2OH$	$H(CF_2CF_2)_2CHO$	84	86	1.295 (25)	59
	3, 3, 4, 4, 5, 5, 5–Heptafluoro–2–pentanol	3, 3, 4, 4, 5, 5, 5–Heptafluoro–2–pentanone	70	64/740	1.3000 (20)	313
C_6	4, 4, 5, 5, 6, 6, 6–Heptafluoro–3–hexanol	1–Chloro–4, 4, 5, 5, 6, 6, 6–heptafluoro–3–hexanol+	68	156/745	1.3560 (20)	313
		2–Chloro–4, 4, 5, 5, 6, 6, 6–heptafluoro–3–hexanol		138/745 (decomp.)		
	3, 3, 4, 4, 5, 5, 5–Heptafluoro–2–methyl–2–pentanol	1–Chloro–3, 3, 4, 4, 5, 5, 5–heptafluoro–2–methyl–2–pentanol	37	129/745	1.3553 (20)	313
C_7	$H(CF_2CF_2)_3CH_2OH$	$H(CF_2CF_2)_3CHO$	70	125	1.298 (25)	59
C_9	$H(CF_2CF_2)_4CH_2OH$	$H(CF_2CF_2)_4CHO$	47	120	1.3039 (25)	59
C_{11}	$H(CF_2CF_2)_5CH_2OH$	$HCF_2(CF_2)_4CF_2Cl$	80	89/30 (46)		59

HALOGENATION OF ALDEHYDES

Halogenation of aldehydes under free radical conditions has been little investigated, although the chlorination of acetaldehyde to give the industrially important chloral has received considerable attention by nearly all major manufacturers of chloral.[391,477]

Razuvaev and co-workers summarized previous investigations on the chlorination of aldehydes and investigated the photochemical and cyclohexyl sulfonyl peroxide-catalyzed chlorination of dichloroacetaldehyde and α, α–dichloropropioaldehyde and their hydrates.[420] They found that in the absence of water, dichloroacetyl chloride and dichloropropionyl chloride are the main products, respectively. In the presence of water, dichloroacetic and dichloropropionic acids are the main products.

$$CHCl_2CHO + Cl_2 \rightarrow CHCl_2COCl + HCl$$

$$CHCl_2CHO \cdot H_2O \rightarrow CHCl_2COOH + HCl$$

The photobromination of paraldehyde at $-10°$ in ether-containing peroxides yields α–bromoacetaldehyde, which is isolated by conversion to diethyl acetal.[104] The photobromination of β–dichloroacrolein produces β–dichloroacryloyl bromide, b.p. $58°/15.5$ mm, n_D 1.5680 (16°), in 69% yield.[287]

$$CCl_2{=}CHCHO + Br_2 \rightarrow CCl_2{=}CHCOBr$$

The chlorination of butyraldehyde in methylene chloride with sulfuryl chloride in the presence of benzoyl peroxide produces α–chlorobutylaldehyde, b.p. $106°/740$ mm, n_D 1.441 (25°), in 79% yield.[66] The chlorination of isovaleraldehyde or β–phenylisovaleraldehyde with carbon tetrachloride in the presence of benzoyl peroxide results in isovaleryl chloride, b.p. 114°, in 60% yield, and β–phenylisovaleryl chloride, b.p. $85°/3$ mm, in 56% yield, respectively.[557]

Sometimes the photochlorination of an aldehyde is accompanied by oxidation. For example, pyruvaldehyde reacts with chlorine in ultraviolet light to give dichloropyruvic acid in 81% yield.[421]

BROMINATION OF ACETALS

Bromination of acetals under free radical conditions has been little investigated. Bromination of acetals with NBS appears to be a free radical process, since the reaction is accelerated by light. Direct sunlight or irradiation with a 60-watt lamp can be used. Solid NBS is added to the acetal at a rate such that the temperature of the reaction mixture is maintained below $40°$.[304] The bromine atom enters the position α to the oxygen function.

$$RCH(OR')_2 + NBS \rightarrow RCBr(OR')_2 + NS$$

Thus, aliphatic diethyl acetals of acet-, propio-, butyro-, and isobutyro-aldehydes are converted to the corresponding α-bromo derivatives.[304] The yields range from 24 to 68%. The bromination of acetals of aromatic aldehydes follows a more complex reaction path than that of aliphatic acetals. Thus, ethyl benzoate is isolated from the reaction of NBS with benzaldehyde diethyl acetal.

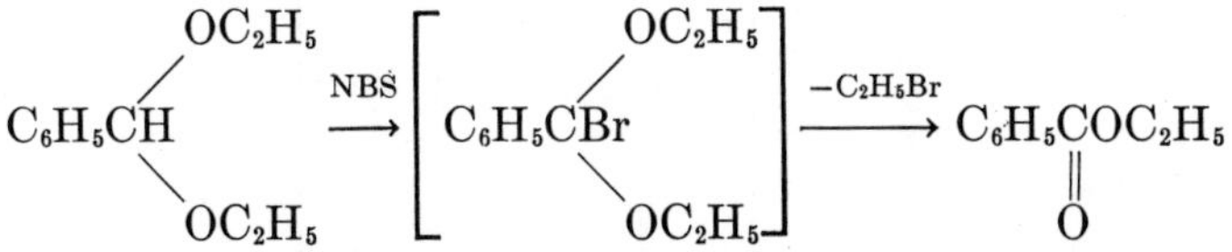

An analogous course is postulated for the reaction of dialkyl acetals of α-keto aldehydes with NBS in the presence of light to give α-keto esters in high yield.[563] This reaction is carried out in boiling carbon tetrachloride.

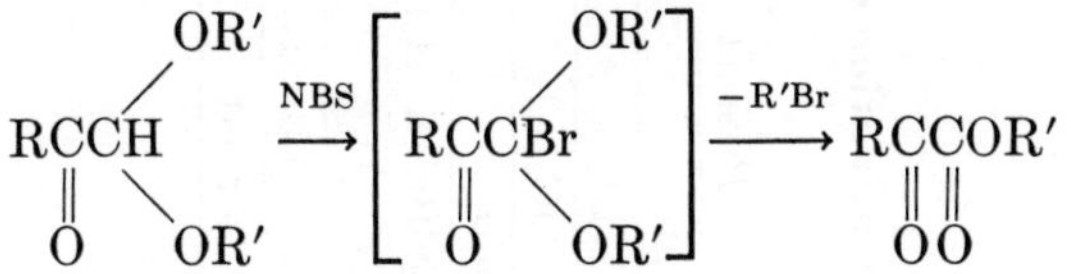

Ethyl pyruvate is prepared from pyruvaldehyde diethyl acetate in this way, butyl pyruvate from pyruvaldehyde dibutyl acetal, α, α, α-trimethyl pyruvate from t-butylglyoxaldiethyl acetal, and ethylbenzoyl formate from phenylglyoxal diethyl acetal.[563]

Table 60. Photobromination of Acetals with NBS

C_n	Acetal	Product	% Yield	°C b.p./mm	n_D (°C)	Ref.
C_5	Pyruvic aldehyde diethyl acetal	Ethyl pyruvate	78	50/14		563
C_6	$CH_3CH(OC_2H_5)_2$	$CH_3CBr(OC_2H_5)_2$	57	67/14	1.4401 (20)	304
C_7	$CH_3CH_2CH(OC_2H_5)_2$	$CH_3CH_2CBr(OC_2H_5)_2$	68	83/30	1.4371 (20)	304
	Pyruvic aldehyde dibutyl acetal	Butyl pyruvate	72	74/15	1.4132 (25)	563
C_8	$CH_3CH_2CH_2CH(OC_2H_5)_2$	$CH_3CH_2CH_2CBr(OC_2H_5)_2$	24	75/15	1.4418 (20)	304
	$(CH_3)_2CHCH(OC_2H_5)_2$	$CH_3CHCBr(OC_2H_5)_2$	59	88/30	1.4345 (20)	304
C_{10}	t-Butylglyoxal diethyl acetal	α, α, α-Trimethyl pyruvate	78	65/15	1.4096 (25)	563
	Phenylglyoxal diethyl acetal	Ethylbenzoyl formate	73	97/2	1.5145 (25)	563

REACTION OF HALOGENS WITH SALTS OF CARBOXYLIC ACIDS

Anhydrous salts of carboxylic acids, in particular those of silver, react readily with halogens. Depending on the mole ratio of the carboxylic acid salt to the halogen, various reactions occur.

When the ratio is 1:1, the main product is an alkyl halide. This reaction is frequently called the Hunsdiecker reaction[237] and is useful for the preparation of primary aliphatic and alicyclic halides. For example, it can be used for the preparation of fluorohalogenohydrocarbons from the corresponding acids and a halogen[62,98,180,183,184,188,203,211]:

$$C_4F_9CO_2Ag + Cl_2 \rightarrow C_4F_9Cl + CO_2 + AgCl$$

$$CF_2BrCO_2Ag + Br_2 \rightarrow CBr_2F_2 + CO_2 + AgBr$$

$$CBrFHCO_2Ag + I_2 \rightarrow CBrFIH + CO_2 + AgI$$

Selected examples of the Hunsdiecker reaction are given in Table 61. These reactions are commonly carried out in an inert solvent such as carbon tetrachloride. In some cases no solvent is employed, and the halogen is reacted with a hot salt of the acid.[98] The temperature of the reaction ranges from room temperature to 100°.[184] Occasionally much higher temperatures, 150–200°, are used.[98,184] Reactions with volatile compounds must be performed in an autoclave.[184] Other salts, such as sodium, potassium, barium, mercury, and lead, can be used, but they often require higher reaction temperatures and the yields of products are usually lower than those obtained by using silver salts.[184] All halogens without exception undergo this reaction.

The Hunsdiecker reaction has been reviewed extensively.[248,264,556] The more interesting recent investigations are those on hydroxy acids,[530] alicyclic dicarboxylic acids,[558] α–substituted carboxylic acids,[296] and the pyrazole series.[60] The Hunsdiecker reaction is a heterogeneous process, and as such it is difficult to investigate and to interpret mechanistically. However, in the last decade much evidence to support a free radical mechanism has been accumulated.[1,41,108,128,487,513,554]

For example, silver salts of cis– or trans–1, 2–cyclohexanedicarboxylic acid react with bromine to give trans–1, 2–dibromocyclohexane in both cases.[1] The reaction of the silver salt of either cis– or trans–4–t–butylcyclohexanecarboxylic acid with bromine produces a mixture containing about 65% trans–4–t–butylcyclohexyl bromide.[128] On the basis of these results Abell[1] and Eliel and Acharya[128] concluded that the Hunsdiecker reaction proceeds by a free radical process.

Some investigators believe that the reaction of a silver salt with a halogen proceeds through an acyl hypohalide, which then decomposes to give the alkyl halide.

$$RCO_2Ag + X_2 \rightarrow 2RCO_2X + AgX$$

The Prevost reaction is evidence for such intermediates; i.e., when the reaction is carried out in the presence of an olefin or an acetylene, the elements of the hypohalide add across the double bond to give esters of halohydrin (I) and 1, 2–diol (II), or a halogenated acetylene (III) is obtained.[264,556]

$$RCO_2Ag + X_2 + R'CH{=}CHR'' \rightarrow R'CH(OCOR)CHXR'' + AgX$$

I

$$2RCO_2Ag + X_2 + R'CH{=}CHR'' \rightarrow R'CH(OCOR)CH(OCOR)R'' + 2AgX$$

II

$$RCO_2Ag + X_2 + R'C{\equiv}CH \rightarrow R'{\equiv}CX + RCO_2H + AgX$$

III

For example, silver acetate and benzoate react with iodine in cyclohexene to give the acetate, b.p. $120°/12$ mm, and the benzoate, b.p. $185°/10$ mm, of 2–iodocyclohexanol–1 in high yield.[46] Butyryl hypobromite reacts with cyclohexene to give the butyrate of 2–bromocyclohexanol–1, b.p. $145°/14$ mm, and dibromocyclohexane.[50] Similarly, benzoyl bromite reacts to give the corresponding benzoate, m.p. $60°$.[50]

Crawford and Simons believe that the complex IV, rather than an acyl hypohalide, is formed as an intermediate in the reaction of a silver salt with a halogen.[99]

$$(RCO_2)_2AgX$$

IV

When 2 moles of a salt of a carboxylic acid is reacted with 1 mole of halogen, an ester of the next lower alcohol is obtained.[264,481,482,556]

$$2RCO_2Ag + I_2 \rightarrow RCO_2R + CO_2 + 2AgI$$

This reaction is sometimes called the Simonini[481,482] reaction. Iodine seems to be the most suitable halogen, since other halogens give poor yields of product. The preparation of esters by this method is, of course, of limited value. When the ratio of silver salt to halogen is 3:2, a combined Hunsdiecker-Simonini reaction apparently occurs, since the products of the reaction are an ester, an alkyl halide, carbon dioxide, and a silver halide.[556]

$$3RCO_2Ag + 2X_2 \rightarrow RCO_2R + RX + 2CO_2 + 3AgX$$

Table 61. Reaction of Halogens with Silver Salts of Carboxylic Acids

C_n	Acid	Halogen	Product	% Yield	°C b.p./mm	n_D (°C)	Ref.
C_2	FCH_2CO_2H	Cl_2	$ClFCH_2$	52	8.5		184
	FCH_2CO_2H	Br_2	$BrFCH_2$	62	17.5		184
	FCH_2CO_2H	I_2	$FICH_2$	55	52	1.490 (20)	184
	CF_2HCO_2H	Cl_2	ClF_2CH	91	−41		184
	CF_2HCO_2H	Br_2	BrF_2CH	88	−15		184
	CF_2HCO_2H	I_2	F_2ICH	93	21		184
	CF_3CO_2H	Cl_2	CF_3Cl	90	−82		180
	CF_3CO_2H	Br_2	CF_3Br	88	−58		180
	CF_3CO_2H	I_2	CF_3I	80	−22		98, 180, 203, 211
	BrF_2CCO_2H	Br_2	Br_2F_2C	81	25		184
	ClF_2CCO_2H	Cl_2	Cl_2F_2C	88	−30		184
	ClF_2CCO_2H	Br_2	$BrClF_2C$	91	−4		184
	ClF_2CCO_2H	I_2	ClF_2IC	78	33		184
	$CBrFHCO_2H$	Cl_2	$BrClFCH$	67	37		184
	$CBrFHCO_2H$	Br_2	Br_2FCH	64	65		184
	$CBrFHCO_2H$	I_2	$BrFICH$	19	104		184
	$ClFCHCO_2H$	Cl_2	Cl_2FCH	73	9		184
	$ClFCHCO_2H$	Br_2	$BrClFCH$	67	37		184
	$ClFCHCO_2H$	I_2	$ClFICH$	35	35/150		184
	$CFIHCO_2H$	I_2	FI_2CH	18	50/50		184
	$BrClCFCO_2H$	Cl_2	$BrCl_2FC$	63			184
	$BrClCFCO_2H$	Br_2	Br_2ClFC	71	80		184

Table 61. (cont.) Reaction of Halogens with Silver Salts of Carboxylic Acids

C_n	Acid	Halogen	Product	% Yield	°C b.p./mm	n_D (°C)	Ref.
C_3	$CF_3CF_2CO_2H$	Cl_2	CF_3CF_2Cl	94	−37		184
	$CF_3CF_2CO_2H$	Br_2	CF_3CF_2Br	98	−20		184
	$CF_3CF_2CO_2H$	I_2	CF_3CF_2I	86	13/760		184, 203
C_4	$C_3F_7\text{-}CO_2H$	Cl_2	C_3F_7Cl	91	−1		184
	$C_3F_7CO_2H$	Br_2	C_3F_7Br	97	12		184
	$C_3F_7CO_2H$	I_2	C_3F_7I	87	41/760		98, 184, 203
	$CF_3CH=CHCO_2H$	I_2	$CF_3CH=CHI$	76	71		183
C_5	$C_4F_9CO_2H$	Cl_2	C_4F_9Cl	89	30		184
	$C_4F_9CO_2H$	Br_2	C_4F_9Br	95	44		184
	$C_4F_9CO_2H$	I_2	C_4F_9I	89	67		184
	$HO_2C(CF_2)_3CO_2H$	I_2	$I(CF_2)_3I$	18	131/760		203
C_6	$C_5F_{11}CO_2H$	Cl_2	$C_5F_{11}Cl$	85	60	1.280 (10)	184
	$C_5F_{11}CO_2H$	Br_2	$C_5F_{11}Br$	91	75		184
	$C_5F_{11}CO_2H$	I_2	$C_5F_{11}I$	89	95	1.320 (20)	184
C_7	$C_6F_{11}CO_2H$ (Undecafluorocyclohexane-carboxylic acid)	Br_2	$C_6H_{11}Br$	54	91/735	1.3205 (20)	62
	$C_6F_{13}CO_2H$	I_2	$C_6H_{11}I$	63	110/736	1.3540 (20)	62
	$C_6F_{13}CO_2H$	Cl_2	$C_6F_{13}Cl$	83	86	1.287 (15)	184
	$C_6F_{13}CO_2H$	Br_2	$C_6F_{13}Br$	90	100		184
	$C_6F_{13}CO_2H$	I_2	$C_6F_{13}I$	90	117	1.322 (20)	184
C_8	$C_7F_{15}CO_2H$	Cl_2	$C_7F_{15}Cl$	80	109	1.292 (15)	184
	$C_7F_{15}CO_2H$	Br_2	$C_7F_{15}Br$	86	123		184
	$C_7F_{15}CO_2H$	I_2	$C_7F_{15}I$	85	137	1.323 (30)	184

HALOGENATION OF ACIDS AND ACID CHLORIDES

Photochlorination and photobromination of aliphatic acids were studied by Michael and Garner around 1900.[324] However, because of inadequate fractionation techniques at that time, the results were qualitative only.

Aliphatic acids and acid chlorides can be chlorinated with elemental chlorine in ultraviolet light or with sulfuryl chloride in the presence of benzoyl peroxide. Light of 3100–4000 A is the most effective.[72] The reactions are usually carried out at the boiling point of the reactants. Carbon tetrachloride can be used as a solvent. In most cases the reactions are completed within 40 to 70 min. The chlorinated products are usually isolated and purified by fractional distillation and are identified by their refractive indices. For more effective fractionation, the chlorinated acids are often converted to the corresponding acid chlorides or esters.[73,257] For example, chlorinated isobutyric acids are converted to methyl esters, and chlorinated n–butyric acids to the corresponding acid chlorides.

Other methods of chlorination have been reported. Thus, acetic acid is chlorinated in ultraviolet light with a mixture of chlorine and either sulfur dioxide[489] or phosphorus trichloride.[496] Photochlorination of butyric acid with chloride in the presence of sulfur and thionyl chloride produces α–chlorobutyric acid in 66% yield.[163] Photochlorination of butyric acid in the presence of a mixture of iodine, phosphorus, and phosphorus pentachloride produces α–chlorobutyric acid, b.p. 104°/20 mm, in 71% yield.[163] Direct photochlorination of butyryl chloride or isovaleryl chloride at 100° produces α–chlorobutyryl chloride, b.p. 130°, in 92% yield, and α–isovaleryl chloride, b.p. 155°, in 89% yield, respectively.[163] α–Chlorobutyric and α–chlorocaproic acids are also prepared by the reaction of a mixture of equimolar quantities of thionyl chloride and elemental chlorine with the corresponding acids in ultraviolet light.[163] Photochlorination of n–caproic acid in the presence of sulfur and phosphorus pentachloride produces α–chloro–n–caproic acid, b.p. 101°/1.0 mm, in 34% yield.[163]

Adipic acid chloride is chlorinated photochemically in the presence of water and iodine to give, depending on the amount of chlorine employed, α–chloroadipic acid (isolated as its methylester, b.p. 138°/10 mm) or α, α'–dichloroadipic acid, m.p. 180°.[523] Adipic acid dichloride is photochlorinated in the presence of iodine to give dichloroadipic acid dichloride in 70% yield.[525] This product is isolated as the dichloroadipic acid dimethyl ester, b.p. 162–168°/8 mm, n_D 1.4705 (14°). Hydrolysis of this ester produces three acids: meso α, α'–dichloro, m.p. 186°, racemic α, α'–dichloro, m.p. 145°, and β, β'–dichloro, m.p. 125°. Chlorination of the dichloride in the absence of iodine produces β, β'–dichloroadipic acid in 61% yield. Chlorination of adipic acid dichloride with sulfuryl chloride in the presence of benzoyl peroxide results in a product which contains 15% α, α'– and 85% β, β'–dichloro derivative. The dichloro acid chloride can be further chlorinated to give α, α', β, β'–tetrachloroadipic acid dichloride in 46–65% yield. In addition, α, α, β, β', α', α'–hexachloro acid dichloride, m.p. 94°, is formed in about 20% yield.[525,541]

Chlorination of adipic acid with sulfuryl chloride in the presence of benzoyl peroxide in a solution of glutaric acid produces meso–β, β'–dichloroadipic acid, m.p. 209° (decomp.), in 20% yield, plus β–chloroglutaric acid, m.p. 130°.[541] Glutaric acid is photochlorinated at 80° to give α, α'–dichloroglutaric acid, m.p. 163°.[524] Chlorination with sulfuryl chloride in the presence of benzoyl peroxide yields β–chloroglutaric acid, m.p. 131°.[524] Chlorination of glutaric acid dichloride results in a complex mixture of products.[524]

Brown and Ash[66] have shown that in free radical chlorinations of aliphatic compounds in solution, the inductive effect of the substituents and the stability of organic radical determine the composition of the products. Groups such as CO_2H and $COCl$ deactivate the α–hydrogen atoms. Thus, in photochlorinations of carboxylic acids and acid chlorides with chlorine or in chlorinations with sulfuryl chloride in the presence of peroxides, substitution of the hydrogen atom for the chlorine atom occurs preferentially in positions further removed from the CO_2H and $COCl$ groups.[486] For example, propionyl chloride is chlorinated with sulfuryl chloride to give an isomer distribution of 40% α– and 60% β–chloropropionyl chloride.[257] n–Butyryl chloride is photochlorinated to give a mixture of products with an isomer distribution of 5% α–, 65% β–, and 30% γ–chloro–n–butyryl chloride.[72] If a molecule has a secondary α hydrogen, a tertiary β hydrogen, and a primary γ hydrogen along the chain, substitution of the β hydrogen atom for chlorine will be favored because of (1) the inductive effect of the CO_2H or $COCl$ group and (2) the following order of carbon hydrogen bond reactivities: primary < secondary < tertiary. Because of this order of reactivity, the isomer distribution between α and γ can sometimes be in favor of α despite the deactivating effect of the CO_2H or $COCl$ group. For example, photochlorination of isovaleryl chloride results in the following chloro isomer distribution: 32% α, 60% β, and 8% γ.[73]

The alicyclic compounds cyclobutanecarboxylic acid, 1, 1–cyclobutanedicarboxylic acid, and their chlorides (I) are chlorinated with sulfuryl chloride in the presence of benzoyl peroxide.[362]

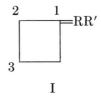

I

R = CO₂H, COCl

R' = H, CO₂H, COCl

Monosubstituted compounds are converted to 2– and 3–chloro derivatives, and the tertiary hydrogen atom in position 1 is not substituted. The disubstituted compounds are converted to 3–chloro derivatives; no 2–chloro isomer is obtained. In all cases *trans* chlorination is predominant. These results in the cyclobutane series suggest an even greater importance of the inductive effect than that observed with aliphatic compounds.

However, a compound such as hexahydrobenzoyl chloride is chlorinated with sulfuryl chloride in the presence of benzoyl peroxide to give α–chloro-hexahydrobenzoyl chloride in 34% yield.[413]

Free radical bromination of carboxylic acid is achieved photochemically with elemental bromine[324] or with NBS.[376,377] Phenyl- or naphthyl-substituted[376,377] acetic acids are brominated to α–bromo derivatives without the use of a catalyst.

Reactions of hydroxy and amino acids with NBS result in degradation and oxidation of the acids.[234] For example, glycolic, methylglycolic, or phenylglycolic acid is converted with NBS to formaldehyde, acetaldehyde, and benzaldehyde, respectively; phenylacetic acid is converted to benzaldehyde; α–aminopropionic acid is degraded to acetic acid.

Halogenation of sulfides is usually considered to proceed by an ionic mechanism. However, the rate of bromination of aryl thioglycolic acids of the structure II is accelerated by light,[369] and therefore the bromination probably proceeds by a free radical path.

$$XC_6H_4SCH_2COOH$$

II

X = H, *p*-CH₃, *p*-Br, *p*-NO₂, *o*-NO₂

Saturated and unsaturated aliphatic acids can be directly fluorinated.[49] Fluorination of butyric acid yields mainly β– and γ–fluorobutyric acids. Fluorination of isobutyric acid produces β–fluorobutyric acid, b.p. 80°/13 mm; the α position is not attacked. Fluorination of crotonic acid produces two stereoisomers of α, β–difluorobutyric acid, while fluorination of oleic acid yields a solid difluorostearic acid, m.p. 81°.

Table 62. Halogenation of Acids and Acid Chlorides

C_n	Starting material	Halogenating agent	Initiator	Product	(% Isomer distribution)	% Yield	°C b.p./mm (m.p.)	n_D (°C)	Ref.
C_2	Acetic acid	SO_2Cl_2	Bz_2O_2	Chloroacetic acid		50			257
	CH_3CO_2H	$SO_2 + Cl_2$	UV	$ClCH_2COOH$					489
	Acetic acid	$Cl_2 + PCl_3$	UV	CCl_3CO_2H			(56)		496
C_3	Propionic acid	SO_2Cl_2	Bz_2O_2	α–Chloropropionic acid + β–Chloropropionic acid	(45) (55)				257
	Propionic acid	Cl_2	UV	α–Chloropropionic acid + β–Chloropropionic acid	(30) (70)		84/10 99/10		71, 73
	Propionyl chloride	SO_2Cl_2	Bz_2O_2	α–Chloropropionyl chloride + β–Chloropropionyl chloride	(40) (60)		52/100 82/100	1.440 (20) 1.454 (20)	257
	Propionyl chloride	Cl_2	UV	α–Chloropropionyl chloride + β–Chloropropionyl chloride	(34) (70)	91	53/100 81/100		72, 324
C_4	n–Butyric acid	Cl_2	UV	α–Chloro–n–butyric acid + β–Chloro–n–butyric acid + γ–Chloro–n–butyric acid	(5) (64) (31)				73, 298
	n–Butyric acid	SO_2Cl_2	Bz_2O_2	α–Chloro–n–butyric acid + β–Chloro–n–butyric acid + γ–Chloro–n–butyric acid		10 45 45			66, 257
	n–Butyryl chloride	Cl_2	UV	α–Chloro–n–butyryl chloride + β–Chloro–n–butyryl chloride + γ–Chloro–n–butyryl chloride	(5) (65) (31)		51/40 66/40 84/40	1.4520 (20) 1.4642 (20)	72, 228, 257, 298, 324, 486

Table 62. (cont.) Halogenation of Acids and Acid Chlorides

C_n	Starting material	Halogenating agent	Initiator	Product	(% Isomer distribution)	% Yield	°C b.p./mm (m.p.)	n_D (°C)	Ref.
	n–Butyryl chloride	SO_2Cl_2	Bz_2O_2	α–Chloro–n–butyryl chloride+		3	52/40	1.4410 (25)	66, 257
				β–Chloro–n–butyryl chloride+		49	53/20	1.4477 (25)	
				γ–Chloro–n–butyryl chloride		48	71/20	1.4597 (25)	
	Isobutyric acid	Cl_2	UV	α–Chloroisobutyric acid+	(33)	60			73
				β–Chloroisobutyric acid	(67)				
	Isobutyric acid	SO_2Cl_2	Bz_2O_2	α–Chloroisobutyric acid+	(15)				257
				β–Chloroisobutyric acid	(85)				
	Isobutyryl chloride	SO_2Cl_2	Bz_2O_2	α–Chloroisobutyryl chloride+	(20)	117		1.4369 (20)	257
				β–Chloroisobutyryl chloride	(80)	151		1.4542 (20)	
C_5	$CH_3(CH_2)_3COCl$	Cl_2	UV	α–Chlorovaleryl chloride+	(5)		75/20		72, 228, 486
				β–Chlorovaleryl chloride+	(65)		91/20		
				γ–Chlorovaleryl chloride	(30)				
	$(CH_3)_2CHCH_2COOH$	Cl_2	UV	α–Chloro–β–methylbutyric acid+	(26)				73
				β–Chloro–β–methylbutyric acid	(70)				
	$(CH_3)_2CHCH_2COCl$	Cl_2	UV	α–Chloro–β–methylbutyryl chloride+	(32)		55/20	1.4535 (20)	73, 324
				β–Chloro–β–methylbutyryl chloride+	(60)		75/20	1.4592 (20)	
				γ–Chloro–β–methylbutyryl chloride	(8)		87/20		
	$(CH_3)_3CCO_2H$	Cl_2	UV	β–Chloro–α,α–dimethyl-propionic acid	(100)	95			73

Table 62. (cont.)   Halogenation of Acids and Acid Chlorides

C_n	Starting material	Halogenating agent	Initiator	Product	(% Isomer distribution) % Yield	°C b.p./mm (m.p.)	n_D (°C)	Ref.
C_6	Caproyl chloride	Cl_2	UV	δ-Chlorocaproyl chloride ε-Chlorocaproyl chloride		99/20 111/20		486
	1,1-Cyclobutanedicarboxylic acid dichloride	SO_2Cl_2	Bz_2O_2	3-Chloro-1,1-cyclobutanedicarboxylic acid dichloride	52	97/14		362
C_7	Hexahydrobenzoyl chloride	SO_2Cl_2	Bz_2O_2	α-Chlorohexahydrobenzoyl chloride	34	95/18	1.4866 (20)	413
C_8	$C_6H_5CH_2CO_2H$	NBS		$C_6H_5CHBrCO_2H$	73			376, 377
	$C_6H_5SCH_2CO_2H$	Br_2	UV	$C_6H_5SCHBrCO_2H$	45	(101)		369
	$p-BrC_6H_4SCH_2CO_2H$	Br_2	UV	$p-BrC_6H_4SCHBrCO_2H$	87	(144)		369
	$o-NO_2C_6H_4SCH_2CO_2H$	Br_2	UV	$o-NO_2C_6H_4SCHBrCO_2H$	87	(138)		369
	$p-NO_2C_6H_4SCH_2CO_2H$	Br_2	UV	$p-NO_2C_6H_4SCHBrCO_2H$	91	(148)		369
C_9	$p-CH_3C_6H_4SCH_2CO_2H$	Br_2	UV	$p-CH_3C_6H_4SCHBrCO_2H$	71	(104)		369
C_{12}	$1-C_{10}H_7CH_2CO_2H$	NBS		$1-C_{10}H_7CHBrCO_2H$	86	(140)		376, 377
	$2-C_{10}H_7CH_2CO_2H$	NBS		$2-C_{10}H_7CHBrCO_2H$	86	(160)		376, 377

HALOGENATION OF ESTERS

Aliphatic esters can be chlorinated photochemically with elemental chlorine,[66,72,73,152,556] with sulfuryl chloride in the presence of benzoyl peroxide,[66] or with NCS.[77] Benzene or carbon tetrachloride can be used as solvents. The chlorinations are usually carried out at 80–120°. Light of 3100–4000 A is used in the photochemical reactions. The reaction mixtures are separated by fractional distillation. Thus, alkyltrichloroacetate is chlorinated at 120° for 7–10 hr by irradiation from a 200-watt tungsten light bulb.[152,536] The chlorinated trichloroacetates are hydrolyzed to the corresponding chlorinated alcohols. This procedure can be used for identification of the products and also for the preparation of aliphatic chloroalcohols.

In photochemical and in sulfuryl chloride chlorinations of esters, two factors play an important role: (1) the deactivating effect of the —CO—

$$\underset{O}{\|}$$

group on the α–C–H bond and (2) the order of reactivity of the hydrogen atoms: tertiary > secondary > primary.[66] For example, methyl butyrate is photochlorinated to give a mixture of methyl β–chloro- and methyl γ–chlorobutyrate.[72] Similarly, methyl n–valerate is chlorinated to a mixture of methyl β–chloro- and methyl γ–chlorovalerate.[72] However, methylisovalerate is chlorinated mainly to a mixture of α–chloro and β–chloro isomers.[73]

In photochemical chlorinations and in chlorinations with sulfuryl chloride of acetates and of trichloroacetate, the alcohol moiety of the molecule is affected.[73,152,536] Thus, chlorination of methyl acetate yields chloromethyl acetate, and chlorination of ethyl acetate yields a mixture of α– and β–chloroethyl acetate.[73]

$$\underset{\underset{O}{\|}}{CH_3COCH_2CH_3} \xrightarrow[UV]{Cl_2} \underset{\underset{O}{\|}}{CH_3COCHClCH_3} + \underset{\underset{O}{\|}}{CH_3COCH_2CH_2Cl}$$

Isopropyl acetate[73] or isopropyl trichloroacetate[152] is photochlorinated to a mixture of α– and β–chloroisopropyl acetate and trichloroacetate, respectively. n–Propyl acetate[66,73] or n–propyl trichloroacetate[152] is photochlorinated to give mainly a mixture of β– and γ–chloro derivatives.

$$\underset{\underset{O}{\|}}{CX_3COCH_2CH_2CH_3} \xrightarrow[UV]{Cl_2} \underset{\underset{O}{\|}}{CX_3COCH_2CHClCH_3} + \underset{\underset{O}{\|}}{CCl_3COCH_2CH_2CH_2Cl}$$

$$X = H, Cl$$

Isobutyl acetate[73] or trichloroacetate[534] is chlorinated to a mixture of $\beta-$ and $\gamma-$chloro isomers. $n-$Butyl acetate[73] or trichloroacetate[534] is chlorinated to a mixture of γ and δ products and β and δ products, respectively. $sec-$Butyl acetate[73] or trichloroacetate[534] is photochlorinated to a mixture of β and β' side-chain products.

$$CX_3COCHCH_2CH_3 \xrightarrow[UV]{Cl_2} CX_3COCHCHClCH_3 + CH_3COCHCH_2CH_3$$

$$\underset{\parallel\ \ \ |}{O}\ \ \underset{CH_3}{\ } \qquad \underset{\parallel\ \ \ |}{O}\ \ \underset{CH_3}{\ } \qquad \underset{\parallel\ \ \ |}{O}\ \ \underset{CH_2Cl}{\ }$$

X = H, Cl

Only a few chlorinations of esters with NCS have been reported, and no study of factors affecting these chlorinations is available. The chlorinations with NCS are carried out in boiling carbon tetrachloride. Benzoyl peroxide is used as a free radical initiator. In most cases $\alpha-$chlorination occurs. Thus, ethyl propionate or methyl adipate is converted with NCS to ethyl $\alpha-$chloropropionate and to methyl $\alpha-$chloroadipate, respectively.[77]

Polyfluoroalkyl borates are chlorinated in ultraviolet light.[474] The first step is the formation of monochlorinated borate, which is further chlorinated to chloroborate, which is very sensitive to moisture.

$$(CF_3CH_2O)_3B \rightarrow (CF_3CHClO)_3B \rightarrow (CF_3CHClO)_2BCl$$

Esters can be brominated with elemental bromine in the presence of peroxides or light. For example, ethyl benzylmalonate under these conditions is converted to the $\alpha-$bromo product.[233] Also, NBS in the presence of peroxide can be used for bromination. For example, ethyl propionate is brominated by this method to ethyl $\alpha-$bromopropionate.[77] 1, 3–Dibromo–5, 5–dimethylhydantoin is also an excellent agent for bromination of esters in the presence of benzoyl peroxide.[55,92]

The bromination of olefinic esters with NBS under free radical conditions results in substitution of the hydrogen α to the double bond.

$$RR'CHCH{=}CHCO_2R'' \xrightarrow{NBS} RR'CBrCH{=}CHCO_2R''$$

R, R' = H, alkyl

R'' = alkyl

Thus, methyl crotonate,[24] ethyl 4–methyl–2–pentenoate,[107,470] methyl 3–methyl–3–acetoxy–4–heptenoate,[5] diethyl mesaconate,[83] methyl sorbate, [210,253] methyl $\beta-$methyl sorbate,[5] and cholesteryl benzoate[42] are all brominated to the corresponding allylic bromoesters.

However, sometimes the bromination yields a dibromide instead of the monobromo product in α position to the double bond. Thus, methylvinyl acetate reacts with NBS in the presence of benzoyl peroxide to give methyl–β, γ–dibromobutyrate.[91] In the absence of a peroxide and in the presence of free radical inhibitors, ethyl acrylate reacts with NBS to form 3, 4–dibromo-propionate.[25] These addition reactions most likely do not follow a free radical course.

Allylic bromination of olefinic esters is sometimes achieved by using bromine or bromoketones in ultraviolet light. Thus, methyl crotonate, ethyl crotonate, or methyl 2–pentene carboxylate is photobrominated in carbon tetrachloride solution to the corresponding allylic bromo deriva-tive.[464] Similarly, cholesteryl benzoate[462,463,465] or cholesteryl tosylate[462,463] is brominated to the 7–α–bromo derivative. Cholesteryl benzoate is also brominated with 2, 4, 6–trichloro–6–bromo- or 2, 4, 6, 6–tetrabromo–1, 4–cyclohexadien–3–one in ultraviolet light to 7–bromocholesteryl bromide, m.p. 139°, in 61% yield.[542]

Table 63. Halogenation of Esters

C_n	Ester	Halogenating agent	Initiator	Product	(% Isomer distribution)	% Yield	°C b.p./mm (m.p.)	n_D (°C)	Ref.
C_3	Methyl acetate	Cl_2	UV	Chloromethyl acetate	(100)	80			73
C_4	Methyl propionate	Cl_2	UV	Methyl α-chloropropionate + Methyl β-chloropropionate	(34) (66)	91	48/30 62/30	1.4176 (20) 1.4263 (20)	72
	Ethyl acetate	Cl_2	UV	α-Chloroethyl acetate + β-Chloroethyl acetate	(65) (35)	80	67/100 87/100	1.4084 (20) 1.4231 (20)	73
	Isopropyl chloroformate	Cl_2	UV	$ClCO_2CH(CH_2Cl)CHCl_2$			95/20	1.4938 (21)	300
	$ClCO_2CH(CH_2Cl)CHCl_2$	Cl_2	UV	$ClCO_2CCl(CHCl_2)_2$			117/20	1.5932 (21)	300
	$CHCl_2CO_2CH_2CH_2Cl$	Cl_2	UV	α, β, β′, β″-Tetrachloroethyl trichloroacetate		62	91/2	1.4991 (20)	500
	Trimethylene carbonate	SO_2Cl_2	Bz_2O_2	α, α′-Dichlorotrimethylene carbonate					100
	Trimethylene carbonate	Cl_2	UV	α, α′-Dichlorotrimethylene carbonate					100
C_5	Methyl butyrate	Cl_2	UV	Methyl β-chlorobutyrate + Methyl γ-chlorobutyrate	(70) (30)	90	49/12 63/12	1.4247 (20) 1.4337 (20)	72
	n-Propyl acetate	Cl_2	UV	β-Chloro-n-propyl acetate + γ-Chloro-n-propyl acetate	(69) (31)	70	63/30 80/30	1.4193 (20) 1.4302 (20)	73
	n-Propyl acetate	SO_2Cl_2	Bz_2O_2	1-Chloropropyl acetate + 2-Chloropropyl acetate + 3-Chloropropyl acetate	(25) (46) (29)		49/20 58/20 59/10	1.4143 (25) 1.4205 (25) 1.4275 (25)	66
	n-Propyl acetate	Cl_2	UV	1-Chloropropyl acetate + 2-Chloropropyl acetate + 3-Chloropropyl acetate	(23) (46) (35)				66

Table 63. (cont.) Halogenation of Esters

C_n	Ester	Halogenating agent	Initiator	Product	(% Isomer distribution)	% Yield	°C b.p./mm (m.p.)	n_D (°C)	Ref.
	Isopropyl acetate	Cl_2	UV	α–Chloroisopropyl acetate + β–Chloroisopropyl acetate	(50) (50)	75	66/100 90/100	1.4226 (20)	73
	Ethyl propionate	NBS	Bz_2O_2	Ethyl α–bromopropionate		42	159	1.4460 (20)	77
	Ethyl propionate	NCS	Bz_2O_2	Ethyl α–chloropropionate		40	146	1.4182 (20)	77
	n–$C_3H_7OCOCCl_3$	Cl_2	UV	2–Chloropropyl trichloroacetate + 3–Chloropropyl trichloroacetate		30 28	94/8 107/8	1.4766 (15) 1.4830 (15)	152
	i–$C_3H_7OCOCCl_3$	Cl_2	UV	$CH_3C(Cl)(CH_3)OCOCCl_3$ + $CH_2ClCH(CH_3)OCOCCl_3$		25 31	72/8 94/8	1.4640 (15) 1.4760 (15)	152
	Methyl crotonate	Br_2	UV	$BrCH_2CH=CHCO_2CH_3$		81	89/16		464
	Methyl crotonate	NBS	Bz_2O_2	Methyl γ–bromocrotonate		83	85/12	1.4959 (25)	25
	$NCCH_2CO_2C_2H_5$	NBS	Bz_2O_2	$NCCBr_2CO_2C_2H_5$			71/1.3	1.4957 (18)	140
C_6	Ethyl butyrate	SO_2Cl_2	Bz_2O_2	Ethyl β–chlorobutyrate + Ethyl γ–chlorobutyrate	(50) (40)		168 185	1.4253 (20) 1.4325 (20)	413
	Ethyl crotonate	Br_2	UV	$BrCH_2CH=CHCO_2C_2H_5$		83	100/14		464
	Methyl valerate	Cl_2	UV	Methyl β–chloro-n–valerate + Methyl γ–chloro-n–valerate	(71) (29)	91	59/8 75/8	1.4312 (20) 1.4379 (20)	72
	Methyl 2–pentene carboxylate	Br_2	UV	$CH_3CHBrCH=CHCO_2CH_3$		71	90/13		464
	$(CH_3)_2CHCH_2OCOCH_3$	Cl_2	UV	Methyl α–chloroisovalerate + Methyl β–chloroisovalerate	(49) (49)		54/12 69/12	1.4277 (20) 1.4342 (20)	73

Table 63. (cont.) Halogenation of Esters

C_n	Ester	Halogenating agent	Initiator	Product	(% Isomer distribution)	% Yield	°C b.p./mm (m.p.)	n_D (°C)	Ref.
	n-Butyl acetate	Cl_2	UV	γ-Chloro-n-butyl acetate + / δ-Chloro-n-butyl acetate	(71) / (29)	75	87/30 / 98/30	1.4292 (20) / 1.4346 (20)	73
	Isobutyl acetate	Cl_2	UV	β-Chloroisobutyl acetate + / γ-Chloroisobutyl acetate	(51) / (49)	75	70/30 / 89/30	1.4218 (20) / 1.4320 (20)	73
	$CH_3CH_2CHOCOCH_3$ ∣ CH_3 (sec-Butyl acetate)	Cl_2	UV	$CH_3CHClCHOCOCH_3$ ∣ CH_3 + $CH_3CH_2CHOCOCH_3$ ∣ CH_2Cl	(66) / (33)	70	101/100 / 113/100	1.4270 (20) / 1.4300 (20)	73
	n-$C_4H_9OCOCCl_3$	Cl_2	UV	$CH_3CH_2CHClCH_2OCOCCl_3$ + / $ClCH_2CH_2CH_2CH_2OCOCCl_3$		33 / 19	95/5 / 115/5	1.4728 (25) / 1.4800 (25)	536
	i-$C_4H_9OCOCCl_3$	Cl_2	UV	$(CH_3)_2CClCH_2OCOCCl_3$ + / $ClCH_2CH(CH_3)CH_2OCOCCl_3$		24 / 27	80/5 / 98/5	1.4658 (25) / 1.4742 (25)	536
	sec-$C_4H_9OCOCCl_3$	Cl_2	UV	$CH_3CHClCH(CH_3)OCOCCl_3$ + / $CH_3CH_2CH(CH_2Cl)OCOCCl_3$ or / $ClCH_2CH_2CH(CH_3)OCOCCl_3$		28 / 25	83/5 / 92/5	1.4671 (25) / 1.4713 (25)	536
	$(CF_3CH_2O)_3B$	Cl_2	UV	$(CF_3CHClO)_3B$		24	100/200	1.3405 (25)	474
	$(CF_3CHClO)_3B$	Cl_2	UV	$(CF_3CHClO)_2BCl$			77/200	1.3490 (25)	474
C_7	Methyl caproate	Cl_2	UV	Methyl β-chlorocaproate + / Methyl γ-chlorocaproate	(77) / (23)	93	80/10 / 101/10	1.4366 (20) / 1.4494 (20)	72
	Methyl adipate	NBS	Bz_2O_2	Methyl α-bromoadipate		30	147/20		77

Table 63. (cont.)   Halogenation of Esters

C_n	Ester	Halogenating agent	Initiator	Product	(% Isomer distribution)	% Yield	°C b.p./mm (m.p.)	n_D (°C)	Ref.
	Methyl adipate	NCS	Bz_2O_2	Methyl α-chloroadipate		38	130/15	1.4420 (21)	77
	Diethyl malonate	NCS	Bz_2O_2	Ethyl α-chloromalonate		38	115/14	1.4375 (24)	77
	Diethyl malonate	NBS	Bz_2O_2	$CHBr(CO_2C_2H_5)_2$		68	117/10		55
	Diethyl malonate	1,3-Dibromo-5,5-dimethyl-hydantoin	Bz_2O_2	$CHBr(CO_2C_2H_5)_2$		75	116/10		55, 92
C_8	$CH_3CH{=}CHCH{=}CHCO_2CH_3$	NBS	Bz_2O_2	$BrCH_2CH{=}CHCH{=}CHCO_2CH_3$		6	75/0.01 (26)	1.5456 (20)	210, 253
	$(CH_3)_2CHCOCH_2CH_2CO_2CH_3$	NBS		$(CH_3)_2CBrCOCH_2CH_2CO_2CH_3$			119/12		469
	$CH_3CH{=}CHC(CH_3){=}CHCO_2CH_3$	NBS	Bz_2O_2	$CH_3CH{=}CHC(CH_2Br){=}CHCO_2CH_3$			101/1	1.5440 (16)	5
	$(CH_3)_2CHCH{=}CHCO_2C_2H_5$	NBS	Bz_2O_2	$(CH_3)_2CBrCH{=}CHCO_2C_2H_5$		81	109/18	1.4848 (20)	107, 470
	Diethyl succinate	SO_2Cl_2	Bz_2O_2	Diethyl chlorosuccinate		50	121/15	1.4334 (20)	413
C_9	$CH_3C(CO_2C_2H_5){=}CHCO_2C_2H_5$	NBS	Bz_2O_2	$(CH_2Br)C(CO_2C_2H_5){=}CHCO_2C_2H_5$		37	72/0.1	1.485 (20)	83
	$(C_2F_5CH_2O)_3B$	Cl_2	UV	$(C_2F_5CHClO)_3B$			117/200	1.3262 (25)	474
	$(C_2F_5CHClO)_3B$	Cl_2	UV	$(C_2F_5CHClO)_2BCl$				1.3330 (25)	474
C_{10}	Methyl 3-methyl-3-acetoxy-4-heptenoate	NBS	Bz_2O_2	$BrCH_2CH{=}CHC(OCOCH_3)$-$(CH_3)CH_2CO_2CH_3$			119/1	1.4901 (28)	5
C_{12}	$(C_3F_7CH_2O)_3B$	Cl_2	UV	$(C_3F_7CHClO)_3B$		37	150/200	1.3250 (25)	474
	$(C_3F_7CHClO)_3B$	Cl_2	UV	$(C_3F_7CHClO)_2BCl$				1.3360 (20)	474
C_{13}	Methyl laurate	NCS	Bz_2O_2	Methyl 2-chlorolaurate		40	178/19	1.4515 (22)	77
C_{14}	$C_6H_5CH_2CH(CO_2C_2H_5)_2$	Br_2	Bz_2O_2 or UV	$C_6H_5CH_2CBr(CO_2C_2H_5)_2$		83	183/14		233

HALOGENATION OF NITRILES

Only a few attempts have been made to systematically study the halogenation of nitriles under free radical conditions.[73,89,94] Chlorination is carried out with chlorine in ultraviolet light, and bromination is carried out with NBS in boiling carbon tetrachloride in the presence of benzoyl peroxide. Most of the work has involved saturated aliphatic nitriles; only a few unsaturated compounds have been brominated.

It is difficult to make general conclusions on the basis of the small number of compounds investigated. However, it appears that the action of the cyano group is similar to that of the CO_2H and $COCl$ groups: the cyano group deactivates the α position, and β–carbon-hydrogen bonds of nitriles are somewhat activated in comparison with other secondary carbon-hydrogen bonds along the molecule. This generalization seems to hold at least for the chlorination of nitriles. Thus, acetonitrile is not attacked by chlorine in ultraviolet light.[73] Propionitrile is photochlorinated to a mixture of 25% α– and 75% β–chloropropionitrile.[73] Butyronitrile is photochlorinated to a mixture of 69% β– and 31% γ–chlorobutyronitrile.[73] Similarly, valeronitrile is chlorinated to a mixture of 75% β– and 25% γ–chlorovaleronitrile.[73]

The reaction path in the bromination of nitriles with NBS in the presence of peroxides is less clearly defined. Hydrogen located α and γ to the nitrile groups can be substituted in preference to the β hydrogen. For example, butyronitrile is brominated to a mixture of isomers containing 76% α and 24% β derivatives.[94] Bromination of valeronitrile yields a bromo isomer containing 30% α, no β, and 70% γ.[94] Acetonitrile cannot be brominated,[94] and bromination of isobutyronitrile yields only the α isomer.[94]

Whereas the photochlorination of nitriles no doubt proceeds by a free radical mechanism, a polar mechanism cannot be ruled out in reactions with NBS. Nitriles are excellent solvents for NBS, and NBS in solution acts like elemental bromine.[234] The situation is particularly complex for unsaturated nitriles. Thus, vinylacetonitrile reacts with NBS in the presence of benzoyl peroxide to give a mixture (13% yield) of γ–crotonitrile and a 21% yield of 3, 4–dibromobutyronitrile.[25] The amount of the dibromo product increases when a small amount of free radical inhibitor, such as catechol, is present. This result indicates that the reaction proceeds by two mechanisms. The substitution reaction most likely proceeds by a radical path, whereas the addition reaction no doubt proceeds by an ionic mechanism.

Both cis– and trans–crotonitrile can be brominated with NBS[25,68,69,93] or with bromine in ultraviolet light.[25,282] Bromination of crotonitrile in carbon tetrachloride in the presence of benzoyl peroxide can produce γ–bromocrotonitrile in as high as 84% yield.[25,68,69] Thus, the expected allylic substitution occurs. However, in the absence of a solvent, α–bromocrotonitrile is obtained.

Table 64. Halogenation of Nitriles

C_n	Nitrile	Halogenating agent	Initiator	Product	(% Isomer distribution)	% Yield	°C b.p./mm	n_D (°C)	Ref.
C_3	CH_3CH_2CN	Cl_2	UV	$CH_3CHClCN$ + CH_2ClCH_2CN	(25) (75)	86	58/80 75/20	1.4096 (20) 1.4370 (20)	73
	CH_3CH_2CN	NBS	Bz_2O_2	$CH_3CHBrCN$	(100)	45	68/50	1.4673 (15)	94
	$CH_2=CHCN$	Cl_2	UV	$CH_2ClCHClCN$		75	58/10	1.4633 (25)	293
C_4	$CH_3(CH_2)_2CN$	Cl_2	UV	$CH_3CHClCH_2CN$ + $CH_2ClCH_2CH_2CN$	(69) (31)	89	65/13 77/13	1.4369 (20) 1.4446 (20)	73, 298
	$CH_3(CH_2)_2CN$	NBS	Bz_2O_2	$CH_3CH_2CHBrCN$ + $CH_3CHBrCH_2CN$	(76) (24)	62	64/20 71/10	1.4652 (20) 1.4754 (20)	94
	$(CH_3)_2CHCN$	Cl_2	UV	α–Chloroisobutyronitrile + β–Chloroisobutyronitrile	(33) (67)				73
	$(CH_3)_2CHCN$	NBS	Bz_2O_2	$(CH_3)_2CBrCN$	(100)	80	62/50	1.4505 (15)	94
	$CH_3CH=CHCN$	NBS	Bz_2O_2	$CH_2BrCH=CHCN$		40	60/4	1.4979 (25)	25
	cis– and $trans$–$CH_3CH=CHCN$	NBS	Bz_2O_2	cis–$CH_2BrCH=CHCN$ + $trans$–$CH_2BrCH=CHCN$		70	74/10 88/10		68, 69, 93
C_5	Vinylacetonitrile	NBS	Bz_2O_2	γ–Bromocrotonitrile + 3, 4–Dibromobutyronitrile	(25) (75)	13 21	90/10 122/10	1.5001 (25) 1.5165 (25)	25, 93
	$CH_3(CH_2)_3CN$	Cl_2	UV	$CH_3CH_2CH(Cl)CH_2CN$ + $CH_3CHClCH_2CH_2CN$	(75) (25)	90	64/5 82/5	1.4407 (20) 1.4489 (20)	73
	$CH_3(CH_2)_3CN$	NBS	Bz_2O_2	$CH_3CH_2CH_2CHBrCN$ + $CH_3CHBrCH_2CH_2CN$	(30) (70)	38	67/10 90/10	1.4777 (15)	94
	$CNCH_2CO_2C_2H_5$	NBS	Bz_2O_2	$CNCBr_2CO_2C_2H_5$			71/1.3	1.4957 (18)	140

REFERENCES

[1] Abell, *J. Org. Chem.*, **22,** 769 (1957).

[2] Adam, Gosselain, and Goldfinger, *Bull. soc. chim. Belg.*, **65,** 523 (1956).

[3] Agre, U.S. 2,682,512 (1954).

[4] Agre and Hilling, *J. Am. Chem. Soc.*, **74,** 3895 (1952).

[5] Akiyoshi and Ueno, *J. Chem. Soc. Japan*, **72,** 726 (1951).

[6] Akopyan, Saakyan, and Avetyan, *Zh. Obsh. Khim.*, **28,** 1221 (1958).

[7] Ali, *et al.*, *J. Sci. Ind. Res. India*, **11B,** 286 (1952).

[8] Anbar and Ginsberg, *Chem. Revs.*, **54,** 925 (1954).

[9] Anderson and Grebe, *J. Org. Chem.*, **26,** 2006 (1961).

[10] Anderson, Putnam, and Sharkey, *J. Am. Chem. Soc.*, **83,** 382 (1961).

[11] Arakawa and Irie, *Pharm. Bull. Tokyo*, **5,** 524 (1957): *Chem. Abs.*, **52,** 15445e (1958).

[12] Arakawa and Irie, *Pharm. Bull. Tokyo*, **5,** 531 (1957): *Chem. Abs.*, **52,** 15445e (1958).

[13] Ash and Brown, *Rec. Chem. Progress*, **9,** 81 (1948).

[14] Asinger, *Monatsh. Chem.*, **64,** 153 (1934).

[15] Asinger, Geiseler, and Schmiedel, *Chem. Ber.*, **92,** 3085 (1959).

[16] Attaway, Groth, and Bigelow, *J. Am. Chem. Soc.*, **81,** 3599 (1959).

[17] Avonda, Gervasi, and Bigelow, *J. Am. Chem. Soc.*, **78,** 2798 (1956).

[18] Bachmann, *J. Am. Chem. Soc.*, **56,** 1365 (1934).

[19] Bader, Edmiston, and Rosen, *J. Am. Chem. Soc.*, **78,** 2590 (1956).

[20] Bader, Edmiston, and Rosen, Can. 584,546 (1959).

[21] Badische Anilin- and Soda-Fabrik, French 960,512 (1950): *Chem. Abs.*, **46,** 5614 (1952).

[22] Baganz, *Ang. Chem.*, **71,** 366 (1959).

[23] Baganz and Domaschke, *Chem. Ber.*, **92,** 3170 (1959).

[24] Baganz and Domaschke, *Ang. Chem.*, **74,** 144 (1962).

[25] Bailey and Bello, *J. Org. Chem.*, **20,** 525 (1955).

[26] Banus, Emeleus, and Haszeldine, *J. Chem. Soc.*, **1950,** 3041.

[27] Barnes, *J. Am. Chem. Soc.*, **70,** 145 (1948).

[28] Barnes and Buckwalter, *J. Am. Chem. Soc.*, **73,** 3858 (1951).

[29] Bartlett, U.S. 2,733,276 (1956).

[30] Bateman, *et al.*, *J. Chem. Soc.*, **1950,** 936.

[31] Bauer and Daniels, *J. Am. Chem. Soc.*, **56,** 378 (1934).

[32] Bauer and Daniels, *J. Am. Chem. Soc.*, **56,** 2014 (1934).

[23] Belohlav and McBee, *Ind. Eng. Chem.*, **49,** 1506 (1957).

[34] Belohlav and McBee, *Ind. Eng. Chem.*, **50,** 1355 (1958).

[35] Belohlav and McBee, *Ind. Eng. Chem.*, **51,** 1102 (1959).

[36] Belohlav and McBee, *Ind. Eng. Chem.*, **52,** 1022 (1960).

[37] Belohlav and McBee, *Ind. Eng. Chem.*, **53,** 1015 (1961).

[38] Bergelson, *Izvest. Akad. Nauk*, **1960,** 1066.

[39] Bergelson and Badenkova, *Izvest. Akad. Nauk*, **1960,** 1073.

[40] Bergmann and Ikan, *J. Am. Chem. Soc.*, **80,** 208 (1958).

[41] Berman and Price, *J. Org. Chem.*, **23,** 102 (1958).

[42] Bernstein, *et al.*, *J. Org. Chem.*, **14,** 433 (1949).

[43] Berson, *J. Am. Chem. Soc.*, **76,** 5748 (1954).

[44] Berson and Swidler, *J. Am. Chem. Soc.*, **76,** 4060 (1954).

[45] Bigelow, *Chem. Revs.*, **40**, 51 (1947).
[46] Birkenbach, Goubeau, and Berninger, *Chem. Ber.*, **65**, 1339 (1932).
[47] Bissell and Shaw, *J. Org. Chem.*, **27**, 1482 (1962).
[48] Bloomfield, *J. Chem. Soc.*, **1944**, 114.
[49] Bockemüller, *Ann. Chem.*, **506**, 20 (1933).
[50] Bockemüller and Hoffman, *Ann. Chem.*, **519**, 165 (1935).
[51] Boekelheide and Goldman, *J. Am. Chem. Soc.*, **76**, 604 (1954).
[52] Bognar and Rákosi, *Chem. Ind.*, **1955**, 773.
[53] Bognar and Rákosi, *Acta Chim. Acad. Sci. Hung.*, **8**, 309 (1955).
[54] Böhme and Dörries, *Chem. Ber.*, **89**, 723 (1956).
[55] Bonafede, *Rev. fac. cienc. quim. Univ. nacl. La Plata*, **29**, 41 (1955).
[56] Booher and Rollefson, *J. Am. Chem. Soc.*, **56**, 2288 (1934).
[57] Boozer and Moncrief, *J. Org. Chem.*, **27**, 623 (1962).
[58] Bost and Krynitsky, *J. Am. Chem. Soc.*, **70**, 1027 (1948).
[59] Brace, *J. Org. Chem.*, **26**, 4005 (1961).
[60] Brain and Finar, *J. Chem. Soc.*, **1958**, 2435.
[61] Brice, La Zerte, and Pearlsen, *J. Am. Chem. Soc.*, **75**, 2698 (1953).
[62] Brice and Simons, *J. Am. Chem. Soc.*, **73**, 4016 (1951).
[63] Brochet, *Ann. chim. Paris*, **10**(7), 295 (1897).
[64] Brook, Warner, and McGriskin, *J. Am. Chem. Soc.*, **81**, 981 (1959).
[65] Brown, in *Vistas in Free Radical Chemistry*, edited by Waters, p. 196, Pergamon Press, New York (1959).
[66] Brown and Ash, *J. Am. Chem. Soc.*, **77**, 4019 (1955).
[67] Brown and Borkowski, *J. Am. Chem. Soc.*, **74**, 1894 (1952).
[68] Bruylants, *Bull. soc. chim. Belg.*, **59**, 107 (1950).
[69] Bruylants, *Ind. chim. belge*, **16**, 485 (1951).
[70] Bruylants and Houssiau, *Bull. soc. chim. Belg.*, **61**, 492 (1952).
[71] Bruylants, Magritte, and Tits, *Ind. chim. belge*, **20**, Spec. No. 588 (1955).
[72] Bruylants, Tits, and Dauby, *Bull. soc. chim. Belg.*, **58**, 310 (1949).
[73] Bruylants, *et al.*, *Bull. soc. chim. Belg.*, **61**, 366 (1952).
[74] Buckles, Johnson, and Probst, *J. Org. Chem.*, **22**, 55 (1957).
[75] Buu-Hoï, *Ann. Chem.*, **556**, 1 (1944).
[76] Buu-Hoï, *Rec. Chem. Progress*, **13**, 30 (1952).
[77] Buu-Hoï and Demerseman, *J. Org. Chem.*, **18**, 649 (1953).
[78] Buu-Hoï and Lecocq, *J. Chem. Soc.*, **1946**, 830.
[79] Buu-Hoï and Lecocq, *C. r.*, **222**, 1441 (1946).
[80] Buu-Hoï and Lecocq, *C. r.*, **226**, 87 (1948).
[81] Calingaert, *et al.*, *J. Am. Chem. Soc.*, **73**, 5224 (1951).
[82] Campaigne and Le Suer, *J. Am. Chem. Soc.*, **70**, 1555 (1948).
[83] Campbell and Hunt, *J. Chem. Soc.*, **1947**, 1176.
[84] Cairns and Englund, *J. Org. Chem.*, **21**, 140 (1956).
[85] Cantzer, Krekeler, and Leutner, German 857,949 (1952).
[86] Carothers, *J. Am. Chem. Soc.*, **55**, 2008 (1933).
[87] Carrico and Dickinson, *J. Am. Chem. Soc.*, **57**, 1343 (1935).
[88] Catch, *et al.*, *J. Chem. Soc.*, **1948**, 276.
[89] Chapman and Williams, *J. Chem. Soc.*, **1952**, 5044.
[90] Churchill and Schaeffer, U.S. 2,680,092 (1954).
[91] Corey, *J. Am. Chem. Soc.*, **75**, 2251 (1953).
[92] Corral, Orazi, and Bonafede, *Anales asoc. quim. argentina*, **45**, 151 (1957).
[93] Couvreur and Bruylants, *Bull. soc. chim. Belg.*, **61**, 253 (1952).
[94] Couvreur and Bruylants, *J. Org. Chem.*, **18**, 501 (1953).
[95] Cox and Swallow, *Chem. Ind.*, **1956**, 1277.

[96] Cox and Swallow, *J. Chem. Soc.*, **1958**, 3727.
[97] Craig and Riener, U.S. 2,783,284 (1957).
[98] Crawford and Simons, *J. Am. Chem. Soc.*, **75**, 5737 (1953).
[99] Crawford and Simons, *J. Am. Chem. Soc.*, **77**, 2605 (1955).
[100] Crocker and Millidge, Brit. 778,734 (1957).
[101] Curtis, Gilman, and Hammond, *J. Am. Chem. Soc.*, **79**, 4754 (1957).
[102] D'ans and Kautzach, *J. prak. Chem.*, **80**(2), 305 (1909).
[103] d'Arcet, *Ann. Chem.*, **28**, 82 (1838).
[104] Darzens and Meyer, *C. r.*, **236**, 292 (1953).
[105] Dauben and McCoy, *J. Am. Chem. Soc.*, **81**, 4863 (1959).
[106] Dauben and McCoy, *J. Am. Chem. Soc.*, **81**, 5404 (1959).
[107] Dauben and McCoy, *J. Org. Chem.*, **24**, 1577 (1959).
[108] Dauben and Tilles, *J. Am. Chem. Soc.*, **72**, 3185 (1950).
[109] Davis and Whaley, *J. Am. Chem. Soc.*, **73**, 2361 (1951).
[110] Denzel, *Ann. Chem.*, **195**, 205 (1879).
[111] De Puy, Thurn, and Isaks, *J. Org. Chem.*, **27**, 744 (1962).
[112] de Sonnay, *Chem. Ber.*, **27R**, 337 (1894).
[113] Di Paco and Tauro, *Ann. chim. Rome*, **47**, 118 (1957).
[114] Dittmer, *et al.*, *J. Am. Chem. Soc.*, **71**, 1201 (1949).
[115] Djerassi, *Chem. Revs.*, **43**, 271 (1948).
[116] Djerassi and Scholz, *Experientia*, **3**, 107 (1947).
[117] Djerassi and Scholz, *J. Org. Chem.*, **14**, 660 (1949).
[118] Donnelly, Lawless, and Wilson, *Chem. Ind.*, **1961**, 1906.
[119] Durrans, *J. Chem. Soc.*, **123**, 1424 (1923).
[120] Duschinsky and Dolan, *J. Am. Chem. Soc.*, **70**, 657 (1948).
[121] Dykstra, U.S. 2,584,992 (1952).
[122] Eaborn, *Organosilicon Compounds*, Butterworths, London (1960).
[123] Eaborn and Shaw, *J. Chem. Soc.*, **1955**, 1420.
[124] Ecke, Buzbee, and Kolka, *J. Am. Chem. Soc.*, **78**, 79 (1956).
[125] Ecke, Cook, and Whitmore, *J. Am. Chem. Soc.*, **72**, 1511 (1950).
[126] Ecke, Kolka, and Burt, U.S. 2,841,593 (1958).
[127] Eibner, *Chem. Ber.*, **36**, 1229 (1903).
[128] Eliel and Acharya, *J. Org. Chem.*, **24**, 151 (1959).
[129] Eliel and Nelson, *J. Chem. Soc.*, **1955**, 1628.
[130] Eliel and Rivard, *J. Org. Chem.*, **17**, 1252 (1952).
[131] Eliel, Rivard, and Burgstahler, *J. Org. Chem.*, **18**, 1679 (1953).
[132] Ellis, *The Chemistry of Petroleum Derivatives*, pp. 491, 686, Chem. Catalog Co., New York (1934).
[133] Ellis, *The Chemistry of Petroleum Derivatives*, vol. II, pp. 726–77, Reinhold, New York (1937).
[134] Emr, *Chem. Listy*, **50**, 668 (1956).
[135] Erlenmeyer and Grubenmann, *Helv. chim. Acta*, **30**, 297 (1947).
[136] Erlenmeyer and Grubenmann, *Helv. chim. Acta*, **31**, 78 (1948).
[137] Evans and Gray, *J. Org. Chem.*, **23**, 745 (1958).
[138] Fainberg and Miller, *J. Am. Chem. Soc.*, **79**, 4170 (1957).
[139] Faseeh, *J. Chem. Soc.*, **1953**, 3708.
[140] Felton, *J. Chem. Soc.*, **1955**, 515.
[141] Feng and Chiu, *Hua Hsüeh Hsüeh Pao*, **25**, 277 (1959).
[142] Fessenden and Freenor, *J. Org. Chem.*, **26**, 2003 (1961).
[143] Finkelstein and Linder, *J. Am. Chem. Soc.*, **73**, 302 (1951).
[144] Ford and Waters, *J. Chem. Soc.*, **1951**, 1851.
[145] Ford and Waters, *J. Chem. Soc.*, **1952**, 2240.

[146] Friedel, *Bull. soc. chim. France,* **28**(2), 171 (1877).
[147] Friedman and Ginsburg, *J. Org. Chem.,* **23**, 16 (1958).
[148] Fritsch, *Ann. Chem.,* **279**, 310 (1894).
[149] Fritsch and Schumacher, *Ann. Chem.,* **279**, 301 (1894).
[150] Fuson and Porter, *J. Am. Chem. Soc.,* **70**, 895 (1948).
[151] Gardner, Wenis, and Lee, *J. Org. Chem.,* **15**, 841 (1950).
[152] Gayler and Waddle, *J. Am. Chem. Soc.,* **63**, 3358 (1941).
[153] Geiger, Usteri, and Gränacher, *Helv. chim. Acta,* **34**, 1335 (1951).
[154] Geiseler and Asinger, *Chem. Ber.,* **90**, 1790 (1957).
[155] George, Prober, and Elliott, *Chem. Revs.,* **56**, 1065 (1956).
[156] Germano and Séchaud, *Helv. chim. Acta,* **37**, 1343 (1954).
[157] Gervasi, Brown, and Bigelow, *J. Am. Chem. Soc.,* **78**, 1679 (1956).
[158] Gilman, Brannen, and Ingham, *J. Am. Chem. Soc.,* **78**, 1689 (1956).
[159] Gilman and Miller, *J. Am. Chem. Soc.,* **73**, 968 (1951).
[160] Goerner and Nametz, *J. Am. Chem. Soc.,* **73**, 2940 (1951).
[161] Gompper and Rühle, *Ann. Chem.,* **626**, 83 (1959).
[162] Green, Remers, and Wilson, *J. Am. Chem. Soc.,* **79**, 1416 (1957).
[163] Griehe, Schulze, and Furst, *Chem. Ber.,* **91**, 1165 (1958).
[164] Groebel, *Chem. Ber.,* **93**, 896 (1960).
[165] Gross, *Chem. Technik Berlin,* **10**, 659 (1958).
[166] Gross, *Ang. Chem.,* **72**, 268 (1960).
[167] Gross, *Chem. Ber.,* **95**, 83 (1962).
[168] Grosse and Ipatieff, *J. Org. Chem.,* **8**, 438 (1943).
[169] Hall and Sirel, *J. Am. Chem. Soc.,* **74**, 836 (1952).
[170] Hall and Ubertini, *J. Org. Chem.,* **15**, 715 (1950).
[171] Harmer, Univ. Mich. Ann Arbor Microfilm 12,582, *Diss. Abs.,* **15**, 1311 (1955).
[172] Harvey, *et al., J. Appl. Chem. London,* **4**, 319 (1954).
[173] Hasegawa, *J. Pharm. Soc. Japan,* **71**, 256 (1951).
[174] Hasegawa, *J. Pharm. Soc. Japan,* **73**, 1326 (1953).
[175] Hasegawa, *Pharm. Bull. Japan,* **1**, 47 (1953).
[176] Hasegawa, *Pharm. Bull. Japan,* **1**, 387 (1953).
[177] Hass, McBee, and Weber, *Ind. Eng. Chem.,* **27**, 1190 (1935).
[178] Hass, McBee, and Weber, *Ind. Eng. Chem.,* **28**, 333 (1936).
[179] Hassel and Lunde, *Acta. chim. Scand.,* **4**, 1597 (1950).
[180] Haszeldine, *J. Chem. Soc.,* **1951**, 584.
[181] Haszeldine, *J. Chem. Soc.,* **1951**, 2495.
[182] Haszeldine, *J. Chem. Soc.,* **1952**, 2504.
[183] Haszeldine, *J. Chem. Soc.,* **1952**, 3490.
[184] Haszeldine, *J. Chem. Soc.,* **1952**, 4259, 4423.
[185] Haszeldine, *J. Chem. Soc.,* **1953**, 3565.
[186] Haszeldine, *J. Chem. Soc.,* **1953**, 3761.
[187] Haszeldine, *J. Chem. Soc.,* **1955**, 4291.
[188] Haszeldine, U.S. 2,716,668 (1955).
[189] Haszeldine and Leedham, *J. Chem. Soc.,* **1952**, 3483.
[190] Haszeldine and Leedham, *J. Chem. Soc.,* **1954**, 1261.
[191] Haszeldine and Marklow, *J. Chem. Soc.,* **1956**, 962.
[192] Haszeldine and Nyman, *J. Chem. Soc.,* **1961**, 3015.
[193] Haszeldine and Osborne, *J. Chem. Soc.,* **1956**, 61.
[194] Haszeldine and Sharpe, *Fluorine and Its Compounds,* Methuen, London (1951).
[195] Haszeldine and Steele, *J. Chem. Soc.,* **1953**, 1199.
[196] Haszeldine and Steele, *J. Chem. Soc.,* **1953**, 1592.
[197] Haszeldine and Steele, *J. Chem. Soc.,* **1954**, 923.

[198] Haszeldine and Steele, *J. Chem. Soc.*, **1955**, 3005.

[199] Haszeldine and Steele, *J. Chem. Soc.*, **1957**, 2193.

[200] Haszeldine and Steele, *J. Chem. Soc.*, **1957**, 2800.

[201] Hauptschein and Bigelow, *J. Am. Chem. Soc.*, **73**, 5591 (1951).

[202] Hauptschein, Braid, and Lawlor, *J. Chem. Soc.*, **79**, 6248 (1957).

[203] Hauptschein and Grosse, *J. Am. Chem. Soc.*, **73**, 2461 (1951).

[204] Hauser and Hance, *J. Am. Chem. Soc.*, **74**, 5091 (1952).

[205] Heath, Lawson, and Rimington, *J. Chem. Soc.*, **1951**, 2223.

[206] Hebbelynck, *Ind. chim. belge*, **16**, 483 (1951).

[207] Hebbelynck and Martin, *Experientia*, **5**, 69 (1949).

[208] Hebbelynck and Martin, *Bull. soc. chim. Belg.*, **59**, 193 (1950).

[209] Heberling, *J. Org. Chem.*, **23**, 615 (1958).

[210] Heilbronn, Jones, and O'Sullivan, *J. Chem. Soc.*, **1946**, 866.

[211] Henne and Finnegan, *J. Am. Chem. Soc.*, **72**, 3806 (1950).

[212] Henne and Haeckl, *J. Am. Chem. Soc.*, **63**, 2692 (1941).

[213] Henne and Haeckl, *J. Am. Chem. Soc.*, **63**, 3476 (1941).

[214] Henne and Hinkamp, *J. Am. Chem. Soc.*, **67**, 1194 (1945).

[215] Henne and Hinkamp, *J. Am. Chem. Soc.*, **67**, 1197 (1945).

[216] Henne, Hinkamp, and Zimmerschied, *J. Am. Chem. Soc.*, **67**, 1906 (1945).

[217] Henne and Ladd, *J. Am. Chem. Soc.*, **58**, 402 (1936).

[218] Henne and Nager, *J. Am. Chem. Soc.*, **73**, 1042 (1951).

[219] Henne and Renoll, *J. Am. Chem. Soc.*, **59**, 2434 (1937).

[220] Henne and Renoll, *J. Am. Chem. Soc.*, **61**, 2489 (1939).

[221] Henne and Richter, *J. Am. Chem. Soc.*, **74**, 5420 (1952).

[222] Henne, Shepard, and Young, *J. Am. Chem. Soc.*, **72**, 3577 (1950).

[223] Henne and Waalkes, *J. Am. Chem. Soc.*, **68**, 496 (1946).

[224] Henne and Whaley, *J. Am. Chem. Soc.*, **64**, 1157 (1942).

[225] Henne, Whaley, and Stevenson, *J. Am. Chem. Soc.*, **63**, 3478 (1941).

[226] Henne and Zimmerschied, *J. Am. Chem. Soc.*, **67**, 1235 (1945).

[227] Henry, *Rec. trav. chim.*, **26**, 65 (1907).

[228] Hertog, Vries, and Bragt, *Rec. trav. chim.*, **74**, 1561 (1955).

[229] Hesse and Krehbiel, *Ann. Chem.*, **593**, 42 (1955).

[230] Hesse, Krehbiel, and Rämisch, *Ann. Chem.*, **592**, 137 (1955).

[231] Hesse and Urbanek, *Chem. Ber.*, **91**, 2733 (1958).

[232] Hopff and Wick, *Helv. chim. Acta*, **44**, 19 (1961).

[233] Horner and Gross, *Ann. Chem.*, **591**, 117 (1955).

[234] Horner and Winkelmann, *Ang. Chem.*, **71**, 349 (1959).

[235] Huang and Wang, *Acta Chim. Sinica*, **22**, 123 (1956): *Chem. Abs.*, **52**, 5285 (1958).

[236] Huett and Miller, *J. Am. Chem. Soc.*, **83**, 408 (1961).

[237] Hunsdiecker and Hunsdiecker, *Chem. Ber.*, **75**, 291 (1942).

[238] Hunter and Edgar, *J. Am. Chem. Soc.*, **54**, 2025 (1932).

[239] Huntress, *Organic Chlorine Compounds*, John Wiley, New York (1948).

[240] Huyser, *J. Am. Chem. Soc.*, **82**, 391 (1960).

[241] Huyser, *J. Am. Chem. Soc.*, **82**, 5246 (1960).

[242] Jacobsen, *Chem. Ber.*, **4**, 215 (1871).

[243] James and Woodcock, *J. Chem. Soc.*, **1951**, 1931.

[244] Jaunin and Germano, *Helv. chim. Acta*, **35**, 392 (1952).

[245] Jaunin and Germano, *Helv. chim. Acta*, **37**, 1328 (1954).

[246] Jaunin and Germano, *Helv. chim. Acta*, **38**, 1763 (1955).

[247] Jenner, *J. Org. Chem.*, **27**, 1031 (1962).

[248] Johnson and Ingham, *Chem. Revs.*, **56**, 219 (1956).

[249] Kaesz and Stone, *J. Chem. Soc.*, **1957**, 1433.

[250] Karrer and Ringli, *Helv. chim. Acta*, **30**, 863 (1947).
[251] Karrer and Ringli, *Helv. chim. Acta*, **30**, 1771 (1947).
[252] Karrer and Schneider, *Helv. chim. Acta*, **31**, 395 (1948).
[253] Karrer and Schwyzer, *Helv. chim. Acta*, **29**, 1191 (1946).
[254] Kharasch and Berkman, *J. Org. Chem.*, **6**, 810 (1941).
[255] Kharasch and Brown, *J. Am. Chem. Soc.*, **61**, 2142 (1939).
[256] Kharasch and Brown, *J. Am. Chem. Soc.*, **61**, 3432 (1939).
[257] Kharasch and Brown, *J. Am. Chem. Soc.*, **62**, 925 (1940).
[258] Kharasch and Büchi, *J. Am. Chem. Soc.*, **73**, 632 (1951).
[259] Kharasch, Fineman, and Mayo, *J. Am. Chem. Soc.*, **61**, 2139 (1939).
[260] Kharasch, Hered, and Mayo, *J. Org. Chem.*, **6**, 818 (1941).
[261] Kharasch, White, and Mayo, *J. Org. Chem.*, **3**, 33 (1938).
[262] Kharasch, White, and Mayo, *J. Org. Chem.*, **2**, 574 (1938).
[263] Kirk and Othmer, *Encyclopedia of Chemical Technology*, vol. 3, p. 730, Interscience, New York (1949).
[264] Kleinberg, *Chem. Revs.*, **40**, 381 (1947).
[265] Kohler and Potter, *J. Am. Chem. Soc.*, **57**, 1316 (1935).
[266] Kolka, Orloff, and Griffing, *J. Am. Chem. Soc.*, **76**, 1244 (1954).
[267] Kon, *J. Chem. Soc.*, **1948**, 224.
[268] Kooyman and Vegter, *Tetrahedron*, **4**, 382 (1958).
[269] Kratzl, *Chem. Ber.*, **77**, 717 (1944).
[270] Krentsel, Topchiev, and Il'ina, *Dok. Akad. Nauk*, **128**, 1192 (1959).
[271] Krieble and Elliott, *J. Am. Chem. Soc.*, **67**, 1810 (1945).
[272] Krieble and Elliott, *J. Am. Chem. Soc.*, **68**, 2291 (1946).
[273] Kumada, *et al.*, *J. Org. Chem.*, **23**, 292 (1958).
[274] Kundiger and Ovist, U.S. 2,822,408 (1958).
[275] Kundiger and Pledger, U.S. 2,813,132 (1957).
[276] Kwiecinski, Maslosz, and Wieteska, *Przemysl Chem.*, **36**, 467 (1957).
[277] Kwiecinski, Maslosz, and Wieteska, *Przemysl Chem.*, **37**, 593 (1958).
[278] La Lande, Knorr, and Aeugle, U.S. 2,758,077 (1956).
[279] Langenbeck, Losse, and Fürst, *Chem. Tech. Berlin*, **5**, 561 (1953).
[280] Larsson, *Kgl. Fysiograf. Sällskap. Lund Förth*, **26**, 145 (1956).
[281] Lawlor, U.S. 2,608,532 (1952).
[282] Leclerq and Bruylants, *Bull. soc. chim. Belg.*, **58**, 5 (1949).
[283] Lecocq, *Ann. chim. Paris*, **3**, 62 (1948).
[284] Lecocq and Buu-Hoï, *C.r.*, **224**, 937 (1947).
[285] Ledrut and Combes, *C.r.*, **231**, 1513 (1950).
[286] Leeds and Everhart, *J. Am. Chem. Soc.*, **2**, 208 (1880).
[287] Levas, *C.r.*, **235**, 61 (1952).
[288] Lieben, *Ann. Chem.*, **146**, 180 (1868).
[289] Ligett, U.S. 2,654,789 (1953).
[290] Litterscheid, *Ann. Chem.*, **330**, 112 (1904).
[291] Longiave, *Chim. ind. Milan*, **36**, 693 (1954).
[292] Looker and Holm, *J. Org. Chem.*, **24**, 567 (1959).
[293] Lorette, *J. Org. Chem.*, **26**, 2324 (1961).
[294] Lorette, Gage, and Wender, *J. Org. Chem.*, **16**, 930 (1951).
[295] Lovelace, Rausch, and Postelnek, *Aliphatic Fluorine Compounds*, Reinhold, New York (1958).
[296] Maekawa, *Bull. Nagoya Inst. Tech.*, **6**, 271 (1954): *Chem. Abs.*, **50**, 11943f (1956).
[297] Maffei, Pietra, and Caltaneo, *Gazz. chim. ital.*, **83**, 812 (1953).
[298] Magritte and Bruylants, *Bull. soc. chim. Belg.*, **66**, 367 (1957).
[299] Malaguti, *Ann. Chem.*, **32**, 15 (1839).

[300] Malatesta, *Ricerca Sci.*, **22**, 1760 (1952).

[301] Markees, *J. Org. Chem.*, **23**, 1490 (1958).

[302] Markownikoff, *Ann. Chem.*, **302**, 1 (1896).

[303] Martin and Sharkey, *J. Am. Chem. Soc.*, **81**, 5256 (1959).

[304] Marvell and Joncich, *J. Am. Chem. Soc.*, **73**, 973 (1951).

[305] Mayo and Hardy, *J. Am. Chem. Soc.*, **74**, 911 (1952).

[306] Mayor, U.S. 2,817,632 (1957).

[307] McBay, Tucker, and Groves, *J. Org. Chem.*, **24**, 536 (1959).

[308] McBee, *Ind. Eng. Chem.*, **40**, 1611 (1948).

[309] McBee and Hass, *Ind. Eng. Chem.*, **33**, 137 (1941).

[310] McBee and Pierce, *Ind. Eng. Chem.*, **39**, 397 (1947).

[311] McBee and Pierce, *Ind. Eng. Chem.*, **39**, 399 (1947).

[312] McBee and Pierce, in *The Chemistry of Petroleum Hydrocarbons*, edited by Brooks, *et al.*, vol. 3, p. 73, Reinhold, New York (1955).

[313] McBee, Pierce, and Marzluff, *J. Am. Chem. Soc.*, **75**, 1609 (1953).

[314] McBee and Roberts, *Ind. Eng. Chem.*, **47**, 1876 (1955).

[315] McBee, Roberts, and Puerckhauer, *J. Am. Chem. Soc.*, **79**, 2326 (1957).

[316] McBee, Roberts, and Puerckhauer, *J. Am. Chem. Soc.*, **79**, 2329 (1957).

[317] McBee and Ungnade, in *The Chemistry of Petroleum Hydrocarbons*, edited by Brooks, *et al.*, vol. 3, p. 59, Reinhold, New York (1955).

[318] McBee, *et al.*, *J. Am. Chem. Soc.*, **62**, 3340 (1940).

[319] McBee, *et al.*, *Natl. Nucl. Energy Ser. VII*, **1**, 207 (1951).

[320] McBee, *et al.*, *Natl. Nucl. Energy Ser. VII*, **1**, 257 (1951).

[321] McBride and Beachell, *J. Am. Chem. Soc.*, **70**, 2532 (1948).

[322] Meidinger, *Z. phys. Chem.*, **B5**, 29 (1929).

[323] Metcalf, *Organic Insecticides*, p. 213, Interscience, New York (1955).

[324] Michael and Garner, *Chem. Ber.*, **34**, 4046 (1901).

[325] Mikheev, *Dok. Akad. Nauk*, **108**, 484 (1956).

[326] Mikheev, *Dok. Akad. Nauk*, **117**, 821 (1957).

[327] Miller, *J. Am. Chem. Soc.*, **62**, 341 (1940).

[328] Miller, *Natl. Nucl. Energy Ser. VII*, **1**, 567 (1951).

[329] Miller, Bergman, and Fainberg, *J. Am. Chem. Soc.*, **79**, 4159 (1957).

[330] Miller and Fainberg, *J. Am. Chem. Soc.*, **79**, 4164 (1957).

[331] Miller and Jones, Brit. 738,992 (1955).

[332] Miller and Koch, *J. Am. Chem. Soc.*, **79**, 3084 (1957).

[333] Miller, Koch, and McLafferty, *J. Am. Chem. Soc.*, **78**, 4992 (1956).

[334] Miller and Walling, *J. Am. Chem. Soc.*, **79**, 4187 (1957).

[335] Milligan, *et al.*, *J. Am. Chem. Soc.*, **84**, 158 (1962).

[336] Mironov, Egorov, and Petrov, *Izvest. Akad. Nauk*, **1959**, 1400.

[337] Mironov, Glukhovzev, and Petrov, *Dok. Akad. Nauk*, **104**, 865 (1955).

[338] Mironov and Nepomnina, *Izvest. Akad. Nauk*, **1959**, 1231.

[339] Mironov, Petrov, and Maksimova, *Izvest. Akad. Nauk*, **1959**, 1954.

[340] Mironov and Ponomarenko, *Izvest. Akad. Nauk*, **1957**, 199.

[341] Misani, Speers, and Lyon, *J. Am. Chem. Soc.*, **78**, 2801 (1956).

[342] Misra and Shukla, *J. Indian Chem. Soc.*, **28**, 277 (1951).

[343] Moelants, *Bull. soc. chim. Belg.*, **52**, 53 (1943).

[344] Molho and Mentzer, *C.r.*, **223**, 1141 (1946).

[345] Molho and Mentzer, *C.r.*, **224**, 471 (1947).

[346] Motsarev and Yakubovich, *Zh. Obsh. Khim.*, **27**, 2786 (1957).

[347] Motsarev, *et al.*, *Zh. Obsh. Khim.*, **28**, 1336 (1958).

[348] Müller and Schumacher, *Z. phys. Chem.*, **B35**, 285 (1937).

[349] Müller and Schumacher, *Z. phys. Chem.*, **B35**, 455 (1937).

[350] Müller and Schumacher, *Z. phys. Chem.*, **B39,** 352 (1938).
[351] Müller and Schumacher, *Z. phys. Chem.*, **B42,** 327 (1939).
[352] Nazarov and Bergelson, *Izvest. Akad. Nauk*, **1960,** 887.
[353] Nazarov and Bergelson, *Izvest. Akad. Nauk*, **1960,** 896.
[354] Nekrasova, *Zh. Obsh. Khim.*, **28,** 1557 (1958).
[355] Nekrasova and Shuikin, *Usp. Khim.*, **22,** 179 (1953).
[356] Nekrasova, Shuikin, and Novikov, *Zh. Obsh. Khim.*, **28,** 15 (1958).
[357] Nesmeyanov, Freidlina, and Belyavski, *Izvest. Akad. Nauk*, **1959,** 1028.
[358] Nesmeyanov, Freidlina, and Kost, *Izvest. Akad. Nauk*, **1958,** 1205.
[359] Nesmeyanov, Zakharkin, and Petrova, *Izvest. Akad. Nauk*, **1954,** 253.
[360] Neubauer, *et al.*, U.S. 2,765,272 (1957).
[361] Neunhoeffer and Schmidt, *Chem. Tech. Berlin*, **10,** 103 (1958).
[362] Nevill, Frank, and Trepka, *J. Org. Chem.*, **27,** 422 (1962).
[363] Noda and Hatotani, *Yûki Gôsei Kagaku Kyokai Shi. (J. Soc. Org. Synth. Chem. Japan)*, **17,** 372 (1959).
[364] Oddo, *Gazz. chim. ital.*, **33**(II), 372 (1903).
[365] Oddo and Cusmano, *Gazz. chim. ital.*, **35**(I), 47 (1905).
[366] Oddo and Cusmano, *Gazz. chim. ital.*, **41,** 224 (1911).
[367] Odelkop, *Dok. Akad. Nauk*, **93,** 75 (1953).
[368] Okawara, Sato, and Imoto, *J. Chem. Soc. Japan*, **58,** 924 (1955).
[369] Oksengendler and Gerasimenko, *Zh. Obsh. Khim.*, **29,** 919 (1959).
[370] Olin Mathieson Chem. Corp., Brit. 744,454 (1956).
[371] Orazi, Corral, and Bonafede, *Anales asoc. quim argentina*, **45,** 139 (1957).
[372] Orazi and Giunti, *Anales asoc. quim. argentina*, **39,** 84 (1951).
[373] Orazi and Meseri, *Anales asoc. quim. argentina*, **38,** 300 (1950).
[374] Orazi, *et al.*, *Anales asoc. quim. argentina*, **40,** 91 (1952).
[375] Orloff, *et al.*, *J. Am. Chem. Soc.*, **75,** 4243 (1953).
[376] Panaiotov, *C.r. acad. bulgare sci.*, **10**(2), 137 (1957).
[377] Panaiotov, *Izvest. Khim. Inst. Bulgar. Akad. Nauk*, **5,** 183 (1957).
[378] Park, Griffin, and Lacher, *J. Am. Chem. Soc.*, **74,** 2292 (1952).
[379] Park and Lacher, *J. Am. Chem. Soc.*, **74,** 2189 (1952).
[380] Park, Lycan, and Lacher, *J. Am. Chem. Soc.*, **73,** 711 (1951).
[381] Park, Lycan, and Lacher, *J. Am. Chem. Soc.*, **76,** 1388 (1954).
[382] Park, Striklin, and Lacher, *J. Am. Chem. Soc.*, **76,** 1387 (1954).
[383] Park, *et al.*, *J. Org. Chem.*, **23,** 1474 (1958).
[384] Park, *et al.*, *J. Org. Chem.*, **26,** 2085 (1961).
[385] Paul and Tchelitcheff, *Bull. soc. chim. France*, **1956,** 869.
[386] Paul and Tchelitcheff, *Bull. soc. chim. France*, **1956,** 896.
[387] Paul and Tchelitcheff, *Bull. soc. chim. France*, **1956,** 1370.
[388] Pereslegina and Finkelshtein, *Zh. Priklad. Khim.*, **32,** 2096 (1959).
[389] Perfogit Societa per Azioni, Brit. 773,131 (1957).
[390] Pestemer, German 936,684 (1955).
[391] Petri and Mahler, German 874,303 (1954).
[392] Petrov and Mironov, *Dok. Akad. Nauk*, **80,** 761 (1951).
[393] Petrov, Mironov, and Dolgii, *Izvest. Akad. Nauk*, **1956,** 1146.
[394] Petrov, Mironov, and Mashantsker, *Izvest. Akad. Nauk*, **1956,** 550.
[395] Petrov and Nikishin, *Zh. Obsh. Khim.*, **26,** 1233 (1956).
[396] Petrov, Smetankina, and Nikishin, *Izvest. Akad. Nauk*, **1958,** 1468.
[397] Petrov, *et al.*, *Dok. Akad. Nauk*, **97,** 687 (1954).
[398] Petrov, *et al.*, *Dok. Akad. Nauk*, **100,** 1107 (1955).
[399] Pickholz and Roberts, Brit. 707,990 (1954).
[400] Pierce and McBee, *Ind. Eng. Chem.*, **41,** 1882 (1949).

[401] Pierce and McBee, *Ind. Eng. Chem.*, **42,** 1694 (1950).

[402] Pierce and McBee, *Ind. Eng. Chem.*, **43,** 1974 (1951).

[403] Pierce and McBee, *Ind. Eng. Chem.*, **44,** 2015 (1952).

[404] Pierce and McBee, *Ind. Eng. Chem.*, **45,** 1969 (1953).

[405] Pierce and McBee, *Ind. Eng. Chem.*, **46,** 1835 (1954).

[406] Pierce and Lovelace, *Chem. Eng. News*, p. 72 (July 9, 1962).

[407] Platz and Stumpf, German 952,093 (1956).

[408] Ponomarenko and Mironov, *Dok. Akad. Nauk*, **94,** 485 (1954).

[409] Ponamarenko and Vzenkova, *Izvest. Akad. Nauk*, **1957,** 994.

[410] Price, *J. Am. Chem. Soc.*, **58,** 1834 (1936).

[411] Price, *J. Am. Chem. Soc.*, **58,** 2101 (1936).

[412] Price, *Chem. Revs.*, **29,** 37 (1941).

[413] Price and Schwarz, *J. Am. Chem. Soc.*, **62,** 2891 (1940).

[414] Quist, *Acta Acad. Aboensis Math. Phys.*, **18**(7), 3 (1952).

[415] Rabcewicz, Zubkowski, and Chwalinski, *Roczniki Chem.*, **10,** 686 (1930).

[416] Rabinowitch, *Z. phys. Chem.*, **B19,** 190 (1932).

[417] Rapp, et al., *J. Am. Chem. Soc.*, **74,** 749 (1952).

[418] Raymond and Tschelitcheff, *C.r.*, **236,** 1961 (1953).

[419] Razuvaev and Dyachkovskaya, *Zh. Obsh. Khim.*, **26,** 1107 (1956).

[420] Razuvaev, Spasskaya, and Etlis, *Zh. Obsh. Khim.*, **29,** 2978 (1959).

[421] Razuvaev, Spasskaya, and Etlis, *Zh. Obsh. Khim.*, **30,** 653 (1960).

[422] Reed, *Chemical Products*, **23,** 299 (1960).

[423] Regnault, *Ann. Chem.*, **34,** 24 (1840).

[424] Reid and Wilkins, *J. Chem. Soc.*, **1955,** 4029.

[425] Reppe and Kröper, German 703,956 (1941): *Chem. Z.*, **1941**(I), 3290.

[426] Reymenant, *Bull. acad. roy. Belg.*, **1900,** 724: *Chem. Z.*, **1901**(I), 95.

[427] Reynolds and Allen, U.S. 2,811,486 (1957).

[428] Rieche and Gross, *Chem. Tech. Berlin*, **10,** 515 (1958).

[429] Ried and Bodem, *Chem. Ber.*, **89,** 708 (1956).

[430] Ried and Bodem, *Chem. Ber.*, **91,** 1981 (1958).

[431] A. G. Riedel de Haën, Brit. 694,405 (1953).

[432] Riedl, German 941,973 (1956).

[433] Riemschneider, *Monatsh. Chem.*, **85,** 1133 (1954).

[434] Riemschneider, *Chim. ind. Milan*, **37,** 531 (1955).

[435] Riemschneider, *Chem. Ber.*, **91,** 2605 (1958).

[436] Riemschneider and Bäker, *Z. Naturforsch.*, **9B,** 751 (1954).

[437] Rinne, et al., *J. Am. Chem. Soc.*, **72,** 5759 (1950).

[438] Roberts and Dev, *J. Am. Chem. Soc.*, **73,** 1879 (1951).

[439] Roberts and McBee, *Ind. Eng. Chem.*, **48,** 1604 (1956).

[440] Robson, et al., *J. Am. Chem. Soc.*, **83,** 5010 (1961).

[441] Rochow, *An Introduction to the Chemistry of Silicones*, John Wiley, New York (1947).

[442] Roedig, *Ann. Chem.*, **574,** 122 (1951).

[443] Roedig and Kiepert, *Chem. Ber.*, **88,** 733 (1955).

[444] Rondestvedt, Grimsley, and VerNooy, *J. Org. Chem.*, **21,** 206 (1956).

[445] Rosen and Stallings, *J. Org. Chem.*, **24,** 1523 (1959).

[446] Ross, Markarian, and Nazzewski, *J. Am. Chem. Soc.*, **69,** 1914 (1949).

[447] Ross, Markarian, and Nazzewski, *J. Am. Chem. Soc.*, **69,** 2468 (1949).

[448] Rothstein, et al., *Rec. trav. chim.*, **73,** 563 (1954).

[449] Ruggli and Schmidlin, *Helv. chim. Acta*, **29,** 383 (1946).

[450] Ruh, U.S. 2,676,193 (1954).

[451] Runge and Zimmermann, *Chem. Ber.*, **87,** 282 (1954).

[452] Russell, *J. Am. Chem. Soc.*, **79**, 2977 (1957).
[453] Russell, *J. Am. Chem. Soc.*, **80**, 4987 (1958).
[454] Russell, *J. Org. Chem.*, **24**, 300 (1959).
[455] Russell, *Tetrahedron*, **8**, 101 (1960).
[456] Russell and Brown, *J. Am. Chem. Soc.*, **77**, 4025 (1955).
[457] Russell and Brown, *J. Am. Chem. Soc.*, **77**, 4031 (1955).
[458] Salellas and Orazi, *Anales asoc. quim. argentina*, **39**, 175 (1951).
[459] Salzberg and Werntz, U.S. 2,065,400 (1937).
[460] Sampey, Cox, and King, *J. Am. Chem. Soc.*, **71**, 3697 (1949).
[461] Sampley and Reid, *J. Am. Chem. Soc.*, **69**, 234 (1947).
[462] Schaltegger, *Experientia*, **5**, 321 (1949).
[463] Schaltegger, *Helv. chim. Acta*, **33**, 2101 (1950).
[464] Schaltegger, U.S. 2,790,757 (1957).
[465] Schaltegger and Müller, *Helv. chim. Acta*, **34**, 1096 (1951).
[466] Scherer, German 907,775 (1954).
[467] Scherff, German 863,656 (1953).
[468] Schgal and Seshadri, *J. Sci. Ind. Res. India*, **12B**, 346 (1953).
[469] Schindler, *Pharm. Acta Helv.*, **23**, 273 (1948): *Chem. Abs.*, **43**, 3792 (1949).
[470] Schmid and Karrer, *Helv. chim. Acta*, **29**, 573 (1946).
[471] Schmitz and Schumacher, *Z. phys. Chem.*, **B52**, 72 (1942).
[472] Schönberg, *Präparative Organische Photochemie*, p. 141, Springer Verlag, Berlin (1958).
[473] Schott and Schumacher, *Z. phys. Chem.*, **B49**, 107 (1941).
[474] Schroeder, *J. Org. Chem.*, **25**, 1682 (1960).
[475] Schumacher, Orazi, and Corral, *Anales asoc. quim. argentina*, **40**, 19 (1952).
[476] Schwabe and Rammelt, *Z. phys. Chem.*, **204**, 310 (1955).
[477] Sconce, Groggins, and Newton, *Unit Processes in Organic Synthesis*, p. 204, McGraw-Hill, New York (1958).
[478] Severson, *et al.*, *J. Am. Chem. Soc.*, **79**, 6540 (1957).
[479] Shelton and Cialdella, *J. Org. Chem.*, **23**, 1128 (1958).
[480] Shostakovskii, Shapiro, and Shmonina, *Dok. Akad. Nauk*, **118**, 114 (1958).
[481] Simonini, *Monatsh. Chem.*, **13**, 320 (1892).
[482] Simonini, *Monatsh. Chem.*, **14**, 81 (1893).
[483] Simons, *Fluorine Chemistry*, vol. I, Academic Press, New York (1950).
[484] Simons, *Fluorine Chemistry*, vol. II, Academic Press, New York (1954).
[485] Skell, Allen, and Gilmour, *J. Am. Chem. Soc.*, **83**, 504 (1961).
[486] Smit and den Hertog, *Rec. trav. chim.*, **77**, 73 (1958).
[487] Smith and Hull, *J. Am. Chem. Soc.*, **72**, 3309 (1950).
[488] Smolyan, Pyryalova, and Kurdyumova, *Usp. Khim.*, **29**, 23 (1960): *Russ. Chem. Revs.*, **29**, 11 (1960).
[489] Solvay and Cie, Belg. 525,032 (1954).
[490] Solvay and Cie, Belg. 540,861 (1956).
[491] Sommer and Evans, *J. Am. Chem. Soc.*, **76**, 1186 (1954).
[492] Sommer and Whitmore, *J. Am. Chem. Soc.*, **68**, 485 (1946).
[493] Sommer, *et al.*, *J. Am. Chem. Soc.*, **68**, 488 (1946).
[494] Sommer, *et al.*, *J. Am. Chem. Soc.*, **68**, 1881 (1946).
[495] Sommer, *et al.*, *J. Am. Chem. Soc.*, **76**, 1613 (1954).
[496] Sonia and Scremin, U.S. 2,674,620 (1954).
[497] Sorkin, Krähenbühl, and Erlenmeyer, *Helv. chim. Acta*, **31**, 65 (1948).
[498] Southwick, Pursglove, and Numerof, *J. Am. Chem. Soc.*, **72**, 1600 (1950).
[499] Southwick, Pursglove, and Numerof, *J. Am. Chem. Soc.*, **72**, 1604 (1950).
[500] Spasskaya, Etlis, and Razuvaev, *Zh. Obsh. Khim.*, **28**, 1827 (1958).

[501] Spasskaya, Etlis, and Razuvaev, *Zh. Obsh. Khim.*, **28**, 3004 (1958).

[502] Speier, *J. Am. Chem. Soc.*, **73**, 824 (1951).

[503] Speier, *J. Am. Chem. Soc.*, **73**, 826 (1951).

[504] Speier, Brit. 683,460 (1952).

[505] Speier, U.S. 2,640,064 (1953).

[506] Spiegler and Tinker, *J. Am. Chem. Soc.*, **61**, 940 (1939).

[507] Stacey, Tatlow, and Sharpe, *Advances in Fluorine Chemistry*, vol. I, Academic Press, New York (1960).

[508] Stacey, Tatlow, and Sharpe, *Advances in Fluorine Chemistry*, vol. II, Academic Press, New York (1961).

[509] Städel, *Ann. Chem.*, **195**, 180 (1879).

[510] Steele and Haszeldine, *J. Chem. Soc.*, **1953**, 1562.

[511] Stevens, *J. Am. Chem. Soc.*, **68**, 620 (1946).

[512] Stuckewisch, Hammer, and Blau, *J. Org. Chem.*, **22**, 1678 (1957).

[513] Sukman, Univ. Mich. Ann Arbor Microfilm 58–5700, *Diss. Abst.*, **19**, 1211 (1958).

[514] Summerbell and Lunk, *J. Org. Chem.*, **23**, 499 (1958).

[515] Summers, *Chem. Revs.*, **55**, 301 (1955).

[516] Suzuki and Miyama, *J. Chem. Soc. Japan*, **75**, 522 (1954).

[517] Takizawa and Hoshiai, *Mem. Inst. Sci. Ind. Res. Osaka Univ.*, **7**, 136 (1950).

[518] Tamborski and Post, *J. Org. Chem.*, **17**, 1400 (1952).

[519] Tedder, *Chem. Ind.*, **1955**, 508.

[520] Tomita and Ueda, *Yakugaku Zasshi*, **80**, 353 (1960).

[521] Topchiev, *J. prak. Chem.*, **2**(4), 185 (1955).

[522] Torssell, *Ark. Kemi*, **10**, 507 (1957).

[523] Treibs and Holbe, *Chem. Ber.*, **85**, 608 (1952).

[524] Treibs and Michaelis, *Chem. Ber.*, **88**, 402 (1955).

[525] Treibs and Walther, *Chem. Ber.*, **88**, 396 (1955).

[526] Tsatsas, *Ann. pharm. franc.*, **12**, 329 (1954).

[527] Tscheou, Shih, and Lee, *J. Chinese Chem. Soc.*, **17**, 150 (1950).

[528] Tsuchuja and Kanazashi, *Bull. Electrotech. Lab. Japan*, **16**, 897 (1952): *Chem. Abs.*, **49**, 160D (1955).

[529] Tyczkowski and Bigelow, *J. Am. Chem. Soc.*, **77**, 3007 (1955).

[530] Umland and Witkowski, *J. Org. Chem.*, **22**, 345 (1957).

[531] Ungrade and Tucker, *J. Am. Chem. Soc.*, **71**, 1381 (1949).

[532] Van Helden and Kooyman, *Rec. trav. chim.*, **73**, 269 (1954).

[533] Veijola, *Suomen Kemistilehli*, **27B**(11), 79 (1954).

[534] Voegtli, Muhr, and Läuger, *Helv. chim. Acta*, **37**, 1627 (1954).

[535] Voronkov and Davydova, *Dok. Akad. Nauk*, **125**, 553 (1959).

[536] Waddle and Adkins, *J. Am. Chem. Soc.*, **61**, 3361 (1939).

[537] Walling, *Free Radicals in Solution*, pp. 369, 381, 385, John Wiley, New York (1951).

[538] Walling and Jacknow, *J. Am. Chem. Soc.*, **82**, 6108 (1960).

[539] Walling and Jacknow, *J. Am. Chem. Soc.*, **82**, 6113 (1960).

[540] Walling and Mayahi, *J. Am. Chem. Soc.*, **81**, 1485 (1959).

[541] Walther and Zimmerman, *Chem. Ber.*, **91**, 630 (1958).

[542] Wander, Swiss 273,397 (1951): *Chem. Abs.*, **46**, 5096a (1952).

[543] Waugh, *N-Bromosuccinide—Its Reactions and Uses*, Arapahoe Chem. Inc., Boulder, Colo. (1951).

[544] Webber and Harthoorn, Brit. 819,240 (1959).

[545] Wenner, *J. Org. Chem.*, **17**, 523 (1952).

[546] West and Barrett, *J. Am. Chem. Soc.*, **76**, 3146 (1954).

[547] West and Schmerling, *J. Am. Chem. Soc.*, **72**, 3525 (1950).

[548] West and Schmerling, U.S. 2,553,799 (1951).
[549] West and Schmerling, U.S. 2,553,800 (1951).
[550] Wheeler, Young, and Erley, *J. Org. Chem.*, **22**, 547 (1957).
[551] Whitmore and Sommer, *J. Am. Chem. Soc.*, **68**, 481 (1946).
[552] Wiberg and Slaugh, *J. Am. Chem. Soc.*, **80**, 3033 (1958).
[553] Wieland and Stenzel, *Chem. Ber.*, **40**, 4825 (1907).
[554] Wilder and Winston, *J. Am. Chem. Soc.*, **75**, 5370 (1953).
[555] Willard and Daniels, *J. Am. Chem. Soc.*, **57**, 2240 (1935).
[556] Wilson, *Organic Reactions*, vol. IX, p. 332, John Wiley, New York (1957).
[557] Winstein and Seubold, *J. Am. Chem. Soc.*, **69**, 2916 (1947).
[558] Winston, Youngblood, and Wilder, *J. Org. Chem.*, **22**, 876 (1957).
[559] Wittig and Vidal, *Chem. Ber.*, **81**, 368 (1948).
[560] Wohl, *Chem. Ber.*, **52**, 51 (1919).
[561] Wohl and Jaschinowski, *Chem. Ber.*, **54**, 476 (1921).
[562] Wolinski, *Roczniki Chem.*, **31**, 1189 (1957).
[563] Wright, *J. Am. Chem. Soc.*, **77**, 4883 (1955).
[564] Wu and Yu, *Hua Hsüeh Hsüeh Pao*, **25**, 289 (1959): *Chem. Abs.*, **54**, 16412i (1960).
[565] Young, Durrell, and Dresdner, *J. Am. Chem. Soc.*, **81**, 1587 (1959).
[566] Young, Durrell, and Dresdner, *J. Am. Chem. Soc.*, **82**, 4553 (1960).
[567] Zaugg, *J. Am. Chem. Soc.*, **76**, 5818 (1954).
[568] Zemplén and Bognar, *Chem. Ber.*, **76**, 452 (1943).
[569] Ziegler, *et al.*, *Ann. Chem.*, **551**, 80 (1942).

Supplementary Reading

1. Alfrey, Bohrer, and Mark, *Copolymerization*, Interscience, New York (1954).
2. Allen, *Organic Electrode Processes*, Reinhold, New York (1958).
3. Ash and Brown, Directive Effects in Aliphatic Chlorination, *Rec. Chem. Progress*, **9**, 80 (1948).
4. Augood and Williams, Homolytic Aromatic Substitution, *Chem. Revs.*, **57**, 123 (1957).
5. Bass and Broida, *Stabilization of Free Radicals at Low Temperatures*, U.S. Govt. Printing Office, Washington, D.C. (1960).
6. Bateman, Olefin Oxidation, *Quart. Revs.*, **8**, 308 (1954).
7. Bevinton, *Radical Polymerization*, Academic Press, New York (1961):
8. Blois, *et al.*, *Free Radicals in Biological Systems*, Academic Press, New York (1961).
9. Bolland, Kinetics of Olefin Oxidation, *Quart. Revs.*, **3**, 1 (1949).
10. Brooks, *et al.*, *The Chemistry of Petroleum Hydrocarbons*, vol. II and III, Reinhold, New York (1955).
11. Burnett, *Mechanism of Polymer Reactions*, Interscience, New York (1945).
12. Burnett and Melville, The Determination of the Concentration of Intermediaries and of Rate Constants in Radical Reactions, *Chem. Revs.*, **54**, 225 (1954).
13. Cadogan and Hey, Free Radical Addition Reactions of Olefinic Systems, *Quart Revs.*, **8**, 308 (1954).
14. Chapiro, *Radiation Chemistry of Polymeric Systems*, Interscience, New York (1962).
15. Cottrell, *The Strength of the Chemical Bonds*, Butterworths, London (1958).
16. Criegee, Herstellung und Umwandlung von Peoroxiden, *Houben-Weyl*, **8**, 5 (1952).
17. Crofts, Compounds Containing Carbon-Phosphorus Bonds, *Quart. Revs.*, **12**, 341 (1958).
18. Dainton, *Chain Reactions*, Methuen, London (1956).
19. Davies, *Organic Peroxides*, Butterworths, London (1961).
20. Dermer and Edmison, Radical Substitution in Aromatic Nuclei, *Chem. Revs.*, **57**, 77 (1957).
21. Dolgoplosk, Erusalimskij, and Tineakova, Generation of Free Radicals in Solutions and Their Reactions in Model Systems, *Izvest. Akad. Nauk*, **1958**, 469.
22. Eaborn, *Organosilicon Compounds*, Butterworths, London (1960).
23. Ellis, *The Chemistry of Petroleum Derivatives*, Chem. Catalog Co., New York (1934).
24. Ellis, *The Chemistry of Petroleum Derivatives*, Reinhold, New York (1937).
25. Evans, Hush, and Uri, The Energetics of Reactions Involving Hydrogen Peroxide, Its Radicals and Its Ions, *Quart. Revs.*, **6**, 186 (1952).
26. Flory, *Principles of Polymer Chemistry*, Cornell, New York (1953).
27. Freidlina, Reaction of Telomerization and Chemical Transformation of Telomers, *Izvest. Akad. Nauk*, **1957**, 1333.
28. Gefter, *Organophosphorus Monomers and Polymers*, transl. by Kosolapoff, Assoc. Tech. Services, Inc., Glen Ridge, New York (1962).
29. Gilman, *Organic Chemistry*, 2nd ed., John Wiley, New York (1944).

30. Gray and Williams, The Chemistry of Free Alkoxy Radical, *Chem. Soc. London, Spec. Publ. No. 9*, 97 (1957).
31. Gritter, Free Radical Chemistry in Solution, *J. Chem. Educ.*, **1958**, 475.
32. Havinga and Oosterhoff, Free Radicals, *Chem. Weekblad*, **47**, 49 (1951).
33. Hawkins, Some Organic Peroxides and Their Reactions, *Quart. Revs.*, **4**, 251 (1950).
34. Hawkins, *Organic Peroxides*, Van Nostrand, Princeton (1961).
35. Hey, Free Radicals, *Annual Reports*, **37**, 250 (1940).
36. Hey, Homolytic Reactions, *Annual Reports*, **41**, 181 (1944).
37. Hey, Free Radicals as Intermediates in Organic Reactions, in *Progress in Organic Chemistry*, edited by Cook, Academic Press, New York (1952).
38. Hey, *Reactions of Free Radicals in Solution*, Univ. Notre Dame Press (1954).
39. Hey and Waters, Some Organic Reactions Involving the Occurrence of Free Radicals in Solution, *Chem. Revs.*, **21**, 169 (1937).
40. Hine, *Physical Organic Chemistry*, McGraw-Hill, New York (1956).
41. Karnojitzky, Orientation donnée á diverses reáctions chimiques par les peroxides organiques, *Chim. ind. Paris*, **83**, 882 (1960).
42. Kato and Moshio, Hydrogen Abstraction Reactions in Free Radical Chemistry, *Kagaku no Ryôki*, **12**, 31, 98, 177 (1958).
43. Kern and Willersinn, Die Katalyse der Autoxydation ungesaettigter Verbindungen, *Ang. Chem.*, **67**, 573 (1955).
44. Kharasch, Inst. intern. chim. Solvay, 8e conseil chim. Univ. Bruxelles, Mecanisme de oxydation, Rapp. et disc., **1950**, 177.
45. Kharasch, Free Radical Chain Reactions in Solution, *The Nucleus*, **1952**, 242.
46. Kharasch, *Organic Sulfur Compounds*, Pergamon Press, New York (1961).
47. Kharasch and Reinmuth, *Grignard Reactions of Nonmetallic Substances*, Prentice-Hall, New York (1954).
48. Kosolapoff, *Organophosphorus Compounds*, John Wiley, New York (1950).
49. Kumada, Recent Advances in Organosilicon Chemistry, *Yûki Gosei Kagaku Kyokai Shi.* (J. Soc. Org. Synth. Chem. Japan), **16**, 379 (1958).
50. Lavin, Coates, and Rakaczky, *Free Radicals, Bibliography and Survey of Publications*, Dept. Commerce, Washington, D.C. (1961).
51. Leffler, *The Reaction Intermediates of Organic Chemistry*, Interscience, New York (1956).
52. Martin, Reactions of Shortlived Free Radicals in the Liquid Phase, *Ind. chim. belge*, **15**, 194 (1950).
53. Mayo and Walling, The Peroxide Effect, *Chem. Revs.*, **27**, 351 (1940).
54. Mayo and Walling, Copolymerization, *Chem. Revs.*, **46**, 191 (1950).
55. McNesby and Gordon, The Oxidation of Liquid Aldehydes by Molecular Oxygen, *Chem. Revs.*, **54**, 325 (1954).
56. Milas, Peroxides and Organic Peroxycompounds, *Encyc. Chem. Tech.*, **10**, 58 (1953).
57. Minkoff, *Frozen Free Radicals*, Interscience, London (1960).
58. Mueller, The Radical State of Unsaturated Compounds, *Fortschr. chem. Forsch.*, **1**, 325 (1949).
59. Mueller, The Nature and Importance of Free Radicals, *Ang. Chem.*, **64**, 233 (1952).
60. Mueller, *Neuere Anschauungen der organischen Chemie*, Springer Verlag, Berlin (1957).
61. Noyes and Leighton, *The Photochemistry of Gases*, Reinhold, New York (1941).
62. Noyes, Porter, and Jolley, The Primary Photochemical Process in Simple Ketones, *Chem. Revs.*, **56**, 49 (1956).

63. Oda, Behavior of Free Radicals in Solutions, *Chem. Revs. Japan*, **5**, 75 (1939).
64. Pryor, *Mechanisms of Sulfur Reactions*, McGraw-Hill, New York (1962).
65. Rice and Rice, *The Aliphatic Free Radicals*, John Hopkins Press, Baltimore (1935).
66. Schönberg, *Präparative Organische Photochemie*, Springer Verlag, Berlin (1959).
67. Sönnerskog, Preparation and Properties of Free Radicals, *Svensk. Kem. Tidskr.*, **70**, 15 (1958).
68. Steacie, *Atomic and Free Radical Reactions*, Reinhold, New York (1954).
69. Szwarc, The Determination of Bond Dissociation Energies by Pyrolytic Methods, *Chem. Revs.*, **47**, 75 (1950).
70. Tobolsky and Mesrobian, *Organic Peroxides*, Interscience, New York (1957).
71. Trotman-Dickenson, *Free Radicals: An Introduction*, Methuen, New York (1959).
72. Uri, Inorganic Free Radicals in Solution, *Chem. Revs.*, **50**, 375 (1952).
73. Voevodskii and Kondratiev, Radicals in Chain Reactions, *Usp. Khim.*, **19**, 678 (1950).
74. Walling, *Free Radicals in Solution*, John Wiley, New York (1957).
75. Walling, Free Radicals, *Chem. Eng. News*, p. 99 (Oct. 1961).
76. Warhurst, Sodium Flame Reactions, *Quart. Revs.*, **5**, 44 (1951).
77. Waters, *The Chemistry of Free Radicals*, Oxford Press, London (1948).
78. Waters, Chemical Reactions Involving Free Radicals, *Science Progress*, **35**, 23 (1947).
79. Waters, *Vistas in Free Radical Chemistry*, Pergamon Press, New York (1959).
80. Weissberger, *The Investigation of Rates and Mechanisms of Reactions*, Interscience, New York (1953).
81. Wheland, *Advanced Organic Chemistry*, John Wiley, New York (1949).
82. Williams, *Homolytic Aromatic Substitution*, Pergamon Press, New York (1960).

Index

A

419

T